The Book of Books

The Book

OLD TESTAMENT

HOLT, RINEHART AND WINSTON • NEW YORK CHICAGO SAN FRANCISCO

# of Books

A TREASURY OF GREAT BIBLE FICTION

EDITED BY IRWIN R. BLACKER AND ETHEL H. BLACKER

Published simultaneously in Canada by Holt, Rinehart and Winston of Canada, Limited.

Library of Congress Catalog Card Number: 65–14442

First Edition

Designer: Ernst Reichl

80975–0115

Printed in the United States of America

Acknowledgments

Grateful acknowledgment is made to the following publishers, authors, and agents who have so generously granted permission to reprint from their publications:

Atheneum Publishers, New York, New York, for the excerpts from *Two by Two* by David Garnett; copyright © 1963 by David Garnett.

A. S. Barnes & Company, Inc., New York, New York, for excerpt from *Judge and Fool* by Vladimir Jabotinsky, translated by Cyrus Brooks, originally published by Horace Liveright, Inc., 1930.

The Bobbs-Merrill Company, Indianapolis, Indiana, for the excerpt from *By Elmer Davis,* edited by Robert Lloyd Davis; copyright © 1964 by Robert Lloyd Davis; also for the excerpts from *Lot's Wife* by Maria Ley-Piscator; copyright 1954 by Maria Ley-Piscator; and for the excerpt from *Adam and Eve* by John Erskine; copyright 1927 by The Bobbs-Merrill Company, Inc.; copyright renewed © 1955 by Helen Worden Erskine.

Crown Publishers, New York, New York, for excerpts from *Voice of the Lord* by Laurene Chinn, copyright © 1961 by Laurene Chinn; and for the excerpt from *Moses, Prince of Egypt* by Howard Fast; copyright © 1958 by Howard Fast.

Curtis Brown, Ltd., New York, New York, for the excerpt from *Jonah* by Robert Nathan, published by Alfred A. Knopf, Inc.; copyright 1934 by Robert Nathan.

Harold S. Davis for the excerpt from *Belshazzar* by William Stearns Davis, originally published by The Macmillan Company, 1925.

John Day Company, Inc., New York, New York, and David Higham Associates, Ltd., London, for the excerpt from *Adam* by David Bolt; copyright © 1960 by David Bolt.

Dial Press, Inc., New York, New York, for the excerpts from *David the King* by Gladys Schmitt; copyright 1946 by Gladys Schmitt.

Doubleday & Company, Inc., New York, New York, for the excerpt from *The Scarlet Cord* by Frank G. Slaughter; copyright © 1956 by Frank G. Slaughter; and for the excerpt from *The Sorceress* by Nathaniel Norsen Weinreb; copyright 1954 by Nathaniel Norsen Weinreb.

E. P. Dutton & Company, Inc., New York, New York, for the excerpt from *Eden* by Murray Sheehan; copyright 1928 by E. P. Dutton & Company, Inc.

Irving Fineman for the excerpt from his novel *Jacob,* published by Random House, Inc., New York, New York, 1941; copyright 1941 by Irving Fineman.

Harcourt Brace & World, Inc., New York, for the excerpt from *Moses* by Louis Untermeyer; copyright 1928 by Harcourt, Brace & World, Inc.; copyright renewed © 1956 by Louis Untermeyer.

W. G. Hardy for the excerpt from his novel *Abraham, Prince of Ur,* originally published by Dodd, Mead and Company, New York; copyright 1935 by W. G. Hardy.

Harper & Row, Publishers, Incorporated, New York, New York, for the excerpt from *Ruth* by Irving Fineman; copyright 1949 by Irving Fineman.

David Higham Associates Ltd., London, for the excerpts from *The Chosen* by Edith Simon, 1940.

Alfred A. Knopf, Inc., New York, New York, for the excerpts from *Joseph and His Brothers* by Thomas Mann, translated by H. T. Lowe-Porter; copyright 1934, 1935, 1938, 1944 by Alfred A. Knopf, Inc.

iv

Dedicated with love

and gratitude

to our parents,

Louis and Sadie Blacker,

Robert and Florence Handler.

Books by Irwin R. Blacker

FICTION

Westering
Taos
The Kilroy Gambit
Days of Gold

JUVENILE

The Bold Conquistadores
Cortes and the Aztec Conquest

NON-FICTION

Irregulars, Partisans, Guerrillas
The Old West in Fiction
The Old West in Fact
Prescott's Histories
The Golden Conquistadores
Conquest
Hakluyt's Voyages

Contents

Introduction

RELIGIOUS THOUGHT and tradition have spread through the world in many ways. For centuries art, poetry and the drama were used to interpret and disseminate both the inspiration and the story of Holy Scripture. In recent times a new literary form—the biblical novel—has developed, capable of reaching a broad and heterogeneous audience.

In a healthy and provocative sense, these books are a new way of looking at the Bible, a new way for artists to enlarge upon their feelings and attitudes, a new form in which to work. If the religious paintings and cathedrals of the Middle Ages and Renaissance reflected the artistic expression of their time, then the biblical novel equally expresses the attitudes and insights of our age.

The recent emergence of the biblical novel as a literary genre is one of the most interesting developments of contemporary literature. At the present time, the flood of novels drawn from Holy Scripture exceeds that from any other source, and probably equals books about the Civil War. During the last half century over two hundred and fifty novels retelling parts of the Holy Scripture have been published in this country alone; a figure which does not include juvenile novels and story books, but only adult novels drawn from both testaments.

This flowering of the biblical novel in an age marked by religious skepticism is anomalous. As a popular form the novel has been developing for over two hundred years, and therefore it is surprising that the biblical novel has been so long coming into its own. This is particularly strange in view of the fact that the historical novel received its first major impetus from Sir Walter Scott's Waverly novels in the early nineteenth century and quickly swept the literary markets of the world. Early European and American novels were as often as not little more than costume pieces, and the historical background was generally either within a generation of the writer's own time or was classical history. Stories of the American Revolution and the development of the country were written in great numbers. In England, Scott, Dickens and Thackeray turned to the history of their own country and its entanglements abroad. Yet neither the serious writer nor Hawthorne's "damned tribe of scribbling women" turned to the Bible as a source for their stories. In the search for materials for historical novels, the Bible now seems an obvious choice. But it was not then. Even though many of its problems and techniques are the same, the biblical novel was to develop in a separate stream.

In all probability, authors refrained from personalizing and fictionalizing biblical characters for fear of offending their readers.

The earliest novel based upon the Bible was William Ware's *Julian; or, Scenes in Judaea,* published in 1841. *The Glory of the House of Israel,* written by G. F. Strauss in 1859, appears to be the first novel based upon the Old Testament. However, the only value of these books lies in their inauguration of this genre.

In 1860, J. H. Ingraham published *The Throne of David,* which he followed up thirty-nine years later with *The Pillar of Fire,* a novel about Moses. The only nineteenth century novelist of significance to attempt an Old Testament theme was Francis Marion Crawford, whose *Zoroaster* contains a single chapter on Daniel; the rest of the book being post-Daniel.

In the first twenty years of this century there were thirty-five biblical novels published and only three of these are of particular interest. Cyrus W. Brady's *When the Sun Stood Still* is a novel about Joshua. Brady, a clergyman who wrote over seventy popular novels and biographies, abandoned the biblical field after one attempt. Sir Henry Rider Haggard, famed for his romances *She* and *King Solomon's Mines,* wrote *Moon of Israel,* a Moses tale, told from the Egyptian point of view, with the Jews as the villains. In *Exodus,* written with the classical scholar Andrew Lang, Haggard fused the story of Moses with that of Ulysses.

However, between 1920 and 1930, thirty biblical novels were published, most of these after the famous Scope's trial of 1925, and they reflect some of the cynicism and irreverence of the period. Robert Graves, Robert Nathan, Elmer Davis and John Erskine wrote with tongue in cheek and treated their respective subjects—Elisha, Jonah, David and Adam—with broad humor.

The biblical novels of the thirties, with the exception of John Erskine's *Solomon, My Son,* were generally serious works, reflecting the mood of the Depression, and many of them are deadly dull. But it was during that decade that Thomas Mann began the Joseph series, which was to take sixteen years to complete. And Sholem Asch began the cycle he worked on until his death.

During the next decade, biblical novels appeared at a much faster pace. Fifty were published between 1940 and 1950. The quality was higher and the public acceptance more general. Gladys Schmitt's *David the King* received serious critical attention and was a major book club selection, as were biblical novels by Lloyd Douglas, Sholem Asch and Thomas Mann.

Whatever started the flow of biblical novels in the forties brought it to flood stage in the fifties, when a hundred and nine novels based upon Bible stories and characters were published.

The range of the novels of the fifties differed only slightly from that of the previous decade. Sholem Asch, Dorothy Clarke Wilson and Frank Slaughter contributed ten to the total. Asch's popularity continues after his death, and Slaughter's simply written romances reach about the same audience each time. Mrs. Wilson's books, published by both religious and trade publishing houses, remain consistently among the best written of the genre.

The first four years of the sixties saw twenty-seven biblical novels published, sufficient to indicate the continuing interest in the Bible as a source for both the reader and the creative writer. The range of persons who have drawn upon the Bible for creative inspiration in the writing of fiction is almost incredible. They include the then-Communist Whittaker Chambers, who translated Felix Salten's *Samson and Delilah;* ex-Communist Howard Fast; clergymen Lloyd Douglas, Father Edward F. Murphy and Rabbi Julius Leibert; housewives Laurene Chinn, author of *The Unanointed* and *Voice of the Lord,* and Irene Patai, author of *Valley of God;* classical scholar W. G. Hardy, author of *Abraham, Prince of Ur* and *All the Trumpets Sounded;* a great neurosurgeon, Wilder Penfield, author of *No Other Gods;* poets Louis Untermeyer, who wrote *Moses,* and Robert Graves who wrote *My Head! My Head!;* and a Zionist revolutionary, Vladimir Jabotinsky, author of *Samson.* Three of Europe's greatest refugee writers wrote biblical novels: Thomas Mann, Franz Werfel and Lion Feuchtwanger.

A number of those who were to become significant writers drew their first books from the Bible. But Robert Graves, as a novelist, has since shifted his ground and gone most frequently to that other stream of Western civilization, classical Greece and Rome. Edith Simon has turned to the Middle Ages. Very few generalities can be made about those who have written biblical novels. Some, like Asch, Douglas, Slaughter, Mann and de Wohl, returned to the Bible time after time. Werfel, Schmitt, Feuchtwanger and Nathan mined the field only once and then moved elsewhere.

The range of Bible subjects which have interested novelists is also wide. There have been ten novels each about Abraham, Moses and David, and these demonstrate the varied approaches to the genre. Florence Bauer's *Abram Son of Terah,* Wilder Penfield's *No Other Gods* and Zofia Kossak's *The Covenant* tell about Abraham's youth and his decision to leave Ur, all extra-biblical. A. L. Chidsey's *Abraham, Father of Nations,* Susan Gates's *The Prince of Ur,* H. R. Rice's *Seeking a City* and M. Todres's *Man of the Ancient World* are examples of books primarily religious and written to educate. Most of the writers have been Christian or reflected Christian traditions. Zofia Kossak has Ab-Ram seeing the Virgin Mary in a dream as "a woman crowned with stars." Sholem Asch has the prophet Isaiah forecast the coming of Christ, whom he sees in a vision.

As with serious historical novelists, writers of biblical novels have not hesitated to tell a story which goes beyond that told in the Bible. In the case of Nathan, Graves, Erskine and Davis, the purpose was to satirize the culture which the writer himself represented. This may have been deliberate—turning David into a glory-seeker (Davis), Jonah into a joke (Nathan), Moses into a hypocrite (Untermeyer)—or it may have been unintentional. With so significant a writer as Thomas Mann, the biblical novel was used to reflect society as he understood it. He considered the last of the Joseph books "remarkably American. For it is the mark of an American Hermes, a brilliant messenger of shrewdness whose New Deal is unmistakenly reflected in

Joseph's magic administration of national economy." And he wrote his brief novel, *Tables of the Law,* as "a polemic against Nazism on behalf of human morality."

If the purposes of the biblical novelist have been varied, so too have the techniques. There is no pattern, but there are several technical approaches which emerge. Many of the novelists have centered their stories upon a single biblical character or story and remained with it. Many have told the peripheral story—the tale of the person who traveled with Moses, the man who fought with David, the friend of the man in the Bible who is familiar to us. Many writers have told what can be considered extra-biblical stories, where the central character is out of the mainstream of the Bible story and only rarely comes in contact with biblical events. Some of the Abraham novels are pre-biblical; some of the Moses novels are focused upon the Egyptians and not the Jews; a few of the biblical novels are set in later, actually post-biblical, periods. These varied approaches are all familiar to a good historical novelist. The reasons behind them are even more obvious in the biblical novel than in the historical.

In the selection of a known story line, the biblical novelist accepts the loss of suspense. His readers know what is going to happen to Moses, to Joseph, to Abraham. They do not know what will happen to the extra-biblical character, or to the character so slightly sketched in the Bible that the novelist must create the rest of the tale. In his historical novels, Kenneth Roberts involves his readers in the fate of his characters and not in the Revolutionary War, the outcome of which is no secret. In *Gone With the Wind* Margaret Mitchell involves her readers with the fictitious Scarlett O'Hara, and only secondarily with the fall of Atlanta. The same technique is used over and over again by biblical novelists.

Where a giant personality of the Bible—Moses, David, Abraham—is the focal point of a novel, the writer has added problems and difficulties. His readers know the characters, have formed their own opinions of them, have visual images of them, interpret their actions in each circumstance from a background already filled in by years of familiarity with the Bible. The writer who tampers with these established images is involved in a dangerous business that could lay him open to the charge of heresy or subversion. Elmer Davis was so attacked for *Giant Killer,* and Louis Untermeyer for his rendition of *Moses.*

If it is difficult for a writer to create the depth of personality and the psychology of his biblical characters because of the *a priori* judgment of his readers, it is even more difficult to make the world in which they live more than a vague and misty backdrop. If the biblical character is ever to be more than a formal symbol, the writer must feed, clothe, house, and kill him, and even develop a love life for him. If the reader is knowledgeable, he has his own preconceptions of daily living in biblical times. For the less knowledgeable reader, the writer must add prosaic elements to an exalted personality or event. This is a difficult task for the historical novelist dealing with periods of history closer to our own, but it is a paramount problem for a serious

biblical novelist dealing with periods so far removed from the present. How
does he create the psychology of a man who is religion-centered for a reader
who is not? How does he create the temper of a society lost in the dim
recesses of the past? The Bible alone does not give the answers. Nor does
Antiquities of the Jews by Flavius Josephus, the historian to whom most
biblical novelists have turned. Modern archaeology and anthropology have
helped many writers gain insights into the time and place of which they are
writing. But even these scientific disciplines are not enough. The only final
solution lies in the understanding and creative skill of an artist. Only the judgment and talent of an artist can make a reader accept an Abraham worried
about his cloak, a Moses concerned with his speech, a Joshua washing his
muddy feet. Many writers avoided the problem by keeping their characters
disembodied from society, moving against an unidentifiable background. Some
have made the rash assumption that there has been no cultural change between the time of the Bible story and the contemporary desert nomad, as if
the very fact of the religious events they are writing about had no impact upon
the people of the country where they took place.

When cultural judgment goes askew, the results can be startling. Part
of this can be blamed upon the artist's inability to see that the culture he is
writing about does not reflect his own. The extreme of this error is demon-
strated in *Jacob* by Jean Cabries and translated from the French in 1957 by
Gerard Hopkins. Here the writer attempted to create within a completely
familiar context.

Fastened at the end of a black chain, the keys of her store cupboards
rattled against her knees . . .

Basmath was standing in front of the old clock, saying, "What was the
matter with him?" Judith, clutching in her arms the basket of linen which
she was bringing in from the wash house . . .

He had rushed to his room, taking the stairs two at a time. Once there,
he had walked up and down in front of the glass, puffing out his chest,
dressed in his brother's blue suit.

Under the roof of the veranda an old lady sat waiting for Rebecca in an
armed chair.

When Abraham died, Isaac had a portrait of his father made in pencil
. . . And he had the picture hung in the entrance hall of the house looking
toward the front door.

What is revealed here is a total lack of understanding of the culture from
which the Bible sprang. The keys, the clock, the blue suit, the looking glass,
the basket of linen from a wash house, the veranda with an armed chair, the
portrait in pencil hung in a hall are all anachronisms and even to this day

would be out of place in the tented culture of the nomadic Middle East. What such ignorance does reflect is the difficulty that any creative artist has in setting his story in a time and place with which he has no personal familiarity.

In setting a logical background for his characters, the biblical novelist has many hurdles to overcome. In the creation of those characters there are additional problems. The Bible character is rarely described physically. A Sara may be referred to in the Bible as "fair." But "fair" may more accurately mean simply that she is beautiful, rather than specifically blond or blue-eyed, as most novelists have interpreted the word, an interpretation which would embarrass any Semite. As the Bible paintings of the Renaissance revealed the culture in which they were made rather than that which they attempted to depict, so have most novelists fallen into the same fallacy. A small problem which may disconcert those reading a few novels about one character is the name attributed to the anonymous personality in the Bible. The Egyptian princess who rescued Moses has a different name in each of twenty-eight novels. Lot's wife also has been given numerous names.

One of the most complex problems facing the Bible novelist is naturally language—tone of voice, or what E. M. Forester has called prophecy. It is the quality which sets a *Moby Dick* apart from a *Caine Mutiny,* or distinguishes a Dostoevsky character from the journalistic caricature of a Sinclair Lewis.

There is no short cut to solution of the language problem. Most readers have been educated to think of biblical prose in terms of the King James or the Douay translations of the Bible. But the writer who turns to archaic English for tone is trapped. And biblical novelists—some of the best—have made the same mistake as the American regional writers of the mid-nineteenth century, who thought that localisms in language could replace those strokes of artistry which create the feeling and empathy so important to the tone of a book. Many Bible novelists have written fine works of art, but not because they used seventeenth century English to create the illusion of biblical Hebrew.

Probably much more difficult for the reader to accept is the novel which changes, arbitrarily, the basic story elements of the Bible. It is difficult to understand why Shirley Watkins, in an otherwise fine book (*The Prophet and the King*), decided that David should have a child by the daughter of Saul, who is recorded as having been barren. It is against all logic for Howard Fast's Moses to be tossed into the river as a child sacrifice to a water serpent god by a primitive people. Vardis Fisher also fell back upon the concept of the Jews as a primitive people (*The Valley of Vision*), bringing them no further forward in history than the later Stone Age, even though his story is set in a Middle East contemporaneous with a flourishing Egypt from which the Jews had long fled.

Critical evaluation of the biblical novel has always been questionable. There are a number of reasons for this, and not all of them can be laid to the novelists, many of whom worked sincerely and created books worth reading.

Probably as important as anything else in tarnishing the image of the

Bible novel have been the motion picture versions of Bible stories. The excursions into sand and sex, scandals and spectacles on the wide screen admittedly satisfy the desires and emotions of vast audiences. Cecil B. De Mille's *Ten Commandments* will probably be one of the most widely seen films in history. Yet, in spite of clumsy attempts to prove the validity of its scholarship, no one takes seriously the gospel according to Cecil. At the same time, no one can seriously doubt that this film does have a place in our culture. It serves a need. It dramatizes simply and effectively at the only level at which many can understand or want to understand the Bible—at its basic, technicolor story level. But most other attempts at Bible films—*Sodom and Gomorrah, Goliath and the Babylonians*—have not had the faintest desire to achieve any standard other than financial success.

If motion pictures have helped to lower the critical opinion concerning the Bible as a source of story material, so has the flood of paperback originals, novels based on these films or created to capitalize on the public's familiarity with a sensuous character. *The Curse of Jezebel,* by Frank Slaughter, is described as "brazen, voluptuous, wanton, lascivious"; and *Jezebel,* by Jefferson Cooper, is "The story of the most voluptuous and ruthless woman of all time." *The Last Days of Sodom and Gomorrah,* by Richard Wormser, are "ruled and ruined by a corrupt and sadistic queen . . . who determined to lure Lot into her cobweb of voluptuous and forbidden temptations," and another book with the same title by Paul Ilton describes how "passions and debauchery explode in history's most wicked city," while *The Road to Sodom,* by Jean Rees, is "ruled by a queen more wicked than Cleopatra . . . more beautiful than Salome. . . . The most powerful story of faith and corruption ever told." So long as bookstalls abound in stories like these—and they always will—the public will be chary and the critics dubious.

Apart from a reader's difficulty in selecting a biblical novel worth reading, there is an attitude which has carried over from the historical novel: a not always unjustified contempt for the genre. This is fairly modern in its origins and stems in part from the thinking prevalent at the beginning of this century. Historical romances engulfed the bookstands. Most of them were not worth the bother to read. The scholarship was poor, the intentions of the writers less than serious. At the same time the very concept of romance was under attack by empirical thinkers in the social sciences and naturalists in the arts. In the words of the Romantic historian Ernest Bernbaum there was born "a naive confidence in the reality of phenomena." The scientific spirit came to dominate the hopes and dreams of men. It brought religious thought and inspiration into disrepute and helped to destroy the image of the serious religious work of art. Many critics, reviewers and scholars put their faith in the reliability of the so-called scientific historians who promised to lead them to an objective and complete report of history. What followed instead was what Robert A. Lively has called, "a regular derogation of such tools as faith and imagination when they are employed for the recapture of the national memories." Today, too many are still seeking photographic realism and have abandoned the search for emotion, faith, simplicity, and—

to use an old-fashioned word—inspiration, of the kind that moves people while recapturing the glories of the past.

In selecting the material for this collection we have roamed far, drawing on all types of writers, foreign and American, who have written significant novels based on the Bible. Most of these writers have attempted to enlarge our understanding of biblical characters and events. A few frankly departed from the Bible as a source, but those were included because what they said was interesting and reflected a point of view in our society.

All have taken the Bible and imaginatively reconstructed those portions of it which interested them. They have brought to their stories insights and interpretations which had meaning for them, and which should have meaning for us even in those instances in which we may disagree with a point of view. For after all, the biblical novel is an opening up, a new look at the old materials and the great foundations of faith through someone else's eyes. It is a dimension added, and—at its best—it is a work of art.

IRWIN R. BLACKER
ETHEL H. BLACKER

Sherman Oaks, California
May 19, 1964.

The Book of Books

1 The Creation of Man

There are many ways of approaching the Bible, and John Erskine did it gently, fondly and with tongue in cheek. His Adam represents all innocents, his Lilith all women. A professor of English at Columbia University and President of The Juilliard School of Music, Erskine brought a love of erudition to the numerous books he wrote. The Bible fascinated him as a source for story material, and after *Adam and Eve* he returned to it a second time with *Solomon, My Son.* Turning to the other two great sources of story material in the Western world, he wrote *Helen of Troy,* based on the Trojan Wars and two novels of Arthur's Britain, *Galahad* and *Tristan and Isolde.* While his scholarship was deadly serious, his fiction was generally as light-hearted as his view of Adam.

And out of the ground the Lord God formed every beast of the field, and every fowl of the air; and brought them unto Adam to see what he would call them: and whatsoever Adam called every living creature, that was the name thereof.

And Adam gave names to all cattle, and to the fowl of the air, and to every beast of the field; but for Adam there was not found an help meet for him.

And the Lord God caused a deep sleep to fall upon Adam, and he slept: and he took one of his ribs, and closed up the flesh instead thereof:

And the rib, which the Lord God had taken from man, made he a woman, and brought her unto the man.

GENESIS: II, 19–22

ADAM AND EVE by JOHN ERSKINE

The Animals

I

GOD MADE MAN, like Himself, lonely. The animals had mates, but man had a soul. God admired this distinction, but man at that time did not.

There's an old story that Adam took his soul among the animals, and tried to make friends with the dog, the horse, the cow and the cat. Up to a point he succeeded, but a day came at last when the divine loneliness could not be endured.

"You mean, you want a mate—like a mere animal?"

"I'm afraid I do," said Adam. "It doesn't sound elevated, as you put it, but I can think of nothing better."

God made Lilith, the most seductive body of a woman the oldest poet remembers.

But a day came when Adam complained of this loneliness also.

"She certainly is beautiful," he said, "and she's aggressively fond of me, but she has no soul."

"No, you have all there is."

"I'm sorry for that," said Adam. "Mate isn't the word—I want another soul."

Then God created Eve, and divided the one soul between them. Not the addition Adam asked for, but division. She became man's wife.

Lilith spoke to the snake, asleep in the garden:

"Lend me your body for a moment, till I break this up."

They used to paint the first temptation so—offering the apple—the serpent's body with the woman's head.

We are familiar with a briefer history of Adam, which says nothing about Lilith. It says nothing of his adventures among the animals, except that he gave names to them. To the land creatures, that is—the fish for some reason remained anonymous. And he ignored the cat, to show his disapproval of the Egyptians, who at the moment were worshipping it. This version says, moreover, that Adam shared with Eve not his soul but his rib. Why do Lilith and soul disappear from the legend, and the rib emerge?

But the condition of the text need not disturb us. I never question an old story myself, not when I like it, and least of all when it recurs daily under my eyes. Adam is not yet at peace. He can reconcile himself neither to be lonely, like a god, nor to be completely mated. On the whole he favors the angels, but he prefers to be a little lower. His naming the animals, what is it but a parable of the scientist in him? He knows the name of a thing at sight. Later he tries to find out what it is.

The difference still remains between Lilith and Eve. We don't state it now, however, in terms of soul. Perhaps Lilith has more soul than the other, if it comes to that. But we say that Eve has temperament, in the artistic or difficult sense, and Lilith, though a beautiful woman, has none. For a man, this formula gives Lilith a charm she may not deserve, an advantage to start with. Most men regret that it also makes her by definition so rare as to be extinct. Even we concede, we who have known her, that the brief and famous account of Adam which left her out was in the large, a prophetic book.

II

Of Adam's social life before he met Lilith the record is meager, but it is essential to our history. Let me sum it up in broad outlines.

The first thing he did was to admire the landscape. At noon precisely he opened his eyes on a broad meadow, green and close-cropped. He saw it from across the road, and along the road a stone wall closed it in. On the other side of the field a second wall ran parallel—he noticed the coincidence. The one near by was covered with a green vine, very glossy. He wondered if the farther wall was so handsomely adorned.

To the right, under maples and oaks, certain animals were huddled, switching away at flies. He recognized the maples, but wasn't sure about the oaks, and in the shade he couldn't identify the animals. He suspected cows. To the left the ground fell away and there was a distance—more fields, more maples, and one apple orchard. Adam's impression was of a good world, well arranged.

He was conscious of observing it for the first time. That is, the first time for anybody. Nothing that happened to him had ever happened before. This perception recurs among his descendants during childhood and youth.

The impulse came on him to walk in the meadow—not a difficult venture, he supposed, if he could climb the wall without harming the glossy vine. But first he must cross the road. The road ran the other way, of course, but no doubt it could be used crosswise. He found it pleasant under foot, except where the cart ruts caused unevenness. But the turf on the other side was painful—the best parts tickled and all the rest tore his skin. He saw the advantage of keeping to the road. There was no essential defeat in giving up the meadow, since the extreme choices remained, the road to the left and the road to the right. "My soul is content," thought Adam, "so long as my will is free."

The vividness of his philosophy diverted his attention from where he was going, and, before he expected, he had turned the corner of the field. The road, oddly enough, bent right into the wall, but where wall and road met there were no stones, only two stout posts, with bars stretched between them. To lean on, obviously. He went up and leaned on the top rail.

There was a cow, as he had thought, one cow, of early middle age. When he looked at the cow, he had to put away the thought that in a good world there might be imperfections. The cow was sitting down, or you might say lying down, except that its feet were under it. It was in a nervous state. It kept up a continuous but practically silent motion with its jaws.

There was a single horse, too. It appeared to be asleep, yet it remained standing, and from time to time it brushed itself off with its tail. The turf where it stood had been entirely dug up. He wondered why it didn't prefer to stand on grass.

Just behind the horse's heels a dog was stretched out, his nose thrust into the dirt.

Adam would have been curious about the dog, but something yellowish was creeping toward him along the top rail of the gate—a fuzzy, elastic something which moved by humping itself up and then stretching out again. It differed from the larger creatures in being interested in him. First it crept up his hand and examined the skin—then on along his arm. Though it tickled, he didn't mind so long as he could see it, but it climbed his shoulder and went on down his back. He understood now why the horse kept brushing himself.

His arm wasn't long enough to reach over his shoulder, and he had just made up his mind to wait till the thing got farther down, when it fell off of itself. There it was on the ground, a small curled mass. He stepped away carefully. Perhaps one oughtn't to lean on a gate.

The road went no further, but there was a stretch of softer grass. It looked softer, and when he tried it, it felt damp. Soon it was positively wet. He lifted his foot to see if there was anything wrong with him, or whether the trouble was altogether in the grass. Then, a few yards ahead, he saw a smooth glistening, very lovely—a pool filled by a spring. It had bubbles at one side, and over them a tiny spout of water from a crack in the rock. At that place the wall was broken—only a few big stones—the water got in around them.

Since there was no delicate vine on these stones, he thought he might walk on them. But they proved not good for walking. He couldn't imagine what had pulled his foot from under him. As though something didn't like him. More than the fall, the thought was disintegrating. He sat down on the cold stone to think it over, and wait till he felt better.

The noise he had made when he slipped brought the dog to the meadow edge of the spring. The beast came slowly, stopped short, and looked at the white figure on the stone. Adam thought it looked sympathetic but he wasn't sure, because the animal didn't look long. After a moment it moved its nose over the moist earth and began to sniff, then stuck out its tongue and patted the water.

"*That* doesn't seem to hurt," thought Adam; "I might try it myself." But there was some dark trick about it—the right way to stick out the tongue. His hair got wet, chiefly, and when he aimed his nose straight, the way the dog did, there was a sharp discomfort in his head, and he couldn't breathe. He got off the stone, discouraged, and walked away. Gates should be avoided. And water.

To the right, behind the spring, a path led up the hill. No broad road with wheel-tracks, but a narrow smoothness. He began with caution, following the windings among trees and bushes. Some of the bushes, he noticed, had red decorations on them, in clusters, and some had black. The color effect, he thought, was ingenious. Were those bright things part of the branch? Or were they put on afterwards? Not all the bushes had them, and they were arranged carelessly. They came off, too—several lay on the ground. Caution to the winds, he reached in his hand. Though the branch never moved—he could swear it didn't—yet it bit him, a thin bite across his wrist, and how it hurt! Bushes didn't like him, either.

He stood quite still and looked down and around, to be sure he wasn't touching anything he shouldn't—quite still and thought hard. He had intended no harm, yet here in the space of a few minutes he had got two separate hurts. He would never confuse them, if they should happen again. When your foot was pulled away, the feeling was broader but not so intense, and it didn't last so long. It made more noise, however.

He looked again at the inscrutable bush. The world was not so well ordered as it seemed. With that discovery came his first taste of sadness, a wound on the inside, yet he might have laughed it off quickly had it not been for the sudden idea that good world or bad, he wasn't entirely welcome in it. Very well, he would leave—who cares to stay where he isn't wanted? In view of what he had got out of it so far, why investigate the world further? Once the question was formulated, however, the answer was inevitable; he knew he would never leave till he had to. "I think I have the love of life," said Adam.

This thought encouraged him, even inspired a sense of pride, and he started up the path again, superior to bushes. Suddenly he came out on a hillside shelf, an open space with more room than was needed. He was on his guard now, but for all he could see there were no stones, and there was no water. The bushes did continue to the edge of the clearing, but there they stopped. Obviously a safe place. He chose a maple root. The path went on through the woods, but he postponed exploration.

Now he could see through the trees, or over them, and his meadow lay below, filled with more sun than before. There at the left was the place he had started from, and straight ahead, at the end of the field, that beautiful distance, with the apple orchard in it. The trees stood symmetrically, in rows each way. Apples must be a methodical fruit.

As he looked, he saw the cow move away from him toward the distance, a little to the right. She had a queer walk, not as though she touched ground, but as though she were suspended from something and swinging. There was no path in the field, but she seemed to know where to go. Her departure emphasized his solitude. He hadn't many companions, and in spite of her restless habit she was a decent creature.

But between her image and his eye a small leaf-like shadow fluttered from a tree, sidewise, and lighted on a bush. He could see the branch tremble with its modest weight. While it was fluttering down it looked broad and loose, but on the branch it was narrow and trim—a bit tilted up at each end. One end suddenly struck at the bush, and to Adam's delight, bit it. Good for the little creature! It didn't like the bush any more than he did! Evidently that was the way—a quick stroke.

Just as he came near, the grayish brown shadow fluttered off—up again, of all things, not down. But it had served its purpose. Adam reached over carefully and gave the red decoration, without warning, a sharp pinch. It came away in his hand, ripe and squashy, and he licked his fingers. But his hand was bleeding.

"I've seen enough of life for one day," he thought. "It's not a bad world, if you sit still. Every time I move I make a mistake." His mind reverted to the spot from which he had first strayed. "I began well," he mused, "if only I hadn't gone too far!"

When he came to the spring, on his way back, the water seemed much darker, and when he reached the gate, the meadow was deserted. The horse and the dog had followed the cow. He was in the midst of a reflection that the pain in his hand was not serious, when he stepped on the tail of a small black creature crouched in a wheel-track. The black thing shrieked across the road, clawed its way up the bark of a tree, and clinging there, turned its head and spit at him. Adam's nerve failed, but he moved to the side of the road and staggered on.

"Just when I was beginning to enjoy myself again!" he sighed. "That's what I call bad luck."

He felt so shaken that when he came to the spot in the road from which he had begun, he was strongly inclined to lie down and stay there. Weariness he had not yet thought of, but lying down would preclude the possibility of error. The grass, however, was still prickly, and if he lay in the road, the spitting black thing might step on him in revenge. He walked on. His thoughts were interrupted from within by memory of the red decoration he had squashed from the bush and licked from his fingers.

When he reached the orchard, the state of the ground surprised him. Grass, of course, he had met before, but here it came in bristles. From what he had seen of the cow, he doubted if she could eat so evenly. At intervals between the trees a dry, wisplike vegetable had been heaped in sizable mounds—pleasant smelling, and graceful in design, but otherwise superfluous. On the whole, he judged it safe to investigate—and under the pressure of his hand the mound sank agreeably. Meant to sit on, no doubt. For the first time Adam sat down of his own will, and made the delicious acquaintance, not of hay, but of rest.

From where he sat he could see the hill, and it was all red. Over it burned a strong unpleasant light, also red. The light was falling slowly into the hilltop, which grew blacker the more it fell. "If there's anything wrong," thought Adam, "I'm sorry, of course, but it's not my fault." But when the red light went out altogether, he missed it, like the cow.

More than ever he wished for another bush, at any cost. A new sensation in him, not comfortable, kept suggesting, he didn't know why, that red taste on his finger-tips. But there was no light, and rest was best—and anyway, if the world was getting lost piecemeal, perhaps it didn't matter.

In the darkness he heard twitterings and chirpings. Perhaps they were there before, but now he noticed them. He wished they would stop. Since they wouldn't he covered himself with some of the mound, and tried not to listen. They persisted, louder. But all at once he forgot them in a larger noise—a far-off baying, lugubrious and fearsome. Some creature was sing-ing, apparently about something it didn't like. He suspected the horse, be-cause the biggest animal would naturally make the biggest noise. What if the horse, for all his quiet deportment that afternoon, had decided to express the general dislike of Adam?

Just before resting on the mound, he had noticed a short stick under the tree near by. Now he groped for it, and felt better with something to hit with. But what if the horse, like that crawling thing on the fence-rail, should be interested in his back? Adam lifted the mound, section by section, and piled it against the tree. He sat down, stick in hand, tree behind him. Let the unfriendly horse sing on! Now he could watch in peace—that is, if he could only see—that is, if there were a little more light—that is, if only his eyes wouldn't close just when he needed them—that is—

2 The Fall

Believing that the story of Adam "remains the story of Everyman," David Bolt, sometime Malayan police official, British soldier in the Indian service and most recently an author's agent in London, retells the story of the Fall of Adam. "Other accounts may explain the origin and physical stature of man," he writes, "but we have yet to find an alternative to the Fall to account for his nature." Of *Adam*, C. S. Lewis, scholar-theologian, said, "there is no patronage, no parody, no allegorization." Lewis believed the book is "splendid," and few reading this account of the Fall would disagree.

> *And the woman said unto the serpent, We may eat of the fruit of the trees of the garden:*
>
> *But of the fruit of the tree which is in the midst of the garden, God hath said, Ye shall not eat of it, neither shall ye touch it, lest ye die.*
>
> *And the serpent said unto the woman, Ye shall not surely die:*
>
> *For God doth know that in the day ye eat thereof, then your eyes shall be opened, and ye shall be as gods, knowing good and evil.*
>
> GENESIS: III, 2–4

ADAM by DAVID BOLT

—BUT THE TREE in the midst of the garden! she said: in the dell, in the forest—which the Lord God has forbidden us!

—Has he? The dragon turned with the speed of surprise to look, first towards the forest, then to the woman's face again. Is it so? Has God said you are not to eat of every tree of the garden?

—No! And she laughed. Because if Igwana had been as close by her as he had said, whether openly or in secret, he might have seen her taking the fruit freely where she found it, and Adam with her. And she said, No—we may eat the fruit of the trees of the garden: only of the one tree, which is in the midst of the garden, God has said, You shall not eat of it, nor shall you touch it, lest you die.

She stood up, stretching her legs as she spoke, wishing Adam would come; conscious of thirst, the sun hot on her shoulders where she stood. I am thirsty! She walked across to the river. The dragon moved down at her side.

9

—The tree you speak of: is it more than another? Or is the fruit of it bitter, that it would harm you?

Ishah, kneeling at the water's edge, cupping her hands to drink, stayed them half lifted. The water drained away through her fingers.

—It is true, she said: it is like the trees of the garden to look at. And whether more than another I cannot tell. But what is bitter?

Waiting for his answer, she forgot her thirst. But he crouched low to lap as if he had not heard, the shining length of scales tilted down in changing colors to the brink, amber and orange, orange and purple, the beauty of wings close-folded like great leaves overlapping. When he had drunk his fill he withdrew backwards a little way, and rested on his belly. In the water the pieces of her face came together again, and were still.

—Tell me what is bitter, she said.

—Is this also hidden from you? Now I begin to see how much God has withheld from you. For how can you savour that which is sweet? seeing you are without the knowledge of bitterness. And as for the fruit, whether it is bitter or sweet, how will you know unless you first taste it? For unless you taste the fruit, you have no knowledge.

Ishah, listening to his voice, saw her own face in the water floating pale and strange on the gentle undulations of the flow, wistful and wise; it was as if she saw it for the first time. He said, Unless you taste the fruit you have no knowledge. . . .

You have no knowledge . . .

And she saw her face as Adam saw it, *You are wise as the bush-tail, Ishah,* and she had said is the bush-tail not wise? and he had said, *Not very wise . . . I did not say it was foolish.*

But it is not very wise.

You see the garden as the cattle, or as the dumb brutes see it: without understanding.

I have told you: your eyes cannot see it.

You have no knowledge.

Unless you taste the fruit.

—God has forbidden it, she said. Shall I taste the fruit, which God has forbidden?

The dragon flexed his talons in the grass, lazily. What is that to me? And she saw her own face in the water, as Adam saw it.

—I will ask Adam, she said. When he returns, I will ask him.

—Ask him, then. But you know already what he will say.

She knew what he would say. He would say, These things are of God, Ishah; Elohim knows. And he would say, Angels are not like the creatures of the garden, that we can go and look for them. How shall I show you such a thing?

She saw her face in the water, her own face, and yet not her own: in imagination shining with light, bright as an angel, wise as Igwana, with all knowledge. She put her hand down slowly to break the spell of it: and the water's chill clasp closed on her wrist.

—But if we die!

If . . .

—You will not die, Igwana said.

His voice was distant, and she lifted her head. He had gone a way up-stream to the river's edge again, where the bank shelved down to the water.

—He said we would die, Ishah said.

—So that you should not eat the fruit. For God knows that in the day you eat it, your eyes will be opened, and you will be as the angels, knowing good and evil.

—Good, we know already! Ishah said.

—And evil?

He entered the water as Leviathan did, easing himself down with no splash, soundlessly, the downward stream was scarcely disturbed. She saw the surface close again over him, the last end-scales of his tail gone down in a bright ripple: and the river empty from bank to bank, as if he had never been.

Only the words remained, lingering on the still air of the afternoon: *You will be as the angels . . .*

She suddenly dipped her hands to drink, cupping them with a little splash that broke the spell of it; laughed for the sweet cool of water on her tongue; swung her legs over to sit, splashing her feet to froth the stream, winced at the cold spray and laughed again, throwing her head back, and the garland of flowers she had braided in her hair flew out into the grass.

She went and fetched it, and began to fasten her hair again, sitting with her ankles in the stream.

Between her two feet the face came again, mirrored: and she regarded it seriously, braiding her hair. The sun behind her head made a halo of bright-ness there, and in imagination she saw herself shining in beauty like Igwana, and Adam beside her shining; lowering her eyelids to consider the picture she made. As the angels . . . Adam and Ishah. And she tried to remember the fruit of the tree; but she had not seen it. And she wondered what it was like.

When she had finished with her hair, she withdrew her feet and stood up, looking to see if Adam was coming; but she could not see him. She went a little way down the river bank, uncertainly; and then turned back. I will not touch it. She began to walk towards the forest.

Only look at it.

Adam, hot from the long climb, swung his aching legs loose over a ledge of rock, grateful for its coolness. At first, coming up from the river valley, he had slackened his pace so that he should not tire the kid; but once among the broken hills it had outdistanced him, sensing the presence of the flock long before Adam found the first dung, or saw any movement. So he let it go on alone, waiting only to see it safe: its bleating once answered, when the horned she-goat leapt down from rock to rock to meet it. And now, having rested, he turned back.

The downward path was easier. But he was too tired to hurry. The sun, which had been behind him all the way up, was now full in his eyes; so that he presently turned aside another way where there were pine trees growing, making his own path down through them; the more slowly for the pleasure of their shade, the silent leaf-mould soft underfoot. He could have lingered there willingly until the cool of the day: but the thought of Ishah in the valley drew him down. And he thought he would rest awhile with her there beside the river, before they went back to the adamah again: a little while. And then the remembrance of it, the little work done that day until now, quickened his stride. He saw the bright street of the thán again winding far below him as he came out of the trees.

Coming down over the grass to the river bank he thought, for a moment, that he had mistaken the place. Not until he had swum the stream, and found the sheltering bough thrown down and shrivelled, the grass crushed where she had lain, was he sure. He called her name.

She had not waited, then.

—Ishah!

But she was gone, and he moved restlessly, unable to account for her going. Waking she must have seen the tracks, must have known that Adam had gone with the kid. The way of man and beast at the water crossing were plain to see, if she had looked for the tracks. And he cast about for hers in the grass; but it was difficult to tell in the grass.

Only at the edge of the bank was the ground soft enough to tell clearly: as if her foot had slipped as she entered the water—and he thought, She had gone another way to meet me.

But it was the dragon, not the woman, whose tracks were in the mud there; not Ishah, but Igwana, the forked talons pressed deep, the dragon, the shining one . . . Then he found the place where Ishah had been, the footprints, lower down, but at the river's edge again.

She is gone with the dragon.

The place was very still. His own shadow was still, tall beside the water; the water lapping gently under the bank, still in the midstream.

A scarlet flower, loose on the grass, puzzled his mind.

It drew his eyes for its colour, a flower in the flowering grasses: one scarlet among the many white. And he remembered that she had braided her hair with scarlet that day. She had made a garland, pricking each stem with her nail and drawing another through it, linking them in a strand. And then, considering the one flower there, Adam dropped down on one knee, and his shadow sprang small to his foot. It was to drink that she had lain there. She had come no farther than the bank. She had not crossed over with Igwana, she had drunk and turned back.

Because he knew she must have returned to the adamah, Adam found her tracks again easily, leading up beside the forest. He went at a slow trot with no more than a glance down as he ran. And he thought, She is gone back to the adamah because it is a working day. And we have made our own Sabbath by the river. He was ashamed, then, because he had been thinking of nothing but the woman and the cool of grass: and she had thought of the work.

With the sun on his shoulders he remembered his thirst, half wishing he had delayed by the thán to refresh himself; half thinking to turn aside again; but he ran on. How shall I answer Elohim, if Ishah works alone? When he glanced down again he had lost the tracks.

For a moment he hesitated. And then, with growing surprise, went back to trace their new direction.

She had turned abruptly into the forest itself, running—the footprints smaller and deeper, with a longer stride. And then after a little way slowing. There was a confusion of signs, as if she had halted, then gone a short way to her right hand, now to her left; as if she were lost in this part of the forest.

He should have turned back, he knew. And he said it, I must turn back. She was not lost, he was sure. But she was not going to the adamah, either. The thought of the work not completed, the unfinished hedge, held him. I will go a little way; and if I don't find her, I will turn back. There was a spray of the young leaves snapped off and thrown down: for no reason that he could tell. Once, she had circled back and Adam, following with relief, set his face towards the adamah again. If Elohim came, he would tell him, I delayed in the forest a little while, but not long; for Ishah's sake, to be with her. And he thought that Elohim had himself made Ishah to be with Adam; Adam with Ishah: and the tracks swerved aside again through a clearing in the trees.

There, in the open suddenly bright with sunshine, she had taken a whole branch and dragged it down to the midst of the clearing.

And Adam knew, then, that she meant him to follow.

The way of the branch along the ground pointed where she had gone. Intent upon the tracks he had given himself no pause to look about him, sensing the direction: now he was so far into the forest it would be as well to go to the adamah this way as by another. But passing among closer trees on rising ground, as the tracks led him on, he knew the place: the ferns growing steeply at his left hand, masking the dell, where the narrow pathway went down to the tree of knowledge. Even before Ishah answered his call, close at hand, he knew that she was within the dell itself.

His first thought was to go to her.

He thrust through the ferns, his feet on the path down, and the cool of the dell flowed back to him in a quiet; and his footsteps slowed, and stopped altogether. He opened his mouth to call her and the thought came to him, The presence of the Lord God is with her.

Because the place was forbidden them; she knew; she would not have gone down of herself.

He went on down more slowly, then, softly, wary of the brightness.

But there was none: only the cool and the half-light. He entered the dell
uncertainly and at first did not see her, turning his head this way and that
to look.

And then he saw her: and was still.

She was standing by the moss mound, her pale shape there as the white
lily by some green pool, his darling, with her hair unbound. And it was like
the hurt in his side the day that she was made: the rush of tenderness within
him, that lifted his heart to his throat, and choked him. Her face was turned
aside, perfectly still, as some forest creature ware of a sound. And yet more
beautiful than any creature of earth or air: the last and loveliest thing God
made. He said, Ishah, and she turned.

In heaven itself he could imagine none more to be desired; nor any
place more blessed than where her feet walked, bringing her to him, the dell
a mist of late sunbeams, a place of dreams about her: the smell of her hair
remembered, and the littleness of her captive hands—trembling: he felt them
tremble, and held them.

—Ishah, he said, and she said, I have something to tell you.

But her eyes fled his own. Not her hands only, but her whole being
trembled with some inward excitement, something held secret to amaze him.
It was Igwana, he knew: how she had seen the dragon down by the river.
He was going to say it; and held his tongue because it would spoil her pleasure. He let her go and she moved restlessly, not looking at him, moving a
little way apart, and stopping again. And he thought of the young hinds
grazing.

—I have been looking at the tree, she said.

Its shadow lay across her, the dark mass of the leaves here and there
speckled with light still. Almost, he had forgotten the tree. He should go from
this place, he knew. All through the forest until he found her he had put off
his weariness but now, when he stood still, when he leaned down to sit, and
lay back against the soft mound of moss, his hands behind his head to watch
her, it was as if he lacked the strength so much as to rise again. And he
thought, if the thing displeased Elohim, he would not have sent the woman to
go through the forest before Adam. He closed his eyes, but not for weariness:
only so that opening them he might see her there still. Blood of my blood,
he said. Flesh of my flesh. And she said, I have been looking at the tree.

It was too late to return to the adamah now. There would be no light to
work by. And he thought, It is too late; watching her.

—And the fruit of it, she said: is it true that we cannot eat the fruit?
Have you seen it, Adam?—have you seen how tender-skinned and ripe it is?

And then she said, I am sure it is good for food.

—Ishah, Adam said.

He stretched out his hand open for hers, to call her back. Don't be foolish. Come, let us go. I know where there is a fruit as yellow and ripe as this.
. . . But he did not rise. The thought of the fruit brought his thirst back
again, worse than before. Shall we eat of the forbidden fruit—and die?

He wanted her to laugh, to run and catch hold of his hands, lending her quick strength to his tiredness for the long climb up to the shelter. But she came slowly.

—You call me foolish, she said. But we have both been foolish; and more than you know. We will not die if we eat of the tree. Do you know why it is called the tree of knowledge? Because its fruit will make us wise, Adam—wise to know all things! Igwana himself has told me.

—Is it true? But he did not think it was true. He caught her wrist, so slender his fingers quite encircled it; touched the sweet curve of her arm.

—It is true, Adam! In the day that we eat the fruit we shall be as the angels.

He held the pale loveliness of her face small between his two hands, infinitely precious to him. As the angels! she said; and he said, What have the angels, that I lack?

—Knowledge! And she drew back with a small fierce movement away from him. They can tell good and evil, they are wise—oh, Adam! Will you be content for ever, to have no more understanding than the beasts? But I am not content for you!

Adam, watching her swift, impatient movements, wanted to smile; and could not; held from smiling by the uncertain truth of her words. She spoke rapidly, urgently; it was as if he were carried away on the stream of her words; no longer listening, but watching her, the movement of her slender shoulders, and her bright hair tossed back. Has Elohim made anything more perfect than this?

It was the movement that gave him warning: the sudden ducking of her bright head in under the tree, her outstretched arm pale among the dark leaves: and he sprang up.

—*Ishah*—!

But he was too late. He caught at her hand, loosening the fruit from her fingers. But she let it go willingly and gave it to him, and slipped away; and he saw that she held another to her mouth.

A moment: and the soft ripple of her laughter came back to him.

—Didn't I tell you? she said. It is sweeter than the honeycomb! Throw yours away then, if you want to. But as for me, Adam, do you still not believe that my eyes will be opened?

And she stood laughing, but softly: fairer than the lily, than the beauty of lilies in the dusk, his darling with her hair unbound—as God made her. Do you still not believe it, Adam, my Adam?

And the thought came to him that God had not made the thing so fair to destroy it, and Adam with her. Not Adam, but God made them one flesh. And he bit through the yellow skin of the fruit in his hand.

And it was as she had said, sweeter than honey and the honeycomb.

They were naked.

He knew his own nakedness as he stood, and lifting his face, saw

Ishah's eyes upon him. In the same moment she turned and fled from the dell.

He might have turned and followed her. But he sat with the yellow fruit in his hand, naked against the grass mound with his knees hunched, his beard on his chest. A trickle of the fruit sap trailed down stickily over his wrist and formed a drop. He looked at the fruit, not seeing it, seeing her image there in naked flight, her face with all the laughter gone out of it.

Even the sound of her was gone.

If she had called him, he would have followed and found her: if she had made so much as a sign or a gesture. And he thought, Let her go, then. The sap on his wrist was sticky, and he wiped his wrist on the grass. In his mouth it had for a little eased his thirst, but now it was worse than before, with a bitter taste.

And he thought it was well with the woman, because she had drunk her fill at the thán, and rested, and afterwards had come up here walking at her ease. But as for Adam, he had neither drunk nor rested from the hill pastures to the dell for her sake. Beside the river she had not waited for his coming, and in the dell she fled from him—it was as though she fled from him—caring nothing for his weariness.

He was angry, then. The fruit he had tasted was gall in his mouth. The thirst tormented him, and he bit into the fruit again more deeply for the first sweetness of it, and got up, and went to the tree for another—one more. And he said, Seeing I have tasted of the tree.

—What is it to me, whether I eat one fruit or two?

He ate seven before his thirst was satisfied. Twice he stopped to listen: and once turned his head to look behind him. Above the high banks the forest ringed the dell with darkness, as it were full of eyes that watched him. And he suddenly snatched up a stone in his hand and flung it high over the bank.

He heard it strike among branches, and then crash down in the ferns. But nothing moved there.

Once, he thought Ishah had returned. He imagined she crept silently, with suppressed laughter, to surprise him. But when he looked the dell was empty.

Not empty: peopled with shadows like living things, creeping closer little by little, moment by moment near; hidden when he looked; watching him all the time.

He left the dell half running, not looking back, in haste from the naked half-light for the refuge of the trees, for the closer darkness to cover him, to lose himself in it safe and be as one with the night and the forest creatures. But even the darkness was alien. He ran wildly, hurting himself among the waiting trees, spewing out the bitter aftertaste of the fruit, but he could not spew it out, it clung in his mouth. There seemed no end to the forest, no way out that he could find or remember: he could find no pathway through the tangled underwoods. The place was quiet for his stumbling. He fell, and there was no sound at all: only the listening for him; the listening and the waiting. And then, when he would have cried out aloud for Elohim the gall rose in his throat and choked him, and he lay as one dead.

And this was death, the absence of God: to be alone in the dark, and afraid.

3 The Murder of Abel

To Murray Sheehan, Adam was more than innocence, he was pompous ignorance. He envisioned a world designed for his use. He neither valued nor appreciated it. He rejected Cain at birth because he resented his son, and he used Eve as a drudge while he spent his time creating meaningless rituals. When Abel was born, Adam appointed this second son to help him with his worship. When Cain, who was raised by a goat and had come to love and understand the world as a beautiful place, joined the family circle, he could not understand either his brother or father. In the selection from *Eden* which follows Murray Sheehan writes of the murder of Abel, of Cain's motives, and of the first realization that men are mortal. For Sheehan, Man has corrupted the world God gave him, and there is nothing irreligious in loving the natural world of God, nor anything religious about empty ritual.

And Cain talked with Abel his brother: and it came to pass, when they were in the field, that Cain rose up against Abel his brother, and slew him.

And the Lord said unto Cain, Where is Abel thy brother? And he said, I know not: Am I my brother's keeper?

And he said, What hast thou done? the voice of thy brother's blood crieth unto me from the ground.

And now art thou cursed from the earth, which hath opened her mouth to receive thy brother's blood from thy hand:

When thou tillest the ground, it shall not henceforth yield unto thee her strength; a fugitive and a vagabond shalt thou be in the earth.

And Cain said unto the Lord, My punishment is greater than I can bear.

Behold, thou hast driven me out this day from the face of the earth; and from thy face shall I be hid; and I shall be a fugitive and a vagabond in the earth; and it shall come to pass, that every one that findeth me shall slay me.

And the Lord said unto him, Therefore whosoever slayeth Cain, vengeance shall be taken on him sevenfold. And the Lord set a mark upon Cain, lest any finding him should kill him.

GENESIS: IV, 8–15

EDEN by MURRAY SHEEHAN

THE SUN WAS SHINING when Cain opened his eyes and found himself suddenly awake. For a moment he could not think where he was. Then the full implication of the sun's having risen and his lying there broke upon him, and he sprang to his feet and ran down towards the bank of the little stream. He saw the two other men coming from their altars, and heard them call to him. But he did not wait to discover what they said. He ran across, stirred up his fire, piled on the wood, and then, when there was flame, he threw on a handful of scented herbs, forgetful of ablutions, ritual, and genuflections.

When he turned, he had leisure now to smile across the stream at Adam and Abel, who stood sourly gazing at him.

He waved a hand of greeting, but they were blind.

"Hello, how are you?" he called, but they were deaf.

Undaunted, he set foot in the stream to return. And only now did Adam come to life. Without a word, he turned and marched into the larger hut.

"Why didn't you wake me for the sacrifice?" demanded Cain, as he came up the bank, smiling at Abel.

"You were sleeping, or pretended to be, when it was time," growled the other.

"Lord, I slept like . . . like a kid," went on Cain gaily, undisturbed by his brother's insolence, which was evidently his sole social manner. "But I sacrificed."

"You can't call that a sacrifice," said Abel. "And neither does the Lord God."

"What makes you think so?" asked Cain.

"Think so?" repeated Abel. "I know it. You forgot to wash yourself."

"Well, I wasn't so very dirty," smiled Cain. "Except . . . except this . . . this garment that I put on yesterday." He did not wish to offend the sensibilities of the other, who approved of sheepskins.

"And you didn't bow," said Abel.

"Heigh-ho, I forgot that," chuckled Cain. "Do you suppose the Lord sets great store by the bowing?"

"And you ignored the way my father showed you last night to move your hands."

"When the heart is right, can the hands be wrong?" was Cain's reply. "I swear I was ready in my soul to glorify the Lord this morning, and I gave Him most hearty thanks."

"Well, He had no respect to your offering, I can tell you that," was the gloomy answer of the younger.

"What makes you think so? In my heart of hearts I awoke this morning with praise, and sang a canticle of love for all the world and all that therein is."

"H'm!" sneered Abel. "Well, look what you're bringing upon us already."

Cain looked up, and saw, in sooth, that the sun was gone. Clouds were piling aloft as he had never seen them in all his life that he could remember.

"Well, what of it? What do you mean?" asked Cain, looking straight at Abel.

"This is the vengeance of the Lord upon you, that's what I mean," said Abel. "This is your doing."

"Nonsense," said Cain. "This is a storm a-brewing, that's all."

"This is a storm descending upon us all in vengeance of your sacrilege, that's what it is, I tell you."

"And I tell you, my fine young fellow, that this is no such thing. Do you think that the Lord God is a pusillanimous creature like yourself, to take vengeance for the washing or the not washing of a pair of hands? For the absence of a crooked knee? For a set of fingers not waved exactly? Nonsense."

"The Lord God will smite you, wait and see."

"The Lord God will not smite me, that I can swear. Or if He does, then so be it. It will not be in wrath. If He will smite me, let Him smite me. I am willing. What the Lord doeth, He doeth in justice, and not in judgment. I am not afraid."

"Impious fool!" raved Abel.

"Impious yourself," was Cain's reply, who was calm again. "There is such peace between God and me as you will never know. Even if God strikes me down, I shall not complain. Which is more, evidently, than you can say. You seem to fear the striking of God's hand. I have more faith in Him."

"Well, look at your sacrifice then, and see what the Lord God thinks of it!"

Cain looked across the stream. The smoke from his fire was curling low, falling from the altar towards the ground, lingering sullenly over the fire like an angry slow serpent. A silence fell upon them, as though an unseen third had been standing there present with them. Then could hear the fire on Abel's altar sputtering and boiling contentedly over some fat morsel of the sacrificial offering.

"And come see how the Almighty accepts my offering," said Abel.

He strode down towards his altar proudly, and stood with folded arms to watch the effect on Cain. Here the smoke was mounting straight and lusty into the upper air.

"It might be explained, you know," said Cain quietly, as he followed Abel, "by some counter current of the air in the one case, and by the draught of the upland on the other side."

"And it might be explained, also you know," mocked Abel, "by the fact that the Lord God has respect to a proper sacrifice in the one case, and has no respect at all to what is no sacrifice, in the other."

Cain did not reply. His eye had been caught by some dark spattering stains that dyed the side of the altar, which had dripped and clotted and gone dry, and here and there seemed fresher and were still wet.

"What are those?" he asked, and his face was darkened.

"Those?" repeated Abel, and looked where Cain pointed.

"Blood," he said calmly. "Blood from the sacrifice that is killed for the Lord each day. The Lord God liveth and reigneth, and He likes His sacrifice hot, fresh-slaughtered to His service."

Cain looked up to the turmoil in the heavens. What did it portend? Was it true what Abel had just said? Was he himself wrong? Had he offended egregiously against the Lord? Did he sin in not taking more seriously this sacrifice enjoined upon him by these men?

The fat in the fire continued to splutter.

"Why are you wroth?" went on Abel, pressing his evident advantage.

"I am not wroth," said Cain.

"And why is your countenance fallen? If you do well, shall you not be accepted? And if you do not well, sin lies at the door."

Cain only looked at him in his empty prating of sin, and would not again be stirred to anger. Abel was baffled in his efforts to prick the man's resentment.

"Well, call your goat," he said at last, sneering.

Cain looked at him a moment longer and then glanced about him.

"Call your goat," came the second gloating sneer.

"Where is she?" asked Cain.

Abel waited a moment before he replied.

"Why, there she is," he laughed, pointing.

"Where?" asked Cain again, looking in the direction indicated.

"There."

And only now did Cain see that he was pointing towards the altar.

"You . . . You . . . ?" he shouted, looking at the man, and his body crouched slightly and he quivered.

Abel answered nothing, but blankly grinned.

Then suddenly Cain had thrown himself upon the younger man, and he had brought down his iron fists upon the other's head, felling him to the ground. His face went dark with anger. A passion mightier than himself was wielding his frame, and its spirit glared from his eyes and tensed the great cords of his fury. It drove him down upon his brother's chest with his knees, and sent his eager thumbs searching into the depths of the throat of the prostrate figure. It clenched his teeth. It maddened him, and Cain did not know what he was doing. Again and again he bore with his full force upon the tender throat. And now his hands were warm, and they were wet, and they were dark.

Suddenly the wild thing left him, and Cain found himself kneeling on the still body of his brother. His hands were sunk in the young man's flesh. There was . . . there was . . . something on his hands. He loosed his grip. He slipped to one side. Abel did not move. What was the red trickle that ran from him like a snake, like an ant-hill pouring out its hosts, like the sap from a tree that is wounded in the spring?

Only, this was red. Red.

Cain looked up from this thing to his hands. From his hands he looked up to the sides of the altar.

Then he knew.

This was blood.

Why did he lie so quiet?

Cain tried to wake him.

"Abel," he whispered, and put his hand on the boy's arm.

"Abel," he whispered again.

Then with a quick movement he drew back from the body, and a terror came upon him, he did not know why. Why would not the boy move? With his eyes still held by the blank face of his brother, he struggled to his feet and stumbled to run away.

But he could not go. There, coming close upon him were the man and the woman, issuing from the shelter, and descending upon the spot where lay their son motionless.

Cain dropped upon the ground and hid his face in his arms, cowering before the wrath to come. It was not fear that moved him, it was a terror bred of uttermost confusion, doubt, and physical exhaustion. He could endure no more.

"What's this!" said Adam suddenly as he came near. "Blood upon the ground at this time of the morning? This will not do. Abel, what is the meaning of this fresh blood?"

There was silence.

"Do you hear me?" blustered the man, stirring the lad's hip with his foot. "Why are you lying there? You know that the Lord God will have no killing except at the time of sacrifice, before the morning altar. I have taught you better than this. Stand up."

As Eve continued to look, suddenly a little wavering wail escaped from her lips, and she dropped to her knees beside Abel's body.

"Adam," she gasped, "this is . . . this is death!"

Stupidly the man was silent for a moment. Why was the woman prating now about death, when the Thunderer was giving no sign?

"Death?" he repeated dully. "Nonsense. What has blood to do with death?"

"But Adam," she wailed again, "this is death . . . this is the death of Abel."

Adam stooped to look at his son, following up the trickles of blood.

"But this is not death, I tell you," he repeated stubbornly. "This has nothing to do with death. There is no sound of thunder in the air. And we . . . we cannot die. The animals die, when we kill them. We do not die. Who would kill us?"

"This is the vengeance of the Lord," cried Eve. "Sent from the tree of the knowledge of good and evil. This is the fruit of the Garden, sent for your disobedience. This is death, sent from the hand of God. The Almighty has killed the child of my body."

Then Adam roused himself and denied it.

"You know nothing about such things," he said. "Do not talk sacrilege. God is my business, and not yours. I know all His affairs and mine. And I tell you, this is not death."

Eve rocked herself.

"But I know, and I know, and I know," she sobbed hysterically. "I don't know how I know, but I know! God said, 'For thou shalt surely die!' And this is death."

Adam was silent, still fumbling with the boy's body, shaking his arm and prodding his side, trying to wake him from his stupor. Then suddenly his wrath flared up in him, and he turned viciously upon the woman.

"Then you have killed my son!" he said. "If the fruit of the Tree has brought this thing upon us, it is not the Lord God Almighty that has done it, it is you. For you offered me the apple in the Garden, and if it had not been for you, I should still have been there, for ever and ever."

He was looking at her now with an old fury that had lasted through the years. He had never forgiven her that thing. He had been saying through all the time since Eden that he was glad they had been delivered from the place. Now his old submerged lie was uncovered, on the surface.

Eve was too deeply sunk in her sorrow to reply.

"The Lord Almighty Jehovah had said that if I ate of the apples, death would come. And He and I understood one another, and I did not touch the apples, and I should never have touched them in all eternity, if it had not been for you. There came no thunder. There never would have come thunder. But you came, and you lured me, woman, to the eating of them, and I fell. If thus death came into the world, and this be death . . . then death be on your shoulders, and my son's blood!"

Adam turned and raised his eyes to heaven.

"There is no righteousness but mine, O Lord," he exclaimed solemnly, and waved his hands in ritual.

"Cursed be God, say I, who devised this thing!" muttered Eve from the ground, as she sat and rocked herself beside the dead body of her son. But, mercifully, Adam did not hear her.

Cain raised himself on one elbow, and brushed back the hair from his eyes.

"I did it," he gasped. "I did it myself."

"You did what?" demanded Adam, looking down for the first time at Cain, not understanding.

"I killed him!"

"You . . . ?" cried Adam, and his eyes sprang wide.

"I killed Abel," continued Cain. "I smote the life from his body and squeezed the breath from his throat. Blood came. And he died."

"You . . . ?" repeated Adam, once more, aghast. "It was not the hand of God?"

Cain raised himself higher.

"And I am glad of it!" he broke forth.

Adam said no word, but his hand went suddenly groping behind him towards the altar, where lay the sacrificial rock for the smashing in of his victims' skulls. His eyes stayed on Cain's face.

"I'm glad of it," repeated Cain, rising to his feet. "If I've brought death in the world, why then it's you, and I . . . and God Himself, all together, who have done the thing. God first, Who thought of death, according to what you said. Then you, who ate of the apples in the Garden. And now . . . I am the killer."

"Sacrilege, too," muttered Adam beneath his breath, who had got the stone in his hand, and was half-crouching to attack his son.

Cain was standing straight.

"For years now you've been bringing death into the world yourself, with your sacrifice, every dawn, in the name of the Lord," he said. "Sheep, and oxen, and . . . and goats."

Adam drew in his breath shortly at the last word, and a sharp light of understanding came into his eyes. He glanced hurriedly at the altar beside him, and his hand wavered with the rock in it.

"You mean . . . ?" he whispered hoarsely. Then, as he continued to stare at Cain, his body seemed to collapse, and a great trembling took hold of him.

For this had his son been done to death! For the sake of . . . No, he would not think of it! For the sake of an animal which, one night . . . No, he must banish the thought! For the sake of . . . God help him to forget the ignominy of his memories!

The man turned and laid down the rock, and again faced up to heaven.

"Vengeance is mine, saith the Lord," he muttered. "I would not touch the man now, not even to his death."

Without another word, he walked away from the presence of the murderer, his eyes turned skywards.

Eve was no longer weeping. There had come a stony glare about her eyes, as she had heard Cain's words. For now she too was remembering the creature whose death had brought about his death who had been dearest to her of all things. She was remembering the birth of Abel, and his black curls. She was remembering how she had been forced, in the earliest days after her travail, to come out, herself, and rescue her firstborn from . . . from that creature. She was remembering how she had fought with the brute for the infant. And fought in vain. And lost him. And here he was, come only yesterday into their midst. And now, so soon, this! And for . . . !

There was silence between her and Cain. At the top of the hill could be heard the stiff wind blowing across the upper world, rising in strength from moment to moment.

When she rose unsteadily to her feet without a word, and drew away from him, the stubborn resistance seemed to melt from Cain in a moment, and his eyes went tender at the sight. He tried to come close to her.

"I am sorry," he tried to whisper to her. But Eve twitched herself away, and went stolidly towards the shelter, into whose depths Adam had retreated.

When she had disappeared, Cain followed after, towards the hut.

"Vengeance is the Lord's," muttered Adam as he saw his son approaching. At the door, Cain stopped, and knelt down upon the ground.

"I have sinned," he said. "I have sinned greatly, in that I have brought death into the world, where there was none before . . . among men." This latter phrase he put in, in very justice to . . . well, to all the dumb things that had died already on the altar in past years.

"What can I do to cleanse me of my sin?" he went on. "What would you have me to do to free my hands from guilt, and make clean my heart within me? Lay what burden you will on my shoulders, take what years you will of my life, let me labor and go heavily laden all the days of my living if you will. But let me be forgiven. I would not live always in the sense of my shame and my wickedness."

Adam had rested silent through all of this. At first he was stubborn, and would not listen. But when the man spoke of burdens to be borne, and labor to be done, the older man in his bereavement opened his ears, and sternly he began to judge within him.

At length Adam opened his lips, and delivered his sentence.

"All the days of your life shall you be as a slave and a beast of burden in my sight," he commanded. "From now on henceforth shall you be a hewer of wood and a drawer of water, to work and to toil with your hands at my command, to go and come at my orders, and do all the things which are laid upon you. Then will I speak to the Lord in your behalf, and strive to gain from Him forgiveness for the grievous offence which you have this day done."

Eve groaned. How could the man at this time speak at such length?

Cain bowed himself.

"So be it," he said.

"Throw now a buffalo skin across my feet," commanded Adam, "for I would sleep a while and forget my great sorrow. Wait you outside until I call."

Cain did as he was bid, and retreated from the presence.

Then there were declarations made in Heaven. Debate they may not be called. God knew what He wanted. There were not two sides to the question to be argued. With Him there never are. Omniscience is unique.

"This will never do," quoth God the Father to Himself, as He sat in ineffable majesty that noontide. "Cain must not rest with these twain, nor be subjected to their nefarious influences."

"Our name is forever on their lips, yet they have no slightest comprehension of Our nature," quoth the second Godhead. "This man who has this day done murder is yet our only hope and stay for the years to come. We must safe-guard him to Our use. And soon, at that, lest he be transmogrified to their likeness and so be lost to Us."

"Yet since he has done murder, must We mask Our plans behind the guise of curses, so that his name may go down to ages yet to come as one who is anathema," quoth Godhead the Third. "We must not encourage murder."

"He killed man, to be sure," said the Son, "and was wrong. But he did it through love and devotion to another. Abel, too, had killed, and albeit his killing was but that of a goat, yet it was done without heart, in hatred and spite, and was sin in Our eyes, beyond that of Cain."

"We shall lift Cain above bondage and ignoble toil," came the closing words of God Himself. "Raise him out of this valley and its labor so that he may have leisure for the contemplation of Our mysteries and secrets. He shall not plough nor sow nor reap, but tend cattle on the hills, and live in the tents of the wanderers, play upon the harp and organ, he and all his children through the age forevermore, and be subtile artificers in brass and iron."

And so it was decided.

Rumblings and tumbled confusions then were heard from the heavens, before the faces of the two remaining men and the woman, and the voice of the thunder was heard, which was to them as the vocables of God.

Adam and Eve cowered in their shelter, and in his lone hut Cain cowered too, caught already into some modicum of the local contagion.

Finally the dread voice of God was heard bellowing the name of Cain from the midst of the whirlwind that was upon them.

"Cain, come forth," it boomed in tones of wrath.

"Aha, not so lightly is he to escape the vengeance of the Almighty," said Adam in his beard. He motioned to Cain in the far doorway to go forth, go forth, into the tempest, and make plain his presence, and be destroyed. It was hard, he felt, that his plans for future leisure and ease must be thus upset. He could have used to good advantage the services of this husky man under his dominion. Still, it was something to have the Lord God so furious in his, Adam's, behalf, so hasty and anxious in retribution of his, Adam's, son. His, Adam's, was high patronage, indeed. It was small compensation for the loss of a laboring hand, but it was something to talk about, at that. He must breed sons and grandsons to whom he could relate the thing.

"Cain, come forth," boomed the voice of God again, in the tempest. The hills took up the sound for miles about and repeated the summons *ad infinitum*.

Then Cain came forth.

His head was high, and there was a new look of bitter scorn about his mouth. His eyes were heavy as they had never been in Eden, and he was thinking thoughts of rebellion against the Universe that he had never before conceived. Was this the God Whom he had thought on in the silent stretches of the night in Paradise? Was this the God Who ruled the stars in their courses, and held true the planets in their vast marches across the sky? Was this the Almighty Father beyond all good and evil, beyond the great silent booming of eternity which he had heard outside the furthest stretches of imagination? Was this the God of Whom there could be nothing said except that He was?

And now was He come down in championship of such a man as Adam?

Cain lifted up his chin and spoke his words clearly.

"Here I am," he said.

"And where is Abel, your brother?" clanged forth the thunder.

"I don't know," shouted the anarch. "Am I my brother's keeper?"

"What have you done?" began the thunder's voice. "The voice of your brother's blood cries out unto Me from the ground. And now are you cursed from this earth, which has opened her mouth to receive your brother's blood from your hand."

Adam turned in the semi-darkness at sound of this, and nodded to Eve significantly. Had he not said as much?

"When you till the ground, it shall not henceforth yield unto you her strength," went on the thunder's accents. "A fugitive and a vagabond shall you be in the earth."

Cain sank down upon the earth which was for him henceforth accursed. Was there no pity in Heaven? He could see no import in the fearful words of the Almighty, except that he was henceforth an outcast.

"My punishment is greater than I can bear," he sobbed, his head sunk down upon his chest. His words hardly carried to the hut where Adam was listening. But they came clearly to the ear of God.

"Behold," he said, "Thou hast driven me out this day from the face of the earth, and from Thy face shall I be hid."

God smiled and shook His head, it was not so. But before Adam He said nothing to disillusion Cain now.

"And I shall be a fugitive and a vagabond in the earth," went on the murderer. "And it shall come to pass that every one that findeth me shall slay me."

God nodded to Himself, and knew the danger that Cain ran. He must protect this wandering child of His from such extinction.

"Therefore," spoke forth the thunder clearly, so that it might surely reach the ears of Adam and Eve, "whosoever slays Cain, vengeance shall be taken on him sevenfold."

There came a blinding flash of lightning, which illumined the whole valley. When it was gone its stunning brilliance and rustle of sharp sound was ended, behold, Cain lay upon the ground before the hut insensate. On his forehead was a mark as of the hand of God, set there for a sign and a symbol, to set him and his sons and his sons' sons to all time as things apart, for ever inviolable at the hands of lesser men, excepting at their peril, sinning against the light.

Then came the rain, and the welded bolts of light and sound, on all sides except the one, to the eastward, even as they had done those years ago when that other man had been driven out of Eden. Adam and Eve lived through again that terrible ordeal, and crouched, and shuddered in their wattled hut, and for a time wondered if it was for them that the display was made.

Cain woke, and roused himself, and moved off to the eastward, and left the valley. The storm raged behind him, and the bellowing accents of God's wrath were heard for miles about, while animals hid in their caves or burrowed deeper in their shelters and there quaked for fear.

But when Cain had run and stumbled eastward, towards the Land of Nod, out of the immediate earshot of that valley where lived the man and his wife, the storm abated somewhat, and Cain was not so hounded in his course.

Neither Adam nor Eve knew when their son left them, for their heads were buried in the multitudinous stuffy coverings of their bed. When at length the storm grew less vehement, and they could look abroad, Cain was gone.

They were alone in the world. As they had been in the beginning, so were they now again, alone, and childless.

They were even more alone than before. For they were comfortless, who had known comfort. A dead child of their bodies lay beyond there in the wet, awaiting sepulture. Their other son was gone, to return no more, to become through all their lives a bane to their rememberance, and a curse upon their lips. The man, and the woman too, now spat upon his memory. Never did they know, more, ever, the revivifying fire of the spirit of Eden.

4 Noah's Ark

In *Two by Two* David Garnett says he started out to write a "frivolous gloss upon the most charming story in the Bible." However, as with most of his books, "a parable kept pushing its way in." No one would question that the story of Noah has meaning for our own time, but Garnett's tale has a great validity in its own right. There is a quiet warmth here, a simplicity which many authors have forgotten is one of the great assets of the Bible itself. Trained as a scientist, Garnett has been writing most of his life. His *Lady into Fox*, written over forty years ago, has become a minor classic. Anyone reading the story about the fictional twins, Niss and Fan, their thoughts about the flood, the tale of Ham's rejection, and the life after the deluge will understand why *Two by Two* has been compared with that earlier masterpiece.

And God saw that the wickedness of man was great in the earth, and that every imagination of the thoughts of his heart was only evil continually.

And it repented the Lord that he had made man on the earth, and it grieved him at his heart.

And the Lord said, I will destroy man whom I have created from the face of the earth; both man, and beast, and the creeping thing, and the fowls of the air; for it repenteth me that I have made them.

But Noah found grace in the eyes of the Lord.

GENESIS: VI, 5–8

And Noah began to be an husbandman, and he planted a vineyard:

And he drank of the wine, and was drunken; and he was uncovered within his tent.

And Ham, the father of Canaan, saw the nakedness of his father, and told his two brethren without.

And Shem and Japheth took a garment, and laid it upon both their shoulders, and went backward, and covered the nakedness of their father; and their faces were backward, and they saw not their father's nakedness.

And Noah awoke from his wine and knew what his younger son had done unto him.

And he said, Cursed be Canaan; a servant of servants shall he be unto his brethren.

And he said, Blessed be the Lord God of Shem; and Canaan shall be his servant.

God shall enlarge Japheth, and he shall dwell in the tents of Shem; and Canaan shall be his servant.

GENESIS: IX, 20–27

TWO BY TWO by DAVID GARNETT

THE RAIN FELL in an almost solid mass—without pause or alteration and the sound of it beating on the roof of the ark never ceased and added to the depression of the company.

Niss and Fan being reasoning creatures who knew good from evil, or at least had ideas on the subject, soon found themselves discussing the rights and wrongs of the Deluge.

Niss started it by the words: "It can't be right."

Fan snorted. "Right! There is no right about it. He has just drowned the entire population of the globe—except for present company. Millions of happy and innocent people."

"He has saved Noah and his family. That is to His credit," said Niss.

"But He has drowned the saddler who was as kind a man as you could find anywhere," said Fan.

"And whom you swindled of a gold dinar."

"What has that to do with it?"

There was a silence while Niss thought about it.

"I suppose if He can hear what Noah says, He can hear you," she said at last.

"Actually Noah always shouts at Him as though He were a very long way off. But I jolly well hope He can hear me," said Fan. "I'm not muzzled. And if you want to know I *despise* Him for that Deluge."

Niss nodded her head. "Yes, I'm with you there. In any case He wouldn't like one just because one was afraid of Him."

"I'm not sure of that. According to Noah, God drowned the world because mankind had become corrupt. I suspect it is the other way round. Power corrupts. Absolute power corrupts absolutely."

"So you think that He just drowned everyone in a fit of temper and decided to make a fresh start?"

"That is the theory—if He exists."

"Oh, come off it. This ark full of animals is proof enough that He exists."

"I don't feel sure," said Fan. "Noah might be the most marvellous weather prophet ever known. Or he may have discovered how to make it rain like the African witch doctors."

"I wish he would discover how to make it stop," said Niss. "But how do you account for the animals coming and for their behaviour?"

"I don't know. Hypnotism possibly. I don't begin to know enough to have an opinion. But I shall try my best to find out. At present, just because we are ignorant and can't be bothered to think it out, we father it all on God."

"You admit it's all a bit odd," said Niss.

"I grant you that. Couldn't be odder," said Fan cheerfully. "All the same you'll agree that if it's God's plan, it's a pretty foul show."

"Foul beyond belief," said Niss.

"That's what makes me suspect that Noah thought it up. It's typical human behaviour."

"What's Noah getting out of it?"

"Everything. An obscure drunkard in a hick town in Palestine whom everyone laughed at, has his revenge on his neighbours, and becomes the sole progenitor of the world to be. You can't beat that."

"Blast it," said Fan throwing away the flint which had broken across the point. Then she lifted her eyes and saw a dark man walking towards them from the south along the seashore.

"Look Niss," she whispered and Niss looked up and saw him. He was limping. He was the first man except Gomer they had seen since they had taken that last look at Noah's family beside the lake, while Gomer was crawling down on them to steal the stallion and the mare.

The young man looked up and saw them sitting there and came towards them. He was Ham's son Mizraim. They looked at him but said nothing. Mizraim threw himself down on the grass beside them and he said only:

"So I have found you."

"Where are the others?" asked Niss.

"I don't know. I ran away from them and came to find you."

Fan saw that he was spent with travel so she put aside the stone she was knapping and brought him a cup of mare's milk and Mizraim drank it without thanking her and put his head down on the turf and slept.

He was still sleeping when Gomer came back with five fish he had caught.

He looked at Mizraim queerly and at once asked the same question as Niss. "Where are the others?"

"Mizraim ran away from them and has come a long way looking for us."

"He may be lying and be Noah's spy," said Gomer.

"He is telling the truth," said Fan watching Gomer's face.

"If I killed him now we could be certain that he would never go back and tell where we are."

Niss gutted the five fish and laid them on the flat stone in the middle of the embers.

"Two men are better than one," said Fan.

Mizraim woke up and stretched and rubbed his eyes.

"Come and eat," said Niss, bringing the fish up from the fire. They ate slowly picking the bones out with their fingers. Occasionally Gomer looked at Mizraim as though by accident and Mizraim looked back, expressionless through lowered eyelids.

"What was it that made you come in search of us?" asked Niss.

"It was old Noah. When we got to the edge of the mountain and the plain and the sea, Noah told us that we should settle there. It was a good place indeed, with the sea for fishing, pasture for our flocks and stone and timber for building. Noah had brought seed corn and slips of vines and he planted a vineyard along the lowest slope of the hill while my father and my uncles ploughed a level field below and sowed wheat and barley and millet and the women made their gardens.

"Everything flourished. There were no birds or beetles or rabbits to peck and pierce and gnaw the crops. The first autumn we had enough corn to make bread and porridge. Last autumn Noah had his first grapes. That made him mad. He watched them all the summer, then when he picked them, I had to tread the bunches all day long in a tub.

"It was about six months after the wine was made that one sabbath he did not show up for evening prayers. My father went first to the cave where he kept the jars of wine, then, as he wasn't there, he went to the vineyard, where the vines were just coming into leaf. There was Grandpapa, dead drunk, lying naked in the last rays of the setting sun.

"Father thought it was a joke to be laughed off: he went and called my uncles. Father thought it funny they should all be assembled waiting for the evening prayer while the old man was lying there naked and sozzled. But my uncles were terribly shocked. Japheth cried out that it was an accident and they took a cloak and covered up their father without looking at him. But my father went on making a joke of it and asking them how they could cover him without looking to see where he was. I suppose Shem must have told the old man about it, because next morning while I was lying enjoying the sabbath rest with my father and brothers, Grandpapa came up in a flaming rage and started to curse us. He cursed my brother Canaan and my father and all the rest of us and said we were to be slaves for evermore and do all the rough work for Japheth and Shem and for all their descendants. We should be bought and sold as slaves. And it was to be for ever and ever. Do you know he talked then just as though he were God?

"My Dad said that Grandpapa would get over it and take the curse off us. But he didn't. Next day Shem started ordering us about and when Canaan told him to shut up and clear out, Shem and his sons came and tied up my brother and whipped him until the blood was running down his back.

"I wasn't going to stand for that. I had been thinking about you ever since you went and wishing I had had the courage to go with you. Then I kept wondering how I could find you. There was all the earth for me to look for you in. And then that night after they flogged Canaan, lying awake I got an idea. I thought that you would have been sure to do what we had done, that is, walk until you got to the sea, where you could get a living fishing. Because you had no goats and cows to milk and no sheep. So you must be living on fish. I knew you were north of us and I thought if I followed the coast I must find you. And that's why I am here."

It was dark. The fire was only a glow of embers. Gomer yawned.

The two girls got up and wandered off: they slept close together that night and were silent. The boys lay by the fire but they were distrustful of each other and for some time lay awake listening and hearing nothing but the sudden unexpected wave breaking on the beach and dragging back the shingle.

Next morning the girls had blown up the fire before the boys awoke and when they did wake they were alone and Fan and Niss were visible far out in the shallows by the rocks shrimping.

Later on Mizraim walked down to where Gomer was mending his fishing line and squatted beside him.

"What's the fishing like?" he asked.

"So so."

"As I came up the coast I could see a lot of islands out at sea."

"What of it?"

"If we went off to an island nobody could come near us."

"How would you get there?" asked Gomer.

"We might build a boat. It would be good for fishing too."

"By golly," said Gomer.

"If that lot could build the ark we could build us a little boat that would sail on the sea. And we wouldn't take twenty years about it either," said Mizraim.

"Let's get on with it," said Gomer.

The temper of the two lads changed and when the girls came back and called to them, they were half a mile along the shore dragging out driftwood.

After that they kept away from the girls while they were working, only coming back to the camp for meals. When Niss said that they needed more fish, Gomer grumbled and told her to go and catch it herself. However, afterwards he set some nightlines along the shore and Mizraim went and helped Fan carry in some firewood from the broken forest. But they did not volunteer anything about their work and the girls were too proud to ask questions.

Mizraim's coming had changed the happy unquestioning relationship between Gomer and the sisters. One day when the boys were working together hauling out seasoned tree trunks, Mizraim looked up and said:

"Niss is your girl, isn't she?"

Gomer looked at him and nodded.

"Well, I'll take Fan."

"That's up to her, mate," said Gomer, grinning suddenly. Actually the idea that Niss was his girl and that Fan wasn't was a new one—and somehow it missed the point of their relationship and spoilt it. But with Mizraim there it could not be helped and anyhow there was the boat to build and seas and islands to explore, which would not have been possible without him.

The first craft they put together was a raft with tree trunks lashed together with withies of willow. They poled it about along the shore. The girls swam out and climbed on and when Fan dived from it, Mizraim lost his balance and fell in and was laughed at because he nearly got drowned and was angry. Later on Fan taught him to swim and soon he was better than any of them in the water. This was a consolation to him for he was lame on land and could not run like the others. The raft was heavy and though it made a good platform for fishing, it was no good as a boat.

The next craft was a catamaran made with two tree trunks kept apart by crosspieces. Gomer sat on one side, Mizraim on the other and they paddled along. But a sail was wanted and eventually the girls made one of interwoven flags. This matting sail was heavy and clumsy but it caught the wind and in a stiff breeze they could go fast and rest from paddling. After they had tried it out they shifted camp, Mizraim and Fan sailing and paddling down the coast, Gomer and Niss riding the stallion and the mare with the two-year-old and the young foal trotting beside them.

The horsemen and fishermen who first went down into Greece were their great-grandchildren and great-great-grandchildren. They worshipped the Python at Delphi and made a god of the poet Apollo. They carried on the tradition which Noah had thought so shocking, that the angels, or the gods, fell in love with princesses and shepherd girls and were the fathers of the most beautiful and most exceptional of the human race. They were not jealous of such strange matings but gloried in them. But long before that time the lizards had come back upon the rocks, the bees were storing honey from thyme and cistus and the young people had traded horses for goats and sheep and cattle and pearls for vines with Noah's kingdom and they had hounds for hunting and to guard their flocks against the wolves. But that is no longer the story of Fan and Niss, but the history of mankind.

5 Abraham and Lot

Few biblical characters have been found more intriguing than Lot's wife. Unnamed in the Bible, she is the subject of numerous poems, many speaking out in her behalf. In *Lot's Wife*, one of the few books which treats of Sodom and Gomorrah seriously, Maria Ley-Piscator envisions her as a sophisticated and dignified princess of Tyre whose final rebellion is an act of dignity. "In love was all my faith. I shall look back at the whole of my life without fear, superstition, vengeance, nor tremble any more with dismay at what was or regret what might have been. I shall look back at the good and the bad. At the love I spent and the love I received—at divine equity—." Mrs. Ley-Piscator has written successfully in German (poetry and novels), French (biography and drama), and English (*Lot's Wife*). A famous dancer and choreographer, she worked with Max Reinhardt in Europe and with her husband, the famous director, in America. The selection which follows describes the separation of Abram and Lot, and Lot's entrance into Sodom where he is corrupted.

> *And Abram said unto Lot, Let there be no strife, I pray thee, between me and thee, and between my herdmen and thy herdmen; for we be brethren.*
>
> *Is not the whole land before thee? separate thyself, I pray thee, from me: if thou wilt take the left hand, then I will go to the right; or if thou depart to the right hand, then I will go to the left.*
>
> *And Lot lifted up his eyes, and beheld all the plain of Jordan, that it was well watered every where, before the Lord destroyed Sodom and Gomorrah, even as the garden of the Lord, like the land of Egypt, as thou comest unto Zoar.*
>
> *Then Lot chose him all the plain of Jordan; and Lot journeyed east: and they separated themselves the one from the other.*
>
> GENESIS: XIII, 8–11

LOT'S WIFE by MARIA LEY-PISCATOR

AT FIRST THERE WAS more excitement than reverence in the shepherds' hearts as they prepared for the meeting between Abram and Lot. Men, women and children had arrived on the mountain between Bethel and Hai which Abram had indicated. They came in solemn procession, dressed in their shepherds' robes, and lined up near an olive grove. They had soft, golden faces and some of the men were rather heavy-set now from good living.

35

Lot was already waiting in the olive grove with his leaders and main drovers. He was dressed in white and so were his men. He ordered the shepherds to go up to the top of the hill behind the grove and wait there for Abram. As he looked at the black-robed crowd assembled there, it seemed as if the mountain had fallen apart, with dark pieces of hope and fear lying about the grove.

While the Patriarch came up the mountain, a rainbow was rendering light to the bright clouds. When he put on the robe of honor—the white cloak of the shepherd, tendered him by two of his shepherds—and went up to the sacred altar built for this last encounter, it seemed to the children of Terah that Abram was clad in the garment of holiness.

"The morning star in the midst of a cloud," said Ti-sar-ilani, barely able to hide her tears.

All fell to their knees, and Lot came up to receive his blessing.

Abram blessed the crowd, then drew Lot to his feet and looked at him and at the fear that played in his face. But the Patriarch's hands were shaking, too, as he blessed his nephew.

"I called for you, nephew, because our days are troubled. This land of Bethel is not able to support us all. We have grown too many. It cannot bear us all so that we may dwell together in peace and plenty."

"Forgive me, my lord, the quarrelings of our shepherds. What is it you want me to do?"

"Look on the land before you. If you will take the left hand, then I will go to the right. Or, if you take the right, I will go to the left, and the quarrel will end."

The children of Terah in the olive grove were watchful, as if they expected some demon to fly out suddenly from the mouth of one of their leaders. They seemed to weigh and judge every word as it came to them.

"The land to the left is so much more fertile," Lot said with a greedy expression in his eyes which had never been there before.

"Yes," said Abram, "even if you should want the right, your senses will always push you against it. Let us separate, my nephew, and you shall take the fertile land."

Lot did not answer Abram. He seemed overwhelmed by his generosity. He stood there with his head bowed, more like a boy who is being told what he has to do than a man making his choice.

And, like a boy, he looked up at Abram after a while with a hostile expression in his eyes.

"This is no longer a quarrel of shepherds, my uncle, for more land and more water. There is more!"

The two men eyed each other.

"I suppose you are right," Abram said after a moment's pause, "but I wish you would explain yourself more clearly so that all can understand. For you know well that I make no decision without my shepherds. Are we not all confronted with your departure? Is not all our destiny played right here and now?"

"You still believe that there is a rebellion of my shepherds against your orders, my uncle." Lot avoided the term "my lord" now. "No. This is not so. Deeper currents are driving us in different directions. We have outgrown through experience and circumstance your visions and can no longer share your destiny. The laws which you have brought down from heaven, the fiery furnaces, and promised lands, the one fearsome God and the Chosen People —we can't believe this any more."

"These are wild fruits of an overripe imagination," said the prophet. "Have you forgotten Canaan?"

"Canaan is no promised land," Lot said contemptuously. "Don't you see that all our days have run out here? Canaan holds more bitterness and suffering for us than even Babylonia and Egypt. The Promise has never been fulfilled."

"May the Lord forgive you," the Patriarch replied slowly.

"That does not make the choice less inevitable," said Lot.

A strange glow had come into Abram's eyes; something glistened there, half tender, fixing itself on Lot.

"What is it, my lord?" Lot had again chosen the word of deference, yet it plagued him. His eyes were shooting restlessness.

"Nothing," replied the Patriarch, sorrowful now. "My soul is torn with anxiety for you."

"There is no need for your soul to be torn," Lot answered harshly. "I am no lost sheep, if I want my own! You have found what you think is a Promised Land. Why should not I?"

"What conceit is this, my nephew? Like a disease, a dangerous infection, it seems to spread over you. It will turn your living spirit into madness, into stone."

"If it be madness to you, some may find wisdom in it. It may be the new race of men and women will rise from such stones!"

Then Abram opened his eyes and beheld all his people. He saw how frightened they were, including Lot. They had gray faces and were bereft of all spirit. He knew that his voice would not reach them at this sorrowful hour. Dismay filled his heart as he said: "Let there be no strife, I pray thee, between me and thee and between my herdsmen and thy herdsmen, for we are brethren. Separate thyself, I pray thee, from me. Which side wilst thou take?"

"East of the plain of the Jordan. Let my tents be pitched forward—"

"Do not go into Sodom, Lot! You are not the man for it!"

Startled surprise swept the young man's face. How was it possible for Abram to know what Lot had even tried to hide from himself until the day before? Sodom? He covered his surprise with anger.

"Why not? Have you already condemned Sodom? And me with it? Is the word given only to you, Abram? Is the right to judge granted only to you?"

"No, nephew. But what is given to me is not given to you. You were born to sing, Lot. You were not born to coin new words. Words have no meaning to you. They will never reach the spring in you. If you persist in so doing, the day you are called to account for your action will make you see defeat. Denounce, recant, eat your words, Lot! Pay the price for being allowed to sing. Be what you are—do not pervert yourself!"

"The old word is still a potent drug. It bribes the conscience," said Lot ironically.

"You will fight a shadow fight in which you are the shadow," the Patriarch said sadly.

"The son of Haran has ceased to be a shadow. He has become alive!"

"I wish you good fortune, nephew," said Abram in a quiet, gentle voice. Then, raising his hand in benediction, he turned slowly away from the olive grove.

Lot watched the majestic figure move down the mountain path.

He screamed after him. He screamed without sound at this inexorable destiny which was separating him from what he loved most, which was driving him forward, forward—to what end?

The journey had become more and more a carnival of the senses. The caravan enjoyed a colorful hospitality all the way down to the valley. Time and again when they halted with their flocks near some habitations, the occupants ran forth and grasped the reins of the camels, begging the "nephew of Abram" to dismount and stay with them. Even before Lot and his wife could enter the house of some rich chief a happy bustle of preparation began for them. An eager, clamoring crowd brought out rugs and furs to spread on the ground so that the distinguished visitors should not touch the earth. Camel saddles were moved into position as back rests for the reclining guests. The coals of fires were stirred, warm or cooling drinks held ready, flowers, baskets of fantastic food and poisonous-looking sweetmeats of unknown spicy fragrance were served; there were smiles on impenetrable faces.

As the weird landscape twisted more and more away from all habitation, one of the shepherds' horns called out a warning. Too late. A slim, shrewd-looking Bedouin chief stopped them just before the border station at the entrance to the valley. Drums were beating and some seers blew on sacred cowrie shells.

The "Shrewd One" explained that a special feast would take place this night in the temple and that the strangers were cordially invited to assist in the rites. He bowed and disappeared. Several armed men had placed themselves at the end of the caravan. There was no withdrawal from such an invitation. Quietly smiling, the men led them toward the temple.

They passed a few houses, large ones, all decorated with crude friezes depicting palms, vines and grapes, acanthus leaves, pomegranates and garlands of flowers. There were also sculptured symbols such as the head of a dragon poised over a woman's breast, or a lion with a snake's tail, or a man and a serpent making love, or a woman embracing a goose.

This was Sodom, they thought. But later they learned that it was not—except for those who had no courage to enter the city.

Yet in a way it was Sodom; splendor and abject poverty, pomp of dress and gaunt nakedness, pearl-embroidered comfort and flea-bitten hopelessness. Lot was not concerned with the ritual offered at the outskirts of Sodom. He was eager to push forward to reach the Six Pillars where Sinna was to meet them. But he realized that an unfriendly move could bring only discomfort.

In a dimly lighted doorway stood the Shrewd One. He bowed deeply and opened a heavy barred portal, ushering in Lot and his wife. Then he approached an old man, sitting in the center of the room, and kissed his hand. The old one, whose face was painted to represent youth, nodded in simulated surprise, smiling at the strangers and making them a sign to approach.

They stepped into what they later learned to be a small temple of Beez. The polished floor was encircled by a low railing decorated for the occasion with palm leaves. At the far end of the room and on a raised dais sat a drummer before an immense hide-stripped, barrellike instrument, his glistening body indolently swaying.

A goat was brought in and tied to the wooden rail in front of the seated worshipers. A garland of heron feathers trailed around his neck and entwined his hind legs. He wore the mask of the mischievous god Beez.

In slow procession the priestesses filed into the room. Their bare oiled bodies were naked except for a shawl passed around their hips, tied with a sash under the painted nipples. Some wore headpieces in the Bedouin manner. All had neck ornaments and bracelets carved in the shape of clenched fists to ward off evil; gold amulets jangled from their wrists.

An old hag with dead eyes, spittle dripping from her wide, painted mouth, approached the drummer. In a high, whining, querulous voice she intoned the first bars of the opening dance, her tongue lashing the crowd with venomous exhortations. The drum and the onlookers answered. The High Priestess, a patrician-like beauty, followed by the other priestesses, prostrated herself now before the goat.

The Shrewd One told Lot and his wife in a low voice that the priestesses had spent from four to six years in the temples at Sodom learning the rites of this festival for the god. What he did not tell them was that the young girls were slaves in the daytime, and only on nights such as this became goddesses.

The bodies of the dancers swayed now. They looked like huge lyrebirds with their tail feathers spread on the floor, increasing, with the tempo of the drum and each whirling turn, the voluminousness of their skirts.

Two priestesses carried a large wooden bowl into the room, circled in sinuous procession three times, then set the bowl before the goat. Gently they pressed the animal's head into the viscous substance, holding it there until its tongue emerged and it consumed the entire contents.

"Beez will drive through their bodies—and make them mad," the Shrewd One explained. "Now they are calling him." The dances began to take on a frenzied air: the great drum accelerated its resounding boom; the eyes of the dancers began to glaze. Sweat beaded the brow and upper lip of the beautiful High Priestess. She whirled about rapidly, her eyes completely closed in anticipation of approaching ecstasy. Her shoulders quivered, her knees sagged. When she seemed about to fall, the priestesses held her up. She twitched violently, ecstatic and rearing. Then, as the ecstasy seemed to take final possession of her, she prostrated herself before the god.

The old hag burst from her place and swung into the center of the room, her body writhing jealously. She threw herself before the goat, flailing the air with her arms. And the drum hammered, beat and hammered in a frenzy.

Now standing over the goat, the hag raised her palms, swaying from side to side, uttering a sharp animal grunt. Then she touched the withers of the animal, caressed his head, embraced the golden mask in an effort to bring the god into herself. Down the goat's body her hands passed, saluting and embracing the flanks, her eyes tightly closed.

As the ecstasy gripped her more violently, her dancing grew more passionate. Her hips became disjointed and her shoulders shook in continuous convulsion as if she had no clavicle. Finally, completely beside herself, she collapsed to the ear-splitting, soul-splintering everlasting and ever-louder boom of the drum, near the prostrate form of the High Priestess.

The other priestesses began to dance and whip the goat with leather-thonged lashes. They untied his front legs and pushed the animal toward the two women who were sprawled on the floor, waiting.

Louder the drum and the whistle of the whips.

The minor priestesses were now mixing with the glassy-eyed crowd. They danced around Lot and his wife with long, lascivious motions, inviting and provoking. The young High Priestess struggled up from the floor. The old one, who had remained still like a tigress before the leap, shot an arm out and dragged the young girl toward the goat. A moment later the two women were battling each other, scratching and tearing their bodies with frenetic passion. Then the old one triumphed. Swaying and teetering drunkenly, she pushed the young High Priestess to the floor. Pitilessly holding the girl down with one hand, the hag embraced the animal with the other and drew it toward the horror-fascinated priestess. The goat rose, stiffened with excitement, and bent over the girl. The drum stopped and the silence became orgasmic.

It was shattered by the girl's scream! The goat had torn her flesh with his sharp horns, ripping her body open.

The drum resumed its orgiastic rhythm. Lot and his wife quickly gained the portal and the armed shepherds, who had been waiting outside, covered their escape.

Ti-sar-ilani's eyes were wide, staring, unblinking. Her mouth was drawn into a witchlike expression. When they reached the caravan, fleeing as fast as they could, the drum was still in a booming fury, and raucous laughter accompanied their flight.

As they rode on toward Moab, a streak of lightning illuminated her tear-bathed face, and in the rumble of distant thunder she could hear the cruel laughter that had haunted her become a triumphant eagle's cry.

6 God's Covenant with
the Hebrews

The great bulk of Zofia Kossak's work has been religious. She completed a trilogy set against the background of the Crusades—*Angels In The Dust, The Leper King* and *Blessed Are the Meek*—before she turned to the biblical novel. After careful research at the British Museum, she wrote *The Covenant* in her native Polish. What follows is her interpretation of what happened when Ab-Ram's personal God became the God of his people and the Lord made His Covenant with the Hebrews.

> *And I will establish my covenant between me and thee and thy seed after thee in their generations for an everlasting covenant, to be a God unto thee, and to thy seed after thee.*
>
> *And I will give unto thee, and to thy seed after thee, the land wherein thou art a stranger, all the land of Canaan, for an everlasting possession; and I will be their God.*
>
> *And God said unto Abraham, Thou shalt keep my covenant therefore, thou, and thy seed after thee in their generations.*
>
> *This is my covenant, which ye shall keep, between me and you and thy seed after thee; Every man child among you shall be circumcised.*
>
> GENESIS: XVII, 7–10

THE COVENANT by ZOFIA KOSSAK

THE SHEEP WERE grazing quietly; not one of them showed any signs of sickness. Had it already got better, or had the shepherds been mistaken? This incident, of no significance in itself, made Ab-Ram wonder. It was not the first time he had been troubled by a feeling that in the tribe things were happening of which he had no knowledge, things which were carefully concealed from him. He did not know how long this had been going on. Accustomed to his people's obedience and confidence, he did not quickly notice that conversations carried on aloud tended to die away when he approached, and that when he asked someone a question he often received a vague answer, embarrassed glances; and that the crowded gatherings in the tent of Aser,

Sephah's husband, broke up hurriedly when he came in. Unfinished sentences
were left hanging in the air, and he was at a loss to know what it all meant.

A day or two after the incident with Aser and Mosa he noticed that
in the oak grove a sapling had been cut down close to the ground, and the
place where it grew had been well trodden. He did not like trees to be cut
down without his knowledge, and he asked several men one after another
what the sapling had been needed for. Each gave him a different answer.
According to Yahiel, the tree had been used as a stake fixed in a pit dug out
on the track taken by the boars. But Aser said he had taken it to give further
support to his tent. Mosa had used it to strengthen the thorn barriers set up
at the valley outlet, as protection against the lions. Undoubtedly they were
all lying. Ab-Ram asked Eliezer what he thought of it.

The old servant seemed to be expecting the question.

"Evil things are occurring among your people, my lord. Every man has
two faces, every man has two tongues. The proverb says: 'double measure
and double weight are equally abominable.' "

"Tell all you know!" Ab-Ram interrupted roughly.

"I know nothing, my lord. I smell the smoke, I do not see the fire. Where
there are reeds there is water, they say. I hear the rustle of the reeds, but I
do not see the water. The people avoid me, for they know that the soul of your
servant has no secrets from your soul . . ."

"Tell me what you conjecture . . ."

"You will not build a wall on conjectures. What have you gained if I
tell you my conjectures, my lord? Your servant judges that the hidden fire-
brand is to be found in the tent of Aser."

"Certainly I have noticed that the herdmen gather there often . . ."

"And I no longer see the son of Aser, little Zabbai . . . That is all your
servant has noticed."

Without a word, Ab-Ram rose and went to Aser's tent. Though he was
white-haired, he retained the stately carriage and easy movements associated
with long-lived families. As he stood at the entrance to the tent he seemed
gigantic and threatening to Sephah, and she fell on her face before him.

"Where is Zabbai, your son and Aser's, woman?"

She burst into tears, and glanced fearfully across her shoulder into a
corner of the tent which was hung with a linen curtain.

"He is not here, my lord," she stammered. "He has gone."

"Where has he gone to? Can he walk so well by himself already? Call
your son."

Without raising her head, she sobbed:

"He is not . . . he is not . . ."

She glanced behind her again. Ab-Ram strode in the direction of her
gaze, and tore away the curtain, to reveal a small stone altar, with two
wooden, clumsily-carved teraphim standing on it. The wood of which they
were carved was fresh, and bore a brownish red stain, as though they had
been soaked in blood. He understood.

Without saying a word, he picked up both the images and went out.

Aser's wife remained kneeling, weeping, and repeating: "He is not . . . he is not . . ."

"Summon all the men of the tribe," Ab-Ram said to Eliezer. "Let them stand before my tent immediately they have watered the cattle. I adjure them in the Name of the Lord Most High that not one of them absent himself."

So ordering, he shut himself away in his tent. Despite his outward signs of calm, he was torn by a terrible anger. So that was it! They had dared to sacrifice a child to a tree, and to carve teraphim! Here, in his tribe, where the One True God reigned. He decided that he would punish the guilty ones harshly, very harshly. And again he asked himself in amazement: did he still rule the tribe, when he had known nothing at all of this that was happening? His authority over the people had slipped from his hands, but he did not know when. And who was to blame?

When evening came on, the cattle had been watered, the camp fires began to flame, and the sky, as usual, was lit up with the soundless laughter of distant lightnings, all the men of the tribe assembled, in accordance with the command. They already knew what had occurred, and their faces reflected their deep anxiety. The chief was sitting before his tent. His face was clouded, and the wooden teraphim lay beneath his feet; the soles of his feet rested on them.

When they were all seated round him, wrapped in their cloaks, Ab-Ram rose and, without speaking, flung the two images into the fire blazing in front of him. The damp oak began to hiss and to scatter sparks. The assembled men fidgeted restlessly, one or two of them rose to their feet, as though about to run and rescue the images from the flames. But no one dared. They gazed at the fire in despair. Others breathed heavily, and sighed. Their faces, customarily expressive of a vegetative tranquillity or animal cunning, revealed their unhappiness.

Pointing with one finger at the smoking images, Ab-Ram asked:

"Who made them without my knowledge and permission?"

"I did," Aser boldly answered, rising to his feet. "Sur told us that Terah son of Nahor had made similar images. I do not think I did evil in doing that which your father, Ab-Ram, did all through his life."

Ab-Ram all but cried out: "Terah son of Nahor did not believe in the gods he carved. But he was afraid of the priests, so he held his peace and went on carving them. He would never have sacrificed his child to them." But it seemed unfitting for him to reveal his own father's weakness. And he was astonished at Aser's bearing. The shepherd did not seem to regard himself as guilty of any offence. Passing his eyes over the assembly, Ab-Ram asked the herdman:

"Do you speak for yourself, or in the name of all?"

Before Aser could reply, shouts arose from all the ring: "Aser speaks truly. He speaks for us all."

Ab-Ram had always thought of his fellow tribesmen as submissive children, whom he could direct as he wished. But now before him were new, strange people.

"Terah son of Nahor, my honoured father," he explained, "did not know the True God, the Lord Most High. So he made images of Marduk or the goddess Damkina. I know the Lord Most High, and you know Him through me. . . ."

They interrupted him, almost shouting:

"We do not know him. We do not even know his name. It is you who know him. . . . We know nothing about him. You have said that he has neither body nor features. How do you know he exists?"

"Silence! Let one speak!"

The shouts died away, the men jostled one another with their elbows and thrust Aser forward. But Aser in turn pushed at Yahiel, who had Ab-Ram's trust. At first Yahiel refused to speak, but at last he began to talk slowly, circumspectly:

"We have made teraphim. What evil is there in carving teraphim? You have wronged us, Ab-Ram, by throwing them into the fire. There was a child's blood on them. Every tribe has teraphim, only you, Ab-Ram, left your teraphim behind in Harran, where they bestow their blessing on Nahor son of Terah. We knew nothing of that and we were of quiet mind, thinking the teraphim were in your tent, as is fitting. But years ago Eliezer the Damascene, returning from Harran, said that our teraphim were standing in the courtyard of your brother. From that time we have known neither quiet nights nor quiet days. We said nothing to you, knowing that your god is a jealous god and will not endure other gods beside him. But Aser sacrificed his son in order to sanctify the wood from which he carved the teraphim. What evil did he do? Sacrifice is acceptable to the gods. We cannot live any longer without gods, Ab-Ram. In the city of Ur there was Nannar-Sin, a strong and friendly god, whom our fathers glorified. Then the Babylonian Marduk came, and he also reigned over the people. He had temples, altars, priests, and servants. Later, in Harran we saw the old god Nannar-Sin reigning as in the past and we rejoiced, for he was the god of our fathers. In Canaan we saw very cruel and vengeful gods, and in Egypt gods with the heads of different animals, and among them unclean animals . . . Everywhere the people have gods and priests and altars, we alone have no one. We have been left without care. At night we are afraid the demons will come and carry us off, or our children, and we have no defence against them. We know that you have your god, Ab-Ram. We think he has forbidden you to reveal his name to us. Is he then a magician whose name cannot be mentioned, because if it is named he loses his power? Even so your god is not very powerful, for Jeser the Hivite told us that you asked your god for the lot to fall in your favour, but he failed to do it. And we have seen the altar to your god in Uru-Salem; we felt ashamed as we remembered the Chaldean and Babylonian temples, which are filled with gold. We do not want to live any longer without gods, Ab-Ram. Why did you burn our teraphim? What harm have they done you? We were never asked before what gods we believe in, whether Marduk or Nannar-Sin. Now allow us to believe in our own fashion.

Aser sacrificed his little son in order to give the teraphim strength and to win the friendship of the gods. Why did you burn the teraphim?"

He stopped, and gave his chief a look of deep affliction.

"Have you ended?" Ab-Ram asked.

Yahiel nodded and sat down, to gaze into the fire, where the wooden images were crackling and smoking.

"Then hearken to my words, Hebrews. Hearken diligently to my words. Yahiel has said that Aser sacrificed his little son so that the child's blood should give power to the gods you have made, and to win their friendship. Then why, when I threw them into the fire and when I trod them with my foot, why did the gods not speak? Why did your teraphim not resist the consuming fire? Aser went to the wood and chose a log, he shed his child's blood over it, he cut it down with his axe, he carved it into human shape and then fell on his knees before it; and he said to you: 'Behold your god! Kneel before him, calling: Save us!' Who caused it to have the power to harm or help? Was it the child, who was not yet fully grown in his own strength? What did you do with the rest of the log? Of a certainty some of it went to make stakes for fences or was chopped up for firewood, or you made stools of it. A god and a footstool from the one stump? Who told you, and marked on the bark: 'from here to here this log is sacred, but here it is ordinary wood?' Perhaps you were mistaken? Perhaps the footstool is the god, or the stake in the fence? Well then! Go and kneel to it!"

"Do not make a mock of us, Ab-Ram," Yahiel said moodily, "for we are simple people and you will not find wisdom among us. We have done as our fathers did before us. Since when has the custom of our fathers become evil and stupid?"

"I will not scoff at you further. You have seen with your own eyes that the teraphim were unable to defend themselves; but of a truth, he who has blasphemed against the Lord Most High shall die the death, for earth and air, fire and water all serve Him. You think He would lose His power if we named Him by name, as if He were a magician hiding like a toad among the stones; but I say unto you that if the Name of the Lord were to be uttered by man all the earth would be riven asunder. For by that Name the worlds arise and fall; the stars are lit and extinguished. He needs no temples or ornaments, for the dawn is His wings, and the sun is the gold of His altars. You do not see Him, yet all that goes on in the world is testimony to His existence. If you do not want to open your own eyes, believe me, your chief. When have I ever lied to you? When have I ever deceived you? I am ready at any moment to die in testimony that God *is*. You complain that you are without protection? It will soon be twelve years since I first began to live, I and all the tribe, under the protection of the True God. Who has suffered any wrong? Whose child has been borne off by demons? No other tribe has been so well protected and spared as you have. Does anything evil come upon you? Have you ever been hungry? Has our camp ever been visited by locusts, disease, or enemies? The Lord Most High, the One Lord has extended His care over you like a tent, and that does not suffice you! Stupid were the words of Jeser the Hivite, for I did not pray that the lot should fall in my favour, only that the Lord should lead me whither He wished. In no other way could I pray to the Lord. For He knows what the morrow will bring, but I do not. He knows what is good and necessary for man, but I might ask for a fruit in which a serpent lurks. It is my honour, my joy, that I am subject to the Lord as the earth is subject to the plough, as the woman to the man, as the child to its father. . . . . He is the Lord, I am the servant. His will is my will. What more do you wish to hear from me?"

"I have heard enough," Eliezer, who was sitting on one side, said hurriedly. "I have faith in my lord; his god is my God."

"It seems I have found greater faith in a servant born in a foreign land than among my own people. What is in your minds? Speak!"

The assembly was silent; the men hung their heads. They were still unconvinced. At last Yahiel spoke mournfully:

"Fine and learned is your speech, Ab-Ram son of Terah, but we have never seen your god. We are not accustomed to believing without seeing. Remove your anger from us and tell your god to give us a sign, that we may believe. We will praise and glorify your god, but let him give us a sign."

Ab-Ram did not sleep all that night. He felt troubled to the depths of his soul; he was profoundly anxious, overwhelmed with grief. Grief for himself, or for his tribe? He did not know. One moment he was angry with his fellow tribesmen for demanding a sign from God; the next he reminded himself that at one time he had been like them. They wanted a sign. Only the Lord could give them that. Would He not be angry at such a request? What sign would completely convince them? For the hundredth time he regretted that the Lord had called him, an unlearned man, to His service, instead of Nergal-Sar, or Melchizedek. They would both have known what to do. But Nergal-Sar had departed almost unknown, and Melchizedek also had died some years since. Both these guides and masters had vanished, as though removed by the Lord's hand so that he, Ab-Ram, should carve his own way. Now, like a hungry man seeking scraps of bread in the larder he recalled all the details of his conversation with Melchizedek concerning people who thirsted for a visible sign. The priest-king had not been indignant, as Ab-Ram was; he had admitted that this demand was proper to human beings. He had mentioned the Egyptian rite of circumcision as a sign and seal that might satisfy the human desire for something visibly testifying that they belonged to God. At that time Ab-Ram had rejected the idea out of hand. But now his anger and grief for his fellow-tribesmen drove him to consider the question in a different light. They wanted a sign: let them have it! A painful, hard, ineradicable sign! Let them suffer! He writhed inwardly at the thought that he would have to begin with himself. He rejected the idea, and sought further. But the conversation with the royal sage, on the rooftop in that stone city, obstinately returned to his memory. "Do according to your measure," Melchizedek had said. The people needed to be given a sign according to their measure. No one dressed a child in the robes of a grown man, for in them it would get entangled, and would perish. Would not that sign be fitted to his people's childish minds? Melchizedek had said that the seal of circumcision testified that the one so sealed was ready to shed his blood for his Lord. Not as men offer children to the gods, but sacrificing his own true body, his own blood, his own pain. This gift could be made to the Lord and be accepted as an acceptable sacrifice. Now Ab-Ram wiped out of his mind the anger he had felt for his tribe since his discovery of the teraphim, and lost the loathing with which he had regarded the idea of circumcision. In fact, he was coming to think that the greater the loathing and fear, the more valuable the offering. Had he not again and again regretted in his soul that, blessed as he was by the Lord, he had nothing with which he could show his gratitude?

These thoughts began to possess him so completely that he looked impatiently for the dawn. The answer for which the people were waiting, and even his own hesitations, were overshadowed by the realisation that he could show the Lord his own gratitude and devotion. It was part of his nature to act at once on every decision he made, and so, shutting himself away in his tent, he set to work. He mutilated himself painfully and clumsily, he could hardly restrain a groan; but he achieved his purpose. Weak and sick, he lay down on the couch. Despite the almost unbearable pain he had a feeling of satisfaction. Now he had truly offered the Lord his own blood, not that of heifers, bulls, or sheep. He lay quietly all that day, defending himself as well as he could from the anxious women, who were alarmed by his sudden illness. He refused food, though they brought him the tastiest of morsels; but he greedily drank water, and demanded only to be left in peace. In the evening he grew feverish. Half asleep, he was visited by visions. The tent seemed to be an ark borne on the waters and falling downward with the waves. In his half-conscious meditations, groaning with pain every time he moved, Ab-Ram felt ashamed of the anger he had displayed towards his own tribe only yesterday. The Hebrew shepherds were only a small part of the great human throng which was crying out for God, and thundering the questions: "Whither go we? What to? Whose are we?" But Ab-Ram, who by the special dispensations of God had come to know the truth, and could have given an answer to this question, had been silent for years, making no attempt to share with others the treasure he possessed.

"But how can I speak?" he asked himself anxiously. He recalled the knowledge and wisdom of the priests, unequalled in all the world; their knowledge of the secrets of the stars and the earth, the several stages of the temple at Ur, each filled with tablets containing all manner of sciences and knowledge. Against that power, which even kings did not dare to affront, was he, a simple, illiterate man, skilled only in the rearing of cattle and sheep, to set himself? The comparison seemed amusing, and he could not help thinking of himself as ludicrous. And he was so dismayed that he again lost strength. But once more, as soon as he closed his eyes, through his feverish brain poured waves which were not the waves of the sea but the generations of the sons of earth, seeking God.

He reached out for a cup of water tinged with wine, which Sarai had set by his head, and the visions vanished. He grew sober. What was it he was thinking of attempting to achieve? Alas! You are driving your flocks to a too distant pasturage, shepherd! You think to measure yourself with kings, to quarrel with the priests of Marduk; and so far you have not subjected even your own tribe to the Lord! You will do much, and very much, if you convince your own people. Think only of them. Give them a sign— the same sign which you have carved in your body. From your own tribe you will create a fortress and sanctuary of the Lord.

The entrance flap was lifted. Eliezer slipped in quietly, and stared at the sick man with eyes expressive of his anxiety. He was surprised and delighted when his master gave him a friendly, though miserable smile. "It is good that you have come, Eliezer," Ab-Ram whispered, painfully moistening his parched lips with his tongue. "Tell the men of the tribe that in a day or two, when I am well again, in the name of the Lord Most High I will give them the sign which they have demanded. Let them wait in peace, untroubled. Bring me some water . . ."

"Live for ever, my lord! I have brought water. The people will rejoice when I tell them what you have said. They were smitten with fear that your god had struck you down, in anger at what they had done."

When the servant had departed, the sick man renewed the broken thread of his meditations. Henceforth his tribe would have no other god and no other faith than that of the Lord Most High. To him, Ab-Ram, it fell to be chief and priest in one, as Melchizedek had been to his people. And one who takes on priesthood must change his name, renouncing his ancestral origin. Of the generations of man one said: "the son of Terah, the son of Nahor, the son of Haran." With the priests it was not so. The father of the priest was the god whose name was included in his new name. Sep-*Sin* . . . Awen-*El* . . . Nergal-*Sar*. . . . And so he, Ab-Ram, should do; but the Lord had not revealed His Name to His servant. The unutterable Name of the Lord was not to be given shape in the mouth of a mortal. As he considered this problem, the name which Melchizedek had persistently repeated years before suggested itself: "Ab-Raham!" And now the name which had once terrified him seemed to have some connection with the innumerable generations of people who were passing in a feverish vision before his eyes. He decided to adopt the name of Ab-Ram.

But was he alone to change his name? In taking the priestly office, would he not draw his wife after him? He felt strongly impelled to do something in recognition of his faithful comrade, Sarai. Nor, indeed, only for her. The words Lot had said when he and Ab-Raham had been riding on the one camel came vividly to mind. O, memory, infallible steward! Like a miser you seize on everything, even things seemingly of no import; you conceal them in your secret places, to bring them out at the suitable moment and to set them before your eyes. When Lot had remarked that the law underestimated women, Ab-Ram had not thought much of the words, he had dismissed them with silence. But now they seemed to him so just, so valuable, that he thirsted not only to distinguish his wife, but in his wife to honour Woman.

Night came on, and with it the fever returned. The pictures were again confused, they erased the bond between dream and reality. Now he seemed audacious, mad, arrogant in his own eyes. His mind swarmed with great intentions, he had decided to be the priest of the tribe, he wanted to change his own name and Sarai's; but what certainty had he that the Lord required all this? Hitherto he had only listened and waited. The Lord had spoken to him when it was His will to speak. But now the servant wanted to compel the Creator.

And, humbled, afflicted, Ab-Ram also, like the shepherds whom he had recently despised for this same weakness, began to implore the Lord for a sign.

"Many years have passed since Thou last spakest to me," he said. "That does not disturb me, for thou art Eternal, and a thousand ages in Thy sight are like an evening gone. It is not for me, but for my tribe that I am anxious. So work, that they may know Thy glory. Make a covenant with me and with all the tribe, that they may descry Thee whom they see not and may know Thee whom they know not. I put my trust in Thee. So work, that others also may trust in Thee. Without Thee there is neither light nor peace. Be our Goel, our King and Guardian. We will be Thy servants. I have never asked thee anything before, O Lord . . . Now I will ask, and will not cease asking. . . . Thou knowest the hearts of men, and knowest that I do not ask for myself, since nothing will diminish my faith. But my people want a sign. Give them a sign!"

The pulse in his temples drummed like a hammer, the pain from his self-inflicted wound pierced through his body, the tent, like an ark, rose, floated, swayed. . . . Ab-Ram had the feeling that, just as once he had been caught up in the air, so again he could see himself below himself; and he thought he heard a voice:

"I will make a covenant with thee and thy people. . . ."

Then everything was confused, was mingled into a single roar that engulfed his memory, his consciousness, his thought.

Only on the fourth day did Ab-Ram emerge from his tent, well, though still weak. He at once summoned the men of the tribe and declared to them:

"The Lord Most High, the True God, has promised to make a covenant with the tribe of Hebrews. Before He does so they must openly renounce all other gods, and must throw all tablets and amulets into the fire, if any possess them, since the Lord will not come where another reigns."

They listened in gloomy silence, taken aback, for they had not anticipated that they would have to renounce the old gods. Of their own choice they had been taken in the snare. If they refused, they would affront the god of Ab-Ram; but if they obeyed they would draw down upon themselves the anger of vengeful demons. Woe! Woe!

Inexorable, stern, Ab-Ram stood in the centre of the ring, naming one after another all the gods known to the tribe. He asked whether they rejected them in their own name, and in that of their descendants. They assented with trembling, looking about them fearfully. They renounced the god Ea, the god En-Lil, the god Anu, the god Enu, the favourite god of their fathers, Nannar-Sin, the goddess Damkina, the goddess Ishtar, the goddess Zirbanit. They renounced the spirits called Anunnaki, Ekimmu, Utukki, and many others. They renounced the demons of the air, the earth, and the water. They renounced the evil Labartu, Ilu, Galu, and Rabisu. As with trembling they pronounced the words of apostasy, they stealthily thrust into the fire their amulets bearing the image of the demon named. Things that hitherto had been as a saving shield, now, after the renunciation, would become a menacing weapon of the affronted spirit. They spoke and acted hurriedly, hoping that the demon would not notice their words and actions in the general confusion.

When all the men had sworn that they would have no other gods but the god of Ab-Ram, when the tablets, images and amulets were cracking and turning to ash in the fire, Ab-Ram began to make preparations to conclude the covenant with the Lord. In his simplicity he behaved as ancient custom directed. So from the flocks and herds he chose a heifer, a goat, and a ram, all without spot or blemish; and he also took a turtle-dove and a young pigeon. After slaughtering the animals he divided them through the middle, not removing their skins or their hooves, but he did not divide the birds. In the centre of the valley he cleared a narrow track of grass some ten paces long, and no wider than one pace, and he set the divided bodies of the animals on either side of the track, each half against its other half, so that if put together they would be as though whole. He did not divide the birds, but set them one on each side of the track, their beaks towards each other. In this labour he was assisted by Eliezer, Sur, Yahiel, Mosa, Aser and several others. The rest of the men surrounded them in a ring, watching the preparations anxiously. They knew that He whose Name might not be pronounced or even known would reveal Himself to their eyes and, in accordance with custom, would pass between the divided carcasses. His steps would be followed by Ab-Ram in the name of the tribe, and thenceforth nothing could violate the covenant thus concluded. The God of Ab-Ram and the Hebrew tribe would become one, just as the halves of the heifers, goat and sheep had been one. One blood in their veins, one heart, lungs, kidneys, liver. No one had ever heard of any of the gods concluding such a covenant with a man before, so the Hebrews rejoiced, even though they were also terribly afraid.

The preparations occupied all the morning till noonday. And the day was burning hot, windless. The path of the Covenant had been made in the middle of the valley, for all to see, far from the shade of the oak grove; and the people sitting about it and waiting for the Coming of the Lord were faint with the heat. Only Ishmael shouted merrily, amused by the whole affair, and Sur had difficulty in restraining the lad from running along the sacred path between the divided animals. Though still very weak, Ab-Ram took a branch and drove off the flies gathering about the carcasses. Seeing this,

Eliezer took a second branch, and the two men silently beat on each side. The dead animals had to be defended from more than flies. The scent of meat attracted the vultures, and they began to circle high above in the sky, gradually dropping lower and lower. Ishmael asked for permission to shoot at them with his bow, and sent arrows flying through the air; Aser and Sur picked up spears and drove off the more persistent of the birds. The time passed slowly, it almost seemed to stand still; the sun roasted them with fire; but no one came. The women brought their men food in platters. They ate but little, drank their fill of water, and again waited. Leaning heavily on his stick, Ab-Ram gazed up at the sky grey with heat; he gazed eastward to the mountains beyond which was the city of Uru-Salem; westward, to where the Great Sea roared; southward to the land of Negeb, dry and burnt; northward to where the city of Harran stood below the snow-covered mountains. He did not know from which direction the Lord would come; his limbs ached intolerably, his head swam with weariness. He swayed on his feet, but he would not sit down. The Lord might come unexpectedly, and he wanted to be ready. Worse than all the weariness and the heat was the fear that the Lord might not come at all. That He had been offended by the impertinent request. Even as Ab-Ram's own people had been astonished, and with reason, for covenants were concluded only between equal and equal, king and king, warrior and warrior, shepherd and shepherd, never between god and man. What frenzy had taken possession of him when he had made such a demand?

The heat streaming from the heavens did not lessen, the air was still sultry. From time to time a sudden afternoon breeze sprang up, sent columns of dust whirling, then dropped again, intensifying the sultriness and bringing no refreshment. The carcasses of the heifer, goat, and sheep began to swell and turn black with the heat. Exhausted by the waiting, the people relieved one another at their posts; some went away, others kept watch. Only Ab-Ram endured the vigil, standing and turning his head in all directions like a crane. He felt an unbearable pressure on his heart. His reason cried: "No one will come. Deceive not yourself and others." An unknown, secret voice replied: "Have confidence! No one will come if you doubt. With your faith you will compel the Lord." So he strengthened himself in the faith that was departing from him. Realising that the weariness of his will would overcome his desire, he yielded himself entirely to the hand of the Lord. He ceased to think of what the disappointed people would say. Calm, still, empty of all impatience, he stood in perfect obedience.

But now dusk crept over the sky. Now the sky began to be lit up by lightnings closer than those of the everyday. Alarmed by the oncoming evening, the vultures flew off; the buzzing of the flies died away. Eliezer thrust his unnecessary spear into the ground. Parts of the carcasses had a bluish hue; the jackals began to steal out of the undergrowth. Even the men who had been keeping watch dozed off; only Ab-Ram kept guard. He watched, resting on his staff.

He watched, resting on his staff, even when a thunder-clap broke so overwhelming and close that the earth trembled, and the sleepers started to their feet. They stood for a moment, then fell to the ground again, stricken with dread. For with their own eyes they saw a great and glowing, fiery ball fall from the sky; amid a deafening thunder it rested momentarily on the point of Eliezer's spear, then fell still lower and rolled between the divided animals. Passing a little beyond them, it disappeared.

The roar of thunder was still rumbling about the earth, shaking the trees, terrifying the hearts smitten with dismay. Only Ab-Ram had no fear. As though in a dream he followed in the track of the flaming ball, strode along the path, smelling the scent of scorched hair. His heart was beating like a hammer. The Lord had come down. He had not abandoned His servant. He had made an everlasting covenant with the tribe of Hebrews.

The others were still lying face downward on the ground, not daring to raise their heads. Forgetting his weariness, the chief called on them to rise. They had seen the Lord pass, dread and terrible. Henceforth they were confederates of God himself. The Lord would keep faith with them, if they kept faith with Him. So long as they did not violate the covenant not one hair would fall from their heads. And now they would receive a token, a seal that they belonged to the Lord, and that no one but God had any right to them. By the light of a torch he laid himself bare before them, and showed them what the sign would be. They listened in amazement, yet ready to obey, assenting to all. The God of Ab-Ram had proved himself a mighty God. Their knees were still trembling with the terror they had experienced. It would be good to be under such protection. If the token which Ab-Ram demanded of them secured them against demons, it was worth a little pain.

Then their chief announced his own change of name. They accepted even this incomprehensible news more easily than they would have done at normal times, when their tongues wagged swiftly and their brains worked clearly. On such a day as today they would not have been astonished to see Ab-Ram rising in the air, or taking fire into his hands. The heaven and the earth were filled with mysteries and menaces, and they were as helpless as lost children.

So they accepted without protest the command to call their chief henceforth not Ab-Ram, nor Ab-Ram son of Terah, but Ab-Raham. Ab-Ram son of Terah, their chief, their goel, their judge, whom they had known as long as they could remember, had vanished without a trace. Instead there was Ab-Raham, the servant and priest of the Lord Most High. His wife also was to receive a new name. Instead of Sarai, henceforth she was to be called Sarah, which means "princess," "eminent," "lady."

Next morning Ab-Ram began the circumcision of all the men of the tribe, from the oldest to the little children. He summoned them in turn, by name, according to their age and rank. Those who were first called suffered no little from the operation. But, as their chief grew more practised, those who came later suffered much less. They all bore the suffering with dignity, regarding the mark as an honourable distinction and guarantee of divine protection in the future.

Ab-Raham felt very happy. As he shed the freely given blood of his tribal brothers—the blood which is the essence of life, is life itself, is the sacred possession of God—he was sanctifying them to the Lord, he was confirming the Covenant made between him and God. The joy of that day was marred for him only by Ishmael, who was unwilling to submit to the rite. Unmoved by the example of his youthful companions in the camp, who obediently though anxiously awaited at their fathers' sides, he fled and hid in the rushes. When at last he was tracked down he struggled and tore himself away, and bit the hands of Sur and Eliezer, who were taking him back. When reduced to helplessness he screamed vociferously. He had to be held still by four men. The sweat beaded Ab-Raham's face, his hands trembled. In his anxiety to spare his only son he added to the boy's pain. Hagar ran like a mad woman round the tent in which the token of the Covenant was being made in the flesh; she cursed Ab-Raham and all his designs, she howled like a wild beast. When the bawling lad was released he took refuge in his mother's arms, and their mingled weeping and their upbraidings of his father were heard for a long time after. The men gathering for the rite behaved as though they had not noticed anything of all this, in order not to bring shame on Ab-Raham, who was already deeply afflicted by his son's conduct.

Meanwhile the women prepared a banquet. Ab-Raham ordered that wine was to be issued abundantly, and as much olive oil as was desired, to anoint the wounds. Myrrh was added to the wine, for it had the property of drugging pain. But the majority of the revellers preferred to drink the wine without the addition of the bitter herb. Some of them had had to endure much more pain when a leopard had torn their shoulder or they had been kicked and trampled by a stampeding herd.

His trouble with Ishmael forgotten, Ab-Raham sat intent and cheerful among the banqueters. Let the armed potentates raise gilded temples to their gods in Babylon, Nineveh, and Egypt. Some new conqueror would destroy them or set new gods up in them. The One God, the True God, the Creator of heaven and earth had founded His indestructible habitation here, in Ab-Raham's people.

He looked back over the past days, the road traversed since that morning when some unknown power had lifted him into the air. Suddenly dazzled with light, he realised that all that had happened during these past years had been significant, had led to the end planned by God. Even his own weaknesses and faults and aimless wanderings and apparent immobility. Every day had brought nearer the time of maturity, thoughts had bored their way into his mind like beetles into a tree. And he realised that all the people he had met in the course of his life had helped in this task: both Nergal-Sar, who had been the first to point to the anticipated Truth, and the Babylonian Hammurabi, who had played such a large part with his attempt to enyoke the Hebrew tribe; both Sep-Sin, who had been afraid of the burden of the Truth, but who when the Lord had seized hold of him had valiantly given his life for it, and the well-remembered priest and king, Melchizedek, to whom Ab-Raham really owed this day. All of them—friends, kinsmen, enemies, even people with whom he had only momentary acquaintance.

Knowingly or not, they had all brought a handful of clay to the edifice planned. His own fellow tribesmen, whom he had regarded as unwise children, had been of great assistance. They had forced him to act, had violated his will, by demanding that he should show them the Lord. Of a truth, without them he would have gone on quietly dozing, forgetting his unfulfilled obligation.

7 The Sacrifice of Isaac

The offering of Isaac by Abraham is one of the oldest biblical stories retold in English, dating back to Caedmon's Seventh Century version of Genesis, and there have been numerous poetic and dramatic versions written through the centuries since. W. G. Hardy, a classical scholar and head of the Department of Classics at the University of Alberta, has drawn his novels from both the classical and biblical streams of history. *The City of Libertines* is a story of Rome, *All the Trumpets Sounded* of Moses, and *Abraham, Prince of Ur* of the patriarch. In the selection which follows Professor Hardy fuses his talents as a scholar and novelist with his passion for archaeology to present his version of the offering of Isaac.

And it came to pass after these things, that God did tempt Abraham, and said unto him, Abraham: and he said, Behold, here I am.

And he said, Take now thy son, thine only son Isaac, whom thou lovest, and get thee into the land of Moriah; and offer him there for a burnt offering upon one of the mountains which I will tell thee of.

GENESIS: XXII, 1–2

ABRAHAM, PRINCE OF UR by W. G. HARDY

THE HILLS ABOUT Beersheba were pleasant with grass, and there was water in the wells. His sheep and his goats and his great herds of asses and of camels throve and multiplied from Bethel in the north, even to Beersheba, which is close to the wilderness in the south of Canaan. Gerar and the horror there was forgotten, or so it seemed when one looked at Sarai and Hagar and Ishmael. But Abraham seemed suddenly to have become an old man.

"What troubles you, my husband?" Sarai would say to him, seeing his bowed shoulders and his gloomy face. "See, Isaac is growing like a weed."

The boy would laugh and run to him and call him father. And Sarai would wonder why Abraham should catch the boy up and kiss him so fiercely and then stride away without a smile at her. She did not know that for Abraham to look upon the face of his son was as death. She did not know either that during the long nights when he was away from her he was wrestling with Yahweh in prayer, but could not come close to him; or that by day the heavens seemed remote to him and even the earth was strange and alien.

Abraham, indeed, was passing through a bitterness of which Sarai could

55

have no conception. For at one moment he told himself that not even Yahweh could expect this of him, to offer up his son. But at the next he remembered Gerar and that the ways of God were not as the ways of men. He recalled, too, how in former days Yahweh had again and again turned His face away from him and had not been appeased until he had abased himself utterly. It was evident to him that Yahweh was a jealous God, who would not permit that anything or any person should be put before Himself. So now, since he, Abraham, loved Isaac beyond all things else, Yahweh was determined that Isaac should be sacrificed to Him.

It did, indeed, come into his mind to defy Yahweh and bid Him do His worst. He would have done so, had he been certain that it would be upon himself that the punishment from Yahweh would fall. He was assured, however, that if he failed his oath a second time, it would be upon Isaac, his son, that some terrible doom would come. Had it not been so at Gerar? And had he not won safety for Isaac by renewing his vow? What still more horrible fate, he kept muttering to himself, might not Yahweh send upon Isaac, more horrible even than that which had threatened him in Gerar, if for the second time he broke his vow? It was a bitter alternative which he faced, and along either road lay unendurable anguish, anguish so poignant that the thought of it made his reason totter. In these days, for that matter, Abraham was not completely sane.

Yet the weeks went by and he had not carried out his promise. He did go up into the hill of Beersheba and raise a dolmen to Yahweh, even a row of pillars such as they built in Canaan in the high places unto Baal. Promises went up from him to his God when each full moon came that on the next he would offer up his son and keep his vow. But when the next full moon would come he would let it pass. Only when the third full moon came he climbed up to the high place and sacrificed a camel foal, a priceless foal which was worth a king's ransom, and prayed to Yahweh to have mercy on him, and to let this cup not be drained by him; or, at least, to let him offer himself in place of his son. All night he lay on the earth and prayed. Yet he could feel no answer in his heart. Only the moon rode cold and high among the silver feathers of the clouds and mocked him.

Even so he could not bring himself to fulfil his oath. But on the next day when he came to his tent for his mid-day meal, Sarai was not at the entrance to greet him, as was her custom. He lifted the tent-flap. Sarai looked at him.

"See what Ishmael has done to Isaac," she said angrily.

Abraham stood as if he were carved from stone. His eyes took it in, unbelievingly and yet as if it were something which he knew would happen. There was a blood-stained bandage about the boy's throat, and his whole body was a mass of bruises. A sign, he breathed to himself, a sign from on high; and the whole tent seemed to whirl about Isaac and Sarai like a crazy pin-wheel, as he forced himself to move over towards his son.

He thought he was shouting, although, in reality, it was only a whisper. "How did this happen?"

"I was just in time. They were in the thicket. Isaac lay senseless. Ishmael had bound him hand and foot, and had put him on an altar of wood." Her voice dropped to horror. "He had a knife—a knife! And he was shouting at Isaac to waken so that he could see himself given as a sacrifice. When he heard me he struck. Praise be to God that he hurried his stroke and did not gash deep." She leaned over her son. "Wake up, Isaac. Look at me."

The tent still wavered. "Hagar?" Abraham said.

Sarai turned to him, and anger crept into her voice. "I went to her. She laughed at me. She said that Ishmael is your first-born, and is more fitted to rule over the Habiru." Sarai rose abruptly and faced her husband. "What will you do with them?"

Abraham did not reply. He had forced the tent-wall to stand still. Yes, he thought, Yahweh had shown his anger. To have one son kill the other would be more cruel even than for Isaac to have died at the hands of the priests of Baal in Gerar. And Ishmael had seen the sacrifice at Gerar. And Yahweh had put it into his mind to do the same to Isaac. Yes, it was a sign and a threat. Yes, he could delay no longer.

"Why don't you say something?" Sarai demanded angrily. "Isaac, our son. I will not have them here. You must send them away, Abraham."

Abraham looked at her strangely as if he did not see her. He glanced at Isaac. Then, he turned and strode from the tent.

"Eliezer," she heard him call. "Eliezer."

For a moment she thought of following him and demanding that he tell her what punishment he would inflict upon them. That is, she told herself bitterly, unless he was still a slave to Hagar, and had spent the night just passed with her. But she looked down at Isaac, lying limp and senseless on the floor of the tent. All other thoughts left her.

"Isaac," she moaned, dropping to her knees and beginning feverishly to sponge his face. "Isaac, look at me."

Meanwhile, Eliezer had come out of his tent, still limping from the wound in his groin. He looked at his master inquiringly.

"Get ready food and water," Abraham told him. "Before nightfall Ishmael and Hagar shall leave my tents. You will go with them."

Eliezer stared at him as if he thought that his master had taken leave of his senses. Through his subtle brain flitted quickly the reflection that, since Gerar, Abraham had not seemed like the same man. Could it be possible that the terrible experiences there had turned his mind? He ventured, however, to expostulate.

"Ishmael is your son!"

"Ishmael," Abraham answered sternly, "has slain Isaac."

"Killed Isaac!" When did this happen? Why—"

"You do not understand," Abraham interrupted impatiently. "Go. Do as I command you. Get beasts and provender and all things ready. Before nightfall they must leave my camp."

"I have given you gold and a store of jewels," Abraham told her. "Eliezer and his men will see you in safety to Egypt. I set you free, you and your son. He has always been your son and never mine. Nevertheless, I wish you both well," he added coldly.

Hagar sat on her beast like a statue carved from stone. She did not even look at Abraham. As clearly as if he heard her speak, however, he heard her say:

"I was never slave to you. I am myself and no man has ever been my master. I would spit upon you, Abraham, if you were worth the spittle. So long as I have my son, what else matters?"

"If Ra-Hotep is still alive," Abraham observed, "tell him this: 'I send Egypt back to you.' He will understand."

She lifted up the reins and her beast started forward. Looking at Ishmael, Abraham felt a pang of regret pierce the armour of his hatred. After all, this was his firstborn.

"My blessing goes with you," he said to the lad. "May Yahweh prosper you."

Ishmael stared at him. In his eyes Abraham caught a glimpse of hatred beside which his own was pale and feeble.

"I do not need your blessing," Ishmael said with unexpected eloquence. "Keep that for Isaac. He will have need of it. And I will not worship Yahweh. Let Isaac worship Him. He hath need of Isaac."

He turned and followed his mother. And his father stood and watched the little cavalcade wind down the path and disappear out of sight. "He hath need of Isaac." Had Yahweh indeed put those words in the mouth of Ishmael?

It seemed to Abraham that he had attained a terrible lucidity, in which space and time were but little things. For his mind walked as through a void, detached, and watched the servants and the ass which was laden with wood and his son, Isaac. Isaac prattled merrily. And around them the stony waste stretched in league after league of rounded, bastion hills, and low clouds scudded across the sky, and now and again sharp drifts of rain drove cold against their faces. For summer was altogether past, and the harvest was gathered in, and the flocks were safe in the steadings, and all nature was barren and draggled at the coming of winter.

Abraham heard the servants grumbling under their breath, and the mud was thick on their sandals. The weather did not, however, dash Isaac's spirits. This was to him an adventure, and he did not know why they had ridden forth from Beersheba.

His father paid no heed to the grumbling of the servants. Nor did he feel the rain. The past and the present were remote from him, and his heart had been so racked by agony that he could feel no more. Only when he heard Isaac's prattle and saw his cheeks, rosy from the wet, and noticed how bright were his eyes, did the sword turn afresh in the wound.

"Father," Isaac said in his childish and excited treble, "where is the end of our journey? It is the third day since we left mother. And it is getting dark."

"God will appoint the place," he told his son.

The boy was satisfied and did not question further. And Abraham thought of the long years when he had failed to fulfil his vow, and of Gerar, and of Ishmael. No, he dared not delay longer. Even while he waited for Isaac to recover from the wound in his throat, Yahweh had shown his anger. An adder had sprung out on the boy while he slept; and at Hebron, on their way up, a bull had rushed to gore him. No, he must not delay longer.

The thought came to him of Sarai in the tents at Beersheba. He wondered what he would say to her when he returned alone. Yes, he told himself, this Yahweh was a ruthless God, a merciless God. Quite suddenly he felt that he could go no longer, but must find an end for it all. He looked around him. They were riding up a valley. As he looked the valley turned and Abraham saw a mountain in front of him and the top of the mountain in the mists was like the face of a man lying down. He knew at once that this was the place which Yahweh had appointed. When he had reached the foot of it he stopped.

"Wait here," he said to the servants. "I and the lad will go up yonder to worship, and then come back to you."

They thought he was mad. He knew and did not care. Taking the wood of the burnt-offering from under the cover which protected it from the wet he gave part of it to Isaac to carry and the rest he bore himself. He took, too, the bowl of fire which he had kept burning for these three days and nights. Then, he and the boy went upward. It grew dark, since the night came on apace in the mist, and they disappeared out of sight of the servants up the mountainside.

In toil and silence they struggled upward. When they reached the topmost level, and the moorland was dreary and deserted about them, and the valleys below them were full of darkness, and in the heavens above them the stars peeped faintly through the ragged scud, and they were utterly alone, Isaac asked:

"My father?"

"Here I am, my son."

"We have the fire and the wood. But where is the lamb for the burnt-offering?"

"My son," Abraham answered heavily, "God will provide a lamb for the burnt-offering."

They came finally to an open space among the stones and the thickets with which the moorland was strewn. Abraham looked upward at the heavens. But there was no relenting. Heavily and wearily he got him stones and built up an altar to the Lord, even to Yahweh. When he had builded it he took the wood and laid it in order thereupon. But the bowl of fire he placed in the shelter of the altar. Then, he looked at the boy and saw how, in the darkness, he watched with eyes that were big with wonder.

"Wait here," he said, and went aside and got down on his knees and prayed to Yahweh, and did not feel that he knelt upon a rock.

"Lord God," he prayed. "Thou seest how I am ready to do Thy will. Is this not enough? Let this cup pass from me."

There was no answer—no, not though he prayed many times and grovelled on the stones in his agony, and beat his forehead against them, and lay in utter misery. Then, after a long time, he saw before his eyes the high place of Gerar, and Isaac lying upon the altar and the boy's eyes wide with horror as he gazed upward at the unclean priest of Baal. And Abraham knew that Yahweh had answered. He groaned and got up and went back to his son.

"You have been a long time, father," the boy said. "I am getting cold."

The words were as a sign to him, a horrible sign of Isaac, his son, cold in death. He put his hands on the boy's shoulders and looked at him. Then he said:

"You know, my son, that I would never do anything to hurt you?"

Isaac smiled back at him. "I know, father."

He bent and hugged the boy closely to him and he thought that his heart would break. And he prayed that he might fall to the ground and die. Nothing happened. He knew then that he must be strong. So he released his son.

"What I must do will seem strange to you, Isaac, my son, my beloved son."

The boy answered: "I am ready, father."

Then Abraham took cords and bound Isaac and lifted him and placed him on the altar. The lad looked up at him trustingly and smiled. Abraham would have groaned; but he knew that he must not. He looked about him wildly. But there was nothing around him, nothing save the darkness and the heaps of stones and the thickets, black and gloomy in the mists. Lifting up his arms to heaven he prayed wordlessly. Again there was no answer, no, not even the smallest sign. All hope died in him and he felt God, like a grim and cruel weight, pressing down upon him until the cords of his brain tightened and he knew that he must make an end. In despair and horror he fumbled for his keen-edged knife. As he felt for it he noticed Isaac and the boy was smiling up at him. Abraham kept his voice still and quiet, although his very being was shattered.

"It is only a little while, now, Isaac, my son. Only a little while. So keep your eyes closed, Isaac, my son."

The boy closed his eyes and lay as if asleep. Abraham drew out his knife and tested the edge of it and knew that to give his son a clean and merciful death he must strike sharp and sure. Marking the place he raised the knife and could not strike. Then a great fear gripped him lest Isaac should open his eyes and see what he was about to do. Drawing in his breath he raised himself up tall and his lips set and the knife rushed downward. Even as it darted he heard a sound close by and checked himself desperately and managed to miss the boy. The knife struck on the stones of the altar and drew sparks of fire and slipped from his grasp and was lost in the darkness. The sound made Isaac stir.

"What was that, father?" he asked, and there was a little quiver of fright in his voice.

"Nothing," Abraham cried out desperately. "Keep your eyes fast closed, my son."

Then he looked about him. But there was nothing on the waste moorland, nothing. Something broke in Abraham's being.

"I cannot," he cried out. "I cannot. Nay, though Thou slay me and the boy, I cannot. Nay, O Yahweh, I will not strike. Strike me if Thou wilt."

It seemed to him that he waited tense for hours for the lightning wrath of his God. None came. He relaxed and lassitude invaded his limbs. He reflected dully that Yahweh would bide his time and prepare some cruel punishment for himself and Isaac. Even so, he could do no more. He must break his vow. For he could not endure to become the slayer of his son, not for his oath or for the fear of some loathsome punishment or for a thousand gods. And he prayed to Yahweh to cease to be his God and to go to some other person. There was no answer. So he knew that Yahweh was waiting, cruel and implacable.

It was at this moment that he heard Isaac stir on the altar and realized that the cords were cutting into him. In a swift rush he lifted him down from the altar and found his knife and cut the cords. The boy still smiled at him. With an oath he flung the accursed knife far from him into the darkness and hugged the boy close, thinking wildly to himself that this was recompense for all the stored-up wrath of his God.

As he thought this and hugged his son, as if past all hope he were risen from the dead, he heard a sound again. He looked. There, hard by, was a ram with its curling horns caught fast in a thicket. In a wild flash of hope he remembered the desert wells of Zara. Leaving Isaac he rushed over and seized the ram. It struggled fiercely. He stunned it with a stone and dragged it over to the altar and laid it upon the wood and felt savagely for his knife. It was not till then that he remembered that he had flung it from him. He could not wait to search for it. So he leaped upon the altar. Baring his teeth he burrowed through the wool into the ram's throat and tore it. After a while there was blood flowing from the altar. Then, Abraham got off and seized the bowl of fire and held it under the wood. He was afraid that the wood would have been wetted with the rain while he had lingered and would not burn. It blazed up fiercely, however, and a great beard of flame rose up into the darkness. Finally, the fire seized hold of the ram and the singed wool, and the stench of burning flesh was as a sweet savour in his nostrils. He looked upward at the heavens. To his amazement the clouds had been swiftly cleared away and the full moon shone out in radiance. Its light, he thought thankfully, was no longer mocking but was true and kindly. So Abraham praised Yahweh, his God, and danced in frenzy about the altar and fell on his knees and bowed himself to the ground. It was then that he thought he heard the voice of Yahweh speaking:

"I am well pleased with thee, O Abraham," the Voice said. "For thou didst not withhold thy son, thine only true-begotten son, but didst bring him to be a burnt-offering to Me. It was I who stayed thy hand and sent the ram into the thicket. For I am not as Baal. Baal is a loathsome god, an unclean god. And the worship of Baal and of Astarte and all the filthiness which surrounds them is abhorrent to Me. Thou shalt not be as the people of Canaan. Thou shalt not sacrifice thy firstborn to me or make thy children pass through the fire or celebrate Me in the ways of this land. For I am a clean God and a mighty God. And I will that thy seed shall be as the stars of heaven and the sands of the seashore, and thy seed shall possess the gates of them who harm them."

Abraham trusted the Lord and lay a great while in adoration of Him, until he heard Isaac say:

"It grows light, father. The dawn will soon be here."

Abraham rose up and went to Isaac and brought him to the altar. The wood and the ram had burnt away. There was nothing left but the dull and wetted ash mingled with half-scorched flesh and charred bones. But Abraham made Isaac kneel by the altar and put his hand upon the ashes and swear that he would bow down to no other God but This. Then, they left the altar and the desolate mountain and came down again into the valley to the men whom they had left there. These lay in heavy slumber. Abraham roused them from their sleep and made them turn at once towards his tents. For his joy would not let him rest.

They rode in sleepy silence back along the way which had seemed so drear. The sun came out fresh and strong after the rain and shone upon them; and the moorland no longer appeared bleak to Abraham. For his very heart sang within him and he kept looking at Isaac, his son, who had been saved to him past all hope. He gave thanks, too, to Yahweh, who had not claimed His sacrifice. Yet there was a still small doubt in his mind, for he knew that he had refused to sacrifice Isaac before the ram had been sent; and it was strange that a God should be so forgetful. It startled him, now that the black cloud which ever since Gerar had seemed to oppress his mind was dissipated, puzzling about the nature of his God, Yahweh, and his own relationship to Him. And it flashed into his consciousness that his idea of Yahweh had changed from time to time.

Unbidden, as he reflected about this, the face of Melchisedek, that wise, dead prince of Jerusalem, rose before him. He heard his words again:

"Each man carries his own God within him, Abraham."

It made him think now that, perhaps, he knew what Melchisedek had meant. Was it that Yahweh, his God, the God of Abraham, was only the image of his own desires and fears, and his visions but the projections of his own deeply hidden thoughts?

He was loath to believe this. Yahweh had been too close to him for too long and it was a comfort to believe that Yahweh was pleased with him again and would cast the cloak of His protection about him and about his son, Isaac. Nor did he wish to think that he had not been under the guidance of a mighty God, himself and the Habiru; or that there might not be a splendid and divinely ordained future ahead for Isaac and Isaac's sons and all the Habiru. How could a man live and be confident unless some God was his protector?

He put, therefore, the thought away from him hastily and cried aloud so that Yahweh might hear:

"There is no God like the God of Abraham and of Isaac. Nay, there is no other god before Him."

In this way he stilled his doubts and rode back in joy to Sarai, his wife.

8 Jacob's Deception of Isaac

With the strange subtitle "An Autobiographical Novel," Irving Fineman alerts the readers of *Jacob* to the fact that his book has several levels of meaning. The biblical tale of Jacob, his forebearers and sons is "the story of the kinship of all generations." At the same time, Jacob addressing a letter to his son Joseph to be read after his death, is a justification for a man's life and an explanation of what he has done. Perhaps, on still another level, it is the author explaining himself to his own children. Looking for meanings beyond those explicitly set down, the reader cannot fail to see that this novel, published at the start of the Second World War, probes the differences between the Jacobs and the Esaus of the world, of the men who live by their wits and the men who live by their brawn, of the loved and the unloved. This is most apparent in the story of the deception of Isaac, which follows.

And Isaac said unto Jacob, Come near, I pray thee, that I may feel thee, my son, whether thou be my very son Esau or not.

And Jacob went near unto Isaac his father; and he felt him, and said, The voice is Jacob's voice, but the hands are the hands of Esau.

And he discerned him not, because his hands were hairy, as his brother Esau's hands: so he blessed him.

GENESIS: XXVII, 21–23

JACOB by IRVING FINEMAN

I HAVE COME to look with no little amusement upon the spectacle most men make strutting in the forefront of events, knowing full well how much they depend upon women not only to nourish and comfort their bodies but to sustain their spirits, how important a role, for all men's posturing, women have long played behind them. And I come to think that the man behind whom no woman stands is a man to be feared.

But the extent to which women will support the Jacobs as against the Esaus among men I first realized when my mother helped me get from my father the blessing he intended for my brother. Since the scandalous acts of men are more often recalled than their virtuous doings, the story of that deception will doubtless be made well known to you; and I am frank enough to call it a deception—and to admit that the deception of a blind man by his son and his wife is a not altogether admirable proceeding. Nevertheless there were extenuating aspects of that event which are not generally considered—especially in the attitude of Esau.

Take for example the matter of his selling his birthright to me before the deception, the circumstances of that event also being generally misapprehended. We were well-grown young men by then, required to provide for ourselves, and Esau could have seen as well as I that the crops that year would be poor because of the long drought we had in the spring. But while I was foresightedly sowing and cultivating my field of lentils he went right on amusing himself, doing what pleased him, hunting and fishing only for the day, not worrying about tomorrow. The strong are apt to be improvident because they feel they can get what they want whenever they want it; they are not given to worrying, to looking ahead very far; perhaps they merely lack the power of imagination . . . But, be that as it may, the time came when I reaped the harvest of my foresightedness; and, the hunt having failed him, Esau, lacking breadstuff as well as meat, came to me one day, faint with hunger, just as I was sitting down to eat.

It was then I learned to my surprise that powerful men, since they have not of necessity, like their frailer brothers, been inured to suffering, are apt not to know how to suffer, are apt not to stand suffering very well. Esau was desperately hungry.

"Feed me, I beg of you," he cried, "some of that red pottage." Never before had the strong and scornful Esau begged anything of me. For the first time in my life I felt that I had the advantage of my brother. Is it to be wondered that I wished to taste my power a little?

I said, "What will you give me for my pottage, Esau?"

He said, "What do you want?" He said it carelessly, as one who, having the world in his grasp, or able to take it when he wished, is in the habit of being generous—which I can truthfully say Esau often was, that is, when he was in a good mood.

But it was not generosity I wanted of Esau that day. Out of the depths of my being rose the wish to see just how much power over my brother my foresightedness, the cunning of my mind, had given me. So long had he shown me how much power over me the mere accident, the chance of his greater strength had given him. I thought of the highest possible price to ask—as one does in any bargaining—as a starting point from which to descend. I said "Sell me your birthright."

To my astonishment, he only laughed. "You would want a birthright!" He said it scornfully. "What do you think that birthright means to me? If I die of hunger you will have it anyway; and as long as I live and have my strength I can seize whatever I want without a birthright. Only the feeble need the support of authority. The strong can take authority when they want it. If I weren't weak with hunger right now I'd take your pottage without so much as asking. Give it to me now and you can have the old birthright."

I could hardly believe my ears. "Swear to it," I said, to make sure, and he swore to it. And in that moment I despised my brother for the weakness of his spirit. No hunger would have moved me to give up my birthright to him.

Nevertheless Esau was incensed later when he learned that I deceived our father into giving me the blessing which went with the birthright. I had said nothing to my father or my mother about his having sold the birthright to me. But knowing it was legally mine and remembering how little he had valued it made it easier for me to fall in with my mother's suggestion that I put on some goatskins and impersonate shaggy Esau before my blind father, and thus get his blessing while my brother was out hunting venison for him.

Knowing I had the birthright already, and being a little fearful of attempting to deceive my father, I did mildly suggest to my mother that I thought I might get along just as well without his blessing. "You may, indeed," said my mother, "but it is just as well in this life to have every possible advantage. And Esau will feel handicapped against you if you have it and he doesn't."

So I went to my father; and curiously enough I had the feeling not that I was deceiving him (although I don't wish to deny that I did so) but that he was deceiving himself; for he obviously suspected I was not Esau and went so far as to say, *the voice is the voice of Jacob's, but the hands are the hands of Esau.* But it was as if he were expressing a long-wished-for idea—it was as if, for the sake of that combination of the sensitive voice which was like his own and the strong and ruthless hand of Esau which he envied, he was willing to be deceived.

> *See, the smell of my son*
> *Is as the smell of a field which the Lord hath blessed:*
> *And God give thee of the dew of heaven,*
> *And of the fatness of the earth,*
> *And plenty of corn and wine:*
> *Let peoples serve thee,*
> *And nations bow down to thee: . . .*

Thus my father in his grandiose and poetic way blessed me, with a promise of wealth and power far beyond anything I have ever dreamed of. I have, for example, never had any desire to have nations bow down to me. Indeed my dreams then and since have been aspirations of a somewhat different sort. However, that blessing was not really intended for me but for Esau, whom it would have suited very well. And this proves, my son, that it is generally foolish to be envious of the blessings of others, because each man has his own peculiar needs.

As it turned out, much of my father's blessings did not come to pass; and what has come to pass, I may truthfully say I have had to struggle and work for; and I might conceivably have done just as well without that blessing, but for the sense of election it gave me, a sense which is helpful to most men and especially to the Jacobs. Perhaps it is because we do not get from our bodies the feeling an Esau gets of physical security in this precarious world that we needs must grasp every aid, every means of support we can find. That is not to say that we are always justified in acting as we do. Indeed, I am not trying to excuse myself before you for anything I have done. Nor is it my intention here to advise you what is right and what wrong so much as to tell you how we behave.

For I often think it would be well if men could observe their own behavior, as an infant does the movements of his own hands and feet. I remember the objective curiousity with which you, my son, used to lie playing with and examining your limbs, even tasting your fingers and your toes, as if intent on learning all about them before you might use them properly. Perhaps in observing these, my acts, you will learn something pertinent to your own.

You will doubtless hear the whole story of that deception told without credit to me, and how Esau afterwards said of me, *Is he not rightly named Jacob—for he has supplanted me these two times: he took away my birthright, and now he has taken away my blessing,* forgetting that he had freely sold me the birthright and that without it the blessing really meant nothing— and that in any case a blessing should really mean no more than a birthright to a strong man who, as he put it, could seize whatever he wanted. You will find, my son, that powerful men are not given to logic or consistency. They have no use for such spiritual concepts and restraints, fortified as they are with the feeling that might makes right. Esau was wild; especially after he ran to my father begging for a blessing, and was told: *by the sword shalt thou live: and thou shalt serve thy brother. . . .* Whatever his failings, my father, a true poet, always said what he perceived. And Esau swore he would kill me.

My father was angry too. Naturally. But it was rather characteristic of him that he was less concerned about the practical consequences of the incident than grieved that a deception had been practiced. It was the principle of the thing he kept harping on, until my mother, irritated by his painful references to the part she—"a woman, a wife and mother" had played in this shady business, burst out, "Women are sometimes driven to deception! Without deception Eve would never have become the mother of mankind. None of us would now be here had she waited for Adam to pick that fruit from the tree. And men, I suppose," her voice was edged with sarcasm, "men never practice deception—your own father Abraham, for example, with his tale about taking you up on Mount Moriah to sacrifice you as a burnt offering at God's command."

"There was no deception about that," said my father. "I was there. Though I was then a small child I remember how my father rose early in the morning, and saddled his ass and took two of his young men with him, and took me and the wood he had chopped for the burnt offering."

"But he left his young men at the foot of the mountain, didn't he—told them to wait there with the ass until he returned?"

"Yes," said my father. "But I remember how he put the wood on my back and took the fire and the knife and we went up and I said, 'Father,' and he said, 'Yes, my son,' and I said, 'We have fire and wood, but where is the lamb for the burnt offering?' and he said, 'God himself will provide the lamb for the burnt offering, my son,' and we went on up together, and my father built an altar and laid the wood in order, and bound me and laid me on the altar, on the wood; and he stretched out his hand and took the knife to slay me. And the angel of the Lord called to him out of Heaven. . . ."

"Did you hear it?" interrupted my mother.

"No. He was not speaking to me; but my father did."

"So he said," said my mother.

"And I remember clearly," persisted my father, "the ram caught in the thicket by his horns."

"That was most conveniently arranged, wasn't it?" said my mother.

"And I remember particularly," my father went on, ignoring my mother's insinuation, "how my father cut me loose and took the ram and offered him for a burnt offering instead of me."

"And then went down," continued my mother earnestly, "and told his young men and all the world how God had forbid him to sacrifice a human being but had provided an animal for a scapegoat. And, though it has all the earmarks of a cunning deception contrived by your clever father, a fine lesson indeed it was in those benighted days when men were given to human sacrifice, and a fine lesson such a deception might still be for the benefit of those who to this day are given to making scapegoats of their fellow men. And a deception, Isaac," said my mother, gently now, but still firmly, "a deception, whether by man or woman, is still needed sometimes when men cannot be persuaded otherwise to do what is best. You would never listen to me when I tried to tell you that the blessing would be wasted on a man like Esau."

"But I've told you again and again, Rebekah, that Esau had the right of priority; he came first," remonstrated my father.

"Right, might; priority, miority!" cried my mother. And no one can be more scornful of law than a woman. "What if Esau did come first? Because the beasts came first on this earth are they given any rights over man?"

Then my mother took me aside and wept that I would have to go away for a while, out of reach of my brother's vengeance. Though I had envied his strength, I had never really feared my brother because I had thought, and still thought, I could, with the help of my brain, cope with him. But my mother said, "Don't be foolish, Jacob. Men like you aren't made for fighting. I don't mean that you should let yourself be despoiled and pushed around as your father was by the Philistines, but you must learn to get what you need and go your own way without strife. Your kind are like women, in that you need peace to do your work. We must have peace in which to bring forth and raise our children. You need peace to bring to pass what is in your fruitful and cunning minds. And yet, strangely, it is just your kind who are apt to make trouble for themselves, to disturb their own peace, to get themselves driven out so that they have to make their own way in the dangerous world. Well, that is your destiny. That's how it works."

It occurred to me then that since she believed in destiny it was odd that my mother had felt moved and justified in deliberately tampering with its working as she had in my case. But the attitude of women toward destiny is something no reasonable man is likely ever to understand. I have told you already about how your mother thought she tricked destiny when you were born.

"And anyway, it is probably for the best," my mother said, wiping away her tears, "that you should have to be parted from me, my son. It is not well for men to be too much attached to their mothers. That, I have sometimes thought, was what weakened your father—he had never really got away from Sarah, his mother; and I merely took her place."

9 Jacob's Wedding

There is probably no author in this book about whom more could be written and with less need than Thomas Mann, Nobel Laureate. The selections which follow were taken from his monumental work *Joseph and His Brothers* consisting of four novels: *The Tales of Jacob, Young Joseph, Joseph in Egypt* and *Joseph the Provider*. Devoting sixteen of his prime creative years to this interpretation of Joseph, Mann brought to the quartet a profound understanding of philosophy and psychology, an appreciation for scholarship, a knowledge of the very countryside where the stories are set, and the genius of a man who towered above his generation like a giant. He has described the task as that of telling "of the primitive occurrences of human life, of love and hate, blessing and curse, fraternal strife and paternal grief, pride and penance, fall and rise, a humorous song of mankind, if one is allowed to call such things by name." During the turbulent years from 1926 to 1942, Mann regarded this quartet as his "refuge, comfort, home, symbol of steadfastness, and guarantee of perseverance in the tempestuous change of things."

> *And Laban had two daughters: the name of the elder was Leah, and the name of the younger was Rachel.*
>
> *Leah was tender eyed; but Rachel was beautiful and well favoured.*
>
> *And Jacob loved Rachel; and said, I will serve thee seven years for Rachel thy younger daughter.*
>
> GENESIS: XIX, 16–18

TALES OF JACOB by THOMAS MANN

The Sisters

THE UNCLEAN BEAST

As THE SEVEN YEARS drew on to their end, and the time approached when Jacob should know Rachel, he found he scarcely realized the truth, yet rejoiced beyond measure, and his heart beat mightily when he thought upon the hour. For Rachel was now nineteen years old and had waited for him in the purity of her blood, invulnerable through it to evil spirits and sickness which might have snatched her from her bridegroom; so that she was indeed, in respect to her bloom and beauty, all that Jacob had so tenderly prophesied:

70

lovely to look at beyond all the daughters of the land, with her full and yet
delicate form, the soft braids of her hair, the thick nostrils of her little nose,
the sweet, short-sighted gaze of her slanting eyes and the friendly night that
rested in their depths; lovely above all in the smiling way the upper lip lay
upon the lower, and shaped the inexpressible charm of the corner of her
mouth. Yes, lovely was she beyond all others; but if I say, as Jacob always
said to himself, that she was lovely most of all before Leah, that does not
mean that Leah was uglier than any other maiden, but merely that she was
the nearest object of comparison, and suffered most of all next to Rachel.
For it is quite possible to imagine a man less enslaved than Jacob to that
single point of view, who might have preferred the elder daughter, despite
the stupid gaze and the "tenderness" of her blue eyes, and the trick she had,
both proud and bitter, of dropping the lids over their squinting stare. For
Leah's rich blond hair hung knotted in her neck, and she had the figure of a
fruitful woman, ripe for motherhood. Much might be said in praise of Rachel,
that she did not vaunt her own charms above her sister's, or take undue
advantage of her lovely little face, the image and likeness of the full moon, as
Leah's might be of the waning one. Rachel was not so untaught as not to
reverence the latter in right of its condition, and indeed at the bottom of her
heart she disapproved of Jacob, that he so utterly rejected the thought of
her sister and turned the brightness of his sole regard upon her—even though
she could not quite put out of her heart all feminine satisfaction in his
preference.

The nuptial feast was set for the full moon of the summer solstice; and
Rachel too confessed that she longed for the coming of the festal day. Yet
in the weeks just before she had been sad, weeping silently on Jacob's shoulder
and against his cheek, answering his anxious query only by a painful smile
and a quick head-shake that dashed the tears from her eyes. What weighed
upon her heart? Jacob did not know—yet often he himself felt sad as well.
Was she mourning over her maidenhead, since now the time of her blossoming drew to an end, when she should become a fruit-bearing tree? Such is the
sadness inseparable from life yet not from joy, and Jacob knew it too. For
the day of high marriage is the day of death and a feast of the solstice; the
moon climbs to her height and from then on turns her face again to the sun,
into which she will sink. Jacob was to know her whom he loved, and begin
to die. For from then on he would not stand alone, living for himself and as
lord of the world; he would be dissolved into his sons and in his person
belong to death. Yet he would love them, they who became the bearers of his
divided and diverse lives, because it was himself which consciously he had
poured into Rachel's womb.

At this time he had a dream, which he remembered long on account of
its strange mood of peaceful sadness. He dreamed it on a warm night of
Tammuz, in the meadows by his flocks, when the moon's sickle stood facing
left in the sky, which at its fulness should usher in the marriage feast. But
in the dream he was still upon his flight from home, or another flight, driven
once more to ride into the red waste; and as before a jackal trotted before

him, prick-eared, dog-headed, with tail held stiffly out behind him, looked round and laughed. It was a repetition of reality, yet the same reality; recurring to work itself out, since the first time it had been left incomplete.

He was riding among loose boulders and dry shrubbery—naught else grew. The evil one wound among rock and bushes, appearing, disappearing, looking round. Once, when he had vanished, Jacob blinked; when he looked again, the creature sat in front of him on a stone, and was an animal still as to the head, the usual dog's head with sharp upstanding ears and a projecting snout whose mouth ran right round to them; but his body was human down to the slightly dusty toes, and pleasant to look on, like the body of a slender youth. He sat on the piece of rock in a careless posture; one leg was drawn up, and he leaned with his elbow upon that thigh so that a fold came across his abdomen; the other was stretched out before him sidewise, the ankle on the ground. This limb, the delicate knee, the long, fine-sinewed, slightly curving leg, was a most pleasant sight. But a fell, the color of yellow clay, began on the slender shoulders, the upper back and breast of the god, merging into the dog's head with the wide jaws and crafty little eyes, which suited the body so ill, was so painful a humiliation of it, that one could only say how lovely, without it, that body might have been. As Jacob rode up he got a strong whiff of the pungent odour which, sad to say, the boy-jackal exhaled. And how sad and strange at once it was to see the figure open its wide jaws and address itself to speech in a labouring, throaty voice:

"*Ap-uat, Ap-uat.*"

"It hath no need, son of Osiris, that thou troublest thyself," Jacob said. "Thou art Anubis, guide and opener of the way, as well I know. And I had marvelled not to meet thee here."

"It was a blunder," said the god.

"What meanest thou?" asked Jacob.

"They were in error," the other said, in his difficult speech, "they who begot me, the lord of the west and my mother, Nephthys."

"I am sad to hear it," said Jacob, "but relate to me how it fell out."

"She should not have been my mother," responded the youth, gradually learning to manage his jaws in speech. "She was the wrong one. The darkness was to blame. She is a cow, it is all one to her. She wears the disk of the sun between her horns, in sign that now and again the sun goes in unto her to beget with her the young day; but the bearing of so many radiant sons has made no abatement in her dull indifference."

"I seek to understand," Jacob said, "that that might be a danger."

"Very dangerous," agreed the other, nodding. "Blindly, in all the good-natured warmth of her cowishness she embraces all that comes to her, and dully passive lets it come to pass, though it happen only on account of the dark."

"That is an evil," said Jacob. "But which had been the right one, then, if Nephthys were not she?"

"Dost thou not know?" asked the jackal youth.

"I cannot precisely distinguish," Jacob answered, "between that which thou tellest me and that which I know of myself."

"If thou knowest it not," the other responded, "then I could not tell thee. In the beginning—not quite in the beginning, but nearly so, there were Geb and Nut. The earth god and the heaven goddess. They had four children: Osiris, Set, Isis, and Nephthys. But Isis was the sister-bride of Osiris and Nephthys of Set the red."

"So much is clear," said Jacob. "And then these four did not keep the arrangement clearly enough in mind?"

"Alas, no," responded Anubis, "two of them did not. What wouldst thou, for we are feckless beings, heedless and distracted from birth onwards. Carefulness and foresight are base earthly characteristics, whereas what all has not carefreeness been the cause of in this life?"

"It is but too true," Jacob confirmed. "One must take care. For to speak openly, it dependeth on the fact that ye are all idols. God knoweth always what He willeth and doth. He promiseth and keepeth to His word. He setteth up a bond and is true unto eternity."

"What god?" asked Anubis. But Jacob answered him:

"Thou feignest. When earth and heaven mingle, then indeed come forth heroes and great kings, but no god, neither four nor one. Geb and Nut, thou hast thyself said it, were not quite the beginning. Whence came they?"

"Out of Tefnut, the Great Mother," came the prompt reply from the stone.

"Good, thou sayest it because I know it," Jacob went on in his dream. "But was Tefnut the beginning? Whence came Tefnut?"

"The secret, the unbegotten one, whose name is Nun, he called her," responded Anubis.

"I asked thee not his name," said Jacob. "But now thou beginnest to speak sensibly, boy-dog. I had no intent to reason with thee. After all, thou art an idol. Relate to me of thy parents' error."

"The darkness was to blame," repeated the evil-smelling one. "And he that carrieth the scourge and the shepherd's crook, he was carefree and distraught. And in his majesty he sought for Isis, his sister-bride, and by mistake he came in the night upon Nephthys, sister of the red one. Thus she received that great god, thinking he was her bridegroom, and they were both enfolded in the utter unconcern of the night of love."

"Can such things come to pass?" cried Jacob.

"With ease," answered the other. "For in its unconcern night knoweth the truth, and in her eyes the lively prepossessions of the daylight are as naught. For one woman's body is like another's, good to love, good to beget upon. Only the countenance distinguishes one from another and is the cause of our choosing one and not another. For the countenance is of the day, full of living fancies, but before the night, that knows the truth, it is as nothing."

"Thou speakest crudely and without feeling," said Jacob, greatly disquiet. "One may have ground to speak thus when one hath a head like to thine and a face which one must cover up only to be able to say that thy leg is pretty and well-favoured as it lies stretched out before thee."

Anubis looked down, drew his leg in beside the other one and put his hands between his knees.

"Leave me out," said he. "I shall one day be rid of my head too. Wouldst thou hear the rest of the tale?"

"What happened?" asked Jacob.

"In that night," went on the other, "the lord Osiris was for Nephthys like Set the red her lord, and she for Osiris like to the lady Isis. For he was on begetting bent and she on conceiving, and to the night naught else was of importance. And they delighted one another in begetting and conceiving, for thinking to love each other they could but beget. Then was that goddess pregnant with me whereas it should have been Isis the true wife."

"Sad," Jacob said.

"When morning came, they parted in great haste; yet might all have been well, had not the god left behind with Nephthys the lotus garland that he wears; Set the red found it and roared aloud. Since that time he seeketh Osiris' life."

"As thou tellest it, so I know it," said Jacob. "Then came the affair with the chest, into which the red one lured his brother, and slew him by its means, so that Osiris, the dead lord, swam downstream into the sea in the sealed-up chest."

"And Set became king of all his lands and sat upon the throne of Geb," concluded Anubis. "But it is not that upon which I would dwell, or which gives this dream of thine its point. For the red one was not for long king of the lands, for Isis gave birth to the youth Horus, who slew him. And lo, as Isis went searching and bewailing through the world, after her lost and murdered lord, and cried unceasingly: 'Come into thy house, come into thy house, beloved, O beautiful child, come into thy house!' there stood beside her Nephthys, wife of his murderer, whom the slain god had in his error embraced, and went beside her whither she went, and they agreed together in their grief and mourned together: 'O thou, whose heart beats no more, O lord of beauty, thee I would fain behold!' "

"That was sad and friendly," said Jacob.

"And that," responded the other from his stone, "is the meaning of the dream. For who else was with her and aided her in her search, her roving and her wailing, then as well as later, when Set found the discovered and rehidden corpse and cut it up into fourteen pieces, which then Isis must seek anew? Who but I, Anubis, son of the unlawful wife, fruit of the murdered one, who was ever at Isis' side in her erring and seeking, and as she wandered she laid her arm about my neck that she might lean upon me, and we lamented together: 'Where art thou, thou left arm of my beautiful God, where shoulder-blade and foot of his right side, where art thou, lovely head, and holy sex, which it seemeth is irreparably lost so that we are fain to replace it with an image made of sycamore wood?' "

"Thou speakest obscenely," said Jacob, "and like to the death-god of the two countries." But Anubis replied:

"And thou, where thou standest, shouldst have more understanding for such matters, for thou art a bridegroom, and shalt beget and die. For in the sex is death and in death sex, that is the miracle of the grave chamber, and sex teareth the bonds of death and standeth up against death, as it happened to the lord, Osiris, above whom Anubis hovered as a female vulture and made his seed flow out of the dead and cohabited with him even as she mourned."

"It is best now that I should awake," thought Jacob. And even as he still thought to see the god swing himself up from the stone and vanish, so that movement and vanishing were the same, he found himself lying under the starry night beside the sheep-pens. His dream of Anubis the jackal soon faded, it returned into his simple recollection of the experience of his journey and he remembered it, after a while, only thus. But a faint melancholy, pleasant to feel, lingered still a while in his soul, in that Nephthys, wrongfully embraced, had yet sought and mourned with Isis, and the bereaved one been cherished and supported by the wrongly begot.

THE WEDDING

At this time Laban and Jacob often took counsel together over the approaching event and the nuptial celebrations, and how Laban in general thought to hold the feast; and Jacob learned that his father-in-law had ambitious plans and meant to celebrate regardless of expense.

"It will cost me," Laban said, "a pretty penny, for there are now many more mouths and I must feed them. But I shall not rue it, for lo, trade is not at all bad, rather fairly favourable in these times, thanks to many circumstances among which we should mention the blessing of Isaac. Therefore it is I can pay for more labour in the court, and have bought two maids in addition to that lazy Iltani, and they are quite seemly wenches, named Zilpah and Bilhah. And on the wedding days I will give these to my two daughters, Zilpah to Leah my eldest and to the second Bilhah. And at the marriage will the maid be thine, and I will give her thee as dowry and her price shall be reckoned as two-thirds of the mina of silver, according to our contract."

"I embrace thee in thanks," said Jacob, shrugging his shoulders.

"But that is the least of it," went on Laban. "For all the feast will be my sole charge, and I will invite people on the sabbath from far and near and have musicians who shall play and dance, and I will lay two bullocks and four sheep upon their backs, and comfort the guests with drink until they see all things double. All that will be a heavy charge but I will bear it and not pull a long face for is it not my daughter's wedding? And besides I have in mind to make the bride a gift, that she may wear it and it will rejoice her heart. I bought it long ago of a traveller, and it cost much money, and I have kept it in the chest: a veil, for the bride to shroud herself in, that she may be holy unto Ishtar and a consecrated one, whose veil also thou shalt lift. It may have belonged to a king's daughter in times past, being the maiden

garment of a daughter of princes, so artfully is it embroidered throughout
with manifold symbols of Ishtar and Tammuz, but she, the spotless one, shall
veil her head in it. For immaculate is she and shall be like one of the *enitu,*
like to the bride of heaven, whom each year at the feast of Ishtar, the priests
at Babel lead up to God before all the people up the steps of the stairs and
through the seven gates, and take from her some piece of her garment and
her ornaments at every gate, and at the last gate her shame, and they lead
the holy maid naked into the uppermost bedchamber of the tower E-temen-
anki. There she receives the god upon the bed in the darkness of the night
and exceedingly great is the mystery."

"H'm," said Jacob. For Laban opened wide his eyes and spread out his
fingers at the sides of his head and put on an air of sanctimoniousness that
in his nephew's view suited him not at all. Laban continued:

"Of course, it is very fine and lovely when the bridegroom hath a house
and court of his own, or is held in great esteem in the house of his parents,
whence he cometh in great pomp to fetch the bride and to lead her in procession by land or by water to his own place, and his inheritance. But thou
as thou knowest art but a fugitive and homeless man, fallen out with thine
own, and sittest with me as my son-in-law, and I make no complaint. There
will be no bridal procession by land or water, and you will sojourn here after
the feast and the nuptial night; but when I have come between you and
touched your foreheads, then we shall do as is the custom of our land in these
cases and lead you with singing round the court and into the bridal chamber.
Thou shalt sit there upon the bed with a flower in thy hand, and await the
bride. For her too, the spotless one, shall we lead round about the court
with torches and singing, and at the door of the chamber we put out the
torches, and I lead the devoted one in unto thee, and leave you, that thou
mayest hand her the flower in the darkness."

"Is that the custom and lawful?" asked Jacob.

"Far and wide, thou sayest it," replied Laban.

"Then will I also approve it," responded Jacob. "And I assume that
there will likewise be a torch burning, or a little lamp with a wick, that I
may see my bride when I hand her the flower and also afterwards."

"Be silent," cried Laban. "Would I might know what thou hast in thy
mind, with thy unchaste speaking, to speak so before the father, to whom
it is moreover painful and bitter to lead his child in unto a man that he may
uncover her and sleep with her. At least in my presence hold thy lewd
tongue and restrain within thyself thy over-great lustfulness. For hast thou
not hands to see, and must thou also swallow up the spotless one with thine
eyes to sharpen thy lust upon her shame and her maiden trembling? Have
respect before the mystery of the high tower!"

"Pardon!" said Jacob, "and forgive me. I have not meant it so un-
chastely in my thoughts as it soundeth in thy mouth. Gladly would I have
looked upon my bride with my eyes. But since it is far and wide the custom
to do as thou sayest, I will be satisfied for the time."

Thus the day of the fullness of splendour came on, and the nuptial feast, and in the house of Laban, the prosperous breeder of sheep, and in his court, there was a slaughtering and a seething and roasting and brewing, so that everything steamed and all was bustle and noise, and all eyes watered from the smoke of the fires that burned under pots and ovens. For Laban was saving of charcoal and heated almost altogether with thorns and dung. And the master and mistress and all that were in the house, including Jacob, hurried on the work and the servants, to make hospitality for so many and to prepare the banquet; for the wedding would last seven days and for all that time the supplies must be inexhaustible, of cakes and buns and fish bread, of thick soups and plantains and milk dishes, of beer and fruit juices and strong waters, not to mention the roasted mutton and joints of beef—else shame and mockery would be the portion of the household. And as they worked they sang songs to Uduntamku the fat, the god of the belly, the presiding deity of feasting, they all sang and composed them, Laban, Adina, Jacob and Leah, Iltani the idle and Bilhah and Zilpah the daughters' maids, Abdcheba the twenty-shekel man, and the latest-acquired slaves. Laban's sons in their little shirts ran boisterously among the press, slipped on the blood from the slaughtering and befouled themselves, so that their father wrung their ears and they howled like jackals. Only Rachel sat still and idle in the house—for she might not see the bridegroom now nor he his bride—and examined the costly veil, her father's present, which she should wear at the feast. It was splendid to see, a magnificent specimen of the arts of weaving and embroidering; it seemed an unmerited piece of good fortune that such a thing should have found its way into Laban's house and his chest; the man who let it go so cheap must have been greatly pressed by circumstances.

It was large and broad, a garment and over-garment, with wide sleeves to put one's arms in at will; so cut that a piece of it could either be drawn over the head to cover it or else wound about the head and shoulders, or else left to hang down the back. And the maiden garment weighed uncertainly in the hand, for it was heavy and light at once, and of unequal weight in different places. The background was of the palest blue, woven thin and fine as a breath of air, a misty nothing, to be squeezed together in one hand, and yet weighted heavily everywhere by the embroidered pictures which covered it with brilliant, glittering colours, carried out in close, fine work, in gold and silver and bronze, and every imaginable shade: white, purple, rose and olive, likewise black and white, all blended together like paintings in bright enamel. And such clever pictures and designs! Here was Ishtar-Mami, in various shapes, a tiny nude figure, pressing milk out of her breast with both hands, the sun and moon on either side. Everywhere the five-pointed star was repeated in varying colours, signifying god; the dove, the bird of the mother-goddess of love, was woven most often in silver thread. Gilgamesh, the hero, two-thirds god and one-third man, was displayed strangling a lion in the bend of his arm. One recognized the human scorpion pair who at the ends of the earth guarded the gate through which the sun goes down to the lower world. One distinguished various animals, sometime paramours of Ishtar and transformed by her—a wolf, a bat, the same who had once been Isullanu, the gardener. But Tammuz, the shepherd, was represented by a brilliant bird, the first partner of her lust, to whom she had decreed weeping year for year; and there was not lacking the fire-breathing bull of heaven, whom Anubis sent against Gilgamesh because of Ishtar's baffled longing and perfervid plaints. The garment slipped through Rachel's hands: she saw a man and woman sitting at both sides of a tree, stretching up their hands to the fruit, while a snake rose up behind the woman's back. And again there was embroidered a sacred tree, with two bearded angels on either side, touching it with scaly masculine cones to make it bear; while above the tree of life the female emblem hovered surrounded by sun, moon and stars. And likewise there were sayings woven into the veil, in broad-pointed signs, lying down or standing straight or slanting. Rachel made out: "I have put off my coat, how shall I put it on?"

She sat and played with the bright-coloured weave, the splendid garment and veil; she wrapped it round her and turned herself about in it, she found new ways to drape its picture-book transparency. Thus she beguiled the time while she waited and the others prepared the feast. Sometimes she had visits from Leah, her sister, who also tried the beauties of the veil upon her own person and afterwards they sat together, and caressed each other, with tears. Why did they weep? They alone knew—though I might go so far as to say that they had different reasons.

When Jacob sat and mused, with swimming gaze, and all the tales that had written themselves in the lines of his face and weighed down his life with their dignified burden came back and were present in his mind, as they had been on the day when he and his red-haired twin had buried their father; then there was one day, and one story, which possessed beyond all others this power of presentness, having inflicted upon him a defeat so devastating to his senses and so humiliating to his feeling that his soul for long could not shake it off, and only regained faith in itself with the advent of a feeling that was like a rebirth and resurrection of those shamed and shattered ones. Present, I say, before all, was the story of his wedding day.

They had all, the people of Laban, washed their heads and limbs in the water of the blessed pond, had anointed and curled themselves to their taste, put on their festal garments and burned much fragrant oil, to receive the incoming guests with a sweet savour. And they came, on foot, on the backs of asses, in carts drawn by bullocks and mules, men alone, men with women, even with children, if they could not be left at home: the peasants and cattle-breeders of the neighbourhood, likewise anointed and curled and clad in festal garments; people like Laban, of the same heavy-handed tribe, with the same prosaic habits of thought. They saluted, hand to forehead, made enquiry into the health of all and sundry, and then settled down in house and court, round cook-pots and shaded tables. Water having been poured over their hands and feet, they smacked their lips and fell to upon the lengthy meal, amid loud invocations in praise of Shamash and of Laban, father of the bride and giver of the feast. The banquet was laid in the outer court round the altar, on the roof of the house and in the wooden galleries; and round the altar were grouped the musicians hired from Harran—they played on harps, drums, and cymbals and likewise danced. The day was windy, the evening still more so. Clouds glided across the moon, hiding her altogether from time to time, a bad omen to many of those present though they did not expressly say so. They were simple folk, and made no distinction between complete darkening and a cloud passing over her face. A sultry wind went sighing through the steading, got caught in the chimney of the storehouses, made the tall poplars creak and groan, and whirling among the savours of the feast, the odours of the anointed guests and the fumes of the cookery, mingled them all together in gusts of vapour, and seemed to try to snatch the flames from the tripods where nard-grass and *budulhu*-gum were burning. Jacob, when he recalled his wedding day, always recognized in his nostrils that wind-driven mingling of spices and sweat and roasted meats.

He sat with the family among the feasting guests in the upper room, where seven years before he had first broken bread with his stranger kin; sat with the master, his fruitful wife and their daughters at a table heaped up with dessert and dainties of various sorts, sweet breads and dates, cucumbers and garlic, and pledged the guests who lifted their glasses to him and Laban. Rachel, his bride, whom soon he should receive for his own, sat beside him, and he kissed from time to time the seam of her veil that enveloped her in its heavy picture-folds. She did not lift it to eat or drink; it seemed the consecrated one's hunger had been satisfied earlier. She sat quiet and silent, only bending meekly her shrouded head when he kissed her veil. Jacob too sat silent and dreamy, with a flower in his hand, a blossoming twig of myrtle from Laban's well-watered garden. He had drunk beer and date wine and his senses were somewhat clouded; his soul could neither free itself for thought nor rouse itself to observation, but was heavy inside his anointed body, and his body was his soul. Gladly would he have thought, gladly comprehended how his god had brought all this to pass; how he had brought the beloved in the way of the fugitive, the human creature whom he had but needed to behold for his heart to elect her and love her for all time and eternity—beyond itself, and in the children whom his love would beget. He tried to rejoice in his victory over time, that hard time of waiting, laid upon him, it seemed, in penance for Esau's undoing and his bitter weeping; to lay it at the feet of God the Lord, in thanks and praise, this triumph, for that it was His; God through him and his not unachieving patience having enforced the time, that seven-headed monster, as once the dragon of chaos, so that what had been but inward wish and waiting was now the present, and Rachel sat beside him in the veil, which in a little while he would be permitted to lift. He tried to partake of this joy in his soul. But with joy it is as with the waiting for it; the longer one waits, the less it is pure joy, the more it is filled with practical activities and living needs. And when it comes, that joy so actively awaited, it is not of the stuff of the divine, but has become bodily present and has material weight, like all life. For the life of the body is never pure bliss, but a mixture, in part unpleasant, and if joy becomes the life of the body the soul does also, and is no longer anything else but the body, with the oil-soaked pores, whose affair that once distant bliss has now become.

Jacob sat, and spanned his thighs, and thought of his sex, whose property this joy had now become, and which very soon might and must approve itself mightily in the holy darkness of the nuptial chamber. For his joy was marriage joy and a feast of Ishtar; it was celebrated with over-eating and drunkenness, wreathed about with the odours of spices—whereas once it had been God's affair and rested in his hand. And as once Jacob had been pained over the waiting, and forced to forget it in life and action, so now he was pained for the sake of God, who was the Lord of life and all the longed-for future, yet, when the hour came to pass, must yield his dominion to the special idols of the physical, in whose sign it stood. And therefore Jacob kissed the little nude figure of Ishtar, lifting the hem of Rachel's veil as she sat beside him, immaculate sacrifice to procreation.

Laban sat opposite, leaning forward with his heavy arm on the table and looking steadfastly at his son-in-law.

"Rejoice, my son and my sister's son, for thy hour is at hand and the day of rewarding, and thou shalt be paid the reward according to law and contract for the seven years that thou hast laboured for my house and my business to the reasonable satisfaction of its head. And the reward is neither goods nor gold but a tender maiden, my daughter, whom thy heart desireth, and thou shalt have her after thy heart's desire, and she shall be submissive to thee in thy arms. I marvel how thy heart may be beating, for the hour is big for thee, truly an hour of life like to be thy greatest hour, great as the hour when in thy father's tent thou wonnest the blessing, as thou hast told me, thou crafty one and son of a crafty woman!"

Jacob did not hear.

But Laban mocked at him with gross words before the guests:

"Tell me, son-in-law, hear me and answer how dost feel? Dost thou quake before the bliss of embracing thy bride? Hast thou not fear as once in that matter of the blessing, when thou wentest in to thy father with thy knees shaking? Didst thou not say the sweat ran down thy thighs for dread and thy voice stuck in thy throat even when thou wouldst win the blessing away from Esau the accursed? Thou happy man, pray that joy take not away thy manliness in the moment when thou needest it most—else the bride might take it ill!"

They all roared with laughter in the upper room, and once more Jacob smiled and kissed the picture of Ishtar to whom God had given the hour. But Laban got heavily to his feet, swaying somewhat, and said:

"Come then, for it is midnight, come up to me and I will put you together."

The crowd pressed close to see Jacob and Rachel kneel down on the paved floor before the bride's father, and to hear how Jacob answered to the questions according to custom. For Laban asked him whether this woman should be his wedded wife and he her husband, and if he willed to give her the flower—to which he answered yes. Asked whether he was well-born, whether he would make rich this woman and fruitful her womb; Jacob answered that he was the son of the great and would fill her lap with silver and gold and make fruitful this woman like the fruit of the garden. Then Laban touched both their foreheads, and stepped between them and laid his hands upon them. Then he told them to stand up and embrace each other and that then they were wed. And he led the dedicated one back to her mother, but the nephew he took by the hand and led him in front of the guests, who crowded after, beginning to sing. They passed down the brick staircase into the paved court and the musicians left their stand and walked before them. Next came boys with torches and after them children in short smocks with censers hanging between chains. Jacob, led by Laban, walked in the sweet-smelling cloud, with the white blossoming myrtle twig in his right hand. He did not join in the traditional songs that swelled up as they marched, and only hummed a little when Laban nudged him and told him to open his mouth. But Laban sang in a heavy bass and knew all the songs by heart; they were sentimental and amorous ditties about loving couples in general, on the verge of their nuptials, and how on both sides they can scarcely wait. They told of the procession, coming out of the wilderness like pillars of smoke, perfumed with myrrh and frankincense; and of the bride-groom walking, with the crown wherewith his mother crowned him on the day of his espousals. All this was about the procession in which they were actually moving, but the allusions did not fit Jacob; his mother was far away, he was a fugitive, and he was not leading his beloved into his mother's house and into the chamber of her who had borne him. Just for that reason, it seemed, Laban sang the more lustily, honouring the pattern in the face of all present lacks, that Jacob might feel how different it was. And then the bride-groom spoke, in the song, and the bride gave ardent answer and they sang in turn long rapturous speeches of mutual praise and longing. Their bed was freshly prepared in the panelled chamber; they pointed one another the way thither, promising the greatest pleasure in the union of their nard-scented loveliness. For his left hand would be under her head and his right hand embrace her, and sweeter than wine from the hills would be their mutual love. Thus they told one another in song, each painting in intoxicated language the other's loveliness. And finally they charged the company to stir not up nor awake from voluptuous slumber either bride or bridegroom until they pleased. They implored the people in song, by the roes and by the hinds of the field, and the company took up the words as they paced and sang them with great heartiness; even the incense-bearing boys sang lustily if without precise understanding. And so they marched, in the windy, moon-darkened night, round Laban's steading, once and twice, and came before the house and before the house door of palm-wood, and Laban pressed through, with the musicians in the lead, and came to the bed-chamber on the ground floor, that likewise had a door, and Laban led in Jacob by the hand. He made light with the torches, that Jacob might see into the room and make out the position of table and bed. Then he wished him blessings on his manhood and turned back to the company that crowded about the doorway. They went away, singing as they went, and Jacob was alone.

After long decades, and in his great age, and even on his dying bed, where he still spoke solemnly of it, Jacob remembered naught more clearly than how he had stood alone in the darkness of the bridal chamber, where it blew, and was draughty, for the night wind burst through the window-openings under the roof and out again through the openings on the side toward the court, getting caught in the carpets and hangings with which, as Jacob had seen by the torchlight, they had adorned the walls, and making a great flapping and clapping. It was the room above the archive and grave chamber, with the teraphim and the receipts. Jacob could feel through the thin carpet they had put down the ring of the little trap door by which one went down. And he had seen the bed and he went towards it with his hands out. It was the best bed in the house, one of three; Laban and Adina had sat on it at that first meal seven years ago: a sofa on metal-covered feet, with a round headrest of polished bronze. They had put covers on the wooden frame, with linen over them, Jacob could feel it, and there were pillows against the headrest. But it was a narrow bed. On the table beside it stood beer and a little food. There were two tabourets in the room, also covered with stuff, and lampstands at the bed's head, but there was no oil in the lamps.

Jacob tried the lamps and discovered their emptiness, as he stood in the wind and the darkness while the train was fetching the bride and filling house and court with the noise of their singing and the trampling of their feet. He sat down on the bed and listened, the flower in his hand. The procession was leaving the house again, with the harps and cymbals at its head, bringing Rachel, his beloved, to whom all his heart belonged, and she walked there in her veil. Laban led her by the hand as he had done Jacob; perhaps Adina was there too, and the music of the wedding songs rose and died away. At last he heard the words:

"My beloved is mine, he is altogether mine:
I am a garden enclosed, full of pleasant fruits and full of the odours
of the finest spices.
Come, O beloved into thy garden!
Eat of thy pleasant fruits, take unto thee the refreshment
of their juices!"

The feet of those who sang were before the door, and the door opened a little so that snatches of the song and the music came through, and then the veiled one was in the room, ushered by Laban, who closed the door quickly and they were alone in the darkness.

"Is it thou, Rachel?" Jacob asked after a little while, during which he had waited for those outside to move away from the door. He asks as one says: "Have you returned from your journey?" when the traveller stands there in the flesh and it cannot be otherwise than that he has returned, so that the question is nonsense, only asked that the voice may be heard and the traveller does not answer but can only laugh. But Jacob heard that she bent her head, he knew it from the faint rustling and rattling of the light-heavy veil.

"Thou beloved, little one, my dove, and apple of my eye, heart of my heart," he said fervently. "It is so dark . . . and bloweth . . . I am sitting here upon the bed, if thou hast not seen it, straight into the room and then somewhat to the right. Come, then, but strike not against the table else a bruise will come upon thy tender skin and also thou wouldst knock over the beer. I am not thirsty for beer, I am only thirsty for thee, my pomegranate. How good that they have brought thee to me and that I sit here no longer alone in the wind. Comest thou now? Gladly would I come to meet thee, but that probably I may not, for it is by law and custom that I hand thee the flower while sitting, and though no one seeth us, yet we will hold to that which is prescribed, that we may be well and truly wedded as we have stead-fastly desired through so many years of waiting."

The thought overcame him, his voice broke. Memories of the time when in patience and in impatience he had arisen for the sake of this hour, laid hold on him mightily and moved him to the depths; and the thought that she had waited with him and now on her side saw herself at the goal of her desires stirred the tenderest emotions of his heart. Such is love, when it is complete: feeling and lust together, tenderness and desire; and while feeling made the tears gush out of Jacob's eyes, at the same time he felt the tension of his manhood.

"Here art thou," he said, "thou hast found me in the darkness, as I found thee after more than seventeen days' journey and thou camest on among the sheep and spoke: 'Behold, a stranger!' Then we chose each other among men and I have served for thee seven years and the time lies at our feet. My doe and my dove, here is the flower. Thou seest it and findest it now, and therefore I will guide thy hand to the twig that thou mayest take it, and I give it to thee and thus we are one. But thy hand I keep, since I so love it, and I love the bones of thy wrist, so well known unto me that I know it again in the darkness, and thy hand is to me like thyself, and like thy whole body, but that is like to a sheaf of wheat garlanded with roses. My sister, my love, let thyself down to me and sit by my side and I will move that there may be space for two and would be for three if needful. Yet how good is God, that He lets us be two alone together, thee by me and me by thee! For I love only thee, for the sake of thy face that I cannot now see but saw a thousand times and kissed for very love, for it is thy loveliness that crowns thy body as with roses, and when I think that thou art Rachel, with whom I have often been, yet never thus, and who waited for me and likewise now waiteth for me, and upon my tenderness, then a bliss cometh upon me stronger than I am, so that it overcometh me. A darkness enfoldeth us, thicker than thy veil which enfoldeth thee, thou purest one, and darkness is bound upon our eyes so that they see naught beyond themselves and are blind. But it is only they, thanks be to God, and not one of our other senses. For we hear each other when we speak, and the darkness cannot part us more. Tell me, my soul, thou too art enraptured by the greatness of this hour?"

"I am thine in bliss, dear lord," she softly said.

"That might have been Leah who spoke, thy older sister," he answered. "Not according to the sense, of course, but in the way of speaking. The voices of sisters are alike, indeed, and words come from their mouths with the same sound. For the same father begot them, upon the same mother, and they are a little distinguished in time and move with separate movement, yet are one in the womb of their origin. Lo, I am afraid, a little, at my own blind words, for I had lightly said that the darkness hath no power over our speech, yet I feel after all that it presseth hard upon my words and sinketh into them so that I fear somewhat before them. Let us be glad of the distinction, that thou art Rachel and I Jacob, and not for instance Esau, my red brother! My forefathers and I, at night beside the flocks, have pondered much upon the person of God, who He is, and our children and our children's children will follow us in our musings. But I at this hour will say and make clear my words, that the darkness may roll back away from them: 'God is the distinction!' And therefore now I lift thy veil, beloved, that I may see thee with seeing hands; and I lay it carefully upon this chair that is here, for it is priceless with pictures and shall be handed down through generations, and be worn by beloved ones without number. Lo, here is thy hair, black but comely, I know it so well, I know the fragrance of it, I carry it to my lips and what power hath darkness over it? It cannot come in between my lips and thy hair. Here are thine eyes, smiling night in the night, and their tender sockets and the soft places beneath them where so many a time I have kissed away the impatient tears, and my lips were wet from them. Here are thy cheeks, soft as down and the costliest wool of goats from strange lands. Here thy shoulders, which feel to mine hands larger than I see them in the day, and here thine arms, and here—"

He ceased. As his seeing hands left her face and found her body and the skin of her body, Ishtar pierced them both to the marrow, the bull of heaven breathed and its breath was as the breath of both that mingled. And all that windy night did Jacob find the child of Laban a glorious mate, great in delights and mighty to conceive, and she received him many times and again and again, so that they counted no more but the shepherds answered one another that it was nine times.

Later he slept on the ground beside her, for the bed was narrow and he gave her room and comfort for her rest, sleeping himself crouching beside the bed, with his cheek against her hand that hung over the edge. The morning dawned. Dim red and hushed it stood before the windows, and slowly filled with light the bridal chamber. It was Jacob who first awaked, from the daylight between his lids, and from the stillness; for until deep into the night the feasting had continued, with much laughter and noise in house and court, and only toward morning, when the bridal pair already slept, had quiet descended. And also he was uncomfortable—though how joyfully—and waked the easier. He stirred and felt her hand, remembering everything and turned his mouth to kiss it. Then raised his head to see his dear one in her slumbers. With eyes heavy and sticky from sleep, still unwilling to focus, he looked at her. And it was Leah.

He dropped his eyes and shook his head with a smile. "Ah," thought he, while even then a chill crept round his heart and into the pit of his stomach, "what madness, what a morning-after mockery! Darkness was hung before mine eyes, and now that they are unblinded they see false things. Are then sisters so mysteriously alike, and show it in their sleep, though no likeness shows itself in their features? Let me look again!"

But he did not look, because he feared to, and what he said to himself was only a panic-struck gabbling. He had seen that she was blonde, and her nose somewhat red. He rubbed his eyes with his knuckles and forced himself to look. It was Leah who lay and slept.

The thoughts tumbled over each other in his head. How came Leah here, and where was Rachel, whom they had brought in unto him and whom he had known this night? He staggered backwards away from the bed into the middle of the room and stood there in his shirt, his fists to his cheeks. "Leah!" he screamed, in a strangled voice. She sat up at once. She blinked, smiled, and dropped her eyelids as he had so often seen her do. One shoulder and breast were bare; they were white and beautiful.

"Jacob, my husband," she said, "let it be so, according to the father's will. For he would have it so and so arranged it, and the gods shall give me that to make thee thank both him and them."

"Leah," he stammered, and he pointed to his throat, his breast and his brow, "since when is it thou?"

"Always it was I," she answered, "and I was thine this night ever since I entered in the veil. And always I was tender towards thee and ready as Rachel, since I saw thee from the roof; and have I not proved it to thee the whole of this night? For say thyself if I have not served thee as well as any woman could, and been strong in desire! And certain am I in my inwards that I have conceived from thee, and it shall be a son, strong and brave, and we shall call his name Reuben."

Then Jacob cast back and bethought himself how he had taken her for Rachel this night, and he went to the wall and laid his arm along it and his forehead on his arm and wept bitterly.

Thus for some while he stood, torn by his emotions, and each time the thought returned, how he had believed and had known her, how all his joy had been delusion and the hour of fulfilment turned to shame, for which he had served and conquered the time, it was with him as though his stomach and his brain turned over within him, and he despaired with his whole soul. But Leah knew no more to say, and only wept likewise, from time to time, as she had done the day before with Rachel. For she saw how little it had been she who had again and again received him, and only the thought that she would now in all probability have a fine son named Reuben came to strengthen her heart.

Then he left her and rushed out of the chamber. He had almost stumbled over the sleepers that lay everywhere outside in house and court, in the disorder from the feast, on covers and mats or on the bare ground, sleeping off their debauch. "Laban!" he cried, and stepped over forms that emitted surly grunts, stretched out and snored again. "Laban!" he repeated more quietly, for torment and bitterness and the fierce demand for a reckoning did not slay in him all consideration for these sleepers in the early morning after the heavy feasting. "Laban! where art thou?" And came before the master's chamber, where he lay with Adina his wife, knocked and cried: "Laban, come forth!"

"What, what!" answered Laban from within. "Who is it calleth me in the early dawn, after I have been sleeping?"

"It is I. Thou must come out!" Jacob cried.

"Oh, indeed," said Laban. "So it is my son-in-law that calleth, and sayeth I, like a child, as though one could tell from that alone who he is, but I know the voice and will come forth to hear what he hath to tell to me in the dawning, though just then I was enjoying my best sleep." And he came forth in his shift, with rumpled hair, and blinking.

"I was asleep," he repeated. "Such a deep sleep and doing me so much good. How comes it thou thyself sleepest not or dost according to thy new state?"

"It is Leah," said Jacob, with trembling lips.

"Of a surety," replied Laban, "and callest thou me in the grey dawn out of beneficent slumber after heavy drinking to tell me what I know as well as thou?"

"Thou monster, thou tiger, thou devilish man!" cried Jacob beside himself. "I tell thee not that thou mayest know it, but to show thee I know it and to bring thee to accounting in my torment."

"Take care of thy voice above all then," said Laban, "that thou lowerest it considerably: that I counsel thee, if thou lettest not thyself be counselled by the plain circumstances. For not enough that I am thy uncle and father-in-law, and thy master to boot, whom it beseemeth not to breathe upon with cries of murder, but also house and court lie full of sleeping guests, as thou seest, who in a few hours will go out with me to the hunt and take their pleasure in the wild and in the reedy places of the swamps, where we will set snares for birds, the partridge and the bustard, or slay a wild boar, that we may pour out a tribute of liquor to him. Thereto my guests strengthen themselves in slumber, and I mar it not, and in the evening the drinking bout shall go on. But thou, when on the fifth day thou issuest out of the bride's chamber, shalt join with us in the pleasures of the chase."

"No pleasures can there be for me in the chase," answered Jacob, "and my poor senses do not set that way, which thou hast confused and brought to shame so that they cry out from earth to heaven. For thou hast deceived me beyond all bounds, with cruelty and shamelessness, and hast privily brought in Leah to me, thy elder daughter, in the place of Rachel for whom I have served thee. How shall I then deal with thee and with me?"

"Hearken now," said Laban, "there are words which thou hadst best

not take upon thy tongue and shouldst shame thyself to utter them aloud;
for in Amurruland there sits as I know a shaggy-haired man who weeps and
tears his fleece and seeks after thy life, and he it is might well speak of
deception. It is unpleasant when a man must blush for another man because
he blusheth not for himself, and thus standeth it at the moment between thee
and me because of thy ill-chosen words. Sayst thou I have betrayed thee?
In what respect? Have I brought in unto thee a bride who was no longer
unspotted and unworthy to mount the seven stairs into the arms of the god?
Or have I brought thee one deformed and incapable in body or who cried out
at the hurt thou gavest her, and was not willing and serviceable to thee in
thy lust? Is it after this fashion I have betrayed thee?"

"No," Jacob said, "not after such a fashion. Leah is great in conceiving.
But thou hast gone behind me and duped me, and made it so that I did not
see and took Leah for Rachel throughout the night, and I have given to the
wrong one my soul and all the best of my strength, so that it repenteth me
beyond my power to utter. This, thou wolf-man, hast thou done unto me."

"And thou callest it betraying and shamelessly likenest me to wild
beasts and evil spirits because I held with the custom and as a righteous man
did not presume to reject that which is sacred and traditional? I know not
how such things are in Amurruland or in the country of king Gog, but in
our land we give not the younger before the elder; that would be to smite
tradition in the face, and I am a respectable man and law-abiding. Thus did
I what I did, and dealt wisely against thy unreason and like a father who
knoweth what is owing to his children. For thou hast bluntly affronted my
love to my eldest born, saying to me 'Leah speaketh not unto my manly
desires.' And therefore hast thou not deserved a correction and called down
upon thee an admonishment? For now thou hast seen whether she speaketh
to thy manly desire or no!"

"I have seen nothing at all," Jacob cried. "It was Rachel whom I embraced."

"Yes, so the dawning hath proven," answered Laban mockingly; "but
the truth is that Rachel, my little one, hath nothing whereover to complain.
For the reality was Leah's but the intent was Rachel's. And now have I also
taught thee the intent for Leah, and whichsoever thou embracest in the
future there will be the reality as well as the intent."

"Wilt thou then give me Rachel?" Jacob asked.

"Of a surety," answered Laban. "If thou wilt have her and pay me the
legal price, thou shalt have her."

But Jacob cried:

"I have served thee for Rachel seven years!"

"Thou hast," responded Laban with dignity and solemnity, "served me
for a child. Wilt thou now have the second, as would be agreeable unto me,
then must thou pay again."

Jacob was silent.

After a little he said: "I will obtain the buying price and see to it that I
contribute the dowry. I will borrow a mina of silver from people with whom

I deal in trade, and I will likewise pay for presents to hang on the bride's girdle; for some possessions have naturally, and without my will, cleaved unto me in this long time, and I am of more substance than when I first wooed for Rachel."

"Again thou speakest without any delicacy," answered Laban, with a smug shake of the head, "and foolishly bringest things to speech which it were better to bury in thy bosom; thou shouldst rather be glad if others also keep silent and dwell not upon them to rebuke thee for them, instead of shouting them aloud and making it so that a man must be ashamed for thee since thou art not for thyself. I will hear nothing of unexpected possessions and provocations of that sort. I will have no silver of thee as dowry and no gear, from whomever it be, as presents for the bride, but rather shalt thou serve me for the second child as long as for the first."

"Wolf-man!" cried Jacob, hardly restraining himself. "And thou wilt give me Rachel only after another seven years?"

"Who hath said so?" countered Laban, superiorly. "Who hath ever so much as suggested such a thing? Thou alone pratest without any reason and in thy haste comparest me to a werewolf; for I am a father and I will not that my child pine after the man until he is old. Go thou now to thy right place and keep thy week and thine honour. Then shall the second be given thee in all stillness, and thou shalt serve me as her husband another seven years."

Jacob hung his head and was silent.

"Thou art silent," Laban said, "and canst not bring it over thyself to fall at my feet. Truly I am curious, whether I shall yet succeed to awaken thy heart to thankfulness. That I stand here in the dawning in my shift, disturbed out of my most needful slumber and deal with thee, it seems is not enough to engender in thee such a feeling. I have not mentioned yet that with the second child thou receivest likewise the second maid which I bought. For to Leah I give Zilpah as dowry, and to Rachel Bilhah, and two-thirds of the mina of silver that I give thee shall be reckoned in. Thus thou hast four wives overnight and a women's house like the king of Babel, thou that sattest so lately barren and forlorn."

Jacob still kept silence.

"Thou cruel man," he said at last, with a sigh. "Thou knowest not what thou hast done unto me; thou knowest and thinkest not on it, I must believe, nor can have any imagining of it in thy iron heart. I have squandered my soul and all the best of me upon the wrong woman this night, and that crusheth my heart together at thought of the right one for whom it was meant and I shall have to do with Leah all the week, and when my flesh is weary for I am only human, and it is sated and my soul all too drowsy for high feelings, then shall I be given the right one, Rachel, my treasure. And thou thinkest it is good so. But that can never be made good, which thou hast done to me and to Rachel thy child, and even unto Leah, who sitteth there upon her bed in tears because I had her not in my mind."

"Dost thou mean," Laban asked, "that after the marriage week with Leah thou wilt have no more manhood left to make fruitful the second?"

"Not that, may God forbid," answered Jacob.

"All the rest is whimseys and moonshine," concluded Laban. "Art satisfied with our new contract, and shall it be so or no between me and thee?"

"Yea, it shall be so," said Jacob, and went back to Leah.

10 Joseph and Potiphar's Wife

Probably the best insights into the Joseph novels of Thomas Mann are his own. He thought about this set of books for ten years before he began it, and when he finally undertook what he describes as a task totalling two thousand pages of manuscript, he had settled in his own mind what he wanted to do with the project and why he wanted to write it. He knew that he wanted "to reproduce this charming story in fresh narrative and with modern means—with *all* modern means, with the spiritual ones and the technical ones." He felt the same temptation which Goethe, his life-long hero, felt "to carry out the short legendary report of Genesis in 'all its details.' " He thought he could do this during a time in his life "when the poetic execution could obtain definite human and spiritual substance as well." To him this meant the need to be exact, to draw into proximity something vague and remote to the point where he could see it with his eyes and grasp it with his hands and "think that finally you have learned the definite truth about it."

And it came to pass after these things, that his master's wife cast her eyes upon Joseph; and she said, Lie with me.

GENESIS: XXXIX, 7

JOSEPH IN EGYPT (JOSEPH AND HIS BROTHERS)
by THOMAS MANN

HE HAD COME HOME, Joseph, the young steward, to see that all was complete, and whether or no Khamat, scribe of the buffet, was deserving of a reproof. He moved about the pillared hall, among the chairs and little tables, the jars of wine in their holders, the buffets laden with pyramids of fruit and cakes. He looked to the lamps, the table of wreaths, floral necklaces, and unguent boxes; and rearranged the sideboard, making the little golden beakers ring. He had spent awhile in these masterly retouchings, and made the beakers ring once or twice, when he started; for he heard a voice, a singing, ringing voice, calling him from some distance; calling the name which he had taken in this land:

"Osarsiph!"

In all his life he never forgot that moment, when in the empty house the sound of his name struck on his ear. He stood with his fan under his arm and two golden beakers in his hands. He was inspecting their polish and certainly he had made them ring as he held them; he listened, thinking he had

90

not heard aright. Yet he must have been mistaken, for he stood thus a long time listening, the two beakers in his hand, and there was no sound for a long time. But at last it came again, that singing voice echoed through the rooms:

"Osarsiph!"

"Here am I," he answered. His voice failed him for hoarseness; he cleared his throat and said again:

"I hear."

Again there was a pause, and he waited motionless. Then it came, singing and ringing:

"Is it you, Osarsiph, whom I hear in the hall, and have you come home alone to the empty house?"

"As you say, mistress," he replied, setting back the beakers in their place and going through the open door into Petepre's northern hall, to speak into the adjoining room.

"Yes, I am here, to see that things are in train in the house. 'Much oversight to put all right'—you know the proverb, and since my master has set me over the house and knows no care save for the bread he eats, for he has put all into my hands, keeping naught back, and will literally be no greater than I in this house—I have given the servants a little extra time to enjoy themselves, but thought best to resign the latter end of the day's pleasures and come home betimes. 'Harsh with thyself, to others merciful'—as you know must be the rule. But I will not praise myself before you, and I am but little ahead of them, they may come at any moment, and Petepre too, the unique friend of the god, your husband and my noble master—"

The voice came ringing out of the twilit chamber: "And seeing after all that is in the house, will you not also, Osarsiph, see after me? Have you not heard that I remained alone and that I suffer? Cross over the threshold and come to me!"

"Gladly would I," Joseph replied, "and would cross the threshold and visit you, but there are many things here in the hall to attend to, and much still to arrange which needs me to cast my eye—"

But the voice sounded again:

"Come in to me. The mistress commands it."

And Joseph crossed the threshold and went in to her.

The Father's Face

Here our story loses its tongue. I mean our present version and repetition in the feast does so; for in the original, as it happened and told itself, it by no means lost its tongue; it went on, there in the twilit room, in an agitated exchange, a dialogue in the sense that both parties talked at once. I prefer, however, to draw over the scene the veil of delicacy and human feeling. For in that long-ago time it went on without witnesses, whereas here and today it is performed before a large audience—a decisive difference, as no one can deny, where a question of tact is involved. Joseph, particularly, was not silent; he could not be silent, but talked very volubly, almost breathlessly, bringing to bear all his wit and charm against the woman's desire, in the attempt to talk her out of it. But just here lies the reason why our story loses its tongue. For he became involved in a contradiction, or rather a contradiction presented itself, as he talked, most painfully affecting and troubling to human feeling: the contradiction between body and soul. Yes, as the woman, in words or by her silence, answered to what he said, his flesh stood up against his spirit, and in the midst of his most fluent and eloquent speech he became an ass. And what a shattering contradiction that is, what restraint it demands from the narrator: when eloquent wisdom is given the lie by the flesh and is manifest an ass!

He fled—for we know that he succeeded in flying—in the state and condition of the dead god; to the woman an aggravated occasion for despair and the raging fury of frustration. Her desire had discovered in him a manly readiness; and the forsaken woman alternately tore at and caressed the garment which he left in her hands—for we know that he left his garment behind him—in paroxysms of frantic agony, with loud outcries of exultation and anguish. The Egyptian woman's cry, repeated over and over again was: *"Me'eni nachtef!* I have seen his strength!"

Something enabled Joseph, in that uttermost extremity, to tear himself away and flee: that something was his father's face. He saw his father's face —all the more detailed versions say so, and we may take it for the truth. It is so: when, despite all his skill of tongues he was almost lost, the face of his father appeared to him. Jacob's image? Yes, certainly, Jacob's image. Not an image of settled and personal lineaments which he saw somewhere in the room. Rather he saw it in his mind and with his mind's eye: an image of memory and admonition, the father's in a broad and general sense. For in it Jacob's features mingled with Potiphar's fatherly traits, there was something of the modest departed, Mont-kaw, and over and above all these were other, mightier traits. Out of bright, brown father-eyes with soft tear-sacs beneath them, it peered at Joseph in tender concern.

This it was which saved him. Or rather, he saved himself—for I would speak in the light of reason and give credit where it is due, not to any spirit manifestation. He saved himself, in that his spirit evoked the warning image. In a situation only to be described as far gone, with defeat very nigh, he tore himself away—to the woman's intolerable anguish, as we must, in justly divided sympathy, admit—and it was fortunate that his physical agility equalled his glibness of speech; for he was able, one, two, three, to twist himself out of his jacket—the "garment," his outer raiment—at which she clutched in the abandon of her love, and to escape, in not very stewardlike array, to the hall, the banqueting-room, the vestibule.

Behind him, in her thwarted love she raced, half in raptures—*"Me'eni nachtef!"*—but yet betrayed beyond bearing. She did frightful things with the garment still warm with his body, which she held in her hands, the precious hated object: covered it with kisses, drenched it with tears, tore it with her teeth, trod it underfoot—dealt with it, in short, much as the brethren had dealt with the veil of the son at Dothan in the vale. "Beloved!" she cried. "Whither do you go from me? Stay! O blissful boy! O shameless slave! Curses upon you! Death! Treachery! Violence! Seize the miscreant! He has slain my honour—help, help! Help for the mistress! A fiend has attacked me!"

There we have it. Her thoughts—if we may speak of thoughts where there was nothing but a whirlwind of rage and tears—had brought her to the accusation with which she had more than once threatened Joseph in the fury of her desire, when she raised her lioness claws against him: the murderous accusation that he had monstrously forgotten himself toward her, his mistress. The wild recollection rose in the woman's mind, she flung herself on it, shrieked it with all her strength—as one hopes, by sheer voicepower to lend truth to the untrue—and our justifiable sympathy must make us rejoice that the insulted woman found this outlet to her anguish, that she could give it an expression, false, of course, yet matching it in horror, which was calculated to enflame all who heard, turn them into allies of her insulted state and make them pant to avenge it. Her yells resounded.

There were already people in the vestibule. The sun was setting, and most of Petepre's household had returned to the house and courtyard. So it was good that the fugitive had a little time and space to collect himself before he emerged. The servants stood rooted to the ground with horror, hearing their mistress's cries; and though the young steward came at a measured pace out of the banqueting-hall and passed with composed mien among them, it was as good as impossible not to connect the impaired state of his clothing with the shrieks that issued from the inner room. Joseph would have liked to gain his room, the special room of trust, to put himself to rights. But as there were servants in the way, and a craving to get out of doors took the upper hand, he crossed over to and through the open bronze door to the courtyard, which was full of the bustle of home-coming. Several litters were drawing up before the harem, containing the secondary wives; the chattering little creatures, under supervision of Nubian eunuchs and scribes of the house of the secluded, had been vouchsafed their glimpse of the feast and were now being returned to their gilded cage.

Whither should the fugitive flee with his black eye? Out through the gateway by which he once had entered? And thence? That he himself did not know, and was glad that he still had space before him in the courtyard and might move as though he were bound somewhither. Then he felt his clothing twitched; and Bes-em-heb, the little dwarf, piped up at him, his face all crumpled with his grief: "Ravaged the field—burnt by the bull—oh, ashes, ashes! Osarsiph, Osarsiph!" They stood halfway between the main house and the gateway in the outer wall. Joseph turned, the little man hanging to him. The sound of the woman's voice came over to him, the voice of the mistress. The white figure stood at the top of the house steps, surrounded by a crowd which poured after her out of the hall. She stretched out her arm, and men followed it running with arms likewise outstretched in his direction. They seized him and brought him back among the courtyard folk running up before the house: gate-and door-keepers, artisans, stablemen, gardeners, cooks and silver-aproned waiters. The weeping midget clung to his skirt and was borne along too.

And Potiphar's wife addressed to her husband's servants thus gathered before and behind her in the courtyard that well-known speech which at all times has been counted against her by all men; which even I, despite all I have done for Mut-em-inet's saga and her cause, cannot fail to condemn. Not on account of its untruth, which might pass as the garment of the truth; but on account of the demogogy which she did not scorn to use to rouse the people.

"Egyptians!" she cried. "Children of Kemt! Sons of the river and the black earth!"—What did she mean by that? They were just ordinary people, and at the time nearly all of them a little drunk. Their Egyptian birth as children of Hapi—in so far as it was a fact, for there were among them Moors from Kush and people with Chaldean names—was a native merit: they had nothing to do with it nor did it help them in the least if they neglected their duties, for their backs were bruised with thick leather straps well laid on, regardless of whose children they were. And now all at once their birth, which had been very much in the background and had no practical value for the individual, was brought to their notice with flattering emphasis—because it could be used to rouse their sense of honour, unite them in a common pride, and make them pant with fury against someone who had to be destroyed. Her challenge bewildered them. Yet it had its effect, combined with that of the good barley beer.

"Egyptian brothers!"—They were her brothers all at once; it went through and through them, they found it thrilling. "Behold me, your mistress and mother, Petepre's chief and true wife! See me as I sit upon the threshold of this house—we know each other well, you and I!"—"We," and "each other"! They swallowed it down, this was a good day for the lower classes!—"But likewise know you this Hebrew youth, standing here half naked on this great day in the calendar, lacking his upper garment, because I have it in my hands. Do you recognize him, who was set as steward above the children of the land and over the house of one great in the two lands? He came down out of his wretched country to Egypt, Osiris' beautiful garden, the throne of Re, the horizon of the good spirit. They brought this stranger to us into this house"—"us" again!—"to mock us, and bring shame upon us. For this frightful thing has happened: I sat alone in my chamber, alone in the house, for I was unwell and was dispensed from appearing before Amun and kept the empty house alone. Then the abandoned one, the Hebrew fiend, took advantage of my being alone and came in unto me that he might do his will with me and bring me to shame—the servant would lie with the mistress!"—she screamed the words—"lie with me to enforce me! But I cried with a loud voice, when he would have done it and have shamed you for his servant-lust; I ask you, Egyptian brothers, have ye heard me cry out with all my strength, in evidence that I repulsed him and defended myself to the utmost, as the law demands? Ye have heard it. But when he too heard it, the abandoned one, that I lifted up my voice and cried, then his boldness failed him and he struggled out of his outer garment, which I have here as evidence and would hold him by it that ye might seize him, and fled away from me with his evil purpose unaccomplished and got him out, so that I stand here pure before you, thanks to my outcry. But he, who was set over you all and over this house, he stands there in his shame, who will be seized of his deed, and judgment shall come upon him as soon as the master, my husband, comes home. Put the clog on him."

This was Mut's speech—it was not only untruthful but provocative. And Potiphar's household stood there stupified and helpless; they had already been not too clear-headed, with all the free temple beer they had had, and now they were completely dazed. They had heard, all of them, that the mistress was infatuated with the handsome young steward and he denied her. And now suddenly it turned out that he had laid hands on the mistress and tried to do her violence. It made their heads go round, what with the beer and what with the mistress's tale; they could not make it rhyme, and all of them were fond of the young steward. Certainly the mistress had cried out, they had all heard her, and they knew the law: it was evidence of a woman's innocence if she cried out when she was attacked. And she had the steward's garment in her hands; it really looked as though she held it as a forfeit when he tore himself away; but he himself stood there with his head sunk on his chest and said not a word.

"Why are you hesitating?" they heard a strong manly voice saying—the voice of Dudu, the gentleman dwarf, who stood among them in a stiffly starched feast-day skirt. "Do you not hear the mistress, that she has been so cruelly insulted and nearly brought to shame, and she commands that the clog be brought and laid upon the Hebrew slave? Here it is, I have brought it with me. For when I heard her lawful outcry I knew where we were and at what o'clock, and quickly fetched the tools out of the whipping-room, to have them at hand. Here they are. Stop gaping, and fetter his lustful hands— bind up this infamous slave, bought long ago on the advice of the shallow against that of the sound; for long enough has he played the master and been set over us who are true-born! By the obelisk! He shall be brought to the house of retribution and death!"

It was Dudu's great hour and he savoured it to the full. And two of the servants took the clog out of his hand and put it on, while little Shepses-Bes whimpered in a way that made the rest of the crowd titter. It was a spindle-shaped block of wood with a slit in it, which could open and shut, holding the culprit's hands helplessly in the narrow hole, weighed down by the heavy wood.

"Fling him in the kennel!" commanded Mut, with a frightful sob. Then she crouched on the step where she was, in front of the open door, and laid Joseph's garment down beside her.

"Here will I sit," she said in her chanting voice that rang across the darkening courtyard, "on the threshold of this house, with the accusing garment by my side. Withdraw from me, all of you, and let no one advise me to go in, that I suffer no harm from my thin garb in the cool of the evening.

I shall be deaf to such pleas, for here will I sit beside my forfeit until Petepre drives in and I receive atonement for my monstrous wrong."

The Judgment

All hours are great, each in its own way, whether great in pride or great in misery. Esau had his, when all went well with him, and he boasted, throwing out his legs. But when he flung out of the tent, crying: "Curse it! Curse it!" and limped away, tears like hazel-nuts rolling from his eyes, was the hour less great, less momentous for the hairy one? So now: we are come to Petepre's feast-hour, the most painful in his life, and at all times inwardly anticipated by him: when he hunted birds, or the hippopotamus, or followed the desert chase; even when he read his good old books, always that hour abode in the background of his thoughts, always he vaguely looked forward to it, ignorant only of its details—though these, when it came, were largely in his hands. And as we shall see, he shaped them nobly.

He rode in between torches, driven by Neternakht, his charioteer; earlier, as I said, than the festivities required, on account of his premonitions. It was a home-coming like many others, when each time he had felt dread in his heart—but this time the dread was to be realized. "Is all well in the house? Is the mistress happy?" Just that she is not: the mistress sits, a figure of tragedy, on your threshold, and your helpful cup-bearer lies fettered in the kennel.

So, then, this was the form which the reality took. Well, let us deal with it. He had already, from some distance, seen that Mut, his wife, somehow frightful to behold, sat beside the door of his house. Yet as he dismounted from his gala chariot he threw out the usual questions—this time they remained unanswered. The grooms hung their heads and were silent. Yes, yes, it was all just as he had always expected, though of course the hour might hold its minor surprises. The car was led away; the crowd drew back into the torch-lighted courtyard; he moved, that Reuben-tower of tender flesh, with his fan and symbol of office in his hand, toward the steps; he mounted them to where she crouched.

"What am I to think of this scene, my dear friend?" he asked, with courtesy and circumspection. "You sit thinly clad in so exposed a place, and beside you is something I am at a loss to understand."

"So it is," answered she. "Yet your words are pale and weak to describe a reality so much more frightful and violent than you paint it. But what you say is true: here I sit, and have that beside me of which you shall soon have frightful understanding."

"Aid me to reach it," he replied.

"I sit here," she said, "awaiting your judgment upon the direst crime ever known in the two lands or probably in all the kingdoms."

He made a sign with his fingers to ward off evil and waited, composedly.

"He came," she chanted, "the Hebrew servant whom you brought to us, he came to me to mock me. I begged you in the hall that sunset evening, I embraced your knees that you might send away the stranger, from whom I boded no good. In vain; the slave was too dear to you and I went away unconsoled. But now the wretch came upon me and would have his lust of me in your empty house, being in manly readiness for the act. You do not believe, you cannot comprehend this abomination? Then see this sign and interpret as you must. Stronger than the word is the sign; in it is nothing to interpret or to doubt, for it speaks the absolute language of fact. Behold! Is this robe your slave's robe? Examine it well, for I am clean before you by this sign. For when I cried out as the wretch assailed me, he was afraid and fled from me, but I held him by his garment and in his fright he left it in my hand. The evidence of his shocking crime—here I hold it before your eyes, the evidence of his flight and of my crying. For if he had not fled I had not his garment; if I had not shrieked he had not fled. Moreover, all your household are witness that I shrieked—ask all the people!"

Petepre stood silent, his head bent. Then he gave a sigh and said:

"That is a very sad affair."

"Sad?" she repeated, stormily.

"I said, very sad," he answered. "It is even frightful; I would seek a yet stronger word, but that I may gather from what you say that, thanks to your presence of mind and legal knowledge, the issue was favourable and things did not come to the worst."

"You seek no word to describe the shameless slave?"

"He is a shameless slave. As the whole affair is a matter of his behaviour, the words I used apply above all to him. And this evil thing must confront me, on this evening of all evenings, the evening of the great day of my elevation to the rank of unique friend, when I come home to celebrate Pharaoh's goodness and grace with a little evening party, to which the guests will soon be coming. You will agree that it is hard."

"Petepre! Have you no human heart in your breast?"

"Why do you ask?"

"Because in this hour of nameless horror you can speak of your new court title and how you will celebrate it."

"I did so but to bring the nameless horror of the hour into sharpest contrast with the homage of the day and set it off the more. It lies in the nature of the nameless that one may not directly speak of it, but only express it by indirection."

"No, Petepre, you have no human feeling!"

"My love, I will tell you something: there are situations in which one welcomes a certain lack of feeling for the sake of the injured as well as of the situation itself, which may be better dealt with in the absence of too much human feeling. What is now to be done, in this dreadful and very sad affair, which mars the day of my own promotion? It must be dealt with and dispatched without delay; for in the first place I quite understand that you will not stir from this spot, where it is impossible you should remain, until you have satisfaction for the unspeakable annoyance you have suffered. But in the second place, everything must be put right before my guests arrive, and that will be soon. Therefore I must hold domestic court without delay, and the trial, praise to the Hidden One, will be brief, for your word, my friend, has sole validity and none other comes into question, so that judgment can be rendered speedily.—Where is Osarsiph?"

"In the kennel."

"I thought as much. Let him be brought before me. Have the exalted parents summoned from the upper storey, even though they may sleep. Let the household assemble before my seat, which I will have set up here, where the mistress sits, that I may raise her after I have given judgment."

His orders were quickly carried out; the only obstacle to them being that at first Huia and Tuia, the brother-sister pair, refused to appear. They had heard of the trouble from their spindle-armed child-servants; these, with mouths like funnels, had poured out the course of events below, and the frightened old folk, like their sin-offered son the courtier of the sun, found that they had always been prepared for something of the sort. Now they were afraid and would not come, because the trial seemed to promise them a fore-taste of the judgment in the lower regions and they felt too weak-headed to marshal their arguments in their own justification, further than the phrase: "We meant it for the best." They sent word that they were near to death and not equal to attending a domestic court. But their son, the master, grew angry, stamped his foot, and ordered that they be helped downstairs, just as they were. If they were on the point of dying, then the fitting place was where their daughter-in-law sat accusing and demanding justice.

So then they came down, on the arms of their child-maids, old Huia's silver beard wagging and his head aquiver; old Tuia with a frightened smile lifting her blank white face, with its slits of eyes, as though she were seeking something. They were placed beside Petepre's judgment seat, where they sat distractedly babbling: "We meant well." After a while they became quiet. Mut the mistress crouched, with her token and forfeit beside her, next to the footstool of the throne, behind which a Moor in a red coat waved a tall fan. Torch-bearers lighted up the group. The courtyard, too, was lighted up with torches, and the household, save those on holiday, were gathered there. And they brought Joseph in his fetters before the judgment seat, with little Sa'anch-Wen-nofer-and-so-forth, who had not let go his skirt; likewise Dudu, pompous and secure in the hope that his great hour was mounting from better to best. The two dwarfs stood there, on the culprit's either side.

Petepre raised his refined voice and spoke rapidly and formally:

"We shall hold a court here, but we are in haste.—I summon thee, Ibis-headed One, who wrotest the laws for men, white ape beside the scale; thee, goddess Ma'at, who representest truth, in adornment of ostrich-feathers. The offering we owe you will be offered later, I stand warrant and it is as good as done. Now the hour presses. I pronounce justice for this house which is mine, and thus I pronounce."

He had said this while holding up his hands. Now he took an easier position in the corner of the lofty chair, supported his elbow, and lightly moved his little hand over the chair-arm as he went on:

"Notwithstanding the host of precautions taken in this house to oppose evil, despite all the words and maxims which should make it invulnerable to harm, yet affliction has succeeded in entering in and breaking for a time the charm which preserved it in peace and tender mutual consideration. Very sad and frightful is all this, there are no other words: so much the more that the evil must come to a head on the very day when Pharaoh's love and grace vouchsafed to honour me with the rank and splendid title of unique friend; one would think that on such a day I must needs be met with courtesy and congratulations from all sides, instead of the frightful news that the order of my house stands tottering. But be that as it may. That beautiful order has for long been gnawed at by affliction, and evil has slipped through the protecting guards, to break in and bring about that which stands written, that the rich shall be poor and the poor rich and the temples desolate. For long, I say, has evil consumed in secret, hidden from most, but not from the eye of the master, who is father and mother to the house, for his glance is like the moonbeam which makes the cow to conceive, and the breath of his words like the wind which bears the pollen from bough to bough in sign of divine fruitfulness. And as from the lap of his presentness all beginning and prospering flow as the honey from the comb, so naught escapes his oversight; however hidden to the many, to his eye it lies open. Let this occasion teach it. For I know the legend that follows my name: that I take upon myself nothing on earth save that I eat and drink. That is but gossip and negligible. Know that I know all; and if the fear of the master and the dread of his all-seeing eye come strengthened anew out of this distress, upon which I sit in judgment, then one may say that despite all its deep sadness it had its good side."

He carried to his nose a little handled malachite scent-bottle, which hung on a chain over his jewelled collar; after refreshing himself he went on:

"Thus were long known unto me the ways by which evil penetrated into this house. And also to me were known the ways of those who in their arrogance and spite, out of envy and hatred, nourished it and prepared its paths— and not only this but even first gave it entrance that it might glide in past all the good words and charms. These traitorous powers stand before my seat, in the dwarfish person of my former guardian of the wardrobe and jewel-caskets, called Dudu. He himself has had to confess to me all his malice and how he opened the way for the consuming evil. Upon him may judgment fall! Far be it from me to deprive him of the virility which the sun-lord was once minded to unite with his puny form. I will not touch it. They shall cut out the traitor's tongue.—Half his tongue," he corrected himself, waving his hand with a movement of disgust as Dudu set up a loud wail. "But," he added, "as I am used to having my clothing and precious stones in the charge of a dwarf, and it is not desirable that my habits should suffer from this misfortune, I will name the other dwarf of my house, Sa'ankh-Wen-nofer-Neteruhotep-emper-Amun, as scribe of the wardrobe, and he shall from now on preside over my coffers."

Little Bes, the nose in his wrinkled face all cinnamon-red from weeping for Joseph, jumped for joy. But Mut, the mistress, raised her head to Petepre's chair and murmured through her teeth:

"What judgments are these, my husband? They touch but the margin of things, they are but trivial. What shall I think of your judgment and how shall I raise myself from this place, if you so judge?"

"Patience!" he answered her as softly, bending down from his seat. "For here each will in his turn have justice and judgment, and his guilt will overtake the culprit. Sit quietly! You will soon be able to rise from your sitting, as satisfied as though you had yourself been judge. I judge for you, my love—though without admixture of all too human feeling—and you may rejoice! For were feeling and its violence to pronounce the judgment, there might be no end to the remorse."

After he had so whispered to her he sat up straight again and spoke:

"Take your courage in your hands, Osarsiph, my former steward, for now I come to you, and you too shall hear my judgment, for which perhaps you have long anxiously waited—to sharpen your punishment I have prolonged your suspense. For I think to lay hold on you roughly and assign you bitter punishment—aside from that growing out of your own heart. For three beasts with ugly names follow at your heels; they are called, if I remember aright, shame, guilt, and mocking laughter. And these, it is easy to see, have brought you before my seat, your head bent and your eyes cast down—as I am not now for the first time aware, for I have kept my secret eye upon you during the torture of the time of waiting I have chosen to inflict. You stand, your head bowed low, your hands in fetters, and utter no word. For how should you speak, since you are not asked to justify yourself, and it is the mistress who witnesses against you, with her own word, which is unimpeachable and of itself would call down judgment; yet there is also the evidence of your upper garment to shame you, and the irrefutable language of things speaks of your presumption, which at last has brought you so far that you have raised your hand against the mistress, and when she would hold you to a reckoning, you are driven to leave your garment in her hand. I ask you, what sense it could have to speak in your own defence against the mistress's word and the plain language of things?"

Joseph was silent, bowing his head even lower than before.

"Obviously none," Petepre answered himself. "You must be dumb, as the sheep before its shearers is dumb—naught else remains for you to do, however glib of tongue and pleasing of speech you are. But thanks to the god of your tribe, that Baal or Adon who is probably like to the setting sun in power, for he preserved you in all your presumption that it came not to the uttermost with your rebellion, but rather thrust you out of your coat—thanks to him, I say, for else you had been at this hour thrown to the crocodile, or your part had been the slow death by fire, if not the torture of the door and the rod. But there can be no talk of such punishments. For you were preserved from the worst and I am not in a position to inflict them. But doubt not that I am minded none the less to handle you roughly; take then your sentence, after your lengthened-out suspense: For I will cast you in prison, where lie the prisoners of the king, at Zawi-Re, the island fortress in the river; not to me any longer you shall belong, but to Pharaoh, and shall be a slave of the king. I will give you into the hand of the master of the jail, a man with whom one does not jest; of whom moreover one may think that he will not be deceived by your beneficent-seeming ways; so that at least in the beginning he will be hard on you. Moreover I will write to the official and advise him of your affair and shall know how to speak of you to him. To this place of atonement, where no laughter is, you shall be taken tomorrow by boat and see my face no more, after those long and pleasant years when you could be near me, fill my cup, and read to me from the good old books. That may well be painful for you, I should not wonder if your downcast eyes were full of tears. Be that as it may, tomorrow you shall be brought to that place of durance. You need not go back to the kennel. That punishment you have already borne, it shall rather be Dudu who shall spend the night there until tomorrow they cut off half his tongue. But you may sleep in your wonted place, the special room of trust, which for this night shall be called the special room of custody before punishment. Also, since you wear fetters, it is but just that Dudu wear them too, if there is another set. If there is but one, Dudu shall wear it.—I have spoken. The trial is ended. Let each one go to his post for the reception of the guests."

No one will be surprised to hear that after such a judgment as this, all those on the court fell on their faces and raised up their hands, crying out the name of their mild and wise lord. Joseph too fell down, in gratitude; even Huia and Tuia, supported by their little maids, did honour on their faces to their son; and as for Mut-em-inet, the mistress, she made no exception; but was seen to bow over the footstool of the judgment seat and hide her face upon her husband's feet.

"My friend," said he, "there is no reason for thanks. I rejoice if I have succeeded in satisfying you in this affliction and have showed myself loving with my power. We may now go into the banqueting-hall and celebrate my feast. For since you have wisely kept the house all day, you have spared your strength for the evening."

So then Joseph went down a second time to the prison and the pit. The story of his rising again out of this hole to a still higher life may be the subject of future lays.

11 Joseph and His Brothers

Thomas Mann was aware of the fuzzy edges of myth and the remoteness of subject as well as the complications of faith in probing the depth of the biblical novel. And yet he believed that "the attainment of the mythical viewpoint is of decisive importance in the life of the narrator; it signifies a peculiar enhancement of his artistic mood, a new serenity in recognizing and shaping. . . ." His approach to the biblical subject is, therefore, quite different from that of novelists like Davis, Nathan and Edith Simon, who seek to explain away the myth by one means or another. Mann's admitted aim was to understand it, live with it, and to develop it in modern terms. At no time does he seek to denigrate his source or to find a realistic explanation for an event which he finds in Holy Scripture. In this way, Mann retains an integrity of material beyond that of most biblical novelists.

And he commanded the steward of his house, saying, Fill the men's sacks with food, as much as they can carry, and put every man's money in his sack's mouth.

And put my cup, the silver cup, in the sack's mouth of the youngest, and his corn money. And he did according to the word that Joseph had spoken.

GENESIS: XLIV, 1–2

JOSEPH THE PROVIDER
(JOSEPH AND HIS BROTHERS)
by THOMAS MANN

I Am He

IT WAS ALREADY the latter part of the afternoon when they came before Joseph's house, for the steward led them thither and not to the great office where they had first bowed and bent their knees. Joseph was not there, he was in his own house.

"He was yet there," the story says, and it is correct. After the merry meeting of the day before, Pharaoh's friend had gone back to his office, but today he could not have left his house. He knew that his steward was at his task; and he waited with extreme impatience. The feast was nearing its climax and it rested with the ten whether they would be on the scene or only

102

hear what happened at second hand. Would they make the youngest come back alone with Mai-Sachme? Or would they all stick together? Joseph's suspense was great: on this point depended his future relations with the brothers. We, of course, are in no suspense: in the first place we know all the phases of the story by heart; moreover we have just been present at the search for the cup and have seen that the brothers did not forsake Benjamin in his guilt, whereas the fact was still hidden from Joseph. So in our wisdom we may smile at him as he wandered up and down and to and fro, from the book-room to the reception-hall, thence to the banqueting-hall, back through all the rooms into his sleeping-chamber, where he feverishly gave this or that last touch to his toilette, like an actor nervously adjusting his make-up before the curtain goes up.

He went to see his wife Asenath, in the women's quarters; they sat together watching Manasseh and Ephraim at their play, and he could not disguise his stage fright.

"My husband and dear lord," said she, "what is the matter? You are nervous, you keep shuffling your feet and listening for something. What have you on your mind? Shall we have a game to divert you, or shall some of my women dance before you?"

"No, my girl," he replied. "Thank you, not now. I have other moves in my head from those in the game, and I cannot watch the dancing; I have too much jigging and juggling to do myself, while God and the world look on. I must get back nearer to the hall, that is the theatre. But for your maids I know a better task than dancing; for I came to tell them to make you beautiful even beyond your beauty, and dress and adorn you; and the nurses must wash Manasseh's and Ephraim's hands and put on their embroidered smocks, for I am expecting very special guests and will present you all as my family so soon as the word has been spoken and they know who I am and whose you are. Yes, you are making big eyes, my shield-maid with the tiny waist! But just do as I say and make yourselves fine, and you shall hear from me!"

With that he was off again into the other part of the house. He would gladly have luxuriated in pure waiting and the pleasure of suspense; but as always there was business to transact: officials to see, accounts and papers to examine and sign, brought to him in his book-room by his reader and his acting scribe. He cursed them mentally, yet welcomed them for their company too.

The sun had declined as he sat over his papers, with one ear cocked. At last he heard a confusion of sounds in front of the house: the hour had come, the brothers were here. Mai-Sachme entered, the corner of his mouth drawn tighter than ever, the cup in his hand. He handed it to his master. "The youngest had it," said he. "After a long search. They are in the hall, awaiting your sentence."

"All of them?" Joseph asked.

"All of them," Mai-Sachme replied.

"You see that I am busy," said Joseph. "These gentlemen here are not here for fun, we are occupied with the business of the crown. You have been

my steward long enough to know whether I can take time from pressing
official business for such petty matters. You and your men can wait."

And he bent again over the roll held open for him by an official. But as
he could see nothing that was written there, he said after a pause:

"We might as well get that little matter over with first. It is a case of
criminal ingratitude, and I must pass judgment. Gentlemen, follow me to
the hall, where the evil-doers are awaiting sentence."

They attended him as he went up three steps and through a hanging out
on to the raised dais of the hall, where stood his chair. With the cup in his
hand he sat down. Servants straightway held fans over his head, for he was
always thus protected the moment he sat down.

A slanting ray full of dancing motes shone from one of the left-hand upper
openings between the columns and the sphinxes and the red sandstone
crouching lions with Pharaoh-heads. It fell upon the group of sinners who had
flung themselves down a few paces from Joseph's chair with their foreheads to
the ground. Spears guarded them on either side. A host of the curious, cooks
and waiting-boys, sprinklers and flower-table stewards, crowded round the
doors.

"Brothers, stand up," said Joseph. "I should not have thought to see you
again, and on such an occasion. But there are many things I should not have
thought. I should not have thought you could do as you have done, when I
had treated you like gentlemen. I am glad, of course, to have my cup back
again, out of which I drank and from which I divine. But I am greatly cast
down by your gross behavior. It is incomprehensible to me. How could you
bring yourselves so crudely to repay good with evil, to offend a man like me
by taking away something he is fond of and which is useful to him? The deed
was as stupid as it was hateful, for you might have guessed that a man like
me would miss so valuable a piece at once and know everything. Did you
imagine that when I saw I had been robbed I could not divine where it had
gone? And now I assume that you have admitted your guilt?"

It was Judah who answered. He became the spokesman for them all this
day, for he had passed through trials in life which they had been spared; he
had familiar knowledge of sin and guilt, and therefore he could fitly represent
the brothers. On their way back to Menfe this had been settled among them
and he had considered what to say. Now, with his garments rent, he stood
among his brothers and spoke:

"What shall we say unto my lord, and what sense would there be in
trying to clear ourselves before him? We are guilty before you, O lord, guilty
in the sense that your cup was found among us, with one of us and that means
with all. How the cup came into the sack of the youngest and most innocent
of us all, who was always safe at home, I do not know. We do not know. We
are powerless to speculate about it before your seat. You are a mighty one of
earth, you are good and evil, you raise up and cast down. We are your
servants. No defence of ours has any worth before you, and foolish is the
sinner who presumes upon present innocence when the avenger demands pay
for all misdeeds. Not for nothing did our old father lament that we would

make him childless in his old age. Lo, he was right. We and he with whom the cup was found are fallen to my lord as slaves."

In this opening speech of Judah's, which was not yet the one for which he is famous, there were points which Joseph preferred to ignore. He therefore answered only the one touching on their slavery, to reject it.

"No, not so," he said. "Far from it. There is no behaviour so bad that it can make a man like me behave inhumanly. You have bought food for the old man your father in the land of Egypt and he is waiting for it. I am Pharaoh's great man of business: no one shall say I took advantage of your crime to keep the money, the goods, and the buyers too. Whether only one of you sinned or all of you together I will not inquire. To your youngest I talked familiarly at table, we were merry together and I told him the virtues of my beloved cup and by its means showed him his mother's grave. It may be he prattled to you about it and all of you concerted the ungrateful plot of stealing the treasure. I assume it was not for the sake of the silver you took it. You wanted to use its magic for yourselves, perhaps to find out what became of your missing brother, the one who left home—how can I tell? But again, maybe your youngest committed the crime on his own, told you nothing and took the cup. I do not wish to hear. The booty was found with the thief. He shall be my servant. But the rest of you may go home in peace to your father, the old man, that he may not be childless and may have food to eat."

Thus the exalted; and for a while there was silence. Then Judah, the man of afflictions, to whom they had given the word, strode out of the group. He trod before the throne, close up to Joseph, took a long breath, and spoke:

"Hear me now, my lord, for I will hold speech before your ears and relate how it all came about and what you did and how it stands with these and with me, with us brothers all. My words will make clear beyond peradventure that you cannot and may not separate our youngest from us and you may not keep him to belong to you. And further, that we others, and in particular I, Judah, fourth among us, cannot possibly ever return home to our father without our youngest. And thirdly I will make my lord an offer and propose to you how you will receive your due in a possible and not in an impossible way. This will be the order of my speech. Therefore let not your anger burn against your servant and stop him not, I beg you, in the speech which I shall make as the spirit gives it to me, and my own guilt. You are as Pharaoh. Now I begin at the beginning and as you began it, for it was thus:

"When we came down hither, sent by our father that we might get us bread from this granary like thousands of others, we did not fare like the other thousands, but were segregated and specially dealt with and led down to your city and before my lord's face. And even there we were unusually treated, for my lord too was strange, I mean he was rough and smooth, soft and hard, in other words he showed two faces. He questioned us particularly about our family. Have you, asked my lord, a father at home or a brother? We have, we replied, a father, he is old, and we have certainly a young brother too, the youngest, late born to him and whom he cherishes as the apple of his

eye and keeps him by the hand because his brother fell away untimely and
is gone. Only this one son of his mother remains to our father, so that he
clings to him beyond measure. Answered my lord: bring him down here to
me. Not a hair of his head shall be harmed. It cannot be, we said, for the
reason we have given. To snatch away his youngest from the father will be
his death. But you replied harshly to your servants: By the life of Pharaoh!
if ye come not with your youngest brother, surviving from the lovely mother,
so shall you not see my face again."

And Judah continued and said:

"I ask my lord whether it was so and so begun or whether it was not so
but began otherwise than that my lord asked after the boy and insisted on his
coming, despite our warning. For it pleased my lord to put it that we should
clear ourselves from the accusation of spying by bringing him down and
thereby showing evidence that we deal in truth. But what sort of clearing is
that and what sort of accusation? No man can take us for spies, we brothers in
Jacob do not look like spies and it does not clear us to produce our youngest,
it is only an arbitrary decision and only because my lord happens to be bent on
seeing our brother with his own eyes—why? On that point I may not speak,
it rests with God." And Jehudah went on in his speech, flung up his leonine
head, put out his hand and spoke:

"Lo, this your servant believes in the God of his fathers and that all
knowledge is with Him. But what he does not believe is that our God
smuggles valuables into the packs of his servants, so that they have their
purchase money back as well as the goods—that has never been, and we have
no tradition whatever of this kind. Not Abram nor Isaac nor Jacob, our father,
has ever found God-silver in his pack that the Lord slipped him. What is not
is not; all that happened was from arbitrary choice and has its source in one
single mystery.

"But can you now, my lord—can you, after we worked on our father
with the famine to our aid and got him to lend us his little one for this
journey—can you, who relentlessly forced his coming, for without that extraordinary demand he would never have set foot in the land, can you, who
said: No harm shall come to him here below—can you hold him as a bonds-
man because they found your cup in his bag?

"That you cannot!

"But we on our side and especially your servant Judah who here holds
speech, we cannot come before our father's face without his youngest—
nevermore. We can do it as little as without him we could have come before
yours—and not on grounds of personal whim but on grounds most potent
and compelling. Your servant, our father, had spoken to us again and said:
Go yet once more and buy us a little food; and we answered him: We cannot
go down unless you give us our youngest brother, for the man down there
who is lord in the land said we must bring him or we shall not see his face.
Then the grey-haired one set up his lament, a song well known and which cut
us to the heart, like the flute that sobs in the gorges, for he launched into song
and said:

" 'Rachel, the lovely and willing, for whom my young years served Laban, the black moon, seven years; heart of my heart, who died on the way and left me, only a furlong from the inn; she was my wife and she gave me to my loving desire two sons, one in life and one in death, Dumuzi-Absu, the lamb, Joseph, the brilliant one, who knew how to get round me so that I gave him all that I had; and Benoni, the little son of death, whom I still have at hand. For the other went out from me, as I willed him to, and all the universe was filled with the cry: Mangled is he, the lovely one mangled! Then fell I on my back, and ever since I have been stiff. But with my stiffened hand I hold this little one who is all I have left, for mangled, mangled and torn in pieces, was the true son. If now you take from me my only one, that the boar mayhap may tread him down, then you will bring down my grey hairs to the grave in such sorrow that it would be too much for the world and it could not bear it. Full to the outermost rim is the world with the cry: Mangled, mangled is the beloved; and were this one given too, the world must be rent asunder and be naught.'

"Has my lord heard this cry of the flutes, this father-lament? Then let him judge after his own understanding if we brothers can come before the old man without our youngest, the little man, and confess: We have lost him, he is missing; whether we could hold out before the soul that hangs on Benjamin's soul, and before the world which is full of affliction and cannot bear more, for it would receive its death-blow in this blow. And above all whether I, Judah, his fourth son who speak, can so come before my father, that you shall judge. For not yet all does my lord know, but far from all; the heart of your servant feels that his word must mount to quite another theme at this hour of our need: it must deal with this mystery here, and can only do so through the revelation of another mystery."

A murmuring rose from among the troop of brothers. They stirred uneasily. But Judah the lion raised his voice against it, spoke on and said:

"I took the responsibility before my father and made myself surety for the little one. Just as now I came close up to your seat to hold this speech, so then I went close up to the father and took my oath before him in these words: Give him into my hand, I vouch for him; if I bring him not again I will bear the blame before you for ever. Such my vow; now judge, O strange man, whether I can go back to my father without the little one, lest peradventure I see an evil too great for me and for the world to bear. Accept my offer! Me shall you keep for your bondman instead of the lad, that you may receive your due in a possible and not an impossible way. I myself will expiate for us all. Here before you, strange man, I take the frightful oath we brothers swore— with both hands I take that oath and I break it in two across my knee. Our eleventh brother, the father's ewe lamb, first son of the true wife, him the beast did not rend; but we his brothers sold him into the world."

Thus did Judah end his famous speech, thus and not otherwise. He stood there weaving to and fro. The brothers had gone pale; yet they were deeply relieved that the secret was out at last. For it is not impossible to go pale and yet feel relieved at the same time. But two of them cried out, and they were the oldest and the youngest. Reuben shouted: "What do I hear?" And Benjamin did just as he had done before when the steward overtook them: he flung up his arms and gave an indescribable cry. And Joseph? He had got up from his seat and glittering tears ran down his cheeks. For it happened that the shaft of light which had been falling aslant upon the group of brothers had now moved round and was coming through an opening at the end of the hall. It fell directly on Joseph's face and in it his tears glittered like jewels.

"All that is Egyptian go out from me!" said he. "Out with you, go! For I invited God and the world to this play, but now shall God alone be witness."

Reluctantly they obeyed. Mai-Sachme put his hands on the backs of the scribes on the platform, urged them towards the door with nods and gestures, and helped them out. The crowds vanished from the entrance—though it is not likely they moved very far; they all stood in and out of the book-room with their heads cocked in the direction of the hall. Some even held their hands to their ears.

And Joseph, heedless of the tears on his face, stretched out his arms and made himself known. Often before now he had done the same and made people stare, giving them to think that some higher power moved in him other than what he was himself and mingled in his single person with a dreamy and seductive charm. But now quite simply—and despite the outstretched arms with a deprecating little laugh—he said:

"Children, here I am, I am your brother Joseph."

"Of course he is, of course he is!" shouted Benjamin, almost choking with joy. He stumbled forwards and up the steps, fell on his knees, and stormily embraced the new-found brother's knees.

"Jashup, Joseph-el, Jehosiph!" he sobbed, with his head tipped back to look up in his brother's face. "You are, you are, of course you are! You are not dead, you have overturned the great abode of the shadow of death, you have risen up to the seventh threshold, you are set as metatron and inner prince—I knew it, I knew it, you are lifted up on high, the Lord has made you a seat like to his own! But me you know still, your mother's son, and you fanned the air with my hand!"

"Little one!" said Joseph. "Little one!" He raised Benjamin up and put their heads together. "Do not talk, it is none of it so great nor so remote and I have no such glory and the great thing of all is that we are twelve once more."

Wrangle Not

He put his arm around Benoni's shoulders and went down with him to the brothers—ah yes, the brothers: how was it with them as they stood there? Some stood with legs apart and arms dangling awkwardly down almost to their knees. They stared open-mouthed into space. Some held their clenched fists upon breasts that heaved up and down with the fury of their

panting. All of them had gone pale at Judah's confession; now they were
crimson, a deep dark red like the colour of pine-trunks, red as that time when
squatting on their hands they had seen Joseph coming towards them in the
coat of many colours. Without Benoni's rapturous cry they would not have
believed or even grasped what the man said. But now the sons of Rachel
came with their arms about each other to stand among them; and a mere
association—for all of them had long since felt that this man had something
or other to do with Joseph—swelled and changed into an identification, and
what wonder that their brains felt as though they would burst? At one moment they would succeed in putting together the sacrificed lamb yonder and
the lord here in his glory; the next moment the two ideas fell apart again.
They had work to hold them together, and that was because their chagrin and
horror were so great.

"Come here to me," said Joseph as he approached. "Yes, yes, I am your
brother Joseph whom you sold down into Egypt; but never mind about that,
for you did me no harm. Tell me, my father is truly alive?—Speak to me, do
not be afraid. Judah, that was a great speech you made. You made it for
ever and ever. I dearly embrace and congratulate you, I greet you and kiss
your lion's head. See, it is the kiss you gave me in front of the Minaeans;
today I give it back, my brother, and it is all blotted out. I kiss you all in
one, never think I am angry that you sold me down here. That all had to be,
God did it, not you. El Shaddei estranged me early from my father's house,
He separated me according to His plan. He sent me on ahead of you to be your
provider—and in His beautiful providence He brought it about that I should
feed Israel together with all strangers in time of dearth. That was a perfectly
simple, practical matter—though physically important, of course; but nothing
to make a shout about. For your brother is no god-hero, no harbinger of
spiritual salvation. He is just a farmer and manager. Remember how your
sheaves bowed down to mine in the dream I prattled about when I was a
young brat, and the stars that made curtsies? Well, that has turned out to
mean nothing so very extraordinary: just that my fathers and brothers would
thank me for what I could give them. When a man receives bread, he says, not
'Hosannah in the highest,' but just 'Thank you very much.' However, bread
there has to be. Bread comes first, before all the hosannahs. Now do you
understand how simple the thing was that the Lord meant, and will you not
believe that I am alive? You know yourselves that I did not stay in the pit,
because the children of Ishmael drew me up out of it and you sold me to them.
Put your hands on me, take hold of me, feel and see that I am your brother
Joseph and I am alive!"

Two or three of them actually did touch him. They cautiously ran their
hands down his garment and timidly grinned.

"Then it was only a joke and you just behaved like a prince?" asked
Issachar. "And you are really only our brother Joseph?"

"Only?" he answered. "That is the best that I am. But you must try to
understand that I am both. I am Joseph, whom the Lord Pharaoh has set as

father and prince in all Egypt. Joseph I am, arrayed in the splendour of this world."

"Then," said Zebulon, "we must not say you are only the one and not the other, for actually you are both in one. We had a glimmering of it all along. And it is good that you are not the lord of the market all the way through, else it would go hard with us. But under your fine raiment you are our brother Joseph, who will protect us from the wrath of the keeper of the market. But you must understand, my lord—"

"Will you drop it, stupid, just leave off this lord business, once and for all—"

"You must see that we have to seek the protection of the keeper of the market against our brother, for in time past we did him ill."

"That you did," said Reuben, with the muscles of his jaw standing out. "It is unheard of, Jehosiph, what I have been ignorant of up till now! They sold you behind my back and never gave me a hint and all these years I did not know that they got rid of you and took money for you—"

"That will do, Reuben," said Bilhah's Dan. "You did this and that behind our backs too and went secretly to the pit meaning to steal the boy. As for the purchase price, it was no great sum, as Joseph's grace well knows. Twenty shekels Phoenician, that was all, thanks to the old man's bargaining powers, and we can settle it any time and you can get your due."

"Wrangle not, men," said Joseph, "don't dispute about what one of you did without the other knowing. For God has put all right. I thank you, Reuben, my big brother, that you came to the pit with your rope to pull me out and give me back to the father. But I was not there. And that was good, for it was not to be so and would not have been right. But now it is right. Now we must all of us think of nothing but the father—"

"Yes, yes," nodded Naphtali, and his tongue went like a clapper and his legs twitched. "What our exalted brother said is quite right, for it must not be that Jacob sits far way in his house of hair or outside it without the dimmest idea of what has happened here: that Joseph is alive and has got high up in the world and has a glittering post among the heathen. Only think, there he sits, Jacob, wrapped in ignorance that we stand here talking face to face with the lost one and touch his garment to convince ourselves. Everything was misunderstanding and wrong information and the father's high-flown lament is as naught and as naught the worm that has gnawn us all our lives. All that is so thrilling it is enough to make a man jump out of his skin—everything in the world is so unbearably awry that we are here and know and he does not know only because he is there and great and foolish distances divide his knowledge from ours; so that the truth can only get a few paces ahead and then lies still and can no more. Oh, if I could just put my hands to my mouth and shout across the seventeen days' distance and say: 'Father, haloo! Joseph is alive and he is as Pharaoh in the land of Egypt, that is the latest news.' But however loud one might shout, there he sits unhearing and unmoved. Or if one could loose a dove whose wings had the speed of lightning, with a screed under its wing: 'Know all men by these presents!'—that the awryness might be

gone out of the world and everybody here and there know the same thing!
No, I can stay here no longer, I cannot stand it. Send me, send me! I will do
it; I will run, defying the fleet stag, to give him good account. For could any
account be better than that which tells the latest news?"

Joseph applauded his zeal, but he said: "Let well alone, Naphtali, do not
be precipitate, for you may not run off alone and no one has a right to say
to our father what I will have said to him and what I planned to say long
ago when I lay at night and mused on this story. You shall all stay with me
seven days and share all my honours and I will set you before my wife the
sun-maid and my sons shall bow before you. After that you shall load your
animals and go up together with Benjamin and tell him: Joseph your son is
not dead but lives, and speaks to you with his living voice and says: 'God
gave me rank among strangers, and folk I know not are subject to me. Come
down here to me, delay not nor fear, dear Father, fear not the land of tombs
whether Abram too came in time of famine. As for the scarcity, and that for
two years now there is no ploughing nor harvest in the world, that will
certainly go on either three or five years more. But I will look out for you,
and you shall settle here in rich pasture. If you ask me whether Pharaoh per-
mits it, I answer you: him your son twists round his finger. And if His
Majesty desire that you should settle in the land of Goshen and on the plains
of Zoan, towards Arabia, I will see to it, you and your children and your
children's children, your flocks and herds and fowl and all that is yours. For
the land of Goshen, also called Gosem, or Gosen, is the place I had long
since chosen for you when you should be sent for, because it is not yet quite
Egypt, not quite so Egyptian, and you could live there on the fish of the
delta and the fat of the land and you need not have much to do with the
children of Egypt, and their old-man cleverness and your own native ways
need not clash. And you would be near to me.' You must speak so to my
father in my name and do it cleverly and skilfully to bring it home to him in
his rigid old age, first that I am alive and that you are all to come down here.
Oh, if I could only go up with you all and coax him into it, I certainly would.
But I cannot, I cannot get away for a day. So you must do it for me: very
lovingly and with great guile, and break these things to him about my being
alive and his coming down. Don't say to him all at once: 'Joseph is alive'; begin
by asking: 'Suppose it were true that Joseph had not died, how would our
lord and father feel?' So he could come on to it gradually. And then do not
blurt out that you are all to come down and settle down below in the land of
the corpse gods; say in the neighbourhood of Goshen. Can you do it like
that without me, sly and loving at once? In these next days we can talk about
how it should be done. Now I will show you my wife, the sun-maid, and my
boys, Manasseh and Ephraim. And we shall eat and drink all twelve of us
together and be merry. And recall old times, yet forgetting much. But while
I think of it: when you get home to our father, tell him all that you have seen
and stint not your description of my glory here below. For his heart has been
sorely bruised, and it must be healed by the sweet music of his son's magnificence."

12 The Birth of Moses

Many authors have turned to the biblical novel because the form helped them say something in addition to the story they retold. Howard Fast's *Moses, Prince of Egypt* seems to have been written for two reasons: to plead for freedom and to attempt to explain the source of monotheism. A popular and controversial novelist, Fast wrote of Moses only a short time after his disavowal of the Communist Party. His previous novels had been drawn primarily from American history and the fight for freedom. His inspiration for this book seems to be derived in part from Sigmund Freud's *Moses and Monotheism*. Fast's Moses learns of his Hebrew background at the time of his Egyptian mother's death when Amon-Teph, an extra-biblical character, secretly teaches him the old Egyptian concept of one God. According to Fast, it was Moses who brought the concept to the Jews, a small tribe that labored in the Egyptian marshes and worshipped a water serpent. An added and interesting complication of Fast's story is the notion that the Pharaoh Ramses, having practiced the Egyptian custom of royal incest, believed Moses to be his own son. Whatever his motives, Fast's novel is intriguing and nothing in it is more interesting than his speculations about the backgrounds of monotheism and the young Moses.

And there went a man of the house of Levi, and took to wife a daughter of Levi.

And the woman conceived, and bare a son: and when she saw him that he was a goodly child, she hid him three months.

And when she could no longer hide him, she took for him an ark of bulrushes, and daubed it with slime and with pitch, and put the child therein; and she laid it in the flags by the river's brink.

EXODUS: II, 1–3

MOSES, PRINCE OF EGYPT by HOWARD FAST

TOGETHER MOSES AND Amon-Teph left the bedchamber of Enekhas-Amon and walked through the darkening corridors to one of the many balconies that looked out upon the river. They were alone on the terrace and they stood at the stone balustrade looking out into the night.

"I had thought to go to the observatory," the priest said, "but I am afraid that death came there first. Since I have despised Osiris during most of my life, I should have no great fear of him afterward; and I am impatient to be with your mother. All that notwithstanding, I cling to life and I am

112

afraid to die. God praise your youth, Moses, for the older we become, the more jealous we are of our little spark of life."

Out of his own thoughts, Moses sighed and wondered why the God Ramses should stoop to trepanning. "Why didn't he kill her and be done with it?" he asked Amon-Teph, his voice so cold and awful that Amon-Teph shuddered.

"When you have loved a woman once, Moses, and have taken her to bed with you, are you ever rid of her?"

"He's rid of her."

"Yes, possibly, I don't know. We are a strange, tortured people, Moses, and the mind of the simplest peasant is a maze that you would lose yourself in. Your mother was in constant pain. Of their own accord people have their skulls opened to relieve the pain, and often enough they live."

"Are you defending Ramses, Amon-Teph?"

"I'm defending you, my son," the priest answered sadly, "Why don't you weep and let the hatred out of your heart?"

Moses shrugged. "No more tears, as you said. And don't be afraid for me. I will bide my time. I begin to find qualities in myself that I never suspected. I think I can be patient. But now we are going to talk, Amon-Teph, and no more mysteries. Look where you have come with your foolish mysteries."

In something close to a whimper, the old priest said, "I can stand all that awaits me, but not your contempt, my son."

Moses turned suddenly and clasped the old man to his bosom, telling him, "No, my father—not contempt." His voice choked, and he shook his head. "Not contempt, my father, my teacher. I am trying to be a man. It is hard."

"I know."

The first edge of the moon arose now about the dark flat edge of the Delta. They remained silent for a time, each struggling with his own emotion, until Amon-Teph was able to say,

"Ask what you wish, and I will answer you the best I can—though I think you know most of it. You bore half a name because the other half waited. You would have been Aton-Moses."

"I suspected as much. But I think I'll remain Moses. There is little point in strutting and posturing now, and I haven't enough vanity to take a name that means my death. There are many reasons why I want to live, Amon-Teph, not only because life is good and sweet, but because I have a score to settle. To tell the truth, I am tired of the gods. You destroyed my fears of Osiris and his creatures of the night—and for that I will be everlastingly grateful—and if Aton is the only god, just and loving, he will not need me to carry his name. I know that you and my mother and perhaps some others dreamed for many years of seating me on the throne of Egypt— well, who am I to judge, as you have made plain to me? But the choice was a poor one, my dear friend. I am not an Egyptian, am I?"

"No—you are not," Amon-Teph admitted. "But Aton warms more places than the River Nile."

"Be that as it may, who am I?"

The priest stared long and thoughtfully at the moon before he answered, and then he turned to Moses and asked him searchingly, "Are you sure you want to know? Can I judge whether you should know?"

Moses cried, "I must know! Can I live in emptiness—out of nothing, no past, no memory?"

"You have the memory of Egypt."

"No! No longer! I want my own! Let me be the judge!"

"Very well," the priest sighed. "But to understand it, you must understand what it meant when the holy Ahk-en-Aton proclaimed Aton as the one living god. He, Ahk-en-Aton, lifted Egypt out of despair and defeat, and brought in a brief age of light and hope—of art and science and fearless inquiry—as in the ancient times when Egypt shone for the whole world like a light in the darkness. And it was his son who raised to the throne beside him Enekhas-Aton, his sister, in the old way of the god-kings. But Tut-ankh-Aton was not the man his father was, and even while he sat on the throne, the glory was fading. The whole great tribe of priests who lived like leeches on the back of the people and who were cast out when Aton triumphed— they were already at work planning and organizing the revolt that overturned the kings of Aton and finally placed Seti on the throne. That you know, and you know how mercilessly Seti destroyed every vestige of Aton worship. Before Seti, Tut-ankh-Aton succumbed to fear and changed his name to Amon—his wife's to Enekhas-Amon, and some bitter whim of Seti gave that name to your mother.

"So think of her, Moses, a girl of great beauty, great birth, the sister of Ramses—I will not call him god again—and beloved of Ramses. He wanted to make her his queen, but she could bear him no children and she bore children to no man. The soothsayers and magicians told him that this was the curse of Aton, and that if she would change her name, she would become fertile and bear him a son. But this, for some reason, for some streak of iron inside her, she could not do. They had terrible, violent battles and he came close to killing her—and her own love for him turned into a malignant hatred. It was at that time she found me out and came to be instructed in the worship of Aton—and because I loved her and had adored her face from the first time I saw her, I could refuse her nothing, and embarked on this venture that ends here.

"In those days, she began the retreat that ended in her seclusion, and very often she would take her barge and go out for days into the endless waterways of the Delta; and sometimes, perhaps because she pitied my dog-like devotion, she would allow me to come with her. Thus it was that we went, one day, along this channel and that one, almost to the Land of Goshen, which lies, as you know, on the eastern edge of the Delta. We were drifting along, the slaves dipping their oars just enough to give us headway in a channel so narrow that the oars brushed the marsh grass, your mother curled up on a mass of pillows in the bow, singing softly—she still sang then—and I standing beside her, when we saw something floating in the water ahead of us. Understand, Moses, there were only the two of us in the boat, and the slaves at the oars, and the helmsman, who was both a slave and a Delta pilot. The thing in the water was a basket, smeared inside with hard clay mixed with bits of cloth, with a child inside it—a child no more than two weeks old. When we picked up the child, the basket was already sodden and beginning to sink. You were that child."

Moses said nothing. He simply nodded and waited for the priest to continue.

"It doesn't disturb you more than this?" Amon-Teph asked gently.

"It has disturbed me since I can remember. I feel better now. Now that I know, I can think about it without being afraid. Where did the child come from, Amon-Teph?"

The old priest spoke slowly, for he had to tell it in his own way now, as if he were compelled to make all of it alive and present; the royal barge lying there in the reeds; the princess under her canopy clutching the child to her bosom; the baby, red-faced from its exposure to the sun, wailing in discomfort and hunger; the princess snapping at him,

"Don't stand there watching, Amon-Teph—find someone to give the child suck before it dies of hunger!"

"But where? Where, in this wilderness?"

"Where the child came from, you fool! Take off that foolish robe of yours and find out where the child came from!"

Amon-Teph nodded as he recalled it for Moses. "I thought I would sink and perish in the morass, but as she willed, I did. Naked in a loincloth, thigh-deep in mud, I waded perhaps a hundred yards along the side of the channel, and then the ground became firmer. The reeds were seven or eight feet high above the water, so I could not see where I was going; but suddenly I was through the reeds on dry ground and there before me were perhaps a hundred men and women and children—who scattered in panic when they saw me and began to run away, leaving behind them the remains of a little fire in which they had burned some incense and leaving behind them, too, a carved cedar box."

It was the carved cedar box, Amon-Teph made clear, that brought them back; for when they realized that they had left it behind, they stopped running and began to return. They had been surprised, but the sight of one muddy Egyptian, a priest, by his shaven head, did not serve to sustain their fear.

"All of you come back!" Amon-Teph shouted. "I'm not going to burn you! I'm a priest of the Great House and I want to talk with you!"

So they returned, warily, and two of them leaped forward and seized the box and dragged it within their ranks. Afterward, Amon-Teph told Moses, they let him see what was in the box. It was a large, black water snake.

"Their god," Amon-Teph told Moses now. "The snake of fertility, to which they made the sacrifice of the child. A very ancient and common prac-

tice—even among our own people two thousand years ago. The same snake
that you will see curled around the legs of Isis—a superstitious and ignorant
cult."

"Who were these people?" Moses whispered.

"One of the slave peoples of the Land of Goshen," Amon-Teph
shrugged. "They are all much the same, Bedouin wanderers from Sinai and
Canaan who received sanctuary in the grasslands during the great droughts
of a century ago—and whom Ramses enslaved. These called themselves
the children of Levi, who was one of the children of Israel, for they keep
an endless record of their ancestry. This was part of the tribe—I imagine
there were six or seven hundred in the whole tribe—and they said they were
related to other tribes who also came from the children of Israel and who
had remained in Canaan and Sinai when these went to Egypt. They spoke
Egyptian of a sort, as well as their own tongue, for you must remember
they have lived long among us. I learned a good deal about them; it was
some time before we left there."

"Tell me what they looked like, Amon-Teph."

The old priest was tiring, and he seemed annoyed that the story must
still continue. "Dirty, bearded, ragged—maybe they would have looked
like you, Moses, had they been raised in the Great House; but they were
skinny, dirty slaves, ignorant and superstitious."

He wanted the story to end; perhaps he, Amon-Teph, was now impatient for the end of many things. He was tired, and he wanted to lie
down and be alone with his sorrow. The rest he told briefly and his listener,
dulled with too much emotion, sorrow and heart-sickness—and the death
of pride in birth and blood; for who could grow up among the lords of the
Great House without such pride?—and the heart-hurting knowledge that he
was a waif, a nobody, a nameless offspring of slaves, thrown by these slaves
in their blind ignorance and superstition as a sacrifice to a water snake—yes,
his listener also desired the story to end. He heard how Amon-Teph had
challenged these people to produce the mother; and when they lied and
denied that it was their babe, he told them that a royal barge of the Great
House lay a stone's throw away, and that if they insisted upon provoking
him, he would return the following day with a squadron of soldiers. Then
he went among them until he found a woman whose full breasts were so
wet they stained the front of her gown, and he ordered her to come with him.

"My mother," Moses said dully.

"Enekhas-Amon was your mother," the priest answered him harshly.
"All your life I refused to tell you this, and I could have died with it as
easily. Not because you were born a slave, but because you have in all truth
become a prince of Egypt, have you forced this out of me. I made this
woman come with me onto the boat, where she gave suck to the child—to
you."

Then came the rest of it—how a pavilion was set up on the shore for
Enekhas-Amon, the mother and the child; how two slaves of the house were
left to guard her while Amon-Teph went back for supplies and to make

arrangements; how they remained there at the edge of the morass for five days, until Amon-Teph found an Egyptian wet nurse whom he could trust; how all of the slaves who were with the barge were sold in the markets of Hatti—for, as Enekhas-Amon said when she returned to the City of Ramses, after four months of quiet hiding in Memphis, the child was hers; and how, with a full measure of wit, gold and threat, the secret was kept.

"But not entirely kept, Moses, my son. No secret is—and while you had a mother, the question of a father remained. Enekhas-Amon would never name a father—she could have—myself, or others of better blood and station who loved her—but she would not. She held that Aton was your father."

"And she believed it?" Moses asked.

"I think so," the old man sighed. "We all believe what we want to believe or what we have to believe. Just as I think that Ramses, the God-King"—his scorn was mixed with fatigue and disinterest—"believes that you are his son."

"No!" Moses cried. "Spare me that!"

Amon-Teph shrugged. "There is much that I would have spared you, but this is the way things are. Ramses, from all I could gather, believes that Enekhas-Amon was waiting for the moment when it would be ripe to proclaim you. Ramses did not wait. . . .

"Well, there it is, all of it; and as for you, my dear son, my dear son" —he had to fight to control his voice; the tears were running from his eyes now, falling strangely upon his loose, pouchy cheeks—"live." His voice was a hoarse whisper. "Live and be strong and good and just. You have been all the life that your mother left to me, and you two gave me what to love and what to live for. You are as noble as any man in Egypt, and when it's all finished, as it is now for me, you realize that we are all brothers, all of the same wit and folly—slave and freeman, noble and peasant. You are what we who loved you desired you should be, and it is the poor, foolish pride of Ramses that makes him claim you for his seed. Let him think so, Moses, and he will not stain his hands with your blood; for whether he faces Osiris or Aton, such a stain would destroy him. Live," the old man gasped, "so that your mother and I can live in you."

Then he kissed Moses and left him; and Moses stood there watching the priest walk slowly and uncertainly into the night.

13 Moses in Midian

The Chosen was the first novel by Edith Simon, who went on to write The Golden Hand and Twelve Pictures, two of the finest historical novels of the past several decades. While well received by the critics when it was published, most of the copies of The Chosen were destroyed by a fire-bomb raid on London during the Second World War. Mrs. Simon was born in Germany and moved to England with her family when she was fourteen. She is the author of three novels which have not yet been printed in the United States and is the translator of Arthur Koestler's The Gladiators. Her research is impeccable and her interest in history profound. In The Chosen she has written about the Exodus from the Egyptian point of view.

Now the priest of Midian had seven daughters: and they came and drew water, and filled the troughs to water their father's flock And the shepherds came and drove them away: but Moses stood up and helped them, and watered their flock.

EXODUS: II, 16–17

THE CHOSEN by EDITH SIMON

WHEN HE HAD toiled up to the summit which spread out in a broad platform, he saw distant smoke mingling with the shreds of mist which played about the rocky teeth.

In the course of the day he found that the ups and downs of the path, leading along the crest-line of a chain of mountains, stretched the distance to the source of the smoke, and very much further than he would have thought. But it would be the end of him were he forced to spend a night on the rocks.

When the sun stood barely a hand's width from the indented horizon, the points of tents seemed suddenly and joyously to leap from behind a low parapet, and he saw that the village well, in a clearing of abundant grass, was quite near.

For several miles all around the ground was earth, as though a well-meaning giant had filled a basin of stone and rubble with great handfuls of it. The well was recognizable by the gibbet-like cross beams built about it, with their rotting winding wheel, and rusty chain encircling a bucket. Its mouth was sealed with a huge slab of stone. By the side of the cross beams thronged a wailing flock kept in order by swathed figures with herdsmen's rods. Closer again, he saw that these were women. He counted them on his fingers: there were seven—a lucky number.

On his approach, they withdrew to the other side of the well, were silent and looked him up and down. Several times he opened his mouth to address them, but the combination of their stares and rigid silence made him incapable of speaking. He sat down on a stone and plucked off the shreds of his sandals, feeling blisters on his feet. The girls then set about shifting the stone slab and by means of the huge chained bucket drew water which they poured into the troughs they had brought with them. The foremost goats locked horns over the troughs whilst the others had nonchalantly scattered. The young women rushed to and fro in an attempt at reassembling them. Only one of the girls remained where she was, looking at the stranger without saying anything; but gradually she smiled.

Moses calculated that she was almost as tall as himself, without appearing sturdy in build. She had blue eyes which shone very prettily out of a reddish-brown surround. Her lips were lighter than the rest of the skin, almost to the degree of the Ethiopian women's, and therefore drew attention to their softly padded, clear outline. She wore a sleeveless blouse and a cloth twisted about her body in such a way that the legs were trousered. Every roundness in her neck, face, and arms reflected the light through many little drops of sweat. As she smiled Moses bade her "Peace."

She returned the greeting and asked, in slightly nasal tones: "Where do you come from?"

"Keme."

"Oh, Keme," she repeated, drawling out the word as though it had three syllables rather than two, and lapsed into a silence deeper than the preceding one, holding her breath and pretending not to look at him.

"Who are you?" Moses asked, trying to control the stammer, smiling the smile that comes naturally in the presence of women.

But already the wide square had become crowded with numerous flocks and their shepherds, unkempt, half-naked, boisterous youths. One or two left their sheep and goats in order to leap after the six scurrying girls, slapping at them with their great hands and roaring with laughter when, through quick wily twists on the part of the pursued, these hands cut heavily into nothing. The others encircled the well and set about driving the first goats away, spilling the troughs, and watering their own beasts.

Shrieking and cursing, the girls stamped their way through the unruly animals. They tried to remonstrate with the shepherds and received slaps and gropings where they least desired them, as well as remarks which made them squeal despite their anger. Nevertheless they were forced to look on as their own flocks thirsted behind the outstretched rods of the shepherds who, in their horseplay, did not care how much water they spilled as long as there was enough for themselves.

Moses saw the blue-eyed girl scramble among animals that strove in the opposite direction; behind her stumbled a shepherd who was holding on to a corner of her garment. She too was both laughing and cursing, but her face looked a little frightened. She almost fell over the last sheep, and gripped at Moses in order to steady herself. "Traveller from Keme," she panted and did not let go of him. Moses brought down his staff on the head of the youth who, after registering an instant's conscious surprise, collapsed where he was.

"Oh, oh," said the girl with the blue eyes. "I wish we hadn't dawdled so. Now they'll take all the water there is, and what about our goats and us?"

"Won't there be any left?" asked Moses pedantically, and moved away from the unconscious shepherd.

"We are very near to the sun up here," she replied, shaking her head and also gazing at the shepherd, "and when one lot of water has gone it takes a whole night to make it come again. And those boys waste so much. I hope you haven't killed him; at first I hoped you had, but such things make too much commotion."

"I will kill them all for you," stuttered Moses, grinning, "come on, you are a strong woman."

"Traveller from Keme," said the girl again, but with a different intonation. She looked quite radiant as she trotted beside him.

Moses hit out with his staff and bellowed with authority. In their first surprise the shepherds left off baiting the other girls and for a moment stared at the stranger. The girls stopped their giggling and shrieking, and rallied round Moses. One of the shepherds, struck across the shoulder, crouched and then fled; another noticed his prostrate comrade on the other side of the well, pointed and yelled; the rest drew away, standing with knit brows until Moses made as if to come after them. They were all quite young. They retreated farther, looking at each other. Quite calm again, the seven girls proceeded to drive away the intruding animals to make room for their own. After a little while the shepherds put their fingers to their teeth and whistled tentatively. Moses glared at them and stammered a long, alliterative Egyptian curse; the shepherds conferred in a dismayed way and withdrew yet a little farther before they dared whistle for their flocks again.

Afterwards Moses helped the girls replace the slab. They told him that they were all sisters, daughters of the lord of that region, Jethro by name. They asked was he going anywhere in particular, would he not come along with them to see their father and be thanked. Now that he looked closely, most of the seven sisters had blue eyes. But they were all rather subdued whilst their eldest sister spoke, brightening only when she had finished and fell behind, seemingly lost in thought.

The village lay in a glade strewn with bushy undergrowth. The girls drove the sheep and goats into an enclosure which, from a distance, seemed to stretch almost vertically up the hillside. As they told Moses, fires were lit there in the evenings and experienced criers stationed to keep away the beasts of the night—though at times this was of no avail.

The tent, or rather block of tents which belonged to their father, reposed in the centre of the village. It was rather a grand affair, not merely of grey felt like the others, but fringed, and extended by huge, tough awnings of canvas striped in brilliant colours. It communicated with the other tents of his household by means of holes cut in its side, which led to corresponding holes in the other tents and were roofed with more canvas stretched over a sort of basket structure similar in appearance to a caterpillar.

"We wonder what our father will say," chattered the girls, "it is just like that old story, isn't it? Two princes first met their wives near wells and through their behaviour induced them to love. Only that the other princes brought earrings of gold, and bracelets, and wine, and greetings from their mothers. We think it might be a Sign. We wonder what our father will think."

The eldest sister went inside to speak to the chief, while the others stayed before the tent, surrounding Moses and causing him to feel nervous because they bade him be courageous and cheery at such great length.

An elderly man with a beard that covered his chest came up and spoke to the girls. "This is Reuel our father's brother," they said, "and this is an Egyptian from Keme who assisted us greatly in the watering of our flocks, and who drove away the shepherds who—ah well . . . Zipporah our eldest sister has just gone inside to tell our father about it."

"And what customs are these?" said the elderly man sternly in a flat, unresounding voice. "Is it correct to leave a friend standing and waiting outside? Should he not receive bread and salt right away?"—He turned to Moses, smiling, "Peace, kind man."

"But we are waiting till our father calls him in," said the girls, their eyes wide open. The elderly man turned slightly away from Moses and anxiously asked the girls whether they knew where Hobal was. "There is going to be a full moon to-night," he said. Before the girls could answer, however, Zipporah came out of the tent. Her face dark and her smile forced, she asked Moses to come inside.

The chieftain was sitting on a horsehair bolster covered with a gaily patterned rug. When he smiled his teeth stood far apart beneath a shaven upper lip, but his chin was obscured by a thick square beard exactly like Reuel's. He lifted in salute one of his hands which had lain neatly arranged on his thighs and showed five miniature nails on otherwise normally shaped fingers, white and clean but seemingly very thin and soft. Beside him sat a woman, sewing, and a man extremely like himself though about fifteen years his junior, who held in his lap a shallow basket covered with a rag. They were quite silent, not a single word rising to the pointed roof above the cheerless, reeking oil-lamp. The woman rose without a glance or smile and fetched a large painted platter.

"Bread," said the chieftain, motioning her to proffer it, "and salt," he added, handing Moses his own pouch. Jethro then introduced himself in a tone guardedly free of patronage for the time being. He praised Moses and thanked him, referring to his eldest daughter Zipporah in an off-hand manner which concealed an amount of suspect regard. He muttered to the woman who got up once more and went from the tent.

"You are from Keme, my daughter tells me?" Jethro opened a new phase in the conversation. He smiled knowingly, his cunning old eyes receding beneath his overhanging brows. Moses said that was so; he was a fugitive from justice. "I know that," said Jethro easily, "but what was your crime?" Moses told him a very roughly outlined story of his origin and up-bringing and finally of the slaying of Hammut the Trader. All the time he could smell food; the clatter of pans being almost unbearable to one who had not eaten for one and a half days. "You must be a very good young man," said the chieftain, "God, no doubt, will reward you."

"What God?" asked Moses, not meaning to be impolite; he wanted to know what god this tribe worshipped.

"There is but One," said the younger replica of Jethro in the background. "Elohim is His name because He unites within Him all the gods who are and ever were. The God of gods, for He is many, although He is One."

"A great god in Egypt is like that too," said Moses goodnaturedly, "He is Himself, and His wife, and His son. On the one hand, He dies, but with the only part of Him that retains life He fathers His Son (who is also Himself) on a female vulture who hovers over His corpse; the Son then gives the Father his own eye for food and so restores Him to life. On the other hand, the Father dies and in the darkness behind the clouds in the shape of His Son begets Himself on His wife and mother who is the one to appear next and in the fullness of time bears Himself again."

"Very complicated," smiled the chieftain; his brother still frowned and said nothing.

"Complicated?" Moses asked unhappily. When the chieftain had explained the meaning of the word to him, Moses went on, eager to interest them: "And the Sun God in Egypt has three different names: one for His ascent, one for His zenith, and one for His decline. This means that He is also three different persons, for in Egypt we bestow on our children double names in order to ensure harmony or adequate unity of the two souls that live within the breast of man. All things merge into one in time; but I myself believe in a different God, more man-made and less man-made than the rest."

The chieftain scrabbled his beard with pale fingers. He raised his eyebrows but kept silent, waiting.

Moses could hardly contain himself; he actually stammered less than usual: "I mean law. Law, thought out and fashioned by human minds, and yet far greater, more all-embracing than the many gods with their earthen foibles."

"And what is it you are thinking of when you say 'Law'?" enquired the chieftain, with a whole-hearted earnestness which endeared him to Moses.

"Justice," said Moses, "tidy living, society mapped out—"

The elderly woman reappeared with two of the girls. They were carrying steaming platters and bowls which they set upon a number of low tables consisting of carven folding stands and large metal discs finely embossed and engraved.

"May your meal be blessed," nodded the chieftain, and with a practised hand plucked a tender piece from the breast of lamb and in the other a mound of rice dripping with butter. The younger man in the background moved closer; he ate nervously, chewing with hasty clicks, swallowing with jerks of his entire neck and, with irritating regularity, swilling a draught from the jug beside him. The women went out again.

"That, my good friend, is all very well," said Jethro, patting his greasy upper lip with the hem of his garment, "but have you a god who will uphold and enforce that tidy pattern of life, that man-made justice presumably based on equality? Have you an image in whom men and women can read this Law, without having to peruse streets of stone tablets whose twentieth paragraph they have forgotten by the time they arrive at the thousandth?"

Moses was so saturated with the happiness of appeased hunger that at first only the most irrelevant thoughts rose to his mind. "Why do you not wipe the grease off your lips with that neat napkin you have yourself grown: your proud square beard?" he thought, which was obviously foolish. "I beg your pardon," he stammered. "Surely the people will love the Just Law more than the man-eating gods? Surely they themselves will joyously add to it, and so keep it fresh and growing in their memories, for a maker does not forget his works."

"If they are as vain as you, stranger from Keme, then maybe," said the younger man, "but few people are quite so certain of being the centre of the universe. Tremble with shame, bow your head, and realize that the God of Gods has merely seen fit to implant the championship for His Own Law in your small soul. Make it visible in His name, instead of your own—which, by the way, you haven't told us—before He shatters you."

"If it was he, then he must also have commanded me to deny him, and sown in me the seed of unbelief which will spread and free the world one day—but I am getting confused. . . ."

"Hobal," exclaimed the chieftain, with a charming smile at Moses, "this man is our honoured guest; and although he has made himself a member of our family by defending our women, he is not quite yet your brother that you may insult and sneer at him. This is my youngest brother, Hobal, a great magician and the prophet of our God; he is rather zealous."

As though in answer, Hobal took Moses' staff from the crook of his elbow, glared at Moses, stretched it towards him, and behold, the staff writhed and hissed. As Moses started back, Hobal became calm again, placed the serpent in the basket beside him, and on looking down Moses saw the staff reposing in the crook of his arm again.

"I once had a friend who could do that," said Moses pleasantly, "he has been lost as a hermit for several years now, but he used to be a great priest at Weset, a physician by profession."

"It is so long since I was last sick—I can never imagine how physicians make a living in the cities," Jethro soothingly changed the subject. But Hobal's teeth were chattering again. He rose shakily, glowered, and went outside.

"He is rather holy," explained the chieftain when the door flap had swung to behind the magician, "almost a living example of that One-ness we were talking about. At every full moon he falls sick, like a woman, only that of course he does not give birth in any way—and by the will of God he talks and contorts himself without remembering anything afterwards. You must talk to him again some other time, you will find him interesting."

"Some other time? Are you offering me hospitality?"

"Besides being martially versed, do you know anything about goats?"

"I've herded sheep. But let me thank you—"

"What a conversation we're having," mused the chieftain. "What did you think of my daughter Zipporah? Not one of the friendly chiefs wants to marry her, and I can't give away the other six before the eldest. I am not boring you? She is extremely short-sighted and has inherited something of the moon-sickness which occasionally runs in our family."

"I should say she was very handsome," said Moses, "she is so tall and candid-looking. Both of my wives are short, and one of them is very wily."

"You had two wives in Keme? In that case you will miss their absence," said Jethro and hooded his blue eyes, "and you are fond of arguing, are you not? Of course," he added after a pensive pause, "I also have a number of sons, But I don't think any of them take after me. The Lord has seen fit to bless me with women to make alliances and increase my herds which will be bequeathed to some unremarkable chieftain after me."

14 The Burning Bush

Dorothy Clarke Wilson is a far better novelist than her critical recognition would indicate. One of the few writers who has written solely from Bible sources, she has shown a respect for her subject, a talent for integrating research and original thinking, a simplicity and charm of style, and a skill in construction. Mrs. Wilson has written five Biblical novels since 1944 when she first published *The Brother,* a novel of the New Testament. Two years later she published *The Herdsman,* about the prophet Amos, and followed this with her most successful volume, *Prince of Egypt,* from which the following selection about the burning bush was taken. This was followed by *Jezebel,* and in 1958 she wrote *The Gifts,* a novel of Jesus. No other writer has probed the Bible so thoroughly for subject matter, and few have worked within the genre more successfully.

Now Moses kept the flock of Jethro his father-in-law, the priest of Midian: and he led the flock to the backside of the desert, and came to the mountain of God, even to Horeb.

And the angel of the Lord appeared unto him in a flame out of the midst of a bush: and he looked, and, behold, the bush burned with fire, and the bush was not consumed.

EXODUS: III, 1–2

PRINCE OF EGYPT by DOROTHY CLARKE WILSON

WHEN NIGHT CAME, he was so close to The Mountain that a stone from his sling could easily have bounded from one of its lower rocky ledges. It had been a longer and more difficult journey than he had expected, but he had finally emerged, just at sunset, into the broad plain which he had expected to find at the west of The Mountain, treeless and sparsely sown with vegetation, but a veritable paradise after the wasteland through which he had journeyed.

He was so weary that he lay down to rest without stopping to eat or to make a fire. In fact, he felt little need for either one. His body was fed and warmed by a consuming purpose, and for the moment he had no fear. The possibility of prowling animals was as remote from his mind as that of the sun's failure to rise.

Though he found it impossible to sleep, his eyes followed without impatience the slow swinging of the stars toward the far horizon. High above his head the fire-edged pillar glowed in a still, shining vapor, more mysterious in its nearness than when seen from a distance. Aloof and disembodied, the solid earth beneath it dissolved into darkness; it too seemed to lie motionless in a void, spirit without body, existence without reason or purpose.

Moses was glad for the hours of solitude. When a man was about to enter into the presence of a god, he had need to prepare himself. What would happen, he wondered, curious rather than fearful, when he set foot on the holy Mountain? Would Yahweh really smite him dead as every desert dweller firmly believed? If so, it was the last time he would lie wrapped in his cloak on the ground, looking at the stars. If Yahweh was that kind of god, he hoped it would be the last time.

There was another reason also why he was glad he could not sleep. For if he slept he might dream again that he was lying on the edge of the burning pit. Each time the dream became more intricate in detail and the figures climbing toward him revealed more and more familiar faces. But after tonight there would be no such unquiet dreams. In the presence of the ultimate truth he would surely find serenity.

He watched the pale dawn reach into the black void. The Mountain again took form. Silhouetted against the yellowing sky, it seemed austere, forbidding. Moses' heart sank. Why should the god have chosen such a terrifying place for his habitation? A fitting home, perhaps, for one who called himself the Destroyer but not for the Creator of all things who had made man in his own likeness! One by one the lesser surrounding peaks reared their heads proudly and donned bright turbans of sunlight. But The Mountain remained towering and aloof, untouched by any radiance save that which emanated from its own mysterious crest.

Moses rose from the ground, removed his clothes, and, using all the remaining water in his small goatskin, bathed himself from head to foot before reclothing himself in his soiled garments. Then, as outwardly calm as if he had been going to release the flocks from their night's shelter, but inwardly quivering with excitement, he moved steadily across the plain. No one knew better than he the enormity of the act he contemplated. He was about to enter into the most holy place of the temple where the image of Re was hidden; to lift the curtain of Amon's sacred bark; to tear aside with rude fingers the mummy wrappings of Osiris. Only for an instant, when the rough prong of rock was less than a hand's breadth from his grasp, did he hesitate.

"Smite me, Yahweh, if you must," he cried soundlessly. "But not yet —not until I've climbed The Mountain!"

Laying his hand firmly on the rock, and finding a crevice for his foot, he swung himself clear of the ground and slowly, one cautious step at a time, worked his way up over the first sheer ledge.

Hours later he cried out again, this time audibly: "Smite me now, Yahweh. Don't torment me any longer. If this is your face that I am seeing, then blind my eyes that I may not look more closely! If this is your voice, stop my ears that I may become deaf! Only let me find peace—"

The jagged walls of the ravine up which he crawled tossed the burning rays of the sun back and forth like jugglers toying with gleaming rapiers. Heat hovered over its narrow, ovenlike depression in throbbing waves. The winds that had risen at noon and blown incessantly across the open wastes up which he had traveled, clutching at his garments, whipping sand and dust into his eyes, were here also, their scorched breath filling the deep crevice like air drawn into an open flue.

He did not know how long he had been climbing. He supposed it was afternoon of the same day, but he could not be sure. There had been periods of intense blackness which might have been either nights or moments. He was vaguely aware of thirst and of other bodily discomforts—blistered feet and hands, knees lacerated from crawling over slippery rocks, the scratching of rough garments clinging to his soaked skin. But they were not important. His search was all that mattered, his search after peace which was leading him into greater agony of spirit than he had ever known.

"Smite me, Yahweh!" he cried again. "Blind me that I may not see—"

But Yahweh did not smite him. And in spite of the blinding dust and barbs of sunlight his vision remained clear and penetrating. He saw every unlovely detail with merciless clarity: the jagged rocks contorted into grotesque shapes, their black surfaces slashed by occasional bare strata of limestone; the twisted limbs of a thorny acacia; the shadow of a vulture's outspread wings. Groanings and mutterings as of a soul in mortal torment filled his ears, whether his own or another's he could not tell. He was no longer a separate entity but a part of some vast activity whose nature he could not even comprehend.

He had long ago lost all sense of direction. He could see neither the plain from which he had come nor the top of The Mountain for which he was bound. His one purpose, to keep traveling upward, became an obsession. He chose the steepest approach to each new eminence, refused to side-pass even the most formidable barrier at a cost of retracing his steps. Sometimes in an upright position, sometimes on hands and knees or with his body stretched full length on the ground, he made his way through the furnacelike grooves, over the strange transfixed stream beds which were as smooth as glass and as black as ebony, up the sheer sides of cliffs with only a few prongs of rock for a foothold, up . . . always up . . . Until finally his feet could discover no more sloping surfaces to climb, his hands no more jagged edges of rock, no more twisted branches of thorny acacia to which they might cling.

If he had found restlessness below, here he encountered turmoil. Winds swept against him with a violence that drove him to his knees. Light flashed before his eyes like blazing scimitars. Heat laid steaming compresses on his throbbing temples, fell like a moist but unsatisfying rain on his parched lips. The earth stirred beneath his body. He realized vaguely that it was sunset and that his whole world, complete but indescribably small, was spread before his eyes. Midian was a cluster of toy rock piles, Ezion-geber a fleck of dust on the tip of a blue blade. The desert of his journeying as a fugitive lay like a small outspread palm, skinflaked and leprose. And Egypt . . . Egypt was the invisible black earth on which the blazing sunset fires were kindled far beyond the horizon.

Night fell swiftly, plunging the mountaintop into a weird half-light which changed its turmoil into chaos. In spite of his exhaustion Moses made his way forward, moving now on hands and knees so that he might not stumble into one of the many crevices. He was very near the goal now. Only a little farther and he would look on the mystery that lay hidden within the glowing pillar. He would look upon it, and that would be the end, for he was sure now that no human being could enter into a knowledge of its reality and live.

"Smite me, Yahweh!" he cried again. "I know now that you must. But not yet. Please—not until I've discovered a little more of truth!"

Hot mists swam before his eyes and entered his nostrils, making it difficult to breathe. Winds lashed him mercilessly. The earth reeled unsteadily. Was it, perhaps, the primeval chaos of which the old minstrel had sung? *"In the beginning, when Yahweh began to create the earth and the heaven, the world was a desolate waste of darkness and wind and water . . ."*

He must have slept finally, for he dreamed again that he was lying on the edge of the burning pit. At first there were no dark naked figures, only the undulating mass of molten fire, brighter and more terrifying than he had ever yet conceived it. Then suddenly they were there, climbing toward him out of the abyss, clinging to its black smooth sides and he was reaching down his hands, struggling, agonizing to reach them. This time there were more than Aaron and Miriam and Jaret and the young Shasu boy. They came in unending swarms through the burning waters, out of the reddened mists— prisoners of war, their bodies lashed together, gold miners of Nubia, slaves from the temple at Karnak, fellahin bent like taut bows to the shaduf, Hebrews with burdens of bricks on their backs.

"Come down, Moses!" they called up to him. *"Come down and help us!"*

No, *no!* So sharply did his whole being recoil from the thought that he awakened from his dream, if dream it was. But he still lay staring into a glowing pit, its depths troubled by such profound disquiet that it might have contained all the naked bodies absorbed into one.

And Moses knew suddenly that his search was over. He had entered the holy place, lifted the sacred curtain, torn aside the divine wrappings. And he recoiled in horror from the truth he had discovered. For there was not only restlessness in the heart of God the Creator. There was an agony so intense that it constantly consumed his very being!

Yahweh did not smite him. He had reserved for this supreme audacity an even more effective punishment: to let him live.

When morning came Moses started to make his way down The Mountain. Descent was surprisingly easy. Viewed from above, the deeply gashed grooves became paths rather than obstructions. Late in the afternoon, he had reached the edge of the bleak wind-blown waste about halfway down The Mountain where he slaked his thirst and filled his waterskin at a small spring. A few stunted acacias nearby gave a meager shelter from the sun. Wearily he sank down beneath one of them, and, since it was already near sunset, decided that it was as good a place as any to spend the night. There was little purpose now in any of his motions. Probably there never would be again. He would go back to his flocks, he supposed, and for the endless years that might remain to him perform the routine duties of a shepherd. Perhaps if he always kept in the wilderness, he would finally forget the toiling figures, and if he refused to look at The Mountain, he might even cease in time to remember its disturbing secret. He would become hard and bitterly resistant, like the stunted acacia that stood alone on the bleak waste some distance from his shelter, its gaunt arms twisted by the winds, its meager leaves darting sharp, defiant thrusts at the enemies assaulting it on every hand.

Even as he watched he saw one such enemy approaching. Emerging from the hot sucking funnels of the precipitous ravines, the winds flung themselves together with a violent impact, locked in furious combat, then, unexpectedly joining forces, went hurtling away, a huge twisting spiral of sand and dust. Seizing the lonely acacia in its turbulent embrace, it clung to the bare, gaunt arms in mad swirling frenzy. At the same instant the setting sun thrust its bright slanting sword into the battle. There was a moment's bitter conflict, the sun and earth and wind flung themselves together in one swift ecstasy of union. The spikes of the thorn tree leaped into flame. The swift-whirling spiral of dust and sand became a pillar of golden smoke, shot through with fire. While Moses gazed spellbound, the tree burned before his eyes, yet it was not consumed. Then, as abruptly as it had come into being, the brief ecstasy of union passed. The fury of the winds subsided. The sun's rays paled. The tree was again a lonely acacia, gaunt and ugly in the midst of a desolate waste.

Moses rose from the ground. He slipped off his sandals.

"Yahweh," he whispered.

He lifted his face to the driving wind, opened his eyes wide toward the sunset's blazing core, and felt the whirling dust which was his own tortured spirit kindle into burning awareness. Blind fool that he had been! Yahweh on a mountain imprisoned in a glowing pit? When he, Moses, had just beheld divinity created out of dust, unspeakable beauty born out of agonizing conflict? Understanding swept through him like a flame. Yahweh had not finished his work of creation. He was still trying, patiently and in desperate agony of spirit, to create man in his own likeness. He would never cease trying until he had fulfilled his purpose, *even though his own being became consumed in the attempt!*

15 The Tenth Plague

Sir Henry Rider Haggard was a novelist in the nineteenth century's romantic tradition. A one-time member of the British colonial service in the Transvaal almost a century ago, he wrote his best-known works against an African setting. *She, King Solomon's Mines,* and other tales about the white hunter known as Alan Quatermain are all over seventy-five years old, and yet they continue to find an enthusiastic audience because they are delightful romances. Haggard's biblical novel, *Moon of Israel,* focuses upon the Egyptians rather than the Hebrews, and most of his characters are fictional, though the story is set against the Exodus. In a word, the book is pure romance. Merapi, the heroine and "Moon of Israel," a Hebrew girl married to a member of the Pharaoh's court, tries to help her people. But the Pharaoh's heart is hardened and the plagues come. In the tenth plague, which is described in the following selection, Merapi herself loses her child.

> *And the Lord said unto Moses, Yet will I bring one plague more upon Pharaoh, and upon Egypt; afterwards he will let you go hence: when he shall let you go, he shall surely thrust you out hence altogether.*
>
> EXODUS: XI, 1

MOON OF ISRAEL
A TALE OF THE EXODUS by H. RIDER HAGGARD

The Night of Fear

THEN CAME THE HAIL, and some months after the hail the locusts, and Egypt went mad with woe and terror. It was known to us, for with Ki and Bakenkhonsu in the palace we knew everything, that the Hebrew prophets had promised this hail because Pharaoh would not listen to them. Therefore Seti caused it to be put about through all the land that the Egyptians should shelter their cattle, or such as were left to them, at the first sign of storm. But Pharaoh heard of it and issued a proclamation that this was not to be done, inasmuch as it would be an insult to the gods of Egypt. Still many did so and these saved their cattle. It was strange to see that wall of jagged ice stretching from earth to heaven and destroying all upon which it fell. The tall date-palms were stripped even of their bark; the soil was churned up; men and beasts if caught abroad were slain or shattered.

I stood at the gate and watched it. There, not a yard away, fell the white hail, turning the world to wreck, while here within the gate there was not a single stone. Merapi watched also, and presently came Ki as well, and with him Bakenkhonsu, who for once had never seen anything like this in all his long life. But Ki watched Merapi more than he did the hail, for I saw him searching out her very soul with those merciless eyes of his.

"Lady," he said at length, "tell your servant, I beseech you, how you do this thing?" and he pointed first to the trees and flowers within the gate and then to the wreck without.

At first I thought that she had not heard him because of the roar of the hail, for she stepped forward and opened the side wicket to admit a poor jackal that was scratching at the bars. Still this was not so, for presently she turned and said,

"Does the Kherheb, the greatest magician in Egypt, ask an unlearned woman to teach him of marvels? Well, Ki, I cannot, because I neither do it nor know how it is done."

Bakenkhonsu laughed, and Ki's painted smile grew as it were brighter than before.

"That is not what they say in the land of Goshen, Lady," he answered, "and not what the Hebrew women say here in Memphis. Nor is it what the priests of Amon say. These declare that you have more magic than all the sorcerers on the Nile. Here is the proof of it," and he pointed to the ruin without and the peace within, adding, "Lady, if you can protect your own home, why cannot you protect the innocent people of Egypt?"

"Because I cannot," she answered angrily. "If ever I had such power it is gone from me, who am now the mother of an Egyptian's child. But I have none. There in the temple of Amon some Strength worked through me, that is all, which never will visit me again because of my sin."

"What sin, Lady?"

"The sin of taking the Prince Seti to lord. Now, if any god spoke through me it would be one of those of the Egyptians, since He of Israel has cast me out."

Ki started as though some new thought had come to him, and at this moment she turned and went away.

"Would that she were high-priestess of Isis that she might work for us and not against us," he said.

Bakenkhonsu shook his head.

"Let that be," he answered. "Be sure that never will an Israelitish woman offer sacrifice to what she would call the abomination of the Egyptians."

"If she will not sacrifice to save the people, let her be careful lest the people sacrifice her to save themselves," Ki said in a cold voice.

Then he too went away.

"I think that if ever that hour comes, then Ki will have his share in it," laughed Bakenkhonsu. "What is the good of a shepherd who shelters here in comfort, while outside the sheep are dying, eh, Ana?"

It was after the plague of locusts, which ate all there was left to eat in

Egypt, so that the poor folk who had done no wrong and had naught to say to the dealings of Pharaoh with the Israelites starved by the thousand, and during that of the great darkness, that Laban came. Now this darkness lay upon the land like a thick cloud for three whole days and nights. Nevertheless, though the shadows were deep, there was no true darkness over the house of Seti at Memphis, which stood in a funnel of grey light stretching from earth to sky.

Now the terror was increased tenfold, and it seemed to me that all the hundreds of thousands of Memphis were gathered outside our walls, so that they might look upon the light, such as it was, if they could do no more. Seti would have admitted as many as the place would hold, but Ki bade him not, saying, that if he did so the darkness would flow in with them. Only Merapi did admit some of the Israelitish women who were married to Egyptians in the city, though for her pains they only cursed her as a witch. For now most of the inhabitants of Memphis were certain that it was Merapi who, keeping herself safe, had brought these woes upon them because she was a worshipper of an alien god.

"If she who is the love of Egypt's heir would but sacrifice to Egypt's gods, these horrors would pass from us," said they, having, as I think, learned their lesson from the lips of Ki. Or perhaps the emissaries of Userti had taught them.

Once more we stood by the gate watching the people flitting to and fro in the gloom without, for this sight fascinated Merapi, as a snake fascinates a bird. Then it was that Laban appeared. I knew his hooked nose and hawk-like eyes at once, and she knew him also.

"Come away with me, Moon of Israel," he cried, "and all shall yet be forgiven you. But if you will not come, then fearful things will overtake you."

She stood staring at him, answering never a word, and just then the Prince Seti reached us and saw him.

"Take that man," he commanded, flushing with anger, and guards sprang into the darkness to do his bidding. But Laban was gone.

On the second day of the darkness the tumult was great, on the third it was terrible. A crowd thrust the guard aside, broke down the gates and burst into the palace, humbly demanding that the lady Merapi would come to pray for them, yet showing by their mien that if she would not come they meant to take her.

"What is to be done?" asked Seti of Ki and Bakenkhonsu.

"That is for the Prince to judge," said Ki, "though I do not see how it can harm the lady Merapi to pray for us in the open square of Memphis."

"Let her go," said Bakenkhonsu, "lest presently we should all go further than we would."

"I do not wish to go," cried Merapi, "not knowing for whom I am to pray or how."

"Be it as you will, Lady," said Seti in his grave and gentle voice. "Only, hearken to the roar of the mob. If you refuse, I think that very soon every one of us will have reached a land where perhaps it is not needful to pray at all," and he looked at the infant in her arms.

"I will go," she said.

She went forth carrying the child and I walked behind her. So did the Prince, but in that darkness he was cut off by a rush of thousands of folk and I saw him no more till all was over. Bakenkhonsu was with me leaning on my arm, but Ki had gone on before us, for his own ends as I think. A huge mob moving through the dense darkness, in which here and there lights floated like lamps upon a quiet sea. I did not know where we were going until the light of one of these lamps shone upon the knees of the colossal statue of the great Rameses, revealing his cartouche. Then I knew that we were near the gateway of the vast temple of Memphis, the largest perhaps in the whole world.

We went through court after pillared court, priests leading us by the hand till we came to a shrine commanding the biggest court of all, which was packed with men and women. It was that of Isis, who held at her breast the infant Horus.

"O friend Ana," cried Merapi, "give help. They are dressing me in strange garments."

I tried to get near to her but was thrust back, a voice, which I thought was that of Ki, saying,

"On your life, fool!"

Presently a lamp was held up, and by the light of it I saw Merapi seated in a chair dressed like a goddess, in the sacerdotal robes of Isis and wearing the vulture cap headdress—beautiful exceedingly. In her arms was the child dressed as the infant Horus.

"Pray for us, Mother Isis," cried thousands of voices, "that the curse of blackness may be removed."

Then she prayed, saying,

"O my God, take away this curse of blackness from these innocent people," and all of those present, repeated her prayer.

At that moment the sky began to lighten and in less than the half of an hour the sun shone out. When Merapi saw how she and the child were arrayed she screamed aloud and tore off her jewelled trappings, crying,

"Woe! Woe! Woe! Great woe upon the people of Egypt!"

But in their joy at the new found light few hearkened to her who they were sure had brought back the sun. Again Laban appeared for a moment.

"Witch! Traitress!" he cried. "You have worn the robes of Isis and worshipped in the temple of the gods of the Egyptians. The curse of the God of Israel be on you and that which is born of you."

I sprang at him but he was gone. Then we bore Merapi home swooning.

So this trouble passed by, but from that time forward Merapi would not suffer her son to be taken out of her sight.

"Why do you make so much of him, Lady?" I asked one day.

"Because I would love him well while he is here, Friend," she answered, "but of this say nothing to his father."

A while went by and we heard that still Pharaoh would not let the Israelites go. Then the Prince Seti sent Bakenkhonsu and myself to Tanis to see Pharaoh and to say to him,

"I would seek nothing for myself and I forget those evils which you would have worked on me through jealousy. But I say unto you that if you will not let these strangers go great and terrible things shall befall you and all Egypt. Therefore, hear my prayer and let them go."

Now Bakenkhonsu and I came before Pharaoh and we saw that he was greatly aged, for his hair had gone grey about his temples and the flesh hung in bags beneath his eyes. Also not for one minute could he stay still.

"Is your lord, and are you also of the servants of this Hebrew prophet whom the Egyptians worship as a god because he has done them so much ill?" he asked. "It may well be so, since I heard that my cousin Seti keeps an Israelitish witch in his house, who wards off from him all the plagues that have smitten the rest of Egypt, and that to him has fled also Ki the Kherheb, my magician. Moreover, I hear that in payment for these wizardries he has been promised the throne of Egypt by many fickle and fearful ones among my people. Let him be careful lest I lift him up higher than he hopes, who already have enough of traitors in this land; and you two with him."

Now I said nothing who saw that the man was mad, but Bakenkhonsu laughed out loud and answered,

"O Pharaoh, I know little, but I know this although I be old, namely, that after men have ceased to speak your name I shall still hold converse with the wearer of the Double Crown of Egypt. Now will you let these Hebrews go, or will you bring death upon Egypt?"

Pharaoh glared at him and answered, "I will not let them go."

"Why not, Pharaoh? Tell me, for I am curious."

"Because I cannot," he answered with a groan. "Because something stronger than myself forces me to deny their prayer. Begone!"

So we went, and this was the last time that I looked upon Amenmeses at Tanis.

As we left the chamber I saw the Hebrew prophet entering the presence. Afterwards a rumour reached us that he had threatened to kill all the people in Egypt, but that still Pharaoh would not let the Israelites depart. Indeed, it was said that he had told the prophet that if he appeared before him any more he should be put to death.

Now we journeyed back to Memphis with all these tidings and made report to Seti. When Merapi heard them she went half mad, weeping and wringing her hands. I asked her what she feared. She answered death, which was near to all of us. I said,

"If so, there are worse things, Lady."

"For you mayhap who are faithful and good in your own fashion, but not for me. Do you not understand, friend Ana, that I am one who has broken the law of the God I was taught to worship?"

"And which of us is there who has not broken the law of the god we were taught to worship, Lady? If in truth you have done anything of the sort by flying from a murderous villain to one who loves you well, which I do not believe, surely there is forgiveness for such sins as this."

"Aye, perhaps, but, alas! the thing is blacker far. Have you forgotten what I did? Dressed in the robes of Isis I worshipped in the temple of Isis with my boy playing the part of Horus on my bosom. It is a crime that can never be forgiven to a Hebrew woman, Ana, for my God is a jealous God. Yet it is true that Ki tricked me."

"If he had not, Lady, I think there would have been none of us left to trick, seeing that the people were crazed with dread of the darkness and believed that it could be lifted by you alone, as indeed happened," I added somewhat doubtfully.

"More of Ki's tricks! Oh! do you not understand that the lifting of the darkness at that moment was Ki's work, because he wished the people to believe that I am indeed a sorceress."

"Why?" I asked.

"I do not know. Perhaps that one day he may find a victim to bind to the altar in his place. At least I know well that it is I who must pay the price, I and my flesh and blood, whatever Ki may promise," and she looked at the sleeping child.

"Do not be afraid, Lady," I said. "Ki has left the palace and you will see him no more."

"Yes, because the Prince was angry with him about the trick in the temple of Isis. Therefore suddenly he went, or pretended to go, for how can one tell where such a man may really be? But he will come back again. Bethink you, Ki was the greatest magician in Egypt; even old Bakenkhonsu can remember none like to him. Then he matches himself against the prophets of my people and fails."

"But did he fail, Lady? What they did he did, sending among the Israelites the plagues that your prophets had sent among us."

"Yes, some of them, but he was outpaced, or feared to be outpaced at last. Is Ki a man to forget that? And if Ki chances really to believe that I am his adversary and his master at this black work, as because of what happened in the temple of Amon thousands believe today, will he not mete me my own measure soon or late? Oh! I fear Ki, Ana, and I fear the people of Egypt, and were it not for my lord beloved, I would flee away into the wilderness with my son, and get me out of this haunted land! Hush! he wakes."

From this time forward until the sword fell there was great dread in Egypt. None seemed to know exactly what they dreaded, but all thought that it had to do with death. People went about mournfully looking over their shoulders as though someone were following them, and at night they gathered together in knots and talked in whispers. Only the Hebrews seemed to be glad and happy. Moreover, they were making preparations for something new and strange. Thus those Israelitish women who dwelt in Memphis began to sell what property they had and to borrow of the Egyptians. Especially did they ask for the loan of jewels, saying that they were about to celebrate a feast and wished to look fine in the eyes of their countrymen. None refused them what they asked because all were afraid of them. They even came to the palace and begged her ornaments from Merapi, although she was a country-woman of their own who had showed them much kindness. Yes, and seeing that her son wore a little gold circlet on his hair, one of them begged that also, nor did she say her nay. But, as it chanced, the Prince entered, and see-ing the woman with this royal badge in her hand, grew very angry and forced her to restore it.

"What is the use of crowns without heads to wear them?" she sneered, and fled away laughing, with all that she had gathered.

After she had heard that saying Merapi grew even sadder and more distraught than she was before, and from her the trouble crept to Seti. He too became sad and ill at ease, though when I asked him why he vowed he did not know, but supposed it was because some new plague drew near.

"Yet," he added, "as I have made shift to live through nine of them, I do not know why I should fear a tenth."

Still he did fear it, so much that he consulted Bakenkhonsu as to whether there were any means by which the anger of the gods could be averted.

Bakenkhonsu laughed and said he thought not, since always if the gods were not angry about one thing they were angry about another. Having made the world they did nothing but quarrel with it, or with other gods who had a hand in its fashioning, and of these quarrels men were the victims.

"Bear your woes, Prince," he added, "if they come, for ere the Nile has risen another fifty times at most, whether they have or have not been, will be the same to you."

"Then you think that when we go west we die indeed, and that Osiris is but another name for the sunset, Bakenkhonsu."

The old Councillor shook his great head, and answered,

"No. If ever you should lose one whom you greatly love, take comfort, Prince, for I do not think that life ends with death. Death is the nurse that puts it to sleep, no more, and in the morning it will wake again to travel through another day with those who have companioned it from the be-ginning."

"Where do all the days lead it to at last, Bakenkhonsu?"

"Ask that of Ki; I do not know."

"To Set with Ki, I am angered with him," said the Prince, and went away.

"Not without reason, I think," mused Bakenkhonsu, but when I asked him what he meant, he would not or could not tell me.

So the gloom deepened and the palace, which had been merry in its way, became sad. None knew what was coming, but all knew that something was coming and stretched out their hands to strive to protect that which they loved best from the stroke of the warring gods. In the case of Seti and Merapi this was their son, now a beautiful little lad who could run and prattle, one too of a strange health and vigour for a child of the inbred race of the Ramessids. Never for a minute was this boy allowed to be out of the sight of one or other of his parents; indeed I saw little of Seti in those days and all our learned studies came to nothing, because he was ever concerned with Merapi in playing nurse to this son of his.

When Userti was told of it, she said in the hearing of a friend of mine,

"Without a doubt that is because he trains his bastard to fill the throne of Egypt."

But, alas! all that the little Seti was doomed to fill was a coffin.

It was a still, hot evening, so hot that Merapi had bid the nurse bring the child's bed and set it between two pillars of the great portico. There on the bed he slept, lovely as Horus the divine. She sat by his side in a chair that had feet shaped like to those of an antelope. Seti walked up and down the terrace beyond the portico leaning on my shoulder, and talking by snatches of this or that. Occasionally as he passed he would stay for a while to make sure by the bright moonlight that all was well with Merapi and the child, as of late it had become a habit with him to do. Then without speaking, for fear lest he should awake the boy, he would smile at Merapi, who sat there brooding, her head resting on her hand, and pass on.

The night was very still. The palm leaves did not rustle, no jackals were stirring, and even the shrill-voiced insects had ceased their cries. Moreover, the great city below was quiet as a home of the dead. It was as though the presage of some advancing doom scared the world to silence. For without doubt doom was in the air. All felt it down to the nurse woman, who cowered close as she dared to the chair of her mistress, and even in that heat shivered from time to time.

Presently little Seti awoke, and began to prattle about something he had dreamed.

"What did you dream, my son?" asked his father.

"I dreamed," he answered in his baby talk, "that a woman, dressed as Mother was in the temple, took me by the hand and led me into the air. I looked down, and saw you and Mother with white faces and crying. I began to cry too, but the woman with the feather cap told me not to as she was taking me to a beautiful big star where Mother would soon come to find me."

The Prince and I looked at each other and Merapi feigned to busy herself with hushing the child to sleep again. It drew towards midnight and still no one seemed minded to go to rest. Old Bakenkhonsu appeared and began to say something about the night being very strange and unrestful, when, suddenly, a little bat that was flitting to and fro above us fell upon his head and thence to the ground. We looked at it, and saw that it was dead.

"Strange that the creature should have died thus," said Bakenkhonsu, when, behold! another fell to the ground nearby. The black kitten which belonged to little Seti saw it fall and darted from beside his bed where it was sleeping. Before ever it reached the bat, the creature wheeled round, stood upon its hind legs, scratching at the air about it, then uttered one pitiful cry and fell over dead.

We stared at it, when suddenly far away a dog howled in a very piercing fashion. Then a cow began to bale as these beasts do when they have lost their calves. Next, quite close at hand but without the gates, there arose the ear-curdling cry of a woman in agony, which on the instant seemed to be echoed from every quarter, till the air was full of wailing.

"Oh, Seti! Seti!" exclaimed Merapi, in a voice that was rather a hiss than a whisper, "look at your son!"

We sprang to where the babe lay, and looked. He had awakened and was staring upward with wide-opened eyes and frozen face. The fear, if such it were, passed from his features, though still he stared. He rose to his little feet, always looking upwards. Then a smile came upon his face, a most beautiful smile; he stretched out his arms, as though to clasp one who bent down towards him, and fell backwards—quite dead.

Seti stood still as a statue; we all stood still, even Merapi. Then she bent down, and lifted the body of the boy.

"Now, my lord," she said, "there has fallen on you that sorrow which Jabez my uncle warned you would come, if ever you had aught to do with me. Now the curse of Israel has pierced my heart, and now our child, as Ki the evil prophesied, has grown too great for greetings, or even for farewells."

Thus she spoke in a cold and quiet voice, as one might speak of something long expected or foreseen, then made her reverence to the Prince, and departed, bearing the body of the child. Never, I think, did Merapi seem more beautiful to me than in this, her hour of bereavement, since now through her woman's loveliness shone out some shadow of the soul within. Indeed, such were her eyes and such her movements that well might it have been a spirit and not a woman who departed from us with that which had been her son.

16 The Flight from Egypt

Mrs. Edith Simon, who now lives in Scotland with her husband and children, approaches history with a fascinated curiosity. She is trying to discover and reveal the actual history behind the myth, to discover how history is made and how its image is distorted by the accounts left by those who participated in the events. There is, of course, validity in this for the historian and for the novelist attempting to create a story beyond the records of the time, but the drive for realism in an area of myth and faith can detract from story telling. However, in *The Chosen* Mrs. Simon has been able to visualize an entire area of biblical implication generally neglected—the impact of the Hebrew actions upon Egyptian society. She attempts to determine within the confines of fiction what the economic and social consequences of the loss of Hebrew labor meant to the Egyptians. And in the humorous passage that follows, she succeeds.

> *And it was told the king of Egypt that the people fled: and the heart of Pharaoh and of his servants was turned against the people, and they said, Why have we done this, that we have let Israel go from serving us?*
>
> *And he made ready his chariot, and took his people with him:*
>
> *And he took six hundred chosen chariots, and all the chariots of Egypt, and captains over every one of them.*
>
> EXODUS: XIV, 5–7

THE CHOSEN by EDITH SIMON

IT WAS NOT before noon that the Weset Temple was informed that the slaves were still fleeing, had passed the hill region and were marching towards the frontier in a straight line that denoted purpose. In the course of less than twenty hours they seemed to have put an uncommonly wide stretch between themselves and the army of the lords.

The new High Priest felt like shutting ears and eyes and going to sleep for a year or so. He dared not ask the questions that preyed on his mind, for certainty of what the answers would be. Yesterday, the day of his supreme triumph—to-day, promise of nothing, or rather, of chaos. Merenptah himself was no better off, it was true; but what good was that if Egypt herself was in the same position?

She was like a great big woman, this Egypt, fat, used to being fed and

139

tended every minute of the day, so flaccid and spreading and large that she could not take care of herself. Yet, if her voracity were not satisfied, the mighty giantess would fall to pieces, crumble to dust. The bed that she rested on had been withdrawn from beneath her colossal weight, so that she had crashed to the ground; a few inches only, but still there had been a crash that had resounded throughout the capital. Those who were to tend and feed her had deserted her; it was as though the roots of a tree had decided to set up business on their own, and walked away—just simply walked away. It was now not merely a matter of catching the roots and hauling them back where they belonged; the tree must continue to live meanwhile, must be tided over pending their return.

But Weset was not Egypt, thus the new High Priest tried to console himself. No? Had not Pithom and Mempi been cleared of brickmakers a week ago, in order to assemble in one centre possible carriers of the danger? Had not messengers reported this morning that the huge fields of the Crown around Weset, those fields only recently made ready for the impending flood, that this miles-wide area had been found to be deserted? Maybe Weset was not Egypt, but she certainly was her heart that kept the blood moving.

The new High Priest shook off his cowardice and called a council.

In the afternoon the messengers of the priesthood travelled far and wide, bearing reports. The first to be affected by the missives, those condemned to death, were lucky—all over Egypt they were no longer to be killed.

In Weset Harbour the great barges which had come to unload were still submerged to the very rim. The sailors themselves were being driven by the ships' masters to do the work, but it was very slow going. Meanwhile fruit and imported game had already begun to rot and sent up the stenches preliminary to disease. Bales of fine linen, unprotected by the customary sheets of sacking impregnated with fluids from the Valley, were being eaten from within their precious folds by all manner of beetles. The entire harbour was a slimy morass on account of the many catches of fish whose rancid bodies had been thrown back into the water. Water rats openly showed their heads in broad daylight. Melons and pumpkins, streaked with the first mildew, rocked in the now turbid bay.

The dockside granaries had been left open overnight, unguarded. Here and there sacks lay loose and emptied, a trail of glossy yellow grains gradually becoming lost in the dust. In a great warehouse which had belonged to the Crete Shipping Company and which was used for storing foreign wines, great puddles of sweet and oily liquid were gradually seeping into the floor of tread-hardened clay that was littered with broken fragments of wine vessels. The neat array of these thousands of vessels had been grossly disturbed; a certain amount of looting had already taken place. The police who were making a tour through the town found in a corner of the warehouse a drunken beggar who, awakened from his stupor, saw to his amazement that he was not going to be executed, but merely imprisoned together with other malefactors.

Furthermore, the huge, stone-reinforced barn of the royal treasury in which had been kept thousands and millions of strings beaded with dried fish had also been invaded, and already many of the harbour prostitutes were returning from the direction of the shopping district, laden with household goods. Rushing to the professional streets, the police found to their relief that the carpenters and potters and tailors were about to close up their shops, fearing a change of currency.

Clearing the procession streets and tortuous alleys of last night's corpses, the police also found that many a white house deplored the loss of water carriers, stable boys, drainage cleaners. Many policemen were impeded in the discharge of their duties by wild-eyed, fashionably-dressed young mothers with screaming babies held precariously in their arms. Nearly every wet-nurse had left Weset, except a few women who could not bear the thought of their charges' starving miserably to death. Most of the ladies and gentlemen had not washed this morning; and, although the citizens gladly missed the familiar sight of the malodorous scavengers, their own houses and grounds were not as sweet as they had been the day before. In a certain suburban market-place a casualty had drowned in the well. The well, too, was not sweet now.

In the fields the ploughs were idle and eerie against the pale horizon. Spades were flung down, crosswise, along the newly-dug channels awaiting the rains, the floods. Here and there a cow had strayed into the maize and was eating it. Of the scarecrows only central sticks, arms, and phalli were left; their ragged clothing had served many a brickmaker for travelling costume. The royal date plantation had been completely denuded of its fruit; here and there lay a rotten or half-eaten fruit testifying to the harvest having been truly ripe. In one of the great threshing clearings straw lay crushed as it had been left; the flails had gone, too. In one haystack a murdered overseer was found with his skull battered in. In the flax fields half a dozen overseers were walking lonely and dejected, looking at the sky, almost insane with worry. One field, bedecked with small and delicate green plants, was wilting under the burning rays of the sun; it bordered a steep stretch of river bank, and the wooden watering see-saw was resting, idle.

The great sand field over on the other side of the river was empty. The two hills of clay were neither shining nor slippery, their colour was dull and they had cracked across. The clay spread out in the centre was for the greater part moulded, but the bricks had not been fanned and were fast changing back into dust. No men, no women, and no children—nothing but a wide vast field of sand and mire. Part of the thorn hedge that led to the enclosure had been torn asunder and taken away as weapons.

Huts and dormitories lay deserted, except for a few sick and dying who crawled, groaned, and screeched at the visitors. The dung fires had gone out; as long as they had flamed, they had spread a semblance of cheer. Vultures were circling over the enclosure, and the flies were an impatient humming cloud, instead of resting and biding their time as was their wont. The architects' corner was desolate; pottery furnaces had grown cold and were surrounded by half-baked and spoiled vessels.

Even the Administration had lost more than half its staff. Overseers and policemen alike had ferried over to the other side, to see whether something might be done. The overseers were also reduced in number. In the unguarded Apis-stud an old bull had broken loose and was running wild, frightening and favoring the cows; he had already fatally gored one of his most promising young sons.

Wherever a new edifice had been begun, it was deserted, and the owner or builder was gazing at it stupefied, wandering about the excavations and scaffolding for hours at a stretch. The mill stones of Weset had stopped turning; to-morrow there would be no bread. All over the city cows were filling the air with agonized lowing; their udders were bursting and nobody milked them. In the great slaughter-houses attached to the cookshops and government dining-houses violet carcasses, ready quartered and disembowelled, were alive with maggots. The Great House itself had lost all its smaller fry, men, women, and children. One refuse carrier was left—he was old, limped, and did not hold with the modern drainage system. There were no cleaning-women and no water-carriers at all—except for two who were nursing scions of the nobility and consequent ambitions. Only the real and the false Head Cook were left—the noble eunuch who held the office, and the famous Assyrian who supervised the actual cooking. Of underlings there were none. In fact, there were almost only noble men and women left in the House of the God on Earth.

The God on Earth sent messenger after messenger to his Weset Temple. The messengers were the young Under Heralds, fresh recruits to the court from their terms at the Library. The proper messenger-heralds had all been armed and included in the now combined palace-and-temple guards. The young and noble erstwhile students breathed importantly, with a sensation of adventure, and were enjoying themselves. Marching with resounding steps in troops of five and six between Palace and Library and Temple, they frightened the artisans, who huddled for news in the square, with sinister, appraising glances.

The Temple and Library were being flooded with messages and messengers. Every official's house, every aristocratic villa sent its high-handed or despairing complaints. The administrations of every industry in Weset sent long and beautifully executed reports on the damage already suffered. The various ships' masters of the Crete and other Shipping Companies came in person, swaying on their stocky legs and cursing volubly. The stately and, for the greater part, ancient members of the Treasury were actually holding their meetings in the poetry class of the Library, since it was the most comfortable, and also since it had become necessary for them to be in uninterrupted contact with the priesthood. In the Music class, which was fairly empty, the Chief of Police set up his desk and secretariat and dealt out instructions to regional officers. In the Chief Magician's cosy study which the jovial old gentleman had vacated for his use, the Field Marshal of the Realm,

Pepi, sat hollow-eyed and twitch-lipped, working out strategical plans which he knew would come to nothing, for the frontier castles could not possibly be notified and fully garrisoned in time.

The overseers of the brickfields, their police colleagues, the stewards of the large estates, the managers of the banks and transport committees, the directors and foremen of the royal mills, the irrigation engineers, master masons, well-to-do private manufacturers, the supervisors of the river islands —all invaded the temple and library buildings, laying further disastrous information, seeking advice and practical help.

Every priest and every priestess was helping in the enormous task of hearing every visitor of import, and making notes of the more immediate matters. Every student, nobly-born or merely prosperous, had been excused his studies and detailed to look after the orderly queuing and comforts of visitors and applicants. Scribes so proud of their intricate art were degraded to painting rough and vulgar designs on the scrupulously white walls of the corridors so that aides-de-camp and messengers might find their way about.

The Master of Sacrifices, only recently appointed to the office, was in a lamentable fluster; for the first time in the Temple's history there was nothing to put on the altar of the God, and the Master of Sacrifices had had to solicit the Chief Magician's aid, so that in the meantime strangely coloured sticks and pills were burning at the foot of the God in ordinary braziers instead of on the burnished hearths which sent up deceptive savours of roasting meat.

Once more the will of the Great House and the will of the Temple were conflicting. Merenptah, in spite of the discomforts imposed on him and his court, was all for holding out until the runaway slaves were brought back again. The priesthood pointed out that the King's own thirst for vengeance would greatly diminish the ranks of the slaves; that, from whatever angle one regarded the matter, it would take time to vanquish them, bring them back all this way, and reorganize them in working bodies; meantime Weset and indeed Egypt would starve to death or, if not that, very shortly become so vulnerable as to be attacked, immediately they heard of it, by all her allies and colonies.

Aided by Sinuhethoth's loyal secretary and his own organizing and political gifts, the new High Priest faced the situation and got down to work. He dispatched armed platoons to every city and province who were to bring back, forcibly if need be, as many of the local serf population as could reasonably and at a stretch be spared. A qualified amnesty was immediately declared which spared every life, from beggarly thief to forger and murderer, would-be Khaemnas, blasphemer, traitor, or personal enemy of the monarch. Every person who repeated any of the rapidly rising legends in connection with the brickmakers and their leaders was, regardless of his rank or wealth, imprisoned, stored, and put to work forthwith.

The daily figure of executions was usually a very high one throughout Egypt. The first batch of criminals spared and stored overnight, as well as the numerous workless and disgruntled executioners, were set to work in the mills and slaughter-houses; the next batch had already been promised to the shipping contractors whose valuable freight was as good as ruined, and every man, woman or child arrested was straight away sent to the fields in an attempt to save something. Already the sudden and prolific advance-guard of informers promised a high tide of spying and denouncing. Quick to take notice, the new High Priest put a good price on Information Received. Gold and precious trinkets were flowing in plenty—and it would take time for it to get round that anyway you could not buy much these days. After one day's hunger, everyone in Weset discovered one or several enemies and consequent offenders against the law, only to deplore their rash action a few hours later when they found that they were richer only theoretically.

All the employees of the State were economically fed from the storage cellars of the Temple, Library, and Palace; but even these were limited, and haste was imperative.

The army in pursuit of the brickmakers received reinforcements and twice-daily messages to hurry. After the first surprise move on the part of the escaped slaves—it had been thought they would barricade themselves in the pass they had gained—it had been impossible to catch up with them, despite the fact that the slaves were encumbered by baggage, women, children, and invalids. True, of the invalids many were found dead or dying by the roadside, enabling the army to follow the track more easily. But it was found that the many chariots which the Temple authorities had generously allowed their army, impeded rather than speeded up their march. For the former brickmakers were taking the shortest road to the frontier, apparently not caring whether they went across hills, rocks, swamp or mud. Many a chariot was lost on such treacherous ground, and as it was impossible to keep the regiments in disciplined marching order; much valuable time was wasted in reassembling or punishing stragglers. Also, the commander had not reckoned with so long-drawn-out a campaign, had caused insufficient supplies to be taken along, so that several hours a day had to be employed in distracted and often unsuccessful search for food. Cultivated land was getting rarer, while there were no forests offering game. Whenever they had encountered ripened crops, the fugitives had taken the harvest along with them. Not a field-hand, not an overseer, was in sight anywhere. All the commander could do was to send emissaries ahead to warn the frontier castles, but it was doubtful whether even these practised spies would be able to overtake the brickmakers by now.

The Hebrews were complaining and almost rebelling, many of them demanding that they halt and wait for the pursuers to catch them up and make them prisoners. But so far they had not reached the stage of action, and although their pace was slowing down, they were still obeying orders and marching on. They had not enough to eat either, and their physical condition had never been any too good in the sand fields. To take their minds off their feet and stomachs they had begun to assert class differences, the field-irrigation serfs and cow-herds insulting the brickmakers, and the drain-cleaners of the city households despising all the rest, unconscious of the fact that in everybody's fancy, if not in reality, the odour of their occupation still clung to them.

The women, children, and invalids took turns on the few ox-carts requisitioned in the fields they passed. In general the women were hardier than the men, and less inclined to give up. Although knowing that most of them would be killed if caught, each of the men was secretly confident he would be one of the survivors, but the women, who did not fear rape, each knew in her heart that her man or son would be a victim.

After four days' almost continuous marching, they reached Lake Shuf which, as had been promised them, lay lopsided in the plain facing the fortresses. It was indeed a large lake, pleasing in appearance on account of its flourishing, high-grown reed. At first glance it seemed like a proper lake, despite the steepness and dryness of its banks. But when one looked more closely one could see the bottom through the hand's depth of murky water.

The lake was very large, and beyond its distant bank was the end of Egypt.

The women filled up their water bags, disregarding the water's greyish colour and stagnant smell; the children caught so many frogs as to make up between them three good-sized sacks, and then collected birds' eggs from those patches of undergrowth which only they could reach.

The Egyptian bank of Lake Shuf was suddenly black and crawling with people; the still air which was usually stirred by nothing under the baking heat except the vapours from the water and the wings and cries of the out-landish birds, resounded and trembled now with the onslaught of conflicting voices. Voices, voices, commands, cries, contradiction; bodies bent on a variety of busy tasks . . .

The nearest fortress sent over a deputation of Hittite mercenaries to see what so gigantic a party was doing there, and to ask for their passports. The deputation did not return. Shortly afterwards two watchmen hurried down from two separate turrets of the castle, each with his separate news: the gigantic company was beginning to cross the lake; a mist was appearing on the horizon, the rains were about to set in, to-morrow, or the day after, the rains were coming: send messengers to Egypt to announce to her approaching rebirth!

Two hours later arrived the first of the Temple guard's emissaries who had managed not to get lost on his round-about route. One hour after this the watchman of the second turret reappeared, reporting that already clouds had formed and were spreading out in their direction.

Half an hour later the fortress commander's arrangements had been made, and the tail end of the exhausted, terrified procession wading the lake observed that soldiers issued forth from the same fortress whose reconnoitring detachment had been so spontaneously killed and left in the rushes.

A quarter of an hour later darkness, whose approach had in the excitement been lost on everyone, fell with its customary suddenness, veiling both pursuers and pursued.

Their hands clasping the shoulders, girdles, skirts of those in front of them, the women in the rear-guard lost the last shred of their valiance and, their voices rusted with fright, wept. The first drops of rain began to fall, gradually increased in number and volume, and fast accumulated to a steady, hissing rush. The night, to the fleeing, was filling up with a consistent screen of sound which sheltered the possible noises of danger, as the darkness hid it from sight. Their feet, wet already, grew clammy as the rest of them became sodden. The chattering of their teeth provided an additional barrier against clear hearing, and they strained their ears while their unseeing eyes began to ache with the useless effort of screwing them up. Would the lake never end? Did it, perhaps, lie in wait for their blind feet with a sudden sheer drop of bottomless water? They were unable to take into account facts that should have soothed them.

One hour later the deputy commandant of the fortress ordered his men to abandon the pursuit and help extricate his three horses and chariot from the mud. It was not until next day that he was wholly informed as to what had been at stake that night.

17 Crossing the Red Sea

Probably no other biblical novelist has had the continuing popularity of Sholem Asch. Probably, too, no other novelist wrote as many biblical novels or brought a richer background of both religious training and creative fiction to the genre. Born in 1880 in the small Polish village of Kutno, Asch was educated in rabbinical theology before he set out for Warsaw at the age of 19. He started writing short stories and plays in Hebrew while still young, and arriving in the United States in 1914, he began to write in Yiddish. With the exception of *Mottke the Thief*, published in 1917, his major works did not appear until 1930. Though capable of writing in English, he continued to employ Yiddish throughout most of his career. After a series of books about his Jewish background, he turned to the biblical novel in 1939 with *The Nazarene*, following this with *The Apostle* in 1943 and *Mary* in 1949. He shifted his ground from the New Testament to the Old, issuing *Moses* in 1951 and *The Prophet* in 1955. His early biblical novels created a stir among the less tolerant of his co-religionists which did not subside until his death in 1958. Whatever the theological controversies which raged about Asch, they did not seem to damage the public acceptance of his work, though he felt called upon to write *What I Believe* in 1941. Simply written, theologically interesting, fictionally well-wrought, his novels have become the cornerstone of a reputation which awaits the full and just assessment which can only come with time.

And the Lord said unto Moses, Wherefore criest thou unto me?
speak unto the children of Israel, that they go forward:
But lift thou up thy rod, and stretch out thine hand over the sea,
and divide it: and the children of Israel shall go on dry ground through
the midst of the sea.

EXODUS: XIV, 15–16

MOSES by SHOLEM ASCH

WHEN THE ISRAELITES had drawn out of Goshen and were on the edge of the wilderness, Moses and Aaron proclaimed again, in the name of God, that the night of the liberation was to be kept as a memorial night by all the generations of Israel; and they repeated the manner of the observance of the festival, with the prescriptions for the slaying of the lamb, and the permission and prohibition as to who might eat of the sacrifice and who might not. And the festival was to be a rehearsal, every year in the years and generations to come, of the act of liberation.

Now it soon became apparent that to the hundreds of thousands of Hebrews who went up out of Egypt (the Egyptian chroniclers, writing under totalitarian pressure, avoided mentioning the exodus as a defeat of Pharaoh) many non-Hebrew slaves had joined themselves. They took advantage of the general panic and confusion to mingle with the Hebrews. Ethiopians, Canaanites, and other Asiatic peoples were among them. And the question arose immediately how they were to be regarded. Were they to be reckoned to the Hebrew people, or were they to be considered camp followers who had no share in the redemption and could not be included among the families of Israel in the celebration of the great festival? The question was placed before Moses, who issued a command in the name of God:

"He that went with us is of us. There shall be one law for the citizen and for the stranger who is in your midst."

Moses was clear in his own mind as to his plans and purposes. During the last warnings which he had issued to Pharaoh he had already revealed that he was not concerned with merely taking the Hebrews for a three-day journey into the wilderness: it was his intention to lead the Israelites out of bondage into the land which had been promised to their forefather Abraham. They would cross the desert and conquer the land. But the ultimate objective was a far higher one. The former slaves were not merely to be a people which conquered a land for itself: they were to be a holy people, a chosen people, a people which by its moral life should be an example to all the peoples of the world, the people of a law which in its justice should express the will of the one living God.

For the fulfillment of this higher purpose he had to bring this people to Sinai, where God had revealed Himself to him and had entrusted him with his mission. There they would receive and accept the laws and commandments of God. There they would be born again, born into the law of God and their new freedom. As the night of Passover had brought the liberation of their bodies, so Mount Sinai was to bring the liberation of the spirit.

If he was to re-educate the people from bondage to freedom, he could not lead it by the shortest route to Canaan, along the seacoast by way of the land of the Philistines. The Israelites had only just emerged from slavery; at the first clash with the Philistines they would turn tail and flee back to Egypt. They must first pass through the swamps of the Sea of Reeds, as he himself had done; they must enter the desert of Sin—only there would they be entirely freed from the Egyptian yoke—and pass into the peninsula and the mountains of Sinai, between the two arms, Suez and Akabah, of the Red Sea.

From his own experiences Moses knew how dangerous would be the passage through the Sea of Reeds, where the growths of hyssop and bamboo concealed innumerable treacherous depths of swamp into which men and cattle sank, never to be found again. He led the people lengthwise along the swamp to the oasis city of Succoth, not far from the earlier treasure city of Pithom, which the Hebrews had built for Pharaoh. He knew quite well that he was still within the shadow of the might of Pharaoh, whose armies could overtake him without difficulty. Only by a miracle of God could he lead this people with its herds in safety through the Sea of Reeds. How the miracle would come to pass he did not know; but he had faith that when the moment arrived, God would show him the way.

The Hebrews, or Israelites, as Moses called them, meanwhile had enough to eat. They baked in the hot sun the cakes of dough which their wives carried in wrappings. They had large supplies of oil, honey, and vegetables; there were also the cattle and fowl which they had brought out of Egypt. Well fed, still intoxicated with the triumph of Jehovah over the Egyptians, they did not perceive the threat which hung over them.

The immense mass of foot travelers, which, together with the cattle, followed Moses and the other guides, raised such a cloud of dust that by day they were concealed as by a curtain of smoke; and in the bright spring nights of the time of the liberation, the light of moon and stars playing on the dust cloud tinged it with red, so that it seemed that pillars of fire advanced before the people on its path.

Moses moved rapidly, urging the people on by night as well as by day, even though he did not know what point in the Sea of Reeds God had designated for their crossing.

The marchers were in high spirits, moving forward tirelessly. The cries of triumph, which kept breaking from the women, the laughing and crying of the children, the lowing of the cattle, the bleating of the sheep made the air quiver. There was as yet no order in the march, and the tribes were mingled with one another.

The third day after they had left Succoth, when they were at the entrance of the desert, where the foothills marked the approach to the sea, Moses received God's command to turn the march in the direction of Egypt, and to pause at the edge of the swampy passage of the Sea of Reeds, between a place called Migdal and the Sea of Reeds itself. They would again be not far removed from Succoth, and opposite Pithom, where the Sea of Reeds ended in the broad Bitter Lakes.

These lakes divided the territory of Egypt from the desert of Shur. The waters, though not altogether free from mud, were considerably clearer than those of the Sea of Reeds. Here it was impossible to advance by laying down rafts of bamboo and reeds. There was only one way of crossing, and that was in boats, as the Egyptian armies did.

The entire area, though it lay on the rim of the wilderness, was studded with garrisons. A caravan road passed near-by through the desert of Shur, linking Egypt with Canaan and Arabia. Here, too, the path lay—through the wilderness of Sin—to the port on the Red Sea, Ezion-geber.

Thus the march was an open challenge to the Egyptians. It was impossible not to mark the progress of the "runaway slaves," not to see their encampments along the foothills or the fires they kindled at night, not to hear the jubilant cries which floated from their midst.

The men slaughtered the fowl and roasted them on open fires; here and there several families assembled and roasted a sheep in a sand bed. The women put on the silk, embroidered garments, which they took out of their bundles, and adorned themselves in finery. With golden rings in their ears, with tiaras and chaplets on their heads, they paraded before the men.

One man in the host put on a pleated skirt, which he had pulled off an Egyptian god in the days of the darkness, donned a heavily curled wig with a mighty helm, which flashed in the sun, and, with rings on his fingers and a bamboo rod in his hand, played the role of "the friend of Pharaoh," of the governor of Rameses, or of the Egyptian high priest. Another had his portion of roast sheep served on a gold plate, while he reclined on an ivory-studded couch, which he dragged with him on his shoulders.

Besides the utensils and robes which they had "borrowed," many of the Hebrews had brought with them out of Egypt weapons of war, bows and arrows, spears, swords, copper-tipped lances, and copper armor. And they clothed themselves like soldiers and officers.

There were also in the camp of the Hebrews many trumpets, cymbals, and rams' horns. The blowing of the trumpets and rams' horns, the clashing of the cymbals, mingled with the throaty singing of the women, the shouting of the men, the laughter of the children, the crackling of the camp fires: and the tumult went up into the moonlit night, a jubilation of freedom, in the heart of Pharaoh's country, in the shadow of the pyramids and by the borders of the Red Sea.

Moses knew well that the liberation was not yet complete, that great trials still awaited him. God had told him that Pharaoh would set out in pursuit and God would let the Egyptian know that He was the Lord. But concerning the manner in which He would save the Israelites, and how He would lead them through the sea, God had told him nothing. Moses only believed that even as God had helped them till now and had revealed the might of His arm to the Egyptians, so He would help them when the next trial came; and he rested in his faith.

But it was not so with the other leaders of the Israelites, with Korah and his circle, with Dathan and Abiram. They went about in the midst of the pealing jubilation of the Israelites heavyhearted and with gloomy looks. After the wonders and miracles which God had performed through Moses, they had of course become believers in the liberation. They had also believed that after Pharaoh had liberated the Bnai Israel, Moses, with the help of God, would perform one more miracle and carry the people over the Sea of Reeds straight into the wilderness, before the three days of the intended festival had expired. But now three days had passed, and Moses had not carried the Israelites into the desert; and Korah, Dathan, and Abiram, together with their circle, trembled before the danger which now confronted them.

Korah called together his intimate followers for a conference. They consisted of leaders of the tribe of Levi and former slave overseers to whom Moses had left important functions in the congregation pending the time when he could reorganize the exodus. The former overseers were under the leadership of Dathan and Abiram, who also brought to the secret conference a few others of like mind with themselves. Here Korah put forward his own plan:

"Moses is wandering blindly in the wilderness. If he could not take us across the narrow swamp passage by Succoth, where the Sea of Reeds is at its narrowest and passage is easy, he will certainly not be able to take this immense multitude, with its possessions, its herds, and its flocks, across the wide stretches of the Bitter Lakes. Where will he get the ships for such an undertaking? Even if Pharaoh himself were to furnish him with ships, there are not enough of them in Egypt to transport this people across the water. The three days of the festival in the wilderness have passed, and Pharaoh must have realized by now that Moses has no intention of bringing the slaves back to Egypt. We may expect any moment to see Pharaoh's chariots in pursuit of us. We must be prepared for that. We must put the whole blame on Moses. We never thought of leaving Egypt. We only wanted to serve God in the wilderness, and it was our intention to return. Moses deceived us. He led us into the wilderness only that he might be able to become ruler over us. The danger is great. If God has not helped Moses till now, and has withdrawn from him, nothing is left to us but to return to Egypt. For Pharaoh will drive us all into the sea, if we do not betimes save as many of the people as we can."

Korah's followers were in accord with him. They knew the Egyptians, and they did not believe that Pharaoh was defeated yet; he was preparing an attack on the Israelites.

And it turned out as Korah had foretold. Despite all the wonders which Moses had wrought, despite all the calamities which had been visited upon the Egyptians, Pharaoh clung to the belief that the power of Moses was temporary and limited, entrusted to him by a god with a temporary and limited rule—not a god of eternal rule; a god, in fact, resembling the Aton whom Amenhotep the Fourth had for a time installed in Egypt. Like Aton, this god could also overcome the gods of Egypt, but for a short time only. Indeed, it was possible that the Jehovah of the Hebrews was none other than Aton, who had returned under another name, this time to make war not on the gods of Egypt, but on the Egyptians themselves, whom he had exchanged in favor of a slave people. If this was so, there was nothing to fear. Just as the gods of Egypt, soon after Amenhotep's death, had conquered his god and driven him from Egypt, so they would conquer him again in his new form.

The heavy blow he had suffered with the death of his beloved son had for an instant so shattered Menephthah that he had let the Hebrews go. When he recovered, he repented of his weakness; he repented of the momentary fear which had overcome him that his gods had by now been decisively defeated by an alien god, that the entire kingdom of Egypt, built on the power of Ra, was in danger of dissolution.

He sent out spies to discover the intentions of the Hebrews. Would they indeed return after their three-day festival, as they had originally said they would? Or would Moses lead them across the narrow passage into the desert? And if Moses planned to lead them through the ring of waters which surrounded Egypt, how would he do it? There was but one way: his God would have to send down His heavenly hosts in the form of mighty eagles, with wings strong enough to lift and carry the immense multitude across the swamps. Other means were out of the question; there were not even ships enough for the task.

But when the miracle held off, when hosts of eagles failed to descend from the heavens, and Moses led the fugitive slaves back and forth along the stretch of the Sea of Reeds between the narrow passage and the Bitter Lakes, without finding a ford, Pharaoh saw the triumph of Ra over Aton, as in the days of Tutankhamen.

Swiftly Pharaoh called a council of "the friends of Pharaoh," the fan-bearers, the high priest, the governor of Rameses, the commander of the chariot brigades, and held forth to them:

"Jehovah, the God of Moses, is none other than the god Aton, the foe of the Egyptian gods, whom Amenhotep the Fourth—may his name be obliterated till the end of time—sought to impose on Egypt. Jehovah-Aton tolerates no gods beside Him. It is true that He was able for a time to overcome the gods of Egypt and to smite the Egyptians with plagues; He was able to desolate their temples, slay the priests, and destroy the images of the gods; but He showed himself to be powerless when Ra arose in the incarnation of Pharaoh Tutankhamen and swept Him out of Egypt, desolated *His* city and temples, destroyed *His* images, and forbade the mention of His name. Jehovah, like Aton, is a god of devastation, not a god of blessings who can help His followers. This is now evident to all who have eyes. He cast terror upon us with His plague visitations so that we hastened to liberate the Hebrew slaves. But He is impotent to save them from our hand. They wander back and forth in confusion. The desert is sealed to them. Jehovah cannot lead them to the other side of the Sea of Reeds. The gods of Egypt have delivered them up to us. Assemble the chariots," said Pharaoh, turning to the commander of the chariot brigades, "and set out in swiftest pursuit. Thou wilt find them, terrified, desolate, and confused, on the shore of the Sea of Reeds. Drive them into the swamps, and let the name of Aton-Jehovah be wiped out forever."

"Son of Ra in his own flesh!" cried the high priest. "Thou wilt hence-forth be likened to Tutankhamen, the avenger of the gods of Egypt!"

"Thou avenger of the gods of Egypt!" exclaimed the governor of Rameses. "Thy victories over thy foes, the Hebrews, will be inscribed to thy eternal glory on the walls of thy pyramids!"

And the commander of the chariot brigades cried: "Thou, Pharaoh, art our power and our glory, and victory is thine! When thou wilt ride forth in thy golden chariot at the head of thy hosts, Ra the god in his own body will set out in his sun splendor, to slay with the rays, which are his spears, his enemies among the gods. Thy charioteers long for thee. They call to thee. Sun of Egypt, lead us!"

"Thou speakest well. I, even I, Ra the god in his own flesh, will lead you into battle against my enemy, Aton-Jehovah. Let my chariot be harnessed."

Clad in the double helmet crown, Pharaoh Menephthah stood upright, for all his years, in the chariot which was to lead the Egyptian hosts against the Hebrew slaves. Four white horses in golden harness tugged at the reins, their hoofs drumming impatiently on the ground. The golden shield which his armor-bearer carried before him blazed like white fire in the sun. With his right arm stretching the bow which he held uplifted in his left, he received the benedictions of his people and the salute of his warriors for the deeds he was about to perform against the god Aton, who had become the god of the Hebrews. Blind temple slaves knelt before him and sang to the accompaniment of harps:

"Thou art like Ra in all that thou dost.
All things happen according to thy heart's desires.
We have seen many of thy wonders
Since thou wert crowned king of the two lands.
When thou commandest, the waters cover the mountains,
The sea hears thee forthwith;
In thy loins is Ra,
Thy creator dwells in thee."

Scribes with styluses and rolls of papyrus knelt in rows and recorded for the generations to be the manner of Pharaoh's departure to do battle with the god of the Bnai Israel.

But of course the departure of Pharaoh at the head of the hosts was only a ceremonial pretense. He was too old and too weak to lead the troops in battle; moreover, it was not the custom for a Pharaoh to take part in an action on the field. No sooner had the chariots reached the desert beyond the city when Pharaoh returned to the palace. His place was taken by one of "the friends of Pharaoh," to whom were henceforth addressed all the panegyrics and prayers intended for the king; and the victories of the substitute were to be ascribed by all the chroniclers to Pharaoh himself.

As far as the eye could see stretched the rows of chariots. The bowmen who drove them burned with eagerness to avenge the name of Egypt; the horses, filled with the fury of battle, flew over the level sands of the desert. At the head rode the surrogate Pharaoh. Clouds of dust rose from the hoofs and wheels, curling like crimson smoke to the heavens and eclipsing the light of the sun. And the host sped irresistibly toward Baal-zephon, where they knew the Hebrew slaves were looking helplessly for a crossing.

On the second day, toward evening, the Israelites descried the clouds of dust rising like fire smoke in the desert. The clouds drew ever nearer, and the Israelites knew that these were Pharaoh's chariots in pursuit. In an instant the encampment was in an uproar. They became like a huge flock of sheep which has suddenly caught the scent of a wolf. They abandoned the possessions to which they had clung so fiercely and began to run. Mothers ran, holding their little ones by the hand, or in their arms. Whither they were running they did not know; and in the confusion of their flight they only drew closer together, so that the center of the encampment became a dense, boiling mass; and men and women pushed against each other and remained locked in one place. A wild cry went up from the encampment, and hands were uplifted:

"God of Israel, help us! God of Israel!"

Moses was in the midst of the camp. He was calm and confident. He knew that the Egyptians would come in pursuit, as God had told him; and he also knew that God would show the Egyptians that He was the Lord. Great indeed was the danger to the Israelites, trapped between the Egyptians and the sea; but though God had not disclosed to him the manner of the rescue, he awaited it with certainty. Had not God shown wonders enough in Egypt?

And the confidence which Moses felt became all the stronger when he heard Bnai Israel, the slaves whom he had led out of Egypt, calling upon Jehovah. At any moment now, before the Egyptians reached the encampment, help would come.

But as he stood thus, and before he had opened his lips to pacify and reassure the masses, he found himself encircled by the Bnai Levi. Their hands were stretched out toward him, their eyes blazed vengeance.

"Did we not know what the end of this would be!" screamed Dathan, his voice carrying through half the camp. "Were there not graves enough in Egypt that thou broughtest us here, to perish in the wilderness?"

But Korah's calm, powerful voice carried even further:

"This is what we always said to him in Egypt. 'Let us serve the Egyptians!' Is it not better to serve the Egyptians than to perish in the desert?"

The words "perish in the wilderness" fell like poison into the ears of the people. The panic intensified, and now a wailing arose, the wailing of beaten slave hordes:

"What hast thou done to us? Why didst thou bring us out of Egypt?"

The danger which Moses now feared was not the approach of the Egyptians, but something more deadly—the work of Korah, Dathan, and Abiram. It was they who threatened to undo all his work. He could see the Bnai Israel turning in an instant, streaming toward the Egyptians, imploring them to take them back as slaves. And now Moses did something he had not dare to do hitherto. He took upon himself the responsibility of Jehovah, even before he had received a command, before he knew how God intended to deal with the Bnai Israel or the Egyptians.

With two powerful arms he flung aside Korah and his aids and thrust his way into the center of the wailing camp. Towering head and shoulders above the mass, he called out in a voice which rang with confidence and power:

"Fear not! You will yet see the help which Jehovah will bring you this day. Even as you see the Egyptians this day, so you shall never see them again. The Lord will do battle for you today. Be silent and wait!"

It was Moses who spoke! Moses, who knew the will of God! He spoke in the name of God! And though the Egyptians hosts drew nearer, and the thunder of hoofs and chariot wheels was clearly audible, the Israelites became calm.

Jehovah would do battle for them. Moses had spoken in his name.

Only when calm had been restored did Moses withdraw from the camp. He went to the edge of the sea, threw himself on his knees before the swelling waters, and lifted his mighty voice:

"Lord God! Lord God! Look upon our need. I have spoken in Thy name. In Thy name I reassured them. Lord God, tell me what to do."

And this time he heard a voice, not in his heart, as hitherto, but sounding in his ear: the voice of God, which he knew so well:

"Why criest thou unto Me? Tell the Bnai Israel to go forward!"

Then, after an interval, the voice spoke again:

"And thou, lift up the staff which is in thy hand upon the waters, and divide them, and the Bnai Israel shall enter into the dryness in the midst of the sea. And I will harden the hearts of the Egyptians, and they will follow after the Bnai Israel. And I will be glorified through Pharaoh and through all his hosts, his chariots, and his horsemen. And the Egyptians will know that I am the Lord."

Like a flash the unrevealed intent, which lay in the words of Jehovah, was made clear to the eager perception of Moses. First God had commanded him to bid the Bnai Israel advance; then afterward He had told him to lift up his staff upon the waters. It was God's will that the Israelites should advance into the sea before it had been split. It was God's desire that thereby the Israelites should show their faith in Him. It was His desire that the Israelites should thereby contribute their portion to the redemption and liberation, demonstrating that they were now the sons of freedom, ready to plunge into the sea for Him. And Moses kept the thing in his heart.

Meanwhile, the clouds of dust had drawn still nearer, the galloping of hoofs, the thunder of wheels, came still more clearly. In another instant the clouds would open and disclose the Egyptians. But the clouds did not open. On the contrary, they became thicker and heavier; they accumulated in smoking folds, and remained hanging, a pall of ever-increasing darkness, between the Israelites and the Egyptians. It was as if an angel of the Lord had erected a terrifying wall of smoke between the encampment and the army.

Pharaoh could no longer see the encampment. He issued the command to dismount for the night.

But no darkness fell on the encampment of the Israelites. There the stars shone with a radiance which filled heaven and earth with brightness.

Now Moses did as God had commanded and lifted up his staff upon the sea.

Suddenly a mighty east wind began to blow and to drive the waters together. Like a pack of wild dogs let loose on a flock of sheep, the winds snapped and hissed and howled at the scurrying waves; and as the waters fled, terrified and foaming, before the onslaught, they gradually divided and began to rear themselves in two towering walls to right and left. It seemed as though, under the fierce pressure of the rushing air, the water had become thick and viscous; and between the two walls there was a flatness. But the flatness was not yet that of dry land; it was a flatness of water still deep enough to engulf human beings.

So the waters remained almost throughout the night. The children of Israel gazed with awe on the gigantic spectacle, and they were aware beyond all shadow of a doubt that something miraculous was taking place. But as yet it did not spell their rescue. Moses, whose custom it was to lead the host like a pillar of fire, did not advance as yet into the water. He was waiting for something.

Moses was indeed waiting for something. He was waiting for another miracle; he was waiting for their life to be divided as the waters were divided; he was waiting for the great division between slavery and freedom. He did not advance before the children of Israel because he wanted them to obey blindly the will of God and enter the waters before these had been wholly divided. He issued the command which God had instructed him to issue. He bade them march forward into the deep swamp between the walls of water, and he stationed himself on the edge to mark how the children of Israel obeyed the command of God.

Here and there one moved forward; but no sooner had he sunk in as far as the knee than he turned and fled back. And Moses waited obstinately, and his thoughts were sharp and hard: "Are they worthy of the miracle? If they do not go in, they are slaves, and they will not be redeemed." And the people too were thinking, thinking wildly and wondering. Something marvelous was happening before their eyes, and yet their rescue was not at hand. Men pushed their neighbors forward, and themselves remained where they were. The people began to be afraid. The night was passing, and in the morning Pharaoh would discover them. And Moses stood there like a pillar of marble, his mighty head uplifted to heaven, his face steeped in moonlight. His lips moved, and prayer welled up in his heart:

"O God, work thy miracle with Israel!"

And then it happened. A man sprang forward from the host, pulling his wife and child with him. He came to the water's edge and cried out:

"Sons of Israel! Show now that you are sons of freedom, and that you are worthy of the redemption. Come! Let us go forward into the sea to meet the God of Israel!"

He advanced. The water rose to his knees. He still advanced. A wave rolled toward him, washed over his thighs; still he advanced, leading wife and child by the hands.

Then a second followed; then ten more; then hundreds. . . . No, they were no longer blind cattle, driven forward by terror. They were freemen, advancing of their own accord and will. Their bundles on their shoulders, their little ones in their arms, they plunged forward into the water. And now the whole sea front was in motion: flocks and herds and human beings. A sound of singing went up, and jubilant cries: "God of Israel!" The first man was up to his breast in the water. He did not pause. He had snatched the little one on to his shoulders, and he still advanced. His wife followed, a bundle on her back. They advanced and the host followed.

The water came up to their throats, up to their lips. And then it happened.

The sea trembled from end to end, as though a mountain had burst in its midst. The two walls of water moved away from each other, and between them a flat, hard path lay, dry and firm. The water retained its own nature, even though it was piled in walls; the children of Israel could see the fish swimming in it. And the earth under their feet had the nature of earth, with the worms and grasses which grow on the earth. For the remainder of the night they marched along the dry pathway, with their children, their possessions, and their cattle. Moses stood at the water's edge, his staff in his hand; at his side stood the youth Joshua, his chosen servant. And only when the last of the host had entered did Moses and Joshua leave the soil of Egypt and follow after.

The morning star had risen, and now began to pale. The dust cloud which had settled like a pall over the Egyptians dissolved, and Pharaoh beheld the children of Israel not as he had expected, wallowing in the waves, but marching on a dry path in the heart of the sea, with a wall of water on either side.

To the surrogate Pharaoh who led the Egyptians only one interpretation of the event was possible. This was Ra, intervening for his hosts, and creating a dry path in the midst of the swampy sea, so that they might ride down the enemy. Indeed, was not Ra now emerging in the heavens, to give them the signal?

"After me! See! Ra has dried the deeps for us! He commanded the waters and they made a path for us, that we may overtake his enemies."

Cries broke from the ranks:

"Ra! Thou has commanded the sea to divide! Ra in his own flesh!"

"Ra goes before us in his heavenly chariot!"

"After me!"

And Pharaoh, at the head of the host, galloped into the waters and the hosts of chariots followed.

This time Moses had believed that when the Egyptians beheld the miracle of the divided sea, they would be terrified, just as Pharaoh had been terrified momentarily by the slaying of the first-born and had let the children of Israel go. But, now bringing up the rear of the advancing Israelites, he turned and saw the Egyptians, blind with hatred and lust of revenge, rushing forward into the heart of the sea. The horses, refreshed by a night's rest, shot fire and foam from their nostrils. The faces of the horsemen and charioteers were like torches. Already the bowmen had stretched their weapons and were pointing the arrows at the backs of the Israelites.

And Moses, whose heart was filled with God, heard the voice once more:

"Stretch out thy hand upon the sea, that the waters may come back on the Egyptians, upon their chariots and their horsemen."

And Moses stretched out his hand upon the sea.

But the walls did not collapse on the Egyptians, as Moses expected. They began to melt. It was like the thawing of a winter sea. Gusts of water fell here and there, flooding the pathway which had been dry a moment before. A thick mud spread under the wheels of the chariots, which began to sink. The horses reared and pulled, lifting their hoofs with difficulty out of the slime. The Egyptians were now in the heart of the sea, sunk in mud, trapped between walls of water, which would soon swallow them up.

"No, Pharaoh, this is not the god Aton against whom thou leadest us to do battle! Thou has deceived us! This is Jehovah, the God of Israel, who fights against us here, as he fought against us in Egypt!"

"It is Jehovah, not Aton! Back! Let us flee!"

These were the last words heard from the Egyptians before the walls collapsed and overwhelmed them.

When Moses issued, the last of the Israelites, on the farther shore, he flung himself on his knees and sang a song of praise to Jehovah:

> *"The Lord is man of war,*
> *The Lord is His name!*
> *Pharaoh's chariots and his host has He cast into the sea,*
> *And his chosen captains*
> *Are sunk in the Sea of Reeds."*

Later tradition added that when Moses sang his song of triumph and praise to the Lord, it was taken up not only by the host which had witnessed the miracle, but by the unborn children in the bodies of their mothers. But when the heavenly hosts, too, began to sing the song of triumph, God turned to them, saying:

"My people, the creation of My hands, are drowning in the waters, and you sing songs of praise to Me?"

The angels stopped singing, and in that same instant Moses broke off his song and did not end it.

18 The Ten Commandments

In all of American letters, there have been few more prolific men than Louis Untermeyer. Poet, novelist, editor, historian, translator, biographer and critic, Untermeyer boasts of being one of the least educated writers in the country. However, more persons have learned more about contemporary poetry from his critical anthologies than from any other source. Beginning with a desire to become a composer and pianist, he abandoned a possible musical career while still young to enter his father's jewelry business, which he in turn abandoned at the age of thirty-eight to devote himself to literature. In 1928 he published his first novel, *Moses,* which he insists is miscalled a novel. He himself believes it to be "a combination of historical reconstruction and poetic fantasia full of speculations." In an attempt to explain away the miraculous in terms of modern realism, he is aware that his book "caused much controversy among the literalists." *Moses* is part of the search which took place in the Twenties for a "rational" explanation that would replace faith.

And Moses turned, and went down from the mount, and the two tables of the testimony were in his hand: the tables were written on both their sides; on the one side and on the other were they written.
EXODUS: XXXII, 15

MOSES by LOUIS UNTERMEYER

THE PEOPLE HAD sanctified themselves, had prayed aloud to Jahveh and offered up sundry private oblations to older and more obscure gods. But they were not at ease. Moses was leaving them for the first time, no one could say for how long. Nor could any one say why. One tale-bearer had it that Moses had quarreled with Aaron and was going into voluntary exile. The women were certain that relations between Miriam and Zipporah were at the bottom of it and that Moses was only doing what every man would do under the circumstances. A more persistent rumor spread that Moses was ascending Sinai to commune with his mysterious God who spoke in words of fire and syllables of thunder. The mountain itself began to take on deific and forbidding outlines. Men swore they heard rumblings in its bowels; children who had scrambled confidently over its knees were forbidden to approach it. It might be the hill of God, but the legends that grew about it were fearful and unholy.

It was the morning of departure. A glistening wind polished the slope until the rocks were root-white. Two trumpets, at opposite corners, blew rings of fine copper. The people came to the mountain, though no man would go nearer than the border of coarse grass. Only Aaron, his sons, Nadab and Abihu, and a few of the elders advanced further than the invisible boundary. The multitude saw Moses make the sign of benediction, saw him ascend into a sky that was like a sapphire laid open.

It was no easy jaunt. Unburdened though he was, for Moses had resolved to fast until illumination entered him, there was contest for every step. The air took on weight, pushing against him. Vine-snares ran out from nowhere, tripping his feet. The sun laid hot hands upon his shoulders. He straightened them and went on. No flocks went with him now, not even a bird. But he was not alone.

He continued reasoning with himself.

"Are they less worthy than the Hittites, the Phoenicians, the Chaldeans?"

"Not less worthy, but more rebellious."

"Am I not, also, a rebel? Am I, therefore, less zealous? If I can keep a promise to myself, can they not keep a covenant?"

"They are not like others. They are a peculiar race."

"For that reason they are a peculiar treasure. They can be a light, not only to themselves. A beacon. A burning bush. A pillar of fire."

What way there was, stopped. Now it was wall and crevice, fissure so smooth that no grass could find roothold. Moses was forced back, found another opening, a gallery piercing the first hump, arranged in rugged and uneven steps. These served him another two hundred feet. He looked down. The plain was a grizzled map, splotched and creased; the towering cypress beside his tent was a round blot, black as sediment of ink. Nothing to look back for. Up. Up. He pushed on. Sometimes he crawled over time-cracked slabs, kneeing his way up; sometimes he took the wiry hands of shrubs and let them pull him over.

At noon, he discovered a thin waterfall and drank of it, listening to its clear nonsense. Two hours later, he watched a small cloud and an eagle mock each other.

"Eternal circling," said Moses. "Is there no altitude where it must cease? Water twisting over the earth. Air winding about the sky. Stars weaving among each other. Space curving to some orbit never to be seen. And all these threaded through the mind of man that contains all and can hold nothing. Order out of chaos. Order everywhere except in his disordered heart."

One more peak. He began the last climb at dusk, working through the sea of granite that was like nothing so much as petrified waves. Night came on as he stood beside the cleft which was the final reach of stone. The summit.

The summit. Stars were close here. The great red planet overhead, the cold blue one pointing the horizon, called him further. They did not hang idly, but burned under the same mandate as the sun. "The law that binds these stars," thought Moses, "that brings Arcturus and the first green blade out, each in his season, is kept in splendor and authority. I must tap that source. The law—"

But he was too tired. It had been a steep ascent. "The law," he murmured, and fell asleep.

The mountains, says Nath, fought with Jahveh for the honor of housing Moses on his pilgrimage. Each claimed to be the only one worthy to receive the visit of Jahveh and his emissary on earth.

"I," said the mountain Tabor, "am above them all. I am the cushion on which Jahveh rests his elbow when he falls asleep; I have caught the tails of comets in my ravines. I am so tall that when all the mountains of earth lay drowned in the flood, the waters did not even reach my ankle. I am the proper stature. Let me bear the prophet."

"I," said the mountain Ararat, "may not be as high as Tabor, but I am holier. It was on me that the ark rested after water had poured one hundred and fifty days from the windows of heaven. I took to my bosom what was left of the human race; I gave them seed for harvest and grapes for a vineyard. Therefore, since I saved his ancestors, let me bear the prophet."

"I," said the height called Migdol, "saved Moses himself and all the multitudes that are with him. Was it not I who hid him in my folds so skillfully that the Egyptians could not find him? When he wished to cross through the sea, was it not I who crouched down and let his people walk over me so that not even their shoes were wet? As I bore them once without complaint, let me bear the prophet again."

"I," said Carmel, "am royal. Kings have made their sanctuaries upon me, temples have been laid at my feet. The other mountains are barren, but I am always blossoming. In spring I go in sprout-green, while the little hills about me skip like lambs. In summer I am crowned and girdled in majesty. Even in winter, I do not put off my color, but crown myself, sitting in stiff and purple clothes. I, alone, can give Jahveh his rightful setting. Let me bear the prophet."

But Jahveh said, "No. The glory of Jahveh will not rest upon proud mountains, nor on hills that dispute because of their eminence. Rather will I choose a lowly mount for one who is meek. I will choose one that has not vaunted or justified itself, even as my chosen servant is silent when others belittle him." So Jahveh gave the word to his angels and Sinai, the most insignificant mountain of earth, was lifted up until it overtopped the others. And it was on Sinai that Jahveh spoke to Moses.

When the world heard the Divine Voice that had not sounded on earth since Abraham, it gave up its dead in a prolonged convulsion. Out of every grave, the souls hurried to Sinai, and from the womb of heaven unborn seers and prophets came to hear revelation. Clouds, blacker than trench-beetles, surrounded the mountain which was miraculously enlarged to accommodate Jahveh and his four hundred thousand angels. As Sinai rose, the heavens descended and, when the two met, a wall of lightnings stood between them and the rest of creation.

The mouth of a cloud opened and shut like a door as Moses walked through. But, although the light was more blinding than the sun reflecting it-

self, it was not due to the presence of Jahveh. It was only the angel Hadarniel and his cohorts, whose bodies are a screen between Jahveh and his universe, a living curtain interposed to preserve men from being shriveled by the direct gaze. When Hadarniel spoke, his words played about the sky in letters of flame; the bodies of his daemons, having absorbed so much of the dazzled atmosphere, were solid light.

Then was heard the voice that tore the elements apart, that entangled water, air and earth before the First Day. But though the mountains pitched like small boats and the air was shaken out like a tent-flap, it was not Jahveh. It was only Kemuel, the porter of the firmament, and his genii of destruction. When Kemuel smiled, two bands of thunder bracketed his mouth; when he laughed, eagles fell from their eyries. He let down a rainbow and Moses crossed upon it.

Here was Sandalphon with his seraphs, gathering the prayers of men and binding them into garlands for the Lord. Sandalphon never knows where Jahveh may be laboring, but he breathes upon each garland which, crying "Holy, holy holy!" rises through space by its own longing until it rests on the brow of the Almighty.

Then Moses felt such heat as first held the fluid universe in a womb of fire. It was not Jahveh but the river Rigyon which follows the Lord and curls about his feet. It is the burning stream of purification in which the angels baptize themselves daily before entering the presence of Jahveh. The river is generated in front of the Throne and is continually renewed by the awe of the holy Hayyot whose perspiration falls in drops of liquid fire. No mortal but one could set foot on those steaming waves.

So when Moses had crossed Rigyon, as had been foretold, and beheld Gallizur whose name is sometimes Raziel, he knew he was near the Source. For it is Gallizur who is the spirit of Order. He arrests the ecstasy of the Hayyot which would otherwise consume the world. He restrains the stars that long to rush back to the divine bosom. He controls the seasons that would empty all their treasures in one lavish hour. He makes a cycle of life and death so that neither has an end and each flows into the other.

Finally there was a blast of diamond-flashing light and Moses beheld the Throne. It was a double dais. On the right sat Jahveh, an infinite transparence, a multitudinous Being whose every facet was promise. On the left sat the Law, exquisitely perfect, clothed in the virgin garments of Truth. And, while the angels held a new day like a canopy above them, Jahveh gave the Law to Moses.

It was the end of his vigil, an end of gathering clouds. The physical man remained on his rock; another self moved freely in an atmosphere more rarified than air on mountaintops. Sense was lost in spirit. Moses no longer saw the stars crowding above him nor the Israelites spread out below. Nothing was visible except his thoughts and these moved in luminous, almost palpable, shapes.

"You have been enslaved," said one of these ideas, "by a sense of time, by the false magic of the tongue, by the lust of the eye. There must be no more idols, neither of flesh nor of stone."

"No more idols," echoed a companion thought, "and no more theft. Do the stars steal from each other to increase their glory? Does one day rob the next one of light? What did you want with the gold of the Egyptians? What led you to their possessions?"

"Covetousness," cried a shape gray as sorrow. "How can God enter when he is shut out by greed? What do you crave beyond his prodigal gifts? Is there not abundance and to spare? Must women dishonor their fathers, must men bear false witness and kill to possess what is thrown away as soon as won?"

"Uncertain hearts, uncertain hands," answered another thought. "Therefore they labor and know not when to rest. Therefore they work hardest to preserve what crumbles first, to capture in many shapes what never can be given form."

"Glory in the least and Order in the highest," sang a new radiance. "There is no other god. The chart of the sun's path or a leaf's progress is drawn by the same hand."

The sky was black now, but Moses saw only layer upon layer of light. The uncovered universe bared its secrets until all space and energy were one. Everything fitted into perfect place. Balance revealed itself everywhere. Pattern within intricate pattern, and nothing interfered with the myriad interwoven cycles. The field was strewn with stars no less than the sky; the structure of an insect was as precise as the shape of a planet; the rainbows crumbled in a sunset and were repeated in a feather. Symmetry was the essence of God; Order his first command. He was obeyed even in the heart of turbulence. The tides might threaten to overwhelm the land, but they were drawn back with a calm relentlessness. Winter might bury the earth, but earth survived. Nothing encroached beyond its season. Nothing broke through the plan which evolved it. Nothing disturbed endless unfolding of endless designs. The elements did not conspire against each other, but penetrated space with harmony . . .

Harmony. Balance and counterbalance. Rhythm, matched to a just measure. Paradox of fulfillment: form moving against and blending with form. Life pitted against death, death regenerating life. Harmony in the least. Benign and imperishable Order. Discipline guiding the stars, holding the worlds in an atom. Over and under, entering everywhere, contradicting nothing, resolving opposition into one expanding whole. Union of law and lawlessness. Unity. Infinite Form, protective and precise. The Law.

Illumination beat upon Moses now, though heaven was black. There were no more questions, only answers widening his sky.

"I have it," cried Moses. "I must bring it to them before it escapes."

Flat chippings of slate were all about him. He picked up one, thin and square as a tablet. Finding a pointed stone, he began to scratch the surface. Automatically, the letters shaped themselves, covering both sides. But the testimony was not complete. The vision was beginning to fade. Hurriedly another slab was incised and covered with square characters.

He began to descend. The voice stayed with him, calling from rock to rock; the flashes increased, showing him new channels through gulfs of stone. Moses descended, wrapped in his vision, oblivious to thunder and lightning.

It was the storm that undid the Israelites. Day after nervous day had passed, and still no word of Moses. Not a sign of his return, not a flare to show he was still there, not even a torch to say he had reached the top. "The wild animals of the desert followed him," said some. "Sinai is pitted with bear-caves," said others. "One scorpion in his path would be enough," said the followers of Korah.

But no one would believe what he said. It was the unspoken terror that troubled them most. It was the mountain. Each day it grew more sinister, more monstrous in its inflamed bulk, more evil in its silence: "Even the birds would avoid it now," said the people; "they are too wise to trust themselves to its shadow." They knew Moses had not been devoured by beasts, for nothing could live, they told each other, in the Mountain of Death. They waited fearfully for the outcome.

It came in thick clouds, gashed with lightning. Oven-black thunder poured from every hole in the mountain. The crannies belched and the smoke (according to Nath) was as the smoke of a furnace. The earth shook and the people abandoned hope.

"Moses has offended the gods of the mountain," they cried in panic. "The spirits of Sinai have seized his nameless God and have slain Moses for his impious words. We are all dead men."

Korah and Abiram gave them hope. "We are not lost yet. There is still a way. Let us disavow Moses and his offense, and placate the gods of the peninsula. Let us sacrifice to the forces of evil that control this world. Let us pay homage to Milcom and Chemosh and Dagon, and we will be spared."

Eager to propitiate the destructive powers at any cost, they tore off earrings and amulets, and rushed to Aaron.

"Here," they cried. "Make us a god that we can see. Moses is dead and his God has perished with him. Be our leader. Give us a god that will be before us, near at hand; one we can understand."

Aaron tried to argue with them, but they were beyond persuasion. They urged, "If you will not help us, you are against us. We will find a leader elsewhere—and we know where to look."

Aaron perceived the hand of Korah, though the man himself was not visible. Would Moses never come? Must he humor this frightened mob? If Moses failed to return, could he—?

"You are children," he temporized. "How can I make a god?"

"With this—" "And this—" "And these." Ear-rings, bracelets, amulets, spoils of the Amalekites, Egyptian silver, metal of every kind was pressed upon him. "And here is Thamri. He helped with the bronze bull at Memphis. Let him make a smaller one for us, and let him plate it with gold."

"But Moses—" persisted Aaron, weakening.

"Will you hold us off until death takes us?" they shouted. "Prepare an altar; sanctify the ground; make proclamation. Erect the god from our sacrifice and let us worship as we did before this man Moses came among us. We go to find wood. Thamri will smelt the gold. Be ready when we return."

As Moses reached the half-way plateau, the storm ended; its last echo was the waterfall with its bolt of silver. Night had gone. Ghosts of dawn wavered along the ridge; below was hollow darkness. Suddenly, the plain was agitated with blowing sparks. Torches, thought Moses, and listened for the drums of attack. A sound reached him, but it was not the voice of mastery nor the crying of the overcome. All he could hear were torn strands of a song. His gaze traced a circular movement in the confusion of lights. He hurried down.

Still at one with his vision, his eyes refused to accept the scene. The details were definite, but they could not be focused in a unit that had any meaning. The rings of celebrants, the lewd words, the blasphemous altar with its glittering reminder of Amen, the conjurations of Dagon and Chemosh. . . . Were these his people? What nightmare had transformed them into half-naked savages falling on one another in their perverted orgy?

The scene converged to a pin-point in which he saw nothing but the image of a golden calf. It expanded a hundredfold, multiplied itself, and danced about Moses in mad spirals. Moses was no longer aware of his body. He swept through the mob to its center, mounted the three sacrilegious steps, and dashed the tablets against the idol. The slabs broke and Moses turned on the people, shouting, "There lies your salvation! You have chosen. You cannot serve God and Amen!"

The circles broke, overthrew each other. Moses added to the maelstrom by calling, "Who is on the Lord's side? Let him come to me!"

Joshua's men and the tribe of Levi were the first to rally. Swords and protests slashed simultaneously. Aaron, signaling his sons to overthrow the metal calf, shouted above the din, "Praise Jahveh, you've come. And in time! Give orders now. Let us exterminate the trouble-makers. We must inspire fear. Let no man discriminate even for his brother. Neighbor must be against neighbor until this rebellious seed is rooted out."

The fury was beginning to leave Moses. "No," he said, "I did not bring them out of Egypt to kill them here in the mountains. Stop them, Joshua, before they murder each other."

A few of the elders, edging through the melee, reached Moses with supplications. He brushed off their hands; the blaze had died, but the smolder persisted.

"No. I want neither excuse nor explanation. Not tonight. The Lord knows you are a fickle race, a turncoat people, and it is only his mercy that keeps him from deserting you. Would to God *I* could! But I cannot. Go. I will talk with you tomorrow. But not until that abomination is destroyed. No man need present himself until the wooden core of that foul thing is burnt, the metal stripped off and reduced to powder. Don't pollute the soil by burying the smallest grain of it here. Take the dust far from the camp and let the winds carry it where it belongs. Scatter it—toward Egypt."

He turned an uncompromising back upon them.

Three weeks had silenced the camp, but apprehension had increased. Men looked back over their shoulders. Moses' days were a succession of appeals.

"Sheep could never have followed you more faithfully," said Aaron, as the two of them sat on the little hill where the idol had been throned. "You have them in your hands now. They'll do anything you say. Give them the law, or a set of laws, and such an accident as last month's won't happen again. I'll see to it," he added decisively, "the more so since I failed to stop them. Still," he went on in self-extenuation, "I've always said it is the spirit of reverence we must encourage. Does it matter what name they call him as long as they worship one god?"

"I think it does," answered Moses. "Chaldea has its own god; so has Philistia. Ours is not like theirs, a choice of warring powers, the selection of one god among many. Our god is God. There is no other."

"Why not tell them that?"

"Because words won't say it. We have no language flexible enough. You can't use the terms of trade and gossip to project infinities—and even if I could find another speech, they wouldn't understand me. And a new tongue?"

"Try the old one. Words are not our masters; they are slaves. Tame them. Twist their necks, if you must, but make them obey you. Whip them into order—into orders. And the people, obeying them, will be keeping your commandments."

"Not mine," said Moses. "God's. I cannot even frame them."

"Don't think of it as a set of formulas. Say it as though you were talking to me, and I'll make notes. Repeat what you were saying before about one god."

"Not one god, Aaron. God. He brought us out of Egypt and the house of bondage."

"Perfect. A magnificent preamble. But it must be made direct and more sonorous; a communication out of Jahveh's own mouth. Let Jahveh speak: I am the Lord thy God which brought thee out of the land of Egypt, out of the house of bondage. Go on."

"We must make it plain that there can be no others."

"Good. But let it all come as though Jahveh were saying it. The people fear words only when tradition or deity repeats them. Making it plain is not enough. It must be a command. This way: Thou shalt have no other gods before me! That has authority. What next?"

Moses felt for a phrase, lost it, and shook his head.

"It's no use, Aaron. Reduced to a clause, it sounds harsh and meager.

Up there, I found union of thought and substance. Nothing was isolated. I saw the thing in its relation to everything. Not a set of strictures, but an integrated, all-encompassing law. It was a sort of vision. But it either gets dense when I try to shape it or it eludes me entirely. Some of it was going as I came down the mountain; the golden calf drove the rest of it out of my head."

"Possibly this will recall the summit," said Aaron, producing two stone tablets. "I've had them pieced together. They seem to contain notes of some kind."

Moses studied the slabs for a time, growing more absorbed while Aaron took care not to jar the abstraction. Suddenly Moses lifted his head.

"Yes. That was it. To destroy idols is not enough. We must have no more statues or paintings of any objects."

"But," protested Aaron, "that would be the death of art."

"Let it die, then," said Moses. "Let it die as long as men worship appearance rather than essence, form and not the spirit, the pattern instead of the Creator who designed it. Earth is rich in living beauty. Must our wonder be imprisoned in stone before we can recognize it? Must we always have a golden calf before us? As for our emotions, the highest feelings cannot be cast in a mold. Pigment and marble never can embody thoughts which have nothing to do with the world of materials. It is only the gods of the heathen who can be represented in line and color. Have we left Egypt only to carry her folly with us? If you insist on command, let it be: Thou shalt not make any graven image or any likeness of anything that is in heaven above or in earth beneath, or in the waters under the earth. Thou shalt not bow to them nor serve them."

"That's eloquent enough, but it lacks power. There should be a threat against those who disobey. The law must have teeth. Something weighty, something more like: For I, Jahveh, am a jealous God, visiting the iniquity of the fathers upon the children unto the third and fourth generation of them that hate me."

"You can't end like that," said Moses. "Is God only an anger, returning hate for hate? Add: And showing mercy unto thousands of generations that love me and keep my commandments."

Aaron hesitated.

"Isn't that making it rather lengthy? But go on. Any more about Jahveh?"

"Yes," replied Moses. "The use of the name. It's being bandied about with too much familiarity. False oaths are supported with 'As Jahveh lives' and 'In the Name of the Lord.' If they cannot use the divine syllables with respect in ordinary intercourse, we must suppress them. We must stamp out the boast that is a blasphemy."

"How would you suppress it?"

"Simply. Thou shalt not take the name of the Lord thy God in vain; for the Lord will not hold the hypocrite and blasphemer guiltless . . . Or a similar construction."

Aaron waited, but instead of more illumination, the light began to fade. After an empty interval, Moses raised cloudy eyes.

"I can't make it out. I see something here about 'rhythms of labor' and 'season of rest,' but the mood that evoked the phrase is gone. Without the mood, the words refuse to come to life—the letter alone is a dead letter."

"What you read sounds something like the Sumerian 'day of rest for the heart'—the ancient Sa-bat."

"That was it. The Sabbath. But not in the civic sense. It is the Lord's Day. The legend has it that he, who rests in action, ceased creating on the seventh day and the earth rested with him. The allegory may be difficult but the fact is simple: Nature finds a breathing-space everywhere. Rest after labor is not only wise, it is holy. Time for meditation, self-searching, recapitulation. Thanks for work accomplished and for leisure won. We must remember the Sabbath day to keep it holy."

Aaron looked applause. "That last sentence is a commandment in itself. It only needs a little amplifying."

"Shall we add," said Moses, "this sentence: 'Six days shalt thou labor and do all thy work, but the seventh is a day of rest and preparation'?"

"Not quite. It isn't enough to tell the people what to do: they want to be told what *not* to do. It's only by limiting their freedom that they'll begin to feel free. They are lost without guide-posts and restrictions—and the more prohibitive the rules are, the happier they'll be. You've stated the positive aspect of the Sabbath, now for the negative: In it thou shalt not do any work. Neither thou, nor thy son, nor thy daughter, nor thy manservant, nor thy maidservant, nor thine ox, nor thine ass, nor any of thy cattle, nor the stranger who is within thy gates . . . I think that includes everything."

"Honoring God and his Sabbath are the impersonal ways. We must know God in his reflections; we must recognize the heavenly Father in our own. If our days are to be long in the land which the Lord has given, we must honor father and mother—the inner circle that encloses God in the family."

"Perfect. I wouldn't dare a syllable in addition. But what about the other negations?"

"They are basic, not particular. Israel has no monopoly of them."

"And the first?" inquired Aaron.

"Thou shalt not kill."

Aaron frowned. "We'll have to qualify that. There'll have to be clause about the right of retaliation. There always will be burning for burning and wound to pay for a wound. It can be acknowledged in a supplementary sentence: an eye for an eye, tooth for tooth, hand for hand, life for life."

Moses shook a determined head. "No, Aaron. That's a survival of Babylon; we have no reason to preserve the code of Hammurabi. Let the injunctions stand without comment. They have force enough."

"And they are?"

"Thou shalt not commit adultery. Thou shalt not steal, Thou shalt not bear false witness against thy neighbor."

"Those admonitions might not be equally popular, Moses, but a state might be governed on the last three alone. In three short sentences you have framed the tenets of chastity, domestic relations, property right, perjury and all that might come under the head of good citizenship. You have developed a genius for condensation. If the mountaintop is responsible for such concentrated power, we ought to move the twelve tribes up there. The last three makes a splendid climax."

"One more. One that sums up the spirit of all. Thou shalt not covet. If they follow this teaching, they will not kill or steal or commit adultery or testify falsely. The other commands forbid the body; this one goes to the source, to the mind. For covetousness is not in the flesh any more than contentment. And it is against greed, against envy that we must fight. Disdaining the good we have and lusting after what we have not, is worse than stupidity; it is the highest blasphemy. For it discredits God."

"I'm afraid I don't put so high a value on metaphysics, Moses. I'm more concerned with the physical man. Heights and a rarefied atmosphere are all very well for the inspired. But if we want to talk to people on their level, we'll have to come down to earth. Let's continue on that plane."

"I think there's nothing more to say."

Aaron examined his notes. "But these are only a few generalities. What you've suggested wouldn't make more than ten commandments."

"Ten are enough. They constitute the Law."

19 The Conquest of Jericho

Frank G. Slaughter, physician turned novelist, has plowed three areas of fiction—the medical novel, frequently set against an historical background; the historical novel, often set in Florida; and the biblical novel, drawing upon both Testaments. Prolific and popular, less a thinker and artist than a storyteller in the classic tradition, his novels have been appealing to a large audience for over twenty years. He attempts very little interpretation, trying rather to enlarge upon the story aspects of his sources. Writing quickly and taking great liberties, he builds his characters and his backgrounds with colorful, melodramatic strokes, but he has brought the Bible stories to many persons who might never otherwise have been exposed to them.

And Joshua the son of Nun sent out of Shittim two men to spy secretly, saying, Go view the land, even Jericho. And they went, and came into an harlot's house, named Rahab, and lodged there.

JOSHUA: II, 1

THE SCARLET CORD by FRANK G. SLAUGHTER

I

NEITHER THE *moreh,* the autumn rains that made it possible to plow and sow the winter grain crops, nor the *gesem,* as the winter rains were called, had been great during the period that the children of Israel dwelt in the land of the Amorites, hard by the fords of the Jord between Abel-shittim and Jericho. As a result, the land was parched and dry except for a narrow band on each side of the river. But the *malquosh,* or spring rains, were abundant, filling the springs and rivulets in the mountain country west of the Jord and bringing ample water to supply an army and a people on the march.

Joshua was impatient to move the army he had assembled westward across the Jord against their first target, the walled city of Jericho. Travelers had reported, however, that the defenses of Jericho were being strengthened and also that some sort of political upheaval had taken place inside the walls, so he was anxious to obtain information as to exact conditions inside the city before they attacked. Salmon was not surprised, therefore, when he received a summons one rainy morning to appear in the magnificent tent, captured from King Og, that Joshua used as his headquarters in the military camp at Abel-shittim. Caleb and several of the leading captains were also present.

170

"Israel has need of you again, Salmon," Joshua said without preamble when the physician had seated himself on a cushion in the circle of men and accepted a cup of wine.

"My supplies are ready," Salmon assured him. "We have ample medicine and cloth for dressing wounds."

"Your skill will be needed when we go against Jericho," Joshua conceded. "I have another task for you now—or rather for the physician called Samma."

Salmon smiled. "He is probably the only Egyptian who would serve Israel now."

"Before we launch the attack against Jericho," Joshua continued, "we must learn everything we can about the city's defenses."

"Don't you have patrols watching the city?"

"The information we seek can be found only within Jericho itself. As the physician Samma, you were able to penetrate the strongholds of Canaan without difficulty, so Jericho should be easy for you."

"The people of Jericho are on guard," Salmon pointed out. "They will be suspicious of any stranger."

"That was exactly my argument against asking you to go," Caleb interposed. "I don't think we should ask it of you or anyone else, Salmon."

"Nor I." Another of the captains, named Khalith, spoke up. "It is one thing to send a man into battle where he has an even chance against his enemies. But if Salmon is taken inside Jericho he will lose his head."

"The life of every one of us must be sacrificed if it is for the good of Israel," Joshua said sharply. "No one person is better than another."

"Then why not go yourself?" Caleb asked.

Before the argument could go any further, Salmon intervened. "Joshua is right," he said. "Any Israelite would be sure of death if he entered Jericho. But as Samma, the physician, I can pretend to come from Urusalim on my way to Damascus. When I display my medicines and skills in the courtyard of an inn, no one will suspect me of being other than what I pretend to be."

"It is settled then," Joshua said with satisfaction. "Now we must decide who will go with you."

"Why should anyone else risk his life?" Salmon objected.

An odd silence descended upon the half circle of men. When no one spoke, Salmon looked inquiringly around at them. "Is something wrong?" he asked.

Joshua spoke, his tone hearty. "We were discussing the risk before you came, Salmon," he said. "And we had decided a soldier should go with you, one of the captains."

"If there is trouble, it would be fine to have a strong sword arm beside me," Salmon agreed. "But with the odds against us if we are discovered in Jericho, fighting skill will make little difference."

"The son of Nun is not concerned about fighting skill," Caleb said dryly. "He wants one of the captains there to inspect the military preparations."

"You are not a soldier, Salmon," Joshua hurried to say. "It would not be fair to ask you to estimate the military strength of Jericho."

"Why not say what you mean?" Salmon said quietly. "You want me to go into Jericho, but you do not trust me to bring back an honest report."

"It is just that we believe a warrior could tell more about the defenses of the city."

"Tell him your real reason, Joshua," Caleb said gruffly. "Because Salmon suggested crossing the Jord at Adamah and attacking the northern cities, you no longer trust his judgment."

Salmon nodded slowly. "Joshua may be right at that. There are—reasons—why I might not advise you well in the case of Jericho. I will take whoever you decide should go with me. He can be disguised as my servant."

"I will go," Caleb said quickly. "If they catch us in Jericho," he added with a grin, "we will at least have the satisfaction of taking a few of their men with us."

The very next day the physician Samma embarked once more on his travels. With him went his slave, Ammiel, a powerful, grizzled man with a craggy face. They journeyed north to Adamah and thence westward across the Jord and into the Canaanite uplands. When finally they approached Jericho, several days later, it was from the direction of Urusalim. And since the physician boasted of healing the sick in that city, as well as in Megiddo, Gibeon, and Beeroth, no one suspected that he was actually one of the hated Habiru from across the Jord to the east.

II

In Jericho, Rahab had long since learned the third lesson of love; namely, that to protect her child, a woman can prostitute her body and feel no shame, no real degradation, only a cold hate for the man who forces her to do so—and a burning determination to kill him at the first opportunity.

The political situation had settled down into a contest that resembled nothing so much as a tense game of *tshau,* or robbers, between skilled players, with the life of each hanging on the outcome. Kalak and Cesera ruled upon the sufferance of Kanofer but plotted constantly against him. And the Egyptian captain busied himself increasing his hold on the military forces. Meanwhile the rains poured down and the hour of doom for Jericho grew daily nearer.

Rahab was busy with preparations for the evening meal in the establishment she supervised for Kanofer—the Egyptian being in Gibeon on a mission to make one last appeal to the Hivites for a defensive union against the Habiru—when Myrnah came running excitedly to her.

"Rahab!" she cried. "I have good news."

Rahab smiled, and some of the harsh lines that had been etched into her face these past weeks were momentarily softened. "It will be a welcome change from what we usually have, Myrnah. What is this news of yours?"

"A physician has just set up shop in the courtyard. He claims to come from Egypt."

Rahab caught her breath. It could not be Salmon, she told herself. Even he would not dare come into Jericho at such a time as this, when every newcomer was suspected of being a spy.

"Let me show Jaschar to him," Myrnah begged. "He may be able to straighten his foot."

"Take the physician to my room," Rahab directed. Even if the newcomer was not Salmon, it would do no harm to let him see the baby's foot. "I will come as soon as I finish what I am doing."

Rahab hurried through her work and upstairs to her room. She heard voices inside and hesitated, her hand on the door, reluctant to enter and hear the verdict of the physician, lest it be unfavorable. Then, straightening her shoulders, she pushed the door open and stepped into the room.

Salmon was examining Jaschar, who lay on his face on the couch, kicking and cooing. Even before she met the physician's eyes, Rahab knew he had already recognized who the baby's father was. A quick warmth burned in Salmon's eyes when they met hers, but he made no other sign of recognition, for Myrnah was in the room.

"I brought the physician and his slave up here as you told me," Myrnah said. "He says he never saw a finer boy."

With an effort Rahab forced a note of calmness into her voice. "You did well, Myrnah. Our guest and his servant must be tired and thirsty; go down and bring them food and wine."

As soon as the servant departed, Rahab ran across the room and threw herself in Salmon's arms. He held her while she sobbed on his breast, and when finally she recovered from her momentary breakdown he dried her eyes with his sleeve. Realizing for the first time that someone else was in the room, she drew away from him.

"It is only Caleb posing as my servant," Salmon said with a smile. "You remember him from the Cave of Yah, don't you?"

Rahab began to laugh, a little hysterically. "Are all the captains of Israel your servants now, Salmon?" she asked.

"They should be," Caleb said with a grin; then he added, "You have changed since last I saw you, girl."

Rahab's face hardened. "For the worse. You find me a harlot, running a brothel."

Caleb shrugged. "Yesterday I was a general; today I am a slave to help my people. I'll wager you are not a brothel-keeper by choice."

"No," Rahab admitted. "And now that you are here, I pray it will not be much longer. What do you think of Jaschar, Salmon?"

"He is a fine, strong boy, like his father."

"You saw the marks on his shoulders then?"

"We did not need to see them," Caleb said. "I would know Joshua's child anywhere."

"I sent for you when he was born, Salmon," she said. "But they told Senu you were away. I—I was hoping you could straighten his foot."

Salmon bent over the baby once more, moving the deformed foot with strong, skilled fingers. When he raised his head Rahab saw the answer to her question on his face. "Nothing can be done then?" she asked.

"If it were only twisted, I might straighten the bones and hold them until they grew in the right position," he said. "But see how the foot points downward because the cord here behind the heel is too short. I can try to stretch it, but there is little hope."

Coming on top of all the things that had happened lately, this was a heavy blow to Rahab. "I suppose this is a—a punishment from Yah because I lay with Joshua when we were not wed," she said slowly.

"The god you worship is a god of kindness," Salmon assured her. "Many children are born deformed. Yah would not do such a thing to you merely because you loved Joshua."

Rahab shook her head slowly. "It seems that I left Yah behind in the Cave on Mount Nebo. Sometimes I think I will never find him again."

Salmon took her gently by the shoulders and made her face him. "You told me once that the temple of Yah is in the hearts of those who love and serve him, Rahab. Never let yourself doubt that for a moment."

"But my baby is a cripple, an outcast," she wailed.

"He is Joshua's son. In Israel he will be respected, if only because of that."

With an effort she gained control of herself. "Do you expect to take Jericho soon?"

"Joshua sent us to study the defenses of Jericho, but Caleb thinks one of the mercenaries at the gate may have recognized him. The man looked closely at us when we came through."

"Then we have no time to lose," Rahab said quickly. "What is it you want to find out?"

Salmon shook his head. "You told me in Memphis how kind Prince Hazor was to you. I would not ask you to betray him by giving us information about Jericho."

"The King is dead, struck down by a traitor's arrow." Quickly she gave them an account of what had happened in the past several weeks, the tragic ending of the ceremony dedicating the gate, Kanofer's taking control, and the uneasy truce that now existed between him and Kalak and Cesera.

"What of the walls?" Caleb asked. "Have they been strengthened?"

"Only at the gate. The towers are mainly to protect the spring. The cracks in the walls have only been plastered over with mud."

"They are still strong," Caleb pointed out. "If the city is well defended by the people—"

"There is no courage left in the hearts of anyone in Jericho. They know Yahweh has given this land to you. Such a fear has fallen upon them that they will melt away before you once the walls are breached."

"That may be," Caleb admitted. "But how shall we breach them?"

"That I do not know," Rahab told him. "But all of Jericho has been filled for months with talk of what you did to King Sihon and King Og."

The door opened and Myrnah came in, her face white. "Soldiers are in the courtyard," she gasped. "They say two of the Habiru are in the house."

III

At Myrnah's words, Caleb's hand dropped to his side where his sword always hung. But as the slave of a physician he wore only a small dagger, a useless weapon against armed soldiers.

"Did you betray us, woman?" he demanded, seizing Myrnah by the wrist.

The slave's eyes almost popped out. "Then you are Hab—"

"Quickly, did you tell them we were here?"

"No, Myrnah gasped. "I did not know they were seeking you."

"These are the friends I told you about, Myrnah," Rahab explained hurriedly. "Where can we hide them while the soldiers are searching the house?"

"I was drying rushes on the roof this morning," Myrnah said. "It is dark already, and they could hide up there beneath the grasses."

"The roof can be reached from just outside this door," said Rahab. "We must move quickly."

"Don't involve yourself in this, Rahab," Salmon begged. "Show us where to go and we will do the rest."

"I owe Kalak a debt," she assured him grimly. "For King Hazor's sake. Hurry up the steps to the roof."

Darkness had already fallen and the night breeze was beginning to ripple the piles of rushes on the roof when they reached it by way of a ladder from the second story. Caleb and Salmon burrowed beneath the piled-up rushes, pulling the dried grass over them until they were completely hidden. But as Rahab turned back to descend the ladder to her room, the sound of men's voices on the floor below stopped her.

She was trapped on the roof.

Rahab's mind raced as she considered the best thing to do in the desperate situation in which she now found herself. At all costs she must keep Salmon and Caleb from being captured, for the information they would take back to Joshua concerning the fear that gripped the people might help capture Jericho. And if the city were taken, she would be free at last from Kanofer and the hateful servitude into which he had forced her.

Suddenly she thought of a way of hiding the presence of the two men beneath the rushes. The soldiers knew her for a harlot—as did all Jericho —so the logical thing to do was to play the part. Quickly she pulled her robe from her shoulders and dropped it to her waist, exposing the upper part of her body as she moved to the opening where the ladder gave access to the roof.

By now the soldiers had reached the second floor in their search and were at the foot of the ladder. "I am up here," Rahab called. "Are you looking for me?"

One of them held a torch above his head and peered upward. "You are early," she called down. "I was cooling myself on the roof before the evening begins." Belatedly she pretended to realize that she was naked to the waist and slowly pulled up the top of her robe.

A man wearing the helmet of an officer elbowed his way through the others to the foot of the ladder. "We do not seek pleasure tonight," he told her. "At least not yet. One of the guards at the gate thinks he recognized a pair of men who came through a few hours ago as Habiru. He says they came here to the inn."

"Two men did come here," Rahab said. "But they left just after dark in time to get out of the city before the gate was closed."

The officer frowned. "We know nothing of their going out. They were seen to come here."

"You can search the roof if you like," Rahab offered.

The captain climbed the ladder and came out on the roof. As he looked around, Rahab moved closer until her body was touching his, hoping to keep his attention from centering on the piles of rushes drying on the roof. "You can see there is nobody here but me," she assured him, then added in a lower tone, "Unless I have a visitor later."

The officer put a hard arm around her waist. He drew her against him and bent to kiss her roughly. Rahab rigidly controlled the shiver of revulsion that went through her and with a lithe movement freed herself from his embrace.

"I don't know where the men went," she said. "But you will have to pursue them quickly if you hope to overtake them in the darkness."

"We will go after them," the captain promised. "They must have gone toward the ford of the Jord and the Israelite camp. But when I return—"

"Rahab waits for no man," she assured him with a shrug.

"Except Kanofer?"

"The Egyptian has gone to Gibeon and will not return for several days. Shall I sit alone and pine for him?"

The captain was already descending the ladder. To keep from re-arousing his suspicions, Rahab followed him down and out into the court-yard. She stood watching until the soldiers disappeared in the direction of the gate. Going back into the house then, she went to the storeroom and searched until she found a length of strong cord. It was scarlet in color, having been wrapped around a dyer's pack, but there was nothing else strong enough to hold a man.

Hiding the cord under her robe, Rahab went quickly up to her room, where Myrnah was guarding Jaschar, and examined the window opening on the west side, away from the city. The distance to the ground was still greater than the length of the rope, she estimated, but she was sure Salmon and Caleb could drop the rest of the way without being hurt. The way of escape was clear at the moment, for the soldiers had gone eastward toward the fords of the Jord.

Salmon and Caleb were still hidden under the rushes when Rahab reached the roof again. They shoved the grass aside and crawled out, picking bits of straw and leaves from their clothing.

"The soldiers have gone toward the fords looking for you," she told them breathlessly. "If you hide in the mountains to the west tonight, you can make your way to the river later."

"We cannot get through the gate," Caleb objected. "They will have doubled the guards by now."

"I have a rope in my room," Rahab explained as she led the way down the ladder. "You can climb through the window and down the wall."

"By the Tablets of the Law!" Caleb said admiringly. "You have a clever head on those beautiful shoulders of yours, girl."

Working swiftly, the men tied one end of the rope to the bench and let the other out the window. Salmon, being the slenderer one, leaned out, Caleb holding his feet, and strained his eyes down in the darkness. When he wriggled back into the room, his face was flushed, but there was a look of satisfaction on it.

"We will have only a short drop from the end of the rope," he reported. Then his face sobered. "But how will we get the baby down the rope?"

"You two must go without us," Rahab said. "We would only hold you back."

"The guards will return and—"

"They will think you escaped them in the darkness. Hurry now, but promise me one thing. When Jericho falls, swear that we will be saved."

"I swear it," Caleb said promptly. "By the name of Yahweh."

"And I," Salmon agreed. He picked up the slender rope by which they planned to escape. "Bind this scarlet cord in the window. Then no one can fail to recognize your house."

"You need have no fear," Caleb assured her. "You nor anyone in your house."

At Salmon's insistence, Caleb went first. He let himself down feet first, while Rahab, Salmon, and Myrnah steadied the bench to which the rope was tied. For what seemed an eternity the rope was tense with the Israelite captain's weight, then suddenly it slackened and they heard a soft thud from outside.

Tensely they waited for a sign that Caleb had safely negotiated the descent. Then a low whistle sounded from the darkness outside and Salmon gave Rahab's arm a quick squeeze in farewell. Wiry and agile, he had no trouble lowering himself from the window. Myrnah and Rahab held the bench until the sudden slackening of the rope told them he had fallen clear, then Rahab climbed up on it and put her head and shoulders through the window.

She could see little outside, but when Salmon's low whistle sounded beneath her, Rahab was able to distinguish two dim figures moving across the rocky ground outside the wall toward the towering black shadows of the mountains to the west. Only when they were out of sight did she step down from the bench and draw the scarlet cord back through the window. Quickly she untied it from the bench and hid it beneath the baby's wrappings where he lay asleep in an improvised crib in the corner.

Dawn was just beginning to break when Rahab awoke with the same strange feeling of impending disaster that had warned her before of danger. She did not realize at first what had awakened her. But when the couch on which she lay seemed to be tilted slowly by a giant hand, she was no longer in doubt, for she had experienced this sensation many times before.

It was an earth tremor, a shaking of the land like an animal roused from sleep, which often presaged an earthquake at this time of the year.

With no thought for her own safety, Rahab leaped from the couch and ran to the corner where Jaschar lay. She took the baby in her arms, protecting it with her body. As she knelt there, another tremor shook the room and a large crack opened in the side that was part of the wall of Jericho. Plaster and broken mud bricks rained down upon the floor, and the groaning of the timbers supporting the roof was like the moaning of giants in pain.

When a few moments passed with no more of the tremors, Rahab called to Myrnah to follow and ran down to the lower floor and out into the courtyard, where they would be better protected from falling debris. Here they crouched, staring wide-eyed at a giant crack that had split the inner wall from top to bottom only a few paces from the houses. Had it occurred in the outer wall, which actually supported the building, the whole thing would have collapsed, burying them in the debris.

People were pouring from their houses now, white-faced with terror. The crash of falling masonry was heard from other parts of the city, and amid the din hundreds of voices could be heard crying out, "Jericho is doomed! Baal has cursed the city."

No one tried to leave the city, for they knew that the Habiru waited not far away, ready to destroy them once they left the protection of the walls. And as the hours passed, reports of the damage were more reassuring. Although the inner wall was breached in a dozen places or more, the outer one had held with only a few cracks. Jericho's main defense was still intact.

To Rahab, the earthquake seemed indeed to be a sign from Yah, sent to reassure her. She even dared to hope now for an early release from the hateful situation in which Kanofer had placed her.

IV

Caleb and Salmon felt the trembling of the earth where they were hiding in the hill country to the west of Jericho. The tremor had not been as severe in the uplands as on the lower ground where the city stood, but as they looked down on Jericho in the early dawn, they could detect some of the damage that had been done to the inner wall.

"Perhaps Yahweh is preparing for the fall of Jericho, as Joshua expects," Salmon suggested.

Caleb grinned. "I care not who breaches the walls, so long as they are breached. But we must get this information to Joshua as quickly as possible. These earth tremors sometimes last a week or more in the springtime. Whatever happens, we must be ready."

"They will be guarding the fords below Jericho," Salmon pointed out. "But we can go back by way of Adamah."

Stopping only to gather fruit and berries on the mountainside to allay their hunger and to drink from the springs that burst from the rocks all through the highlands here—now that the *malquosh* had soaked the earth once more—Salmon and Caleb made their way northward toward the next crossing of the Jord above the fords of Jericho, opposite the town of Adamah. The way was rough, for there were no roads here. And in truth, they did not dare follow a travelled path for fear the soldiers of Jericho would be lying in wait along the roadside to capture them.

Every few hours they felt a new tremor of the earth, but since none was as strong as that which had occurred during the first night, they pushed on each day until darkness fell and then slept in a cave. Early the third morning they reached the road leading from Tirzah in the uplands eastward to the Jord and shortly came down into the deep valley where the river flowed.

On Salmon's previous visit to Adamah, when he had been spying out the cities of Canaan, he had noted the great earth cliffs on the west bank of the Jord. He had been certain then that a few men could block the river here by digging away the undercut bank and allowing great masses of dirt to fall into the stream. Now, they saw, this had already happened to a small degree. A section of the overlying bank had fallen into the Jord during the recent earth tremors, slowing the flow of its waters.

More significant, however, was a giant crack that had cut almost halfway through the cliff, leaving a mass of earth large enough to block the Jord completely, hanging, so to speak, in the air.

Salmon discovered the crevice while inspecting the crossing. He stopped at the edge of the earth cliff, for it seemed that hardly more than a nudge would send the whole mass tumbling.

"Come here, Caleb," he called, and when the gnarled captain stood beside him, he pointed down into the great crevice. "A hundred men digging here could dislodge this mass of earth into the river and block it."

Caleb knelt at the edge and dropped a stone into the crevice. A moment later they heard it strike water well below them.

"Ten men could do it," he agreed, "but we will take no chances. A hundred should be more than enough. Then the carts with our supplies and even the battering-rams and siege towers can pass over the Jord without any trouble." He got to his feet. "Joshua must know about this at once."

On the east bank of the Jord they met an Israelite patrol stationed there to give warning of any attempt by the Canaanites to deliver a flanking attack.

Supplied with fresh sandals and food by their fellows, the travelers trudged on southward and reached the Israelite encampment at Abel-shittim in the late afternoon.

To their surprise, they found the place almost deserted and were informed that the main body of the troops and the people were encamped on the banks of the Jord at the fords, waiting for the river to lower before crossing into the region controlled by the King of Jericho on the west bank. No one seeing the battering-rams and the rude siege towers on their great wooden wheels waiting on the bank of the river could doubt that the armies of Israel were embarked at last on the long-expected attack against Jericho.

Joshua's tent was pitched on the very bank of the stream, near the sumptuous canopy housing the Ark of Yahweh, which was said to contain the tablets of a covenant made by their god with the Israelites.

Joshua had been studying a rough map drawn on a sheet of papyrus. He looked up quickly when Salmon and Caleb were ushered in, and the physician was almost shocked at the burning light in the Israelite leader's eyes.

The Joshua with whom he had conferred in this very tent a few days ago had been strong and secure in the belief that he was obeying the will of Yahweh. But the man who faced them now was fired by something more, the consuming flame of a fanatic zeal that neither knows nor admits opposition.

"Salmon! Caleb!" he cried. "I was afraid you had been taken in Jericho. We were moving against it to take the city and release you."

"We were almost captured," said Caleb grimly. "But you would have found only our heads."

"Three days ago when the earth began to tremble," Joshua told them, "I recognized it as the voice of Yahweh urging us on against Jericho. We began to move that very day in preparation for crossing the river."

Salmon had the strange feeling that he was already watching a great event from a distance, as he had watched the destruction of King Og and his men from the hillside above Edrei. Nor could he throw off the conviction that everything taking place here had somehow been ordained already and nothing any of them could do would really hinder or help it, leaving all of them to play out their appointed roles with no volition of their own.

"When will you cross?" he asked Joshua.

"When Yahweh cuts off the waters of the Jord."

Caleb shot him a startled glance. "And when will that be?"

"He spoke to us once in the earthquake, telling us the time had come to move on Jericho. When it is time to cross the river, he will speak again."

"We found a great crack in the earth cliffs at Adamah," said Caleb. "It was made by the tremors we have been feeling these past few days. Salmon thinks a hundred men could push it loose and block the river."

"Yahweh has already spoken then," Joshua said, as if he had expected to hear this information all along. "Take the hundred men tomorrow, Salmon, and loosen the earth cliff. Did you learn anything else in Jericho?"

"One of the mercenaries guarding the gate recognized Caleb," Salmon explained. "We were forced to escape at night before the earth tremors occurred and learned but little of their defenses. But we could see from the hills the next morning that the inner wall was breached in several places by the earth tremors."

"And the outer?"

"It is still strong," said Caleb. "Only battering-rams can break it down."

"We will make camp on the plain before Jericho and wait for the voice of Yahweh," said Joshua. "If he does not breach the walls for us, then we will attack them with rams!"

Caleb shook his grizzled head. "Yahweh has given us victory so far, Joshua, but only when we fought for it. I say move up the rams and the siege towers at once. The people of Jericho are afraid. When they see our strength arrayed before the city, they might even open the gate to us."

Joshua shook his head. "They will not surrender without a battle. I have caused *herem* to be invoked against Jericho."

"The curse!" Salmon exclaimed in horror. "Why would you doom everyone in Jericho to death for defending themselves?"

Joshua's face hardened. "You know the Lord God of Israel has given the land of Canaan to us, Salmon."

"Would you kill every living thing because of that? Our god also teaches kindness and love one for another."

"I intend to destroy everything until they yield up the whole land to us."

"We promised immunity to one family," Caleb told him. "The house of a harlot. She let us down from the wall with a scarlet cord when the guards sought us."

"I will give orders that the harlot and her household be spared," Joshua agreed.

"Her name is Rahab," Caleb said quietly. "She will mark her window with the scarlet cord."

"And she will have with her a babe," Salmon added, "bearing the same marks as those on the back of the son of Nun."

For a moment it seemed that Joshua would strike them both; he even raised his fist. Then he dropped it. "I have given my word and the woman will be saved," he said harshly, but suddenly his anger broke the bonds within which he had been rigidly holding it. "I will be father to no harlot's brat, Salmon," he snapped. "It could be yours as well as mine. You were in Egypt with her."

"The child is yours," Salmon said evenly. "Caleb knew that without seeing the marks upon its back. Rahab will not ask you to acknowledge it if you are so stiff-necked as to deny your own seed. She asks only that she and hers be spared when Jericho is destroyed."

"That shall be—but no more." Joshua turned abruptly back to his map.

Outside, Caleb found his voice in an explosive burst of indignation. "By the altars of Baal!" he snapped. "What has come over Joshua? He must be possessed by a demon."

"He is possessed," Salmon agreed, "but not by a demon. You might say he has been possessed by a god—"

"I wager he did not resist," Caleb said shortly. "He was already beginning to *think* himself one."

"Joshua cannot let anyone be superior to him in anything," Salmon agreed as they walked across the camp toward Caleb's tent. "Remember when he lost the skirmish to the forces of King Og?"

Caleb nodded. "It was then that he invoked *herem* against Bashan. Jericho is a similar case."

"How? Joshua has never even been in the city."

"He hates Rahab for shaming him," Caleb explained. "The King of Jericho honored her by making her his concubine, so now the whole city has become a target for Joshua's anger."

"Hazor is dead."

"But his city still stands."

Salmon shook his head slowly. "I don't want to believe that of Joshua, Caleb. He must be convinced that Israel cannot live in Canaan side by side with the Canaanites."

"We live here with the Amorites," Caleb pointed out.

"Look what is happening to our people since they began to intermarry with the Amorites and the Moabites. You can find a golden image of Baal in half the tents, and the men openly visit the temple of Ashtarth to lie with the sacred women.

"Joshua may be right, Caleb," Salmon continued. "And you and I could be wrong. Yahweh may indeed have given him the power to conquer Canaan and destroy its people so that we of Israel will turn away from the false gods we have been pursuing."

"Then you will have to believe Yahweh will block the waters of the Jord for us to cross. And that he will shake down the walls of Jericho and let us in." The old warrior shook his head. "That is asking too much, Salmon. Battles are won by fighting, not by praying."

"Remember the crevice in the earth cliff at Adamah? It needs but little help from us to block the Jord."

"I will not sit by and wait for rivers to cease flowing or walls to be shaken down before me." Caleb clenched his massive fists. "If these two hands grip a sword in a good cause, Yahweh will give victory to my arms. But I must make the first thrust." He smiled. "If you don't understand my words, I am saying, 'Take the hundred men to Adamah tomorrow morning and make sure the earth cliff falls into the Jord.'"

Salmon smiled too. "I had no intention of waiting," he admitted. "Yahweh has put a gift of healing into my hands. But I must still dig out poisoned arrowheads and dress wounds with soothing balm."

"One thing I do know," said Caleb. "I have not eaten a full meal for three days, and my belly cries out for meat and wine. Let us go and find some."

They had just finished their meal when the trumpets blared out a summons for the people to assemble. As Caleb and Salmon joined the crowd on the riverbank, they saw Joshua standing on one of the portable siege towers high above the crowd. With the sun shining on his dark head, he seemed godlike as he waited—lost in some distant contemplation—for the people to come together.

The trumpet blared out again, and as the echoes from the opposite bank of the Jord died away Joshua spoke. Even his voice had changed, Salmon realized with a start. Its tones had become deeper and more sonorous, like the voice of a king.

"Sanctify yourselves," Joshua told the waiting throng, "for tomorrow the Lord will do wonders among you." Turning to the priests, he ordered, "Take up the Ark of the Covenant, and pass before the people."

A hush claimed the whole of the camp of Israel while the priests brought the Ark of the Covenant from its tent, covered with a rich cloth against the profane gaze of those not holy enough to approach it. Moving slowly with an impressive tread, the priests bore the Ark up and down along the bank of the swiftly rushing stream, passing twice before the silent people and the tall figure standing on the siege tower with arms folded. Only when the sacred symbol once more reposed within its tent did Joshua speak again.

"Come hither and hear the words of the Lord your God," he commanded. "Hereby you shall know that the living God is among you and he will without fail drive out from before you the Canaanites, the Hittites, the Hivites, the Perizzites, the Girgashites, the Amorites, and the Jebusites. Behold, the Ark of the Covenant of the Lord of all the earth is to pass before you into the Jord.

"Now therefore, take twelve men from the tribes of Israel, from each tribe a man. And when the soles of the feet of the priests who bear the Ark of the Lord, the Lord of all the earth, shall rest in the waters of the Jord, they shall be stopped from flowing and the waters coming down from above shall stand in one heap."

That night Salmon was awakened in his tent by another strong earth tremor. There was no fear in the camp of Israel, however, for Joshua had told them the trembling was caused by the footsteps of Yahweh walking upon the earth to aid them. And such was the trust of Israel in their leader and in the favor of Yahweh that no one dared to doubt his words.

Nor was Salmon surprised when, halfway to Adamah with a hundred men shortly after dawn, he met a patrol from that city bringing the exciting news that the tremor during the night had loosened the great cliff of earth on the west bank of the river where the waters had undercut it. In the early hours of the morning the earth had tumbled into the river with a great crash, blocking the flow of the stream completely. The waters were piled up far above the crossing, according to the report of the patrol, while the stream below the newly formed obstruction had trickled to a mere brook, carrying only the flow from a few springs that entered the Jord between Adamah and the fords east of Jericho before which Israel was encamped.

V

All day long, the Israelites crossed the Jord almost on dry land, women leading children and domestic animals, asses, goats, dogs, and sheep. Horses pulled the chariots, heavily loaded with supplies of war, as well as the great clumsy battering-rams and mobile siege towers on huge wooden wheels. They were helped by the strongest men, who labored in the mud of the ford, pushing the great wheels and levering them up with heavy poles when they gouged holes into the river bottom.

At the head of the multitude moved a band of the best fighting men, guarding against attack. Behind them, the mass of the people with their posessions were strung out in a broad pattern like a V. The flocks came first after the fighting men, followed by the herds, and behind them were more warriors protecting the flanks from attack. By the time the first column had reached the place called Gilgal chosen for the new camp, a little more than halfway between the river and Jericho, the end had not yet finished crossing the Jord.

Gilgal was located in a flat area particularly suited for such an encampment, with an ample water supply from a stream forming its southern boundary in a small canyon. Long after night had fallen the Israelites labored, setting up tents, dispersing the flocks on the grassy hillsides with shepherd boys to look after them and armed patrols to guard against a surprise attack by the enemy. When morning dawned, a formidable sight indeed met the eyes of the soldiers patrolling the walls of Jericho. Spread out in full sight was the might of Israel, with the great war machines waiting for the beginning of the final attack.

Joshua had not yet ordered moved up a portable shelter Salmon had devised to cover the spring that supplied Jericho with water and deny it to the inhabitants. The shelter was ready when it was needed. Meanwhile, since this was the season of the Passover, when the children of Israel were accustomed to celebrate their escape from Egypt, it was decided to defer any more intensive movement against the city until the celebration was finished.

On the morning after their arrival at Gilgal, Joshua called the people together and announced that on each of the succeeding six days the entire forces of Israel would march around Jericho, with the Ark of the Covenant borne before them and the ram's-horn trumpets of the priests blasting out defiance to the city's defenders.

At the announcement, a murmur of surprise ran through the crowd. None of the captains spoke, however, until Caleb asked, "What is the meaning of this play-acting, Joshua?"

"Do you dare call the commands of Yahweh play-acting?"

"I will obey the commands of Yahweh," said the old soldier, "when I know they come from him."

"I speak the words which the Lord our God puts into my mouth," Joshua told him.

"What shall we do on the seventh day when the play-acting is finished?" Caleb inquired. "Will the soldiers cease to prance and boast and be ready to fight like men?"

"On the seventh day we will march around the walls seven times."

"And when we are all too exhausted to fight? What then?"

"Our god will deliver Jericho to us," Joshua said evenly.

For a long moment there was a deep silence while the people stared up at Joshua in a state of awed wonder, as if he had indeed become, as he claimed, the mouthpiece of Yahweh. Only when Caleb snorted and stamped away was the spell broken.

Joshua dismissed them then, and they scattered to their tents to discuss this strange method of warfare about which none of them had ever heard before and which, in truth, had never been used in the history of mankind. A second important topic of conversation, particularly among the captains, was the rapidly approaching breach between Caleb and Joshua.

Salmon found his old friend sulking in his tent and gnawing his beard. "Now I know Joshua is possessed," Caleb burst out angrily as soon as Salmon came in. "Were those the words of a soldier—or a self-chosen prophet?"

"I could not help believing it will all happen as he said."

"You are not alone," Caleb admitted reluctantly. "I too had to fight hard not to believe it."

"Why do you try then?"

"Why do I try?" the old captain spluttered. "Because after Joshua I am the first captain of the hosts of Israel. Suppose the army of Jericho decides to attack us on the seventh day when we have marched ourselves into exhaustion? What better time could they choose?"

"Remember how the waters of the Jordan were stopped?"

"You saw the reason for that at Adamah. It was caused by the earthquake."

"Joshua was waiting for the river to go down before we brought news concerning the condition of the earth cliffs at Adamah," Salmon pointed out.

"He might have waited a month then. Or a year."

"But the cliff *did* fall into the river," Salmon reminded him. "And just when we needed it to be blocked."

Caleb threw up his hands in disgust. "Have I no friend in Israel any more? You, of all people, Salmon, should not be taken in by this business of Joshua posing as a god."

"You and I have been friends for a long time, Caleb—"

"And shall continue to be, I hope."

"If we are not, it will not be of my choosing," the physician assured him. "Are you sure you don't fight Joshua because of envy? After all, but for him you would be chief of our armies."

Caleb poured a cup of wine with a shaking hand. He drank it slowly and wiped his lips with his sleeve before he spoke. "I had not thought my friend would accuse me of envy," he said, a little sadly.

"I too envy him," Salmon admitted.

"You envy Joshua?" Caleb asked in surprise. "In your own field of work you are greater than he is in the art of war."

"I envy him the love of Rahab, for one thing," Salmon admitted. "Once, too, the captains looked to me in matters of strategy. Now Joshua makes such decisions for himself and I am not consulted."

"Nor am I—or any of the captains," Caleb growled. "Take this foolishness of walking around Jeri—"

"It may not be foolishness, Caleb."

"Why not?"

"We have decided to celebrate the Passover before attacking Jericho. If we only sat here, the people in the city might decide we fear to attack and be heartened. But if we parade our might, they will know we outnumber them at least several times and can attack whenever we choose. Besides, this is still the season of earthquakes. Who knows whether or not by the time we launch our attack another earthquake may damage the walls more than they have already been damaged."

"You will be telling me next that Yahweh will deliver Jericho to Joshua by shaking down the walls—while we only stand by and watch," Caleb said disgustedly.

"It could happen," Salmon reminded him. Before Caleb could snort his disbelief, Salmon went on, "We know Yahweh raises up a leader for Israel when she is in need. He gave us Moses to lead us out of Egypt. And now he has raised up Joshua to lead us in conquering Canaan. Neither you nor I can go against the will of Yahweh, Caleb. And we should not want to if it is for the welfare of Israel."

"Not even when it means I must yield to the son of Nun?"

"I have yielded, although it meant giving up the woman I love—because I believe Joshua's way is Yahweh's will."

"You are stronger—and more forgiving—than I am then," Caleb growled. "But I will try—if Joshua does not push me too far."

And so the armies of Israel paraded around the walls of the Jericho the next day in all their warlike might, with the trumpets sounding before them. Joshua marched immediately behind the Ark, which was borne by the priests, with Caleb just behind him at the head of the army, as befitted the second-in-command. Marching in the rear, as usual, Salmon looked up at the walls, and his heart took a sudden leap when he saw a scarlet cord hanging in the window of one of the houses.

On the first day the soldiers of Jericho, safe within the protection of the thick walls, peered and shouted insults at the marching Israelites. But as the days passed, the mockery died away. Soon they only stood and watched while the long line of fighting men daily wound its way around the city, their arms clanking in a martial din. Soon the fear of Jericho's people was a heavy dank miasma, palpable even at this distance from the walls.

All during the week they had felt earth tremors. On the sixth day Salmon climbed one of the hills west of Jericho in order to look down into the city, and saw that considerable damage had been done to the inner wall. It still held, however, and the outer one appeared to be intact, a formidable barrier to an attack by frontal assault.

More than once during that week, when he returned from treating one of the minor complaints that always seemed to arise with nightfall, Salmon saw Joshua standing at the edge of the camp, a majestic and somehow lonely figure, staring across at the forbidding walls of Jericho. Whether or not there was any doubt in Joshua's mind that Yahweh would indeed deliver up Jericho as he had promised the people, Salmon could not know, of course. A year ago he would have felt free to stop and talk to his former comrade, but an invisible wall seemed to have been reared between them now, a wall he did not know how to surmount.

When Joshua addressed the troops on the morning of the seventh day, however, Salmon could detect neither doubt nor lack of decision in his voice. "Today Jericho will be delivered up to us," he promised them. "When we have marched around the walls the seventh time, the priests will blow a loud blast on the trumpets and we will launch the attack against the city."

As his words died away a sudden tremor shook the earth, throwing many of them to the ground and overturning one of the siege towers with a mighty crash. Plainly audible in the hushed silence that followed were the terrified shouts of the people inside Jericho and the sound of falling masonry.

"Hear me, O Israel!" Joshua shouted, his face suddenly aglow. "Yahweh marches with us today! Forward!"

Again the long line filed around Jericho, with the priests marching as before in the lead, each blowing on a long curved ram's horn. The wailing of the people within the city was like a deep animal howl of despair as the army of Israel continued the slow, deliberate march. When the seventh turn had been completed Joshua, resplendent in full military regalia and wearing his armored tunic, lifted his hand.

"At my command, you will shout," he ordered. "For the Lord has given you the city. All that is within Jericho shall be devoted to the Lord for destruction. Only Rahab, the harlot, and all who are with her in her house shall live, because she hid the messengers that we sent.

"But you," he warned, "keep yourselves from the things devoted to destruction, lest you take away any of the devoted things and make the camp of Israel a thing for destruction and bring trouble upon it. All silver and gold and vessels of brass and iron are sacred. They shall go into the treasury of the Lord."

Joshua's upraised fist swung downward in the agreed-upon signal. As one man, the multitude set up a great shout, not only the soldiers, but the people in the camp who were watching.

At the shout and the sudden blast of trumpets, the massed troops began to close in upon the city, pushing before them the battering-rams and the siege towers, from which bowmen were already laying down a covering hail of arrows to protect the men who would place the long scaling ladders against the walls. The attack upon Jericho had finally begun!

VI

Thinking of it later, Salmon could not remember whether or not the earth had been trembling before Joshua finished speaking. But he knew he would never forget the sudden shock that threw him and many of the attackers to the ground before they were halfway across the open space separating them from the walls of Jericho. Joshua—miraculously, it seemed —stayed erect, although the earth was quivering now like a living, demented thing and a great crevice had opened out before them, stretching straight toward the doomed city of Jericho.

"It is the voice of Yahweh!" Joshua shouted again, and his voice carried to all the troops, even above the crashing roar of the earthquake and the terrified cries of the people, attackers and attacked alike.

Salmon staggered to his feet, but another shock sent him to his knees once more. He rose again and stumbled on, his eyes fixed on the window looking down from the wall of Jericho in which the scarlet cord was displayed.

The crash of masonry and the screams of the dying made a pandemonium of sound now. Salmon saw a great crevice open up and swallow a group of Israelite soldiers like ants, but had no time to wonder at the strange phenomenon of the god of Israel killing his own troops. He could not take his fascinated gaze from the walls of the city, which were slowly tilting outward, as if pushed from within by a giant hand.

Almost intact, a huge section of the outer wall collapsed and overturned, revealing the great breaches torn through the inner bastion by the previous shocks. Houses were tumbling everywhere, but through the dust of falling masonry he could see that several sections of wall were still standing. In the midst of one was a window, and across it, plainly visible, was bound a scarlet cord.

At Joshua's shout of exaltation the Israelite warriors who had been thrown down struggled to their feet. Seizing their spears, they moved toward the walls, which were still crumbling apart and falling to the ground. Dust filled the air, but Salmon held his breath and plunged on with only one thought in mind, to reach the house where Rahab would be waiting. In the excitement and the blood lust that always went with *herem,* he knew that something could easily go wrong and she and those with her might still be injured in spite of Joshua's order.

Stumbling over great boulders—so recently shaken loose from the masonry of the wall that they were still moving—coughing and choking from the dust and barely able to see, Salmon pushed on.

Now he was past the first wall and into the rubble-filled area between it and the inner one. Pausing for a moment, he peered through the haze, looking for Rahab's house, which, since it was built across the walls, could be entered only from the inner one.

Already the butchery of the inhabitants had begun, and the screams of the dying penetrated even through the roar of falling rocks and the groaning of those sections of the walls that had not already fallen. Above the screams sounded the exultant cries of the Israelite warriors as they went about the bloody task of carrying out the *herem*.

An Israelite soldier loomed suddenly out of the dusty haze beside Salmon, instinctively stabbing at him with his spear until he recognized the physician and deflected the point at the last moment. Belatedly Salmon remembered that he was armed with nothing save the bronze knife he carried at his belt for cutting away clothing and slitting cloth for bandages.

The air cleared for an instant and he was able to distinguish the wall of a house that looked like Rahab's, still standing to the right of him. Turning, he plunged toward it and lurched into a courtyard that seemed familiar. He moved on, caroming against a wall as he stumbled over a pile of rubble, and half falling through a door leading into the lower floor of the house.

"Rahab!" he shouted. "Rahab! Where are you?"

Guided by a woman's scream, Salmon turned toward another room and found himself facing a soldier of Israel with spear upraised, ready to strike a woman cowering in the corner. Even as he struck the spear aside, Salmon recognized her as the old slave who had brought him to Rahab in this very house only a short while before.

"This is the house with the scarlet cord," he shouted into the astonished face of the soldier. "Harm these people and Joshua will have your heart."

The man still stared stupidly at him, but Salmon paid no more attention to him. Kneeling, he lifted Myrnah's head and saw that she was not hurt, only pale with fear and shock. "Where is your mistress?" he demanded.

"In—in there," she gasped, pointing toward another room. "With the baby."

"Guard this house well," Salmon ordered the soldier. "It is under the protection of Joshua."

The man nodded and lifted his spear once more. Whimpering with fear and relief, the slave woman scuttled through the open door leading to the adjoining room. There Salmon found Rahab with the baby clutched to her breast. Her body was bent over so that if the walls fell they would strike her first, so she did not see him.

He touched her shoulder gently, and she looked up with eyes that were wide with horror. Then a sudden light of gladness burned in them.

"Salmon!" she cried. "Yahweh has delivered up Jericho to Joshua."

Salmon felt as if a band of the Hittite metal had been forged about his heart, but this was no time to consider his own feelings. "We must get out of the house," he told Rahab, lifting her to her feet. "This section of the wall may fall at any time."

With Rahab carrying Jaschar and followed by Myrnah and Senu, who had appeared out of the dust and rubble from somewhere in the building, Salmon led them from the house. Hardly were they clear of it when the roof collapsed with a groan of rending timbers and the outer wall tilted slowly away to crash upon the rubble pile forming all that was now left of the once formidable defenses of Jericho.

"Yah protected us, Salmon!" Rahab cried, her eyes shining. "He kept the walls standing until you could find and save us."

An Israelite captain came into the courtyard, followed by a dozen warriors, their spears and knives dripping blood. With a surge of relief Salmon recognized his friend Khalith.

"This is Rahab and her family," Salmon called to him. "Give me soldiers to protect them."

"The harlot?" Khalith peered at them through the murky dust-filled air that shrouded the city in a pall of destruction.

"Did Joshua call me a harlot when he gave the order, Salmon?" Rahab asked quickly. At the hurt in her voice he knew he dare not tell her the truth. And yet if he could, he would have spared her some of the heartbreak she must experience when she met Joshua again.

"The house where you were staying was known to be a brothel," Salmon explained. "He spoke without thinking."

Khalith detailed six Israelite warriors as a guard for them. "You will be safe with these men," Salmon told Rahab. "I must see to the wounded."

"Where is Joshua?"

"He led the soldiers across the walls," said Khalith. "You will find him wherever the fighting is thickest for the rest of the day."

As Rahab and her guard moved off into the dust cloud, Khalith wiped sweat from his face. "You will have little work today, Salmon," he said. "Jericho's defenders were jellied with fear. Only a few mercenaries and one Egyptian captain dared to fight against us. Joshua cut him down in one thrust."

And indeed, as Salmon went about the city looking for those who might need his services, he saw that Khalith had been almost correct. Stunned by the earthquake that had leveled the walls and let the armies of Israel pour into the city unimpeded, the people of Jericho had resigned themselves to death from the very beginning of the attack.

Sickened by the butchery, Salmon made his way through the gate shortly after sunset and down the ramp to the spring outside what was left of the walls of Jericho. His elaborate plan for securing the spring would not be needed now—further proof, it seemed, that Yahweh did indeed speak through the voice of Joshua.

Salmon doused his head with water and drank deeply, but even quenching his thirst could not cure the sickness in his heart. Butchery like this, even in the name of Yahweh, he could never understand. Nor could he believe that it was really the purpose of the god they worshipped, however warlike they believed him to be.

Parts of the city were aflame already. As the raging fires swept through the flimsy roofs of the houses—most of them covered with dried rushes that caught like tinder—the people who had hidden in the hovels and huts built into the very walls of the city were driven out, along with the rats and vermin who skulked there. Rats and vermin the soldiers spared; they had no quarrel with them. But men and women, old and young, and children of every age they cut down with their spears and battle-axes.

A ring of soldiers surrounded the entire city now, driving back with naked spears anyone who managed to burst through, forcing them to choose between death upon the weapon or in the raging holocaust that had once been the proud city of Jericho.

A line of men led from the gate to the camp, carrying the wealth of Jericho, ornaments and utensils of gold and silver, images of Baal and other gods, tools of iron, cooking pots of copper, metal-reinforced helmets and shields—all the loot that fell to the conquerors of a fallen city. Some of the booty, Salmon knew, would find its way into the tents of the people, in spite of Joshua's strict order that everything of value was to be dedicated to Yahweh by being placed in the temple treasury. That was expected, however, and not even the priests worried about it, so long as the major share found its way into their hands.

At the Israelite camp at Gilgal the priests were busy in the open space before the tent housing the Ark of the Covenant, counting and recording the booty in the light of flaming torches. There, as he had expected, Salmon found Rahab's father, Chazan, busy at his task as chief of the scribes, recording on a long papyrus roll each item and its estimated value.

"Yah will bless you for giving Rahab back to me, Salmon," the old man cried, embracing him.

"She earned her freedom," Salmon assured him. "But I am glad I reached the house first."

"Rahab told me that but for you they would have been killed." Chazan's face sobered. "Have you seen Joshua? She has been asking for him."

"He is still in the city, seeing that it is burned, down to the last stone."

Chazan looked across the plain toward the red glare that now masked what had been a proud city. "What can I tell Rahab about the change in Joshua? I would like to soften the blow for her."

"Don't say anything yet," Salmon advised. "When Joshua sees the baby, he will know it is his beyond any question. He may feel differently then."

The old scribe shook his head slowly. "It takes an understanding and tolerant person to play god, Salmon. I am afraid Joshua is neither."

"Where is Rahab?"

"In my tent, over there at the edge of the camp."

Salmon frowned. "I thought your tent was in the center of the camp, near Joshua's."

"The women are already saying Rahab bewitched you and Caleb so she would be spared from Jericho. It seemed better for her to be at one side of the camp, at least until the *herem* is over."

As Salmon moved through the camp he saw that the women were already beginning to gather in little groups. And as they talked their eyes went to Chazan's tent, where Rahab and those who had escaped from Jericho with her were quartered. A few even stopped him to demand why a harlot should have been spared from the curse put upon Jericho and to predict that bad luck for the whole camp would come because of her.

20 Deborah and Barak

The author of three biblical novels and one post-biblical novel, Nathaniel Norsen Weinreb brought a storyteller's approach to his books. Only in his *Esther* did he remain close to the Bible source. In *The Babylonians* he centered his story on extra-biblical characters, though Jeremiah and other biblical figures do appear. In *The Copper Scrolls,* probably the only novel drawn to date from the Dead Sea Scrolls, he created fictional characters against an Essene background. *The Sorceress* was written in 1954. Here Weinreb renames the biblical hero Barak, calling him Dael on the grounds that Barak was either a title or nickname which means *lightning.* He does not hesitate to weave his own story through the biblical background, creating a romance between Deborah, the Judge, and Barak, the General, whereas the Bible specifically refers to Deborah as another man's wife. Weinreb also follows the common practice of attributing Nordic qualities to Semitic characters; as in giving Deborah "butter-yellow" hair. Well-educated and story-wise, Weinreb has written short stories and dramatic scripts for radio. He also worked as a story analyst for a motion picture studio.

And the Lord sold them into the hand of Jabin king of Canaan, that reigned in Hazor; the captain of whose host was Sisera, which dwelt in Harosheth of the Gentiles.

And the children of Israel cried unto the Lord: for he had nine hundred chariots of iron; and twenty years he mightily oppressed the children of Israel.

And Deborah, a prophetess, the wife of Lapidoth, she judged Israel at that time.

And she dwelt under the palm tree of Deborah between Ramah and Bethel in mount Ephraim: and the children of Israel came up to her for judgment.

And she sent and called Barak the son of Abinoam out of Kedesh-naphtali, and said unto him, Hath not the Lord God of Israel commanded, saying, Go and draw toward mount Tabor, and take with thee ten thousand men of the children of Naphtali and of the children of Zebulun?

JUDGES: IV, 2–6

THE SORCERESS by NATHANIEL NORSEN WEINREB

SLOWLY DEBORAH LED Dael down the narrow trail which wound its way to the encampment of Israel on Mount Tabor. The battle, she knew, was but one day—perhaps two at the most—away. The rains had come and the pores of the plain had opened to receive the waters from the sky. Already the normally dry and flat land now was soggy and heavy with the rainfall, mud lay thick over everything, and here and there the earth had sagged under the weight of the fall of rain, creating huge pits and craters. The footing was treacherous, the scouts had reported. Another day of downpour, and Israel would be ready to strike. Deborah took a quick glance at the sky above and breathed a little prayer that all she could see were the low, fat, scudding clouds that hovered ominously over all.

Slowly Dael became aware of the stir of life and the throb and hum of domestic activities around them in the pitched tents or in the natural shelters of caves. As they moved downward, he caught glimpses of family life—here a woman bent over the mortar and pestle of her mill, pounding the corn or barley that would make tomorrow's bread, there a man blowing upon the flames of a small fire, a group seated around an eating mat. Snatches of song, the soft insidious tinkle of the *kinnor* harp and the exotic, lonely wail of wooden flute floated up lazily to them.

At first Dael had debated the virtues of having the warriors accompanied to the mountain by their families. But he had finally decided that to leave them alone in their homes, unprotected, at the mercy of Sisera's raiders, would not only endanger their lives but would fill the spirits of their men with doubt and anxiety. So he had agreed that the wives and children accompany the fighters.

Thicker and more profuse grew the temporary homes and the people who now dwelled in them. Around Dael there swirled the odors of cooking, hot and savory goat's flesh being roasted, the aroma of freshly baked bread, the vinegary pungence of wine. In a small tent a dark-haired mother was nursing her babe, while near her another mother was shoveling food, piled high on a bone spoon, into the smeared and gurgling mouth of an older child.

"The children are everywhere!" Dael mused.

"And why not?" came Deborah's soft answer. "Whom but for the children do we fight? So that their generation may have the peace that ours did not?"

He looked quizzically at her, wondering at a hidden meaning in her answer, whether there was anything personal in it, then decided not to explore further.

When he said he had seen enough of the camp and was satisfied as to its location, she urged him forward. "Only a few paces more," she said, pointing to a wide and unguarded space to their right. "There is something

I most desire for you to behold." She wet her lips nervously. "The Ark," she added.

He stiffened with surprise, his glance touching hers hotly. "The Ark!" he finally burst out. "What need is there for me to see it?"

"There is need, Dael. You are the chosen leader of Israel," she answered. And in her mind she added: *Chosen but not yet dedicated.* Still, she began to pull him forward, but his feet remained rooted against the stones of the trail. She continued to tug at him and, to gain time, he asked, "Why is not the Ark guarded?"

Deep in her throat the laugh arose, then died as quickly as it had sprung into life. "Because there is no need for man to guard the Ark. For what greater protection than the power of Jehovah Himself can there be?"

Slowly she led him into the open enclosure. There Dael saw a portable tent shrine of the kind he had seen on the walls of certain houses in Memphis that had the picture writing on them. As he neared it, he saw that it was made of ram's skin dyed red, with a domed roof, and large enough to hold two or three persons. As he hesitated, Deborah confidently swung aside the low-hanging canopy and waited for Dael. "Fear not," she encouraged him, "for the Lord is here, and with thee as well."

She pushed him forward gently, and Dael, stooping slightly, entered the interior, surprised to find little more in there than a single lamp, suspended from a pole, blazing heartily against the darkness of the corners of the sanctuary. Directly under the lamp, in the center of the portable shrine, stood a squared box with four rings on each corner.

"For the carrying poles," Deborah explained, pointing to the circlets of metal, "and constructed by some of our finest craftsmen. See for yourself." Her hand indicated the cover of the box, which, Dael noticed at once, gleamed a dull yellow.

"It is made of pure, beaten gold," she went on, "as are these two images."

Dael's interest quickened immediately. As a worker in metals, not as a leader or fighter now, he bent forward, his hands already running with loving and knowing knowledge over the smooth surface which, despite the coolness of the night, still appeared warm to him.

His fingers touched a pair of small statuettes, child-faced and fruited with spread wings, which hovered over the lid. The two little figurines were deftly molded into the gilded cover of the chest of cedarwood by their entwined feet.

"But one is broken!" he exclaimed sharply, pointing to the left wing of one of the cherubim, which had a crack in it and seemed to droop.

Her smile was wan in the pale light. "Remember you how once I spoke of this?" she recalled. "I said then that the Ark needed mending and that no craftsman had been found who could make the repairs."

He nodded, concentrating on the metal figures. It really would not be hard to do, he mused. First to melt the wing off, then shape it carefully to the right size, and then, with infinite care, mold it back onto the body again.

Perhaps he would even place the wing a little higher, to make it look more protective, more defiant.

Dael felt Deborah's hand on his. "Now," came her hushed voice, "take your hand and open the lid and gaze within. Come, fear not. With my hand on yours you will open the Ark."

She felt his fingers tremble, then steady themselves as they found the edge of the lid and lifted—slowly, carefully, until the golden cover stood upright on rigid hinges. Together, the close-cropped head close to the butter-haired one, they bent over the box. All Dael could see inside the Ark were two large stone tablets about three feet in length and a foot wide.

"Reach within, take them out and read," she urged. And with a sudden confidence he had not felt before, he obeyed her. He found the tablets stone-cold to his touch. Carefully he brought them out, hugging them to his chest, greatly fearing that he might drop one and shatter it to bits. Deborah, a strange smile on her lips, took one of the flat stones from him. The other he brought closer to the suspended lamp.

"Read, Dael."

He concentrated on the letters which were carved in a beautiful and archaic style. Then, as the phrases combined in familiar groups before his eyes, he began to read in a voice that grew louder and stronger as he mouthed each syllable.

His voice never faltered as he read the Commandments of the covenant made between Jehovah and Moses, how Jehovah was the one and only God and there could be no others but He, how no images of Jehovah should be carved for worship, and His name not to be invoked for evil intent, how to remember the seventh day for Him and keep it holy.

" 'Honor thy father and mother, that you may live long in the land the Lord your God is giving you,' " his voice rang, and then faltered as he remembered Abinoam, his father, and how he had died. *And have I honored him?* he asked himself. He paused. He had come to the bottom of the first tablet. But before he could reach out for the second one in Deborah's arms, her own voice, beautiful in its trained and poetic expression and phrasing, went on for him.

" 'Thou shalt not commit murder.'

" 'Thou shalt not commit adultery.'

" 'Thou must not steal.'

" 'Thou must not bring a false charge against your neighbor.' "

And she finished with the laws that forbade the coveting of a neighbor's wife, his male or female slave, his ox, ass, or anything that was of his possession. And when she had concluded, she gently took the tablet, replaced it within the Ark, while Dael did the same with his. He closed the lid tenderly, his eyes dark with thought.

"Of what you found here, or what you read, does it appear to you that Jehovah is nothing but another blood-smeared war god?" she demanded quietly. "Does a god of war speak thus, and in such terms? Does a war god forbid murder and false witness and theft and adultery and coveting? In what you read was there only blood lust? Do you really believe that Jehovah, who inspires such a philosophy of life as revealed in the commandments, can be nothing but a savage deity of fierce desert tribesmen?"

He made no answer, his head bowed.

"More than that is Jehovah," she insisted. "A whole world will someday live according to the concepts you have seen enscribed here. Jehovah is more than a mere tribal god; He is for *all* to share. And to love. For, yes, Jehovah is a god of love," she continued softly. "You know the phrase. 'In the image of God He created him. Male and female created He them,' " she whispered. "Hear me, Dael. For in those two words 'male and female' speaks the essence of Jehovah. For Jehovah speaks of love now, of love between man and woman and for the children that are born from such unions of love. Therefore, Jehovah is a god of love and so shall forever be for all mankind. Not of war, Dael, but of love . . ."

He lifted his head and looked at her. For some time now, perhaps since his return from Egypt, he had longed to tell her that he thought she was right. But perhaps pride and stubborness had tied his tongue with thongs of silence.

His hand caressed the Ark. "Why?" he asked, more of himself than of her, "do the words of the Commandments seem so different now? I knew them, had read them before. But now, at this time . . ." His voice, soft with wonder, faded.

Deborah made no vocal answer at first, her eyes cast downward, with only the insect-shaped eyebrows raised high. A slight smile trembled on her mouth. But when she spoke, she looked at him. "Perhaps," she answered, "you had to live the words before you could understand them."

Slowly he nodded. She was right. Call Him what you might, Jehovah the god of war, or the god of peace, the fact remained that, because of love for this woman, he, Dael, had gone through many ordeals gladly and was prepared to face more. It came upon him again, as it had when Ard's bitter words had lashed at his conscience, that it was necessary to fight first for the love, or peace, a man desired. I know now, he admitted in silent and rueful thought, that I cannot live aloofly in a world, I cannot be an island, not to partake of events and affairs which will lead to a better life for all. No man can so live alone. If I fight for Jehovah, the god of war, so that He may become a god of peace, I will have shared in the struggle of all mankind and shall share in the fruits that later must come.

Deborah was beginning to move out of the sanctuary when he stopped her. "I wait here," he said, his hands running over the broken wing of one of the cherubim. "Have fetched for me a strong hand bellows and a fine chisel. And order a hot fire built for me outside." He grinned at her amazed expression.

"The broken wing," he explained. "I would repair it so it may fly high in victory for Jehovah . . ."

Later it was told by those who remembered, and mouthed and repeated by countless generations, until it was finally enscribed in the books of the land, that Jehovah had been pleased and gratified that Dael had laid his gifted and gentle craftsman's hands on the Ark of the Lord. For otherwise, asked the chronicles, would Jehovah have opened the heavens that very night and sent forth such a downpour as had never before been beheld by the eyes of man?

For hours the rain never stopped, and with it Jehovah also hurled his lightning bolts, his crashing thunder, the whistling wind, and even great icy stones of hail that shrieked as they rent the sodden clouds and buried themselves in the soggy earth of the plain with great splashes of mud that curtained the scene. And where these hailstones nosed into the soft and yielding ground, other spouts of water streamed upward, so it was as if the rain poured from both above and from within the earth itself. The great plain became riddled with pits, and where there were no depressions on the land, the mud was like a treacherous, clinging sea of brown.

And there were those who huddled in fear that night as the rain and hail drummed against the tent walls or on the stone shelters, and whispered that Jehovah, the God of Israel, and Hadad the weather deity of Canaan, were already locked in a personal, mighty combat of their own.

And when the dawn lanced the eastern horizon, hardly able to pierce the thick, rain-sodden clouds that scudded close to the earth—clouds that were borne on the high wind—Dael ben Abinoam, he who was known as Barak, knew the time for battle was at hand.

He did not need a grim Obed, leader of the Benjamite and Ephraimite forces, already encamped at the south shore of the Kishon, to meet him and tell him the plain was in an almost untenable position and that the river was rising furiously all along its banks.

By the end of the first watch of morning, Obed returned to his men with instructions to select those who were fit for battle and to march openly out on the level ground, where Sisera's scouts would see them, report them, and bring the chariots into the open for the battle.

As Obed returned to the southern camp, Dael ordered his captains and lieutenants gathered unto him to begin the selection of the warriors. In a small valley, part of a cuplike depression grooved against the flank of Mount Tabor, Dael commanded that the northern tribes stand before him for the battle selection. And the men of Naphtali, Issachar, Zebulon, and Western Manasseh heard and obeyed. Under their banners, damp and heavy with water, but still wind-whipped proudly, they stood, the warriors who were this day to meet the might of Jabin and Sisera.

Standing on a low edge of rock, Dael again beheld the banners—the flag of Ephraim, with the single horn on the goat bobbing and darting in the wind; the pennant of Manasseh, the half tribe of the son of Joseph, with its bull's image nodding at the goat; the symbol of Zebulon, its twelve-oared, bird-shaped boat rocking in the gusts; the sign of Issachar, the strong old man, bearded and bent under his pack, but all-eternal, all-wise.

And proudest of all the flags, it seemed to Dael now, was that of Naphtali, of his own tribe and his own people and of his own blood. Great artistry had gone into the creation of that banner, the leaping gazelle who freely and joyously sprang under the protecting rays of a crimson-and-gold sun. The gazelle leaps to freedom, he thought, with proud and quickening heart, a freedom we shall this day wrest from the iron jaws of Canaan.

Yet he knew that under the cold and impersonal scrutiny of any man of war the situation of Israel could be considered hopeless, even with the rain. Nine hundred chariots and twenty thousand of Jabin's best fighters awaited only nine thousand of the warriors of Israel. Canaan was fruitful with horses, vehicles, weapons of bronze and iron, spears, bows, axes, javelins, swords, while Israel had little more than clubs, stones, a few swords, some meager supplies of bows and arrows, flint knives, boomerangs.

And faith . . .

Faith that they would win, that they must win to preserve their integrity, their very way of life, to continue existing, to save the land and keep the peace for their children and their children's children for all time.

But was faith, an ideal, enough? Would that be strong enough to hammer down the iron chariots, break through the sturdy shields of Jabin?

Almost unseeingly he stared before him. They *must* believe, his intellect told him, just as he himself now believed. He had come to the road of faith after a long and indifferent detour. But if he did not believe—believe that in Jehovah would be found peace, even if it meant war first—would he be here now? And would the others be with him? They, too, must share the same convictions. There were no mercenaries among the men of Israel. They had come willingly and without coercion. The farmers and the laborers, the artisans and craftsmen and the scribes and poets and musicians had all come when they had been summoned. No officers had, at sword's point, forced them into combat. Even now those who might be faint of heart were free to leave when the selections began. And men who came to fight willingly, he thought, his resolve strengthening, could not easily be defeated.

And there was more, he pondered. For the first time in the history, for the really first, recorded time, the tribes of Israel were uniting against a common foe. True, the great Joshua had invaded the land, but he had come with no great and summoned army; his military achievements had been more in the nature of quick, guerrilla-like raids, infiltrations and the conquest of certain Canaanite settlements. And with him had been no single and unified fighting cohort, merely parts of tribes, of wanderers, of men even foreign to Israel who had attached themselves to the invaders. But now Israel—at least half of it—stood together against the foe, stood as an army, as an individual host. And perhaps, he thought, it was the start, the beginning of many such armies until Israel would be mighty and ready to resist any and all who threatened it. Perhaps in future centuries men would point to this day and say to their children:

"It started then . . ."

He straightened his shoulders, glanced at his captains. "Let the selections begin," he ordered quietly. He stepped aside as three musicians, lifting the rams' horns to their lips, blew the blasts that rolled and echoed and were hurled against the mountain and then returned to the ears of all. Only dimly he heard the laws of the selection being mouthed by the captains. Those men who had built a new house and had not yet dedicated it, those who had planted a new vineyard or who had a new wife, still virgin, those who were fearful and faint of heart were commanded to step forward and be excused from warfare.

Dael's eyes stung with pride as not a single man stood forth to be counted. He knew, as well as did his officers, that many among the Israelites could have met the requirements but refused. For, he understood now, what good were houses and vineyards and wives and children if there was no peace, if all could be destroyed or taken away?

He stood with the others as the priests and Levites made the dedications to Jehovah and sanctified the fighters for battle. Then, as the sacrifices began, he strode from the ledge, seeking Deborah, finding her huddled against a rock. She was wearing a robe of light wool, and around her shoulder was strapped an inkhorn that swung from her right hip. In the wide belt were stuck several pens, and in her left hand she carried a small untouched and unrolled scroll of horse leather. Her hair was swept back from her forehead by a band of lapis-lazuli-blue, and on her feet she wore long thonged boots.

He frowned as he saw her, his eyes touching her equipment with a severe glance. "You cannot stay here," he finally said. "We sweep down into battle soon after Obed moves out into the plain. Return you with the other women up the mountainside, where it will be safe."

But she smiled at him and shook her head. "I go not with them," she answered quietly, "but venture down with the fighters." She touched the scroll in her fingers. "This day I will write of the great victory I shall see, so that all men may read of it later."

Dael's face was hard. "I so order you to return," he said shortly. "The field of battle is not for women."

She continued to smile at him. "I do not go forth to battle, merely to record," she replied. "I will not be hurt. I will watch and write what I see. And why not?" she mused as if to herself. "Perhaps in other times other women will do as I do today. Write what they see when their men fight." The smile left her lips and she came closer. "Dael, can you not understand? This must be written down as it happens, so that men will remember and have the word before them always. Perhaps there will come times when they will need the spirit of confidence and hope and faith to move them, and they can read what I will this day enscribe, and their hearts will be refreshed."

He looked away from her. "I want you not here," he insisted stubbornly. "It is your life that concerns me. That—and nothing more. I cannot lose you. Not now. Not after—"

Her lips were both cool and clinging against his mouth. When she broke away, her smile was wistful. "Fear not, beloved," she assured him. "For Jehovah is this day with me, as He will be with you. I will be in no danger but watch from a distance. Go now," she added kindly, "for it is time."

He nodded, opened his mouth as if to speak again, then turned sharply on his heel and walked away, hardly hearing her call after him, "I will take care."

And thus the first general of a united Israel and perhaps the first woman ever to witness a battle and enscribe it for the future parted.

And now, having crossed the south bank of the Kishon, the men of Benjamin and Ephraim advanced boldly upon the Plain of Esdraelon.

Watching from their hidden positions near the base of Mount Tabor, Dael and his men saw Obed leading his own fighters as they made their way laboriously through the mud. No mail, no armor weighed them down. They wore loose mantles, kilts, or loincloths as rank by rank they wheeled and faced the high ground to the west where surely the great chariots of Sisera must hurtle upon them. In their hands were clubs, oxgoads, daggers, a few homemade spears. Some of the captains carried awkward and bulky-looking swords. Other men held the wooden boomerangs. A few had their bows slung over their left shoulders.

And some, Dael noticed, had nothing in their hands but stones . . .

Still onward they went, toward the west, knowing that soon the thunder of the wheels must meet them. Stubbornly, courageously, and yet quietly they moved forward under the murky, windswept skies, pierced now by the peaks of Mount Carmel ahead of them and of Mount Tabor to their right.

"Look, my lord." It was Heldai, one of his captains of a hundred, who touched Dael, pointing to his own right. Dael's eyes followed the gesturing finger, and he froze into stiffened attention.

For now the might of Sisera was advancing upon Israel.

From the west they came, from Harosheth, from the place of the setting sun, the picked twenty thousand of Canaan, with their nine hundred terrible war wagons, with their blades already glinting dully in the light as they turned on the hubs, with their trained war horses who knew how to kill, with their drivers and archers and spearmen and cavalry poised for the conflict. Already wheels were churning and working heavily on the drenched upland as they came pouring down toward the soggy plain.

It was an awesome sight to behold, this powerful army of banners and pennants and death. First, approaching slowly, majestically, almost in arrogant defiance, were the great chariots of six spokes, with driver, spearman, and archer on the swaying platforms. In three tightly packed rows of three hundred the massed vehicles neared the host of Israel, each chariot moving panel to panel, each horse's shoulders in line with the others, stepping high, their plumes bobbing, the jingle of the tiny pomegranate bells on their bellybands already reaching the ears of the men at the base of the mountain. Red and gold and blue shone the enameled panels, bronze glinted from spears and swords and mail. As if turned by a single hand, eighteen hundred wheels churned the mud that could not blanket the rising, rolling boom of the oncoming chariots.

Sisera, Dael saw at once, was taking no chances, meeting the nearing Israelites, who were on foot, as if they were a mighty army themselves. For not only was there a solid wall of chariots to the front, but, protecting their rear and front were the checkreined and impatient chargers of the cavalry, the riders sitting stiffly and proudly upon the ornamented saddles, their javelins already naked in their hands.

And behind the chariots and the cavalry trudged the foot soldiers, the spearmen, the archers, the axmen, and the slingers.

Dael's breath caught harshly in his throat and escaped in a trembling sigh. "Sisera is determined to win," he pointed out to Heldai. "The battle formation is perfect. The chariots to break through the front, the cavalry to attack from the flank and to the rear, and the foot soldiers to move in to finish the deadly work." He glanced quickly at the captain beside him and wondered if his own face was as pale as that of Heldai.

On and on rolled the war wagons, forward trotted the horses of the cavalry, ahead surged the masses of the infantry, some slowly removing their bows and notching the arrows into the strings. And already the sounds of battle were starting, the occasional neigh of a horse, a shrill command, the creak of leather, the sucking sound of hoofs in mud.

But the men of Israel never faltered, also moving forward through the heavy mud into the very jaws of death, heads up, stride confident, shaggy hair flowing in the wind, faces lifted. And leading them was the sturdy figure of Obed, his crude sword already raised.

Watching them, Dael shivered—whether from pride or fear, he was never to know. For a fleeting moment he thought: It is folly, madness, fanatical and fantastic. How can we win against such a war machine? The men of Ephraim and Benjamin will be shattered by the first charge of the chariots, will be crushed in the vise of the cavalry and annihilated by the foot soldiers.

But still the men of Israel marched on, coming ever closer and closer to the chariots, which were picking up speed, the bladed scythes whirling faster now, the figures on the platforms steadying themselves against the lurch and bounce by holding onto the panel straps. And along the flanks, the riders began to spur their horses, lifting their feathered javelins high in the air.

"Soon . . ." Dael heard Heldai breathe beside him.

Shorter grew the distance between Israel and Canaan, closer and closer came the chariots. They had reached the flat plain now and were close enough for Dael to make out clearly the high and protective panels, even the inlaid ornamentation. The tremendous wheels, heavy with steel at the hubs, were churning the heavy mud.

And high rose the hoofs of the charging horses, their flanks already bespattered by mud, their handsome trappings soaked and soggy. The proud crests and haughty plumes still danced on the heads of the beasts, but the constant bouncing and jogging caused these ornaments to act as hindrances now, slipping over the eyes of the horses, blinding some of them until a charioteer had to cut them off with his sword.

The cavalry, too, swung into action, their riders low in the saddles now, the javelins held level as they moved against the advancing Israelites. And from the rear the footmen and archers either stood or knelt as they unstrung their bows. Cloud after cloud of arrows whispered their song of death as they soared skyward and then landed in the midst of the men of Benjamin and Ephraim, no longer walking now, but running into the fray. And the flung spears hissed their own deadly tune as they pierced the air and sought their targets of flesh.

It was becoming a blurred scene now—the rocking chariots, the plunging horses, the running men who closed in against the Canaanites. Almost with bare hands the ragged, lean, gaunt tribesmen leaped upon the war horses, tearing bridles from them, their knives glinting dully as they whipped at tendon and sinew. And the land was covered with sound now, the yelling, the blaspheming, the prayers, the exhortations, the neighing and screaming. With a sickening feeling Dael saw the men of Benjamin and Ephraim fall, like the mown wheat, as the arrows and spears cut them down, as horses' hoofs tramped them into the bloodied mud, as scythed wheels chopped and slashed, as chariot warriors, leaning out of the platform, hacked with sword and ax.

But not a man of Israel turned backward. With bared teeth they leaped upon all who came at them, hanging from bridles, poles, from harness, clambering onto the very chariots themselves, and, while the vehicle was still in motion, engaging the fighters there in hand-to-hand combat. Forward and onward, not to be stopped, sometimes scrambling over their own dead, they flung themselves at the enemy, using oxgoads to pierce eyes and bodies, hammering with the stones in their fists, unmindful of the death around, in front, and above them.

And now the mud began to take its toll. The chariots' wheels were biting helplessly against the soft and yielding ground. Whips flashed over the flanks of the horses, the muscles of their haunches strained as they sought to extricate themselves from the sticky embrace. Here and there a chariot began to founder, then to slip, then overturning entirely, the spokes spinning slowly against the leaden sky. And into these overturned wagons others crashed, borne forward by the momentum of their charge. Loud and terrible were the screams now, the whinnying of horses already entangled in their own harness.

And like lithe cats, the men of Israel leaped upon these stalled vehicles and savagely struck at all before them, at drivers and horses and warriors alike, slashing and cutting. Many were already armed with Canaanite weapons, which they used against their former owners. Others, seizing emptied chariots, were charging frenziedly into the ranks of the Canaanite-manned wagons with smashing impact that crushed and shattered the vehicles. Here and there little piles of chariots, either mired or overturned, began to dot the plain. Furiously—but more helplessly now—the cavalry wheeled, unable to use its lances for fear of killing their own men.

Dael felt Heldai look at him, and the man from Naphtali nodded his head slowly.

"Now," he ordered tersely. As Heldai was about to rise, Dael stopped him with a hand on his elbow. "Before you give the signal, do your chosen ones have the torches hidden in the pitchers?"

Heldai nodded. "And the rams' horns as well, my lord."

Dael also arose, feeling at his waist for the sword. He regarded Heldai soberly. "We will charge down the mountain now," he said quietly. "And may Jehovah be with us." As Heldai nodded, Dael asked, "And the woman, Deborah?"

The tight smile stretched briefly over Heldai's face. "She will be safe. She told me you need have no great fear over her."

Dael nodded again. "So be it," he said. "Now we go into battle. Let the signal be sounded."

And again a ram's horn—five times—called out, and then men of Naphtali, Issachar, Zebulon, and Manasseh, who had been hidden, rose as one and began their wild charge down the mountainside to the plain below.

"*Cherev l'Adonoi!* The word for the Lord!"

By the twenties, then the fifties, then the hundreds and thousands, they stormed down Mount Tabor, screaming their great battle cry—leaping, lean, bearded men, unkempt, with their long hair streaming in back of them, their crude weapons held high before them. In front they were led by Heldai and Dael, closely flanked by those who bore live torches, whose flames were guarded against extinguishing by the pitchers in which the brands had been thrust.

"*Cherev l'Adonoi!*"

With a roaring fury they sprang and bounded from their ambush upon the field of battle. The Canaanites, already desperately fighting for their lives, heard the new sound with dulled ears, and then, with amazed and frightened eyes, beheld the second assault upon them.

In moments, it seemed to Dael, he was closed in battle.

He almost stumbled over the body of a Canaanite officer at his feet. In one smooth and liquid motion he dropped his own sword, retrieved the finer blade of the slain man, waved it high, and urged his men forward. Before him loomed a Canaanite, his teeth bared and grimacing. Dael easily skipped aside, bent his knee slightly, and thrust the sword under and upward. The Canaanite never finished his plunge, whirling once, twisting upon Dael's weapon until the fighter had to force the sword free by jerking at it savagely. As he turned, a spearman charged upon him, the point held low and steady. But Heldai, swinging a battle-ax, let it fly from his hand into the face of the enemy. Grinning at him, Dael plunged ahead, his eyes seeking a free chariot. Already around him the sound of the battle was reaching a maddening pitch, and the torches of the Israelites, which had already made the remaining horses crazed with fear and utterly unmanageable, began to be applied to the chariots. Here and there spurting flames raced along panels and pole. Mounds of mired chariots started to burn hotly. Others, set afire and allowed, like mobile torches, to run free on the battlefield, careened into other vehicles, smashing into panting groups of struggling men.

As he ran forward Dael felt a jarring impact on his shoulders, and he crumpled to the ground, trying to roll from under the Canaanite whose hands were reaching for his throat. Over and over both men turned, with Dael's newly found sword knocked from his grasp. With a free hand he tugged at his waist, slipping the bronze dagger out, jabbing fiercely upward again and again. Blood spilled in a sudden tide over him, and the weight was gone from his body. When he rose to his feet he did not even look at the slain warrior below him.

Another figure reared up at him, ax raised high in the air. Bending swiftly, Dael ducked the first blow as the ax thudded into the ground. He whirled, but not in time to prevent his enemy from wrenching the ax from the earth and raising it to strike again. From the corner of his eye Dael beheld part of a broken chariot wheel. Even before the ax could descend, he had lifted the half-moon of jagged spoke and broken scythe blade and hurled it into that screaming mouth.

His eyes smarting from the pall of smoke that was beginning to hover over the field of combat, he still sought for a chariot, finally seeing one, still unbroken and with its two horses under control, managed by a single driver. He ran toward it, waiting as it bore past him, reaching upward with one hand, vaulting onto the platform. Still half crouched, he coiled himself for the spring upon the driver, the blade in his hand ready for the thrust. He was about to leap when the driver turned and stared.

Dael lowered his knife, sagged against the lurching back of the chariot, grinned weakly at Ard—Ard, blood-smeared, soot-streaked, but wearing Canaanite armor, made of leather and circles of iron fastened against it.

"*Dael!*" Ard began to rein the plunging horses, but Dael merely waved for him to let the beasts continue. He rested for a moment, getting his breath, thankful that Ard, who had gone to fight with his own tribe at the start of the battle, was safe and alive.

"Truly you have the luck of the brave!" Dael shouted. "In one more instant I would have been forced to find a new trainer."

"Or I a fighter!" grinned Ard. He tapped his chest, pointing at the armor. "Behold this. From a Canaanite captain of a hundred. He gave it to me most willingly. This chariot too."

"Gave?" Dael shouted again.

Ard nodded. "In fact, he had no more use of it after my persuasion."

Dael laughed harshly, then looked at the platform of the chariot. There a huge two-bladed sword of iron rattled against the bouncing floor. He picked up the weapon, grunted at its weight, and began to swing it from both hands. "Drive into the footmen!" he ordered.

"What?" Ard screamed with indignation. "Am I your chariot driver then? *I* secured this wagon. Get yourself one of your own!"

But he obeyed Dael, driving into the huddled groups of archers and spearmen who were still valiantly trying to stem the tide of battle. But it was hopeless now. More and more of the Israelites had found chariots and, like Dael and Ard, were thundering into the helpless infantry, hacking at them with sword and ax as they swooped by, returning again and again until they broke whatever ranks they had and began to flee.

To flee westward, toward the city of Harosheth.

To the Kishon, the swollen, flooded Kishon.

And now, as if their very discipline had been shattered by fear, mud, surprise, torch, and blood, the Canaanites began a headlong retreat to their headquarters, hoping to cross the river and thus regroup for another attack. But upon them now from every side, from flank and rear, came the men of Israel, on foot, on horse, in chariots, laden with weapons, carrying torches in pursuit of their foe.

Those Canaanites who still had chariots drove them desperately westward, not stopping to pick up any of their own men who pleaded with them to be spared from the death behind them and at their sides. Although the retreat continued, the battle did not end, with smaller bands of Israelites and Canaanites fighting along the way.

Then, as they neared the Kishon, a new terror unfolded itself before the eyes of the Canaanites. When they had crossed the Kishon four days earlier, it had been a quiet stream, moving slowly, placidly, against its narrow banks. Now, swollen by rain and flood, it was a raging torrent, a turbulent barrier which had spread far beyond its banks and was already pounding against the wheels of the approaching chariots of Jabin.

Dael and Ard, in swift pursuit, knew what faced their enemies. In front of them was this wild and tumultuous stream; to their back came the screaming, battle-maddened, blood-crazed men of Israel.

There was no time for debate or decision now, no moments for planning or deliberation. Without hesitation, the leading chariots plunged into the roaring waters.

For a moment Dael thought they would emerge safely. Horses swam, heads high, and the chariots, although teetering from side to side, still managed to keep afloat. Half carried, half pushed by the angry Kishon, they headed for the middle of the river.

Then it happened.

The weight of the scythed wheels was too much; the burden of the ornaments and tassels and plumes could not combat the snarling raging waters as they closed over chariot after chariot. One by one they went down, twirling over and over in the water, being tumbled along by the force of the flood before disappearing for all time. But the other chariots still kept coming, rolling or pitching over the banks and into the stream. And behind them raged another storm, that of Israel, who dove into the waters and helped the Canaanites drown, thrusting horses' heads under the surface and keeping them there, clawing at drivers and warriors, wrenching them out of the chariots and then slitting their throats. The banks became heaped with the dead. The Kishon turned ruddy, and its foam was flecked with pink.

Dael and Ard, furiously maneuvering their chariot, were almost charged into by another wagon, whose driver was an Israelite. Splattered with mud, with a sword cut still open on his cheek, the driver made a hasty salute.

"I come from Obed," his voice rasped. "He ordered me to find you and tell you that victory is ours!"

Supporting himself by the strap, Dael leaned out. "In what manner?"

The messenger smiled despite the wound. "In back of us the Canaanites are asking for surrender. And their great general, Sisera, has fled the field."

"Sisera? *Fled?*"

It was inconceivable at first, hard for the mind to grasp or imagine. Sisera, the great general, the genius of the chariots, fleeing?

"This is true?" Dael shouted again.

"Both Obed and Nun confirm it," the messenger screamed back. "The Canaanites want our mercy and plead for surrender."

Dael continued staring at the other for a long time, hardly aware of the diminishing sounds of the battle, not knowing when Ard finally calmed the plunging horses, alighted from his chariot, and stood silently at their heads.

Jabin's lips pursed, his pink jowls shook as he laboriously signed the document, held out his hand silently to the scribe who placed the sand box in his palm. The King of All Canaan dipped stubby fingers into the grained surface, pinched the sand, and scattered it carefully over his signature. He stared at it for a moment, lifted it, and handed it to Dael.

"Here is your peace, Barak," the monarch said.

In back of him, Dael could hear the slight stir made by the Canaanite officials and the elders of Israel who now, four days after the defeat of Canaan on the Plain of Esdraelon, were witnessing the peace pact established between Jabin and the tribes of the children of Abraham.

As Dael started to read, he heard Jabin say: "It is all there. No longer will Canaan raid against Israel. And workers in metal, smiths and craftsmen, can continue their peaceful pursuits."

"And enforcement of the worship of Baal?" Deborah's clear voice rang out.

Jabin glared at her, his pink pate turning a shade darker. Then he shrugged. "Worship of Baal by Israel will not be enforced." He continued to stare at this woman, whom some called sorceress and who, others whispered, could be the first queen of Israel if she so chose. He could not help his resentment. She was a woman, and in his entirely male world there was no position of any authority for a woman at all.

"Peace, at least," Jabin's voice rumbled. And peace, he thought, bought at such a terrible price—nearly his whole army destroyed, his general, Sisera, fleeing from battle, only to be slain by the hand of a Kenite woman in whose tent he had sought sanctuary. And if he were to count the loss of his champion, Og, and his wagers—the price was even greater. Still, he mused, it could have been worse. There would be peace now within the land, and Canaan was still intact. Better yet, perhaps now Israel would unite with Canaan against common foes, since there would no longer be warfare between them.

Dael finished reading the document and folded it carefully before thrusting it into his waistband. Jabin looked at him, a suspicion of a smile on his mouth.

"It is satisfactory, Barak?"

"It is," Dael answered solemnly. "Fair and satisfactory."

"And I will honor it," Jabin said, "and see to it that you do as well, since you are now King of Israel."

Dael, also smiling, shook his head. "I am no king, nor wish I to be one," he said. "But I will honor the peace."

"It is what I desire too," Jabin agreed. "Someday you will see that my words will bear fruits of truth. Canaan and Israel will be as one, with the same cultures and religion merging for the good of all."

Dael regarded him. "And would Canaan have prevailed, would you still have felt this way?"

Jabin shrugged. "Perhaps not. Perhaps, had I been victorious over you, I would have marched forth against Egypt. Although," he continued, shaking his head, "it is no longer Egypt which should be feared, but a new power which is rising in the north."

"The wolf of Assyria?" Dael asked quietly.

Jabin nodded glumly. "A new enemy. Not quite ready, perhaps, but ever growing in strength. And one which we will have to fight one day."

"And perhaps then," Deborah broke in, "it will be *Israel* which will defend Canaan against the invader."

Again Jabin peered at her, his little blue eyes speculative and narrow upon her. Still trying to overcome his suspicion and resentment against her as a woman, he made speech directly with her for the first time.

"I am told you witnessed the battle and recorded it in words," he said. "I would that it were given me to hear this poem. Or at least part of it." His curiosity was natural. He had never before met a woman who could read and write.

Deborah, inclining her head somewhat, murmured that she would be pleased to oblige the king and would recite from memory portions of her descriptions of the combat. Then she lifted her head, her eyes half closed as she began to intone:

> "*Awake, awake Deborah,*
> *Awake, awake, utter a song*
> *Arise, Barak, and lead thy captivity captive,*
>   *thou son of Abinoam . . .*
> *Then fought the kings of Canaan*
> *In Taanach by the waters of Megiddo*
> *They fought from heaven*
> *The stars in their courses fought against Sisera.*
> *The brook Kishon swept them away*
> *That ancient brook, the brook Kishon*
> *The earth trembled, the heavens also dropped*
> *Yea, the clouds dropped water*

And the mountains quaked at the presence of the Lord
Then did the horse hoofs stamp
By reason of the prancings
The prancings of the mighty ones. . . ."

21 Jephta's Vow

Lion Feuchtwanger approached both the biblical novel and the historical novel with the respect of a man who has thought profoundly about his craft. To his novels he brought a great learning, a scholar's desire for knowledge, and the ability to read comfortably in Greek, Latin, Hebrew and the significant modern languages. A creative artist who understood what he was trying to do, Feuchtwanger believed that "If a historical novel accomplishes only part of what it sets out to do, it affords the reader an experience that no other form of literature can give him. The reader can at one and the same time live the very lives of the characters and yet watch them from a distance. He does not merely understand, he actu-ally feels that the problems of these long-passed men and women, however different they may seem, are the same that concern him and will some day concern his grandchildren." To the biblical novel he brought another concept, ". . . many of the men we read about in the Bible have an air of historical truth lacking in the characters of other ancient literatures . . . these Hebrew authors . . . were conscious that their own time was a link in an immense chain, a bridge between past and future." Internationally renowned for his historical novels, *Proud Destiny, Power,* the Josephus trilogy, Feuchtwanger drew upon the Bible only once in *Jephta,* written in 1957.

> *And Jephthah vowed a vow unto the Lord, and said, If thou shalt without fail deliver the children of Ammon into mine hands,*
>
> *Then it shall be, that whatsoever cometh forth of the doors of my house to meet me, when I return in peace from the children of Ammon, shall surely be the Lord's, and I will offer it up for a burnt offering.*
>
> JUDGES: XI, 30–31

JEPHTA AND HIS DAUGHTER by LION FEUCHTWANGER

THE MARCH OF Jephta's men to the Jabok was as arduous as he had foreseen. More than one man dropped out. But Jemin showed his mettle. At the appointed time Jephta arrived at the Nahal-Gad with his troops.

The same day Gadiel also arrived, bringing a stronger force of armed men than Jephta had hoped for. He feared that such a large body moving across country could not have remained unobserved. However, Gadiel had seen to it that there was considerable activity in the camp outside Mizpah, and he had also sent raiding parties out into Ammon's territory; so the enemy was not likely to discover that the men had been pulled away from Mizpah.

Scouts reported the movements of Bashan's warriors. The enemy marched down Pharaoh's great highway, but then, as Jephta and Jemin had foreseen, most of the companies of light-armed men and even some groups of mounted men turned aside and took the shorter road leading to the ford of the Jabok.

The force that Bashan was sending to King Nahash was unexpectedly strong and was accompanied by a large baggage train. It approached slowly. Jephta and Jemin were able to make their preparations at leisure and with all due care. They occupied the heights on both sides of the Nahal-Gad gorge so they could block the entrance and the exit with all possible speed. As Gadiel had brought so many men with him, Jephta was able to post a strong detachment on the far bank of the Jabok as well, to catch, as they crossed the ford, any of the enemy that might escape from the gorge. All went so well that Jephta could not have wished for anything better. Only one thing was missing: Yahweh's Ark had not yet arrived. Slow, awkward Shamgar had not come on time.

At the earliest glimmer of dawn on the morning when the enemy was due to reach the gorge, Jephta stood, together with Jemin and Gadiel, on the height from which he intended to direct the battle. For days past there had been torrents of rain. But now the rain had ceased and there were flashes of clear sky between the clouds. However, Jemin, who could read the weather signs, said the warm southwest wind would bring still heavier rain—indeed, there would probably be a thunderstorm, and that would not make it any easier for the men of Bashan to get through the gorge.

And so they waited in the thicket there on the hilltop, well concealed, keeping watch. At last the enemy came into sight. It seemed to be a very long column: the scouts had not exaggerated. With a grim smile Jephta saw how unconcernedly they marched along. He could well understand their carefree attitude. The longest, hardest part of their journey lay behind them; ahead of them there was only one more difficult feat: descending the gorge of Nahal-Gad and fording the Jabok. Compared with what they had accomplished already, it would be child's play. But there, Jephta thought merrily, is where you are mistaken. Not many of you will see the end of this day. He gazed at his standard and cried out to his god: "O Yahweh, I confess it: I did strive to avoid this battle that is fought in your name. But if you are just, then grant me this: I had good reasons. Be that as it may, those are bygones; now I fight for you with all my heart, breath and blood. Do your part and give me your blessing."

Now the enemy vanguard had reached the gorge; they entered, disappearing into the ravine, and Jephta could no longer see them. Yet with his mind's eye he saw them proceeding on their fatal journey. The rainy season had swollen the brook Gad into a torrent; still, there was little danger that the current would sweep anyone away. Briskly the men wound their way along the banks of the river, some of them even jumping from stone to stone in the middle of it.

Now the mounted men entered the gorge, and it was time for Jephta to give the signal to block the entrance. Yet he delayed. The column was seemingly endless, and there were still countless troops outside the gorge to the north. But Jephta did not mean to let the cavalry escape. He gave the signal.

A detachment of his heavy-armed warriors stormed down upon the enemy, broke up their column and occupied the entrance to the gorge. The same operation was repeated at the exit, where the Gad flowed into the Jabok. From the hills overlooking the gorge, Jephta's bowmen showered arrows on the trapped enemy, and the spearmen flung their javelins. Confusion and death reigned in the gorge. Jephta's men had orders to aim first at the horses. The wounded animals tried to escape, lashing out on all sides, and their neighing mingled horribly with the yells of the fighting men; the terror of the animals increased the confusion of the men. And now Jephta himself and his own guard attacked the dismayed warriors below, cutting them down with their good swords. And Jephta's heart swelled with pleasure.

Veteran warriors that they were, Jephta's men blocked the entrance to the gorge so that those trapped inside could not make their way out again. But the men of Bashan who had not yet reached the gorge were very many, they had superior numbers, and instead of fleeing, as Jephta had expected, they took up the challenge and threatened to overwhelm Jephta's men at the entrance to the ravine. Jephta had to go to the aid of his men, leaving it to his archers and spearmen to deal with those who had been trapped; he himself had to lead his forces into the northern hills in order to rout the enemy there.

The air had become heavy. Jemin had not been deceived; there was a spring thunderstorm coming up, with livid, yellowish dark clouds that reduced visibility. But this much Jephta saw at once when he reached the hilly land to the north: the enemy was not only before him, but coming at him from all sides, streaming out of the hills to his right and to his left.

And then Jephta realized another thing which for a moment made his heart stop beating: the forces advancing on him from the east were not Bashan's tall warriors, they were not Emorites, they were men of Ammon, soldiers of King Nahash. It was not Jephta who had outwitted Nahash, but Nahash who had outwitted him! Clearly the king had discovered his plan and outflanked him to the east. Now too Jephta realized why Bashan's troops had come on so slowly. Nahash had given them orders to delay so that he might have time to carry out his flanking movement.

The first heavy drops of rain fell. The first gusts of wind swept by. If it had been only a matter of wiping out those in the gorge, the thunderstorm would have been to Jephta's advantage. As it was, it helped the enemy.

And behold! Even the *god* of the enemy was coming to join the battle —the *baal* of Bashan, the winged bull god! All this time Jephta had been wondering where he was: had Bashan, like Gilead, to fight without the help of their god? Yet now all was clear: the *baal* had merely been cleverly hidden far back in the column, biding his time. Now the time had come, now he was swaying on toward Jephta, to avenge himself on the man who had stood on his mountain, on the roof of his house, and mocked him. Surrounded by a throng of warriors, borne by four gigantic men, he came swaying on, inexorable, unwieldy, a monster with heavy copper wings. And his, Jephta's, god was not there. They had abandoned him, that old stubborn priest and Shamgar, the fool, his brother. It had been their only task—to have Yahweh's Ark there in the hour of need. And they had not even been capable of that, those blunderers!

For an instant the sun pierced the thick clouds and the *baal* gleamed with a sudden wild, terrifying brilliance. Yet Jephta was not afraid. He would not flee, he would throw himself against the braggart bull god, seize him by his wings and pull him down into the mud, and his and his warriors' feet should trample him into the mire.

A dense throng of guards surrounded the *baal*. Jephta had no hope of capturing the god. The wisest thing to do was to fight his way back to his main force on the Gad. Yet his fierce, overwhelming desire to seize the enemy god and tread him into the dirt was stronger than his common sense and his knowledge of war; his lust for battle burned too hotly, driving him on toward the *baal* of Bashan. The intoxication that had often sent his father Gilead rushing forward now seized him too.

He shouted: "For Gilead and Yahweh!" And at his side Gadiel shouted: "For Gilead and Yahweh!" And Jemin shouted: "For Yahweh and Jephta!" And the trumpeters blew their rams' horns, sounding the *terua gedola,* the great battle cry, the standard bearer in front of Jephta raised the standard with the cloud and the lightning, and Jephta's old comrades from the land of Tob uttered their war cry: "Hedad, hedad!" and stormed ahead against the impenetrable wall of warriors surrounding the image of the *baal*.

The brazen image was heavy and those who bore it, strong though they were, advanced only slowly; it seemed as though the god were falling back, melting away into the yellowish dark clouds. Jephta laughed his husky, jovial, boyish laugh, thrust out his beard, and egged his men on, jeering at Bashan's bull god: "There it goes, Bashan's calf! It is creeping away to hide! But we shall catch it!"

Now, however, the enemy had discovered Jephta's standard, and it exasperated them no less than the *baal's* image did him. They were superior in number, and they made a tremendous thrust forward, pressing Jephta and those with him very hard. The standard bearer fell. Another seized the staff and raised the standard high; then he too was slain. And then alien, hostile hands grasped the staff. Jephta's men wrenched it away from them, only to be cut down in their turn. And finally Emorite hands seized the standard irresistibly and swept it away into their own ranks. Swiftly, passing from hand to hand, Jephta's cloud and lightning receded into the distance. The standard was lost. Yahweh had averted his face from him. From now on he must fight without the protection of the god.

There were few of his men left, and all now realized that they had advanced dangerously far. They were surrounded, cut off from their main force, a little island in a sea of enemies. Yet they acted as if they did not perceive the danger. It was like a silent conspiracy. They shouted, sang and went on fighting, furiously, doggedly, and of good cheer, drunk with battle.

None was more ecstatic than Gadiel. He laughed, babbled and talked gibberish. Eleven battles he had fought in, but none had been like this, with fighting on all the four fronts at once. "It is magnificent, Jephta, it is glorious!" he cried again and again, until a sword sliced his throat. He collapsed, grotesquely gurgling, clutching the man next him and dragging him down. Jephta envied him. Gadiel had died in the midst of what he liked best: fighting, drunk with fighting, a good soldier of Yahweh.

Now the storm broke with all its force, roaring upon them from all sides, and the rain blinded them. Jemin, fighting at Jephta's side, remained cheerfully unconcerned. He still believed in victory. For the moment they had to cut their way out from among the enemy, and that was no longer difficult, since in the streaming, wind-whipped rain no man could clearly see his adversary. Even in this tempest Jemin's practiced eye was quick and sharp, and he discovered a bushy knoll where their pursuers would neither seek nor reach them. There they could rest, regain their breath, and gather strength again.

They fought their way through, Jephta and Jemin in the lead. Jephta struck out around him, another Gideon, another Hammerer. In his immediate danger he thought only of the very next step, thought only: On! Up! Upward through the thicket! Up the hill! He no longer thought even what purpose their climb had. It was good to think only this one thing: Upward!

They reached the height. They dropped down on the muddy earth, exhausted, panting in the heavy greenish torrents of rain. They were safe.

Jemin rejoiced aloud. Well indeed had Yahweh done to send his thunderstorm! The storm had saved them. Jephta did not contradict him, but he knew it was not so. It was the *baal* that had sent the lightning and thunder; they did not come from Yahweh. Yahweh was granting him only a short respite so he could meditate and repent. Then he would destroy him. And rightly so. The god had warned him through Abijam, through the mouth of the singer Jashar, through Ja'ala, through his friend Par. He ought to have listened and to have gone to the sons of Ephraim. But he had been presumptuous, madly confident in his own strength. He had yielded to his own greed for more power and more glory. He had not been content with being captain of the hosts and judge as well, he had wanted to be the lord of a great realm, and to that end he had even thought of giving away his daughter to the Ammonites and their god Milkom. In truth it was neither Yahweh nor Milkom who had been his god: his god had always been only Jephta. And that was why Yahweh now averted his face from him, withholding his Ark, and depriving him of his battle standard; and now the enemy would come upon him, and he would die miserably here in the mud.

Jemin broke in on his sullen brooding. He touched his arm, pointing toward the east. Jephta glanced up, and for the twinkling of an eye he saw, indistinctly swaying among curtains of rain, a familiar and longed-for thing. He did not dare to trust his eyes and that momentary vision. But obviously

Jemin had also recognized what he saw in the distance. It was no mirage, no mere vision: it was real. What he had for an instant seen swaying toward him was Yahweh's Ark.

Yet between it and him, more solid than the most solid wall, there was still the dense, innumerable body of the enemy forces. How were they to join each other, Shamgar with the Ark and he with his sword? But now that he knew it was indeed Yahweh who had sent the thunderstorm, and Yahweh's countenance, not Milkom's, that glared among the flashes of lightning, his old energy returned to him. He would fight his way to the Ark. He willed it. He must do it. He would do it.

He stood up slowly, yet once more with strength in his limbs. He tore out of his breast whatever still belonged to Milkom; he summoned up all the power of his will, and in his heart he cried out to Yahweh: "You have the right to punish me, for I was cold in your service. Worse than that: I betrayed you. I meant to deliver up to the sons of Milkom and of Kemosh the daughter you gave me, she who is like a hind, the lovely one. But do not punish me. Do not do it. You have sent the storm, your lightning has opened my eyes, I see you, I recognize you, I revere you. The mountains of Sinai and Lebanon and Hermon are no more than the toes of your feet—and what am I in your sight? I humble myself, I confess myself a worm. Only hear me and punish me no more. Do not remain squatting on your high seat. Come down and fight for me as you did for my father Gilead, who was not a better man than I and who did not believe in you more firmly than I. Let me not bring shame upon my tribe in the eyes of Ammon and of western Israel. Slay me if that is your will, but first let me behold victory. Let me advance to your Ark. Let my men rejoin the others. Send out your hornet, the *zirea,* this frantic terror, and send it not into our bones, but into the marrow of the enemy's bones. I am remorseful for what I have done. I am very remorseful. But now if you will cease tormenting me, I will be a faithful son to you."

Jephta stood there, his lips moving. He spoke only in his heart, and if now and then he uttered a word aloud, the storm and the driving rain swept it away unheard. The others saw him speaking to the storm and the storm-clouds, saw his resolute face, and realized that he was making one last mighty effort, pleading and bargaining for victory with someone riding in the storm. They saw him raise his clenched fists in the air; then they saw him opening his hands as though making an offering.

Jephta indeed mutely, urgently, passionately was crying out into the storm: "And if you hear me, Yahweh, and rescue me, then I will make a sacrifice to you, one such as you have never yet savored. If you hear me and grant me victory, then I will slaughter the best of the enemy to you upon your stone, even though it should be King Nahash himself, who is my good friend, and if he is not among my prisoners, then, when I return, I will offer up to you as a burnt sacrifice whosoever first comes running toward me from my home, though he may be the dearest to me of all. But hear me and do not let me be defeated."

So Jephta cried out in his heart. And in the distance he saw the Ark of

Yahweh swaying onward, rising, disappearing, and rising again. Then his heart filled with great joy. He felt it: the god in the Ark had heard him.

He shouted—and now his hoarse voice rang out through the pounding rain and the cracking, splintering branches of the trees: "See Yahweh's Ark! Let us reach the Ark and the god! Follow me!" He plunged through the thicket, taking immense strides, sometimes running, thrusting aside whatever was in his way. His strength had increased tenfold. He struck, slashed, fought his way toward the Ark. The others followed him; his strength and confidence inspired them and they pressed forward, fighting, through tumult, storm, and darkness. Many were wounded and sank to the ground, there was shrieking and groaning, dark rain, the blare of horns, and clouds, torrents, thunder, and lightning, but Jephta's men pressed forward, they came ever nearer to the Ark.

The tide of battle turned. Although they were superior in number, the enemy gave way, their ranks opening before Jephta. His name, "Yahweh Opens the Gate," took on new meaning. Yet in all the excitement and ecstasy of battle he could not understand why the Emorites, beyond any doubt brave men and with the advantage on their side, had turned and were fleeing in all directions. It must be that Yahweh had sent forth the *zirea,* the hornet, the panic; he had spread the great terror among them.

And now Jephta reached the Ark. It glistened in the rain, its worn brown timber gleaming as if new, and those who bore it through the midst of all the perils and this furious tempest stood breathing heavily, jubilant and happy. And there was Shamgar, his drenched garments fluttering and slapping around him, clinging to his puny body; yet there he stood, laughing, foolish and happy. Jephta fondled the wood of the Ark with his callused hands; it was real, and he stroked it softly, he kissed it. To the bearers he gave the order: "Raise the Ark high!" His peremptory command gave the exhausted men new strength and they raised the Ark on high.

Everyone saw it. It was one of Yahweh's miracles that his Ark had come safely through the hosts of his enemies. But there it was in the midst of embattled Gilead; it swayed in the air, and all could feel it was so high and light because the god had left it and was now in the storm and clouds, fighting for Gilead. His breath drove Gilead forward as it blew Ammon and Bashan away.

Their overwhelmingly strong enemy was routed and in full flight. Jephta's men and Gilead's shouted their victory. The harsh blare of their rams' horns and their ferocious shouts of "Hedad!" and "Jephta!" and "Gilead!" rang out louder even than the uproar of the thunder and the storm.

And it turned out that Jemin had been right: the wild storm did indeed come from Yahweh. For the rivers Gad and Jabok swelled and fought for Gilead. The ravine and the banks of the Jabok became impassable death traps. The only way of escape left open to the enemy was northward. But there, it seemed, some invisible thing drove them back. They despaired, many pulled their cloaks over their heads and let themselves be struck down without a struggle. Only a few of the warriors of Bashan and Ammon escaped.

That whole day Jephta's rollicking gaiety continued. The next morning, too, he woke filled with a blithe sense of his great victory.

He considered the tasks before him. First of all he must deal with those in the seven northern provinces who had grown slack in their loyalty.

But instead, he gave orders to move south, to Mizpah. To his astonished lieutenants he explained that before he dealt with Bashan he wanted to force King Nahash to make peace quickly, lest he ally himself with Ephraim.

In his heart he knew that something else kept him from marching northward. In the north were the women, Ketura and Ja'ala, and what he had sworn to Yahweh was: "I shall offer up to you as a burnt sacrifice whosoever first comes running toward me from my home." Confusion and his sore need had caused him to use words that were not clear; was his camp in the land of Tob to be regarded as his home? In any case it was wiser and more prudent to go to Mizpah and avoid the north, where he might meet the women. There was an obscure, evil curiosity in him to learn which one of his people in Mizpah Yahweh would send to meet him, so that he might lay his hand on him and fulfill his pledge.

Everywhere on his journey he was hailed with jubilation and reverence. There might indeed be some few who wondered whether Jephta had done right in attacking the Ephraimites and who feared that Yahweh might be angry. But the great majority had unlimited confidence in him and felt nothing but joy in his great victory. And the whole land rang with satisfaction at the boisterous joke Jephta had permitted himself and his men at the ford across the Jordan. The men of Gilead were grave and dignified and seldom laughed; but whenever they thought of what had happened at Zafon they nudged each other and burst out again into peals of laughter. "*Shibboleth,*" and "*Shalom,*" and other words that began with *sh,* and they were mirthful over the stupid, clumsy Ephraimites who could not manage to pronounce such simple words correctly even to save their lives.

On this journey to Mizpah Jephta did not have his standard borne before him. He was waiting for the new standard the artist Latarak was making for him. But as they approached the city of Mizpah he made his way over the Hill of Obot and there, at the burial place, he had the old standard brought out. The boulders were rolled aside and he entered the cavern to give to his father the dented, crumpled standard with the cloud and the lightning, the witness to his plight and his victory.

He groped through the half-darkness and the evil-smelling chill of the place. Faintly the *teraphim* shimmered ahead of him. He laid the standard down before his dead father and rendered an account to him. "Your son Jephta," he told him, "has won a victory the like of which has not been seen since Barak and Deborah defeated the Kana'anites. For long years to come Ammon and Moab will not dare to invade Israel again. I bring you the battle standard that was the witness of my sore need and of my victory. But I confess to you, I no longer delight in it. For in my anger and pride I slew those who brought it back to me, and that was not well. I fear it gave offense to Yahweh. The last time I was here with you I boasted that I would not act rashly, as you acted, but would curb myself. I was lying: I too have let my wild impulses master me. Help me, if you can, so no evil shall come of it. Today at least all is well. Today I am the victor and report to you: through your son Jephta the name of your clan has become glorious."

When he came out into the open air, his heart was light again. Filled with the happiness of victory he journeyed on toward the walls of Mizpah, past the Remet-Habonim, the hill of the dead children.

And now, everywhere around Mizpah, all was jubilation and everything confirmed the greatness of his victory. Through the town gates a festive throng came pouring out to meet him, singing, shouting, and making loud, joyful music.

Amid the din of harps, flutes, and zithers he heard a strange and yet familiar sound: Ja'ala's drum. How could that be? He was in Mizpah. It was to Mizpah he had gone, not to his camp in Tob. Or was he in Tob after all? He was bewildered, as in a dream.

But this was Mizpah, this was real, and there, leading the procession of dancing girls, was Ja'ala, his daughter.

He was drawn down in a black and terrible vortex. "Whosoever first comes toward me," he had sworn. "Even the dearest to me of all," he had sworn.

Meanwhile Ja'ala came dancing toward him with those savage and yet marvelously light steps of hers, and she beat her drum and sang: "A mighty warrior is Yahweh, he sent the waters against the enemy and drowned him. But Jephta, on whom his blessing lies, fought with his sword. Great among the heroes is Jephta. His father, the judge Gilead, slew four thousand in his great battle, but the judge Jephta slew fourteen thousand with the sharpness of his sword. Crimson carpets are spread before Jephta's house to celebrate his return. All the people and the stones of the city of Mizpah sing praises to Jephta, the judge and captain of the hosts, the victor."

So Ja'ala sang. But Jephta's broad face darkened in a terrifying way, twisting into a distorted grimace. He would have liked to burst out into grief and fury, lashing about him, tearing his beard, rending his garments.

The women were aghast. Ja'ala had wished to be there so her father could fulfill his promise and take her with him on his proud, victorious entry into Rabat-Ammon, and when she had begged her mother to let her welcome her father ceremoniously in Mizpah, Ketura had unhesitatingly given her permission. They had wanted to give him a happy surprise; but clearly they had not succeeded.

With a tremendous effort Jephta controlled himself. His hoarse voice was hoarser than ever as he gasped out: "I thank you, Ketura. I thank you, Ja'ala, my daughter. I thank you all. But it is not yet time to tread the crimson carpets. The war is not yet ended. First I must have Ammon under my heel."

He did not enter Mizpah but encamped outside the walls as he had done before the battle. He ordered a day of rest for the troops that had come with him.

He himself could not sleep. Through his head went the verses of the song

of Deborah praising the woman Ja'el. Ja'el—Ja'ala. Ja'el had driven the
tent peg through the forehead of Sisera, the captain of the Kana'anite hosts.
Sisera's mother had expected her son to return victorious with immense
plunder, but instead he lay there dead. For him, Jephta, his daughter had not
waited in vain. He had returned as a victor with great booty, but he had come
to slay her.

He remained restless. Shortly after the beginning of the third watch of
the night he rose and walked through the sleeping camp, past the astonished
guards. He walked out into the night, up a hill. A half-moon, low in the sky,
cast a dim light. The land all about lay empty, ancient, in deathly silence,
deathly stillness.

Jephta stood on the hill, broad-shouldered, tall, alone, thrusting his chin
out into the air, clenching his teeth.

Yahweh had made a fool of him, had played a cunning trick. First he
had made Nahash suggest that he, Jephta, should deliver up his daughter to
Milkom; then, because he had not immediately rejected that temptation, the
god had taken a mocking revenge by exacting his daughter's blood for himself. Oh, the god had delicate tastes! The child Ja'ala was an exquisite morsel.
She felt more intensely, her eyes saw more penetratingly, her skin and all her
being was smoother and finer to the touch than that of others. That was why
Yahweh wanted her for himself. The god, infinitely greedy, wanted to savor
her.

But Jephta was not a man to be ordered about, even by Yahweh. He
thought of the *akko,* the ibex. He was strong, out of nothing he had got himself a great army and a great territory. If now after his victory he married his
daughter to the Ammonite, then he could weld together the great realm that
he had envisioned on Mount Hermon, and he could do it without Yahweh,
even in spite of Yahweh.

He laughed aloud into the night, insolently. "If Milkom is for me," he
declared in a challenging voice, "I am content. If Yahweh is for me, I am
content. But even if I alone am for myself, I shall be content with that."

Terror came upon him at the sound of his own words, chilling his blood.
He remembered the spirits that roam in lonely places and preferably by night,
and the strongest of those spirits was Yahweh. He was helpless against
Yahweh. There was no way out. If he did not sacrifice his daughter, then the
god would take what he had been promised and would also destroy Jephta for
having broken his word.

He crouched down. Once again he lived through the shame and rout on
the heights above the Nahal-Gad. Once again he heard himself uttering his
vow amid the storm clouds. In his heart he had known perfectly well that it
was his daughter he was offering Yahweh as the price of victory. Only he had
tried to trick the god by words of double meaning, as once he had tricked the
King of Bashan and even King Nahash. But Yahweh was no little king.
Yahweh could not be deceived.

Nevertheless the god might have made it easy for him, his favorite, to
fulfill his oath: he might have sent, say, young Ibzan to meet him, his favorite

servant. But in the arrogance of his victory, he, Jephta, had provoked the god further: he had yielded to a fatal lust and had slaughtered the allies whom the god had sent him. If Yahweh now sent his daughter to meet him, it was not a whim, a sly trick; it was a punishment.

So he crouched there on the hill, Jephta, judge in Gilead, captain of Gilead's hosts, victor at the Nahal-Gad, overwhelmed by comprehension and remorse, staring out across his land now gray in the first light of dawn.

The people of Mizpah assumed that in order to make the most of his victory Jephta would at once march against King Nahash, who still held the city of Yokbecha. But the days passed and Jephta did nothing.

Jelek, that shrewd and sensible man, came to the camp and asked his brother outright why he did not force Nahash to make peace. The fields must be tilled, and in the houses and at the sheepfolds there was need of the men who were idling away their time in camp. Jephta told him to leave it to him, the captain of the hosts, to decide when and how he would finish the war. He spoke with such violence that Jelek fell silent.

Jephta admitted to himself that his brother was right. But he knew whatever he undertook would fail as long as he had not paid his debt to Yahweh. He must fulfill his vow, and at once.

Yet still he made no preparations; he was like a man paralyzed. With his inner eye, in cruel clarity, he saw his child, his Ja'ala, lying bound on Yahweh's stone. He saw her tensed throat, saw the knife in his hand, saw the hand guiding the knife, saw her body heave and slacken, saw her blood flowing over the stone. This strong man who had so often calmly gazed on fighting and slaughter grew dizzy with helpless protest.

He brooded on how he could extricate himself from the consequences of his oath. Generally a man swearing an oath challenged the god to punish him if he did not keep it; this was an intrinsic element in the oath. He had not done so, and so his oath was not binding. Yet even while he quibbled in this way he knew his oath *was* binding. Yahweh had nodded and accepted. Yahweh had done his part; now it was for Jephta to do his.

Then from Bashan came Par, his faithful friend, disturbed by rumors of the assault on the Ephraimites. "It is said," he recounted, "that the men of Ephraim came to help you and that they were massacred. By our own men. Of course I know this cannot be true. It seems to me that many people must have misunderstood many things. Our men were drunk with battle, the men of Ephraim, haughty as they are, doubtless provoked them, and in the tumult of victory many thoughtless things are done, all unintended. But now the whole of western Israel is enraged against you, and they say Ephraim means to attack Gilead. I beg of you, my Jephta, tell me the truth of what happened."

Absently, reflectively, Jephta gazed on his friend, standing there before him so anxiously and yet so full of trust. "The detachments that fought against Ephraim," he answered at last, "were under Jemin's command. He can tell you what happened."

Jemin came. "The captain," he recounted cheerfully and proudly, "had ordered the men of Ephraim to leave the land of Gilead before the full moon. But on the day before the full moon they were still encamped before Bet-Nobah. Thereupon the captain said they ought to be slaughtered like roaming wild beasts. So then I took thirteen hundreds—for the captain of Ephraim also had thirteen hundreds, and I did not want to have any unfair advantage—and went to the Ephraimites and spoke to them. But they answered insolently, slighting our captain. So then I acted according to his words and rid him of that plague."

There was silence. Broad, sturdy Par breathed hard. He had to sit down.

"You have reported well, Jemin," Jephta said. "Those were my precise words. You understood me exactly."

When he was alone with Par, Jephta went on: "Now you know what happened. I do not believe that more than two hundred of the Ephraimites escaped. Of our own men some eight hundred perished."

Par remained silent. Then—and it was the first time that Jephta had ever known such a thing to happen—this quiet man broke into wild sobbing. "Why did you do it, Jephta?" he asked.

"For reasons you cannot understand, O valiant husband of my sister," Jephta answered. "I myself scarcely understand them."

Very quietly Par said: "You asked me for Yahweh's treasure. I handed it over to you. It was for Yahweh that you won victory at the Nahal-Gad. Then every drop of blood in me rejoiced."

Jephta grinned and took up the theme: "And then I killed the Ephraimites, Yahweh's friends. It was for that I consumed his treasure. I have committed a *ma'al,* I have robbed Yahweh of what was his. That is what you mean to say, is it not? Why do you not accuse me before Abijam?"

Now Par's voice was plaintive as he said: "I remember the day when you lay in your tent and let us look into your breast. And see, Yahweh had inspired you with his breath, and you wanted to unite all of the tribes of Israel into one people. But now the god's breath has knocked you down and you have split Israel even worse than before. I wanted to return to Yahweh's settled land. But now you have turned all Israel into a wilderness in which every man is free to indulge every whim. I have lost you, my Jephta. Now I have nothing more, only Kassia and the wilderness in the north."

"You mean to go away from me, Par?" Jephta asked. He shook his head in amazement. "Long ago in the wilderness," he said musingly, "when I stoned the man who asked to take back his slave Dardar, you understood me at once."

"Explain to me what you have done, Jephta," Par pleaded. "Tell me!"

Jephta knew that if he told his friend of the appalling penance that Yahweh had imposed on him, then Par would stay with him. But he wanted no man's pity, not even that of Par. He would settle the matter of his oath and of Yahweh alone.

He let Par go.

But now he could not wait any longer, he had to gather his courage and tell Ja'ala his secret.

He asked her to walk with him toward the northern hills. She had been grieved because it had made him angry when she came to meet him outside the gate of Mizpah. Now she looked forward excitedly, yet full of trust, to what he would say to her.

He saw how gaily she walked at his side, and it was almost with terror that he realized how deeply he loved her—more than Ketura, more than himself, more than all the power and all the glory of the world. He could not raise the knife against his child. He would take her by the hand, and Ketura too, and flee into the remotest wilderness. But the wilderness was no refuge from Yahweh. The god would rise up from his seat on Mount Sinai, he would find him wherever he might be, and say to him: I heard your vow and granted you victory, and now, oath-breaker, where is your sacrifice? And Yahweh would slaughter him and all who were his.

Everywhere around Mizpah there were fields and pens and sheepfolds. They had to walk a long way before they found a little wood where they could sit down and talk. Jephta saw his daughter's calm face light up from within, saw how intensely she enjoyed his companionship, and realized that she loved him as much as he loved her. A proverb came into his mind, one he had heard from old Tola: "You cannot kill the lion if he does not love you."

Ja'ala talked eagerly of her own affairs. Her father's victory had not surprised her. Ever since he had asked her if she would like to go to Rabat with him, she had known he would wage war on Ammon, and would defeat the enemy. Ingenuously she confided that she had composed the song in praise of his victory even before the battle had been fought.

Jephta listened to her childlike voice. He saw her eyes. How much clear, deep life there was there! And suddenly he uttered a groan, a wailing cry, tore his garments, beat his breast, and exclaimed: *Echah!* and: *Chah!* and: *Ach!*

"O my daughter," he said, "how much sorrow you bring on me with your loveliness and your love! Your love made you run out to meet me, and you sang for Yahweh and for me, and now the god wants you completely for himself—all of you, not merely your song. *Echah, echah!* What a terrible god is Yahweh!"

Ja'ala looked at him in dismay. She heard his words without understanding them. Then she realized that it was she herself whom he was lamenting, and that some dreadful thing lay in store for her. Often she had watched a wounded animal as it died, observing with avidity how the blood and the life poured from the creature, yet at the same time full of deep sympathy with its suffering. This time she herself was to be the victim. Cruel, suffocating agony swept over her. She slid off the tree stump on which she had been sitting, and lay there, deathly pale, her eyelids closed.

Jephta caressed her, pressed her to him, moved her limbs until the breath of life returned to her. She gazed at him with a smile that wrung his heart, and begged: "Let me rest a little longer, my father, and then tell me more, if such is your will."

He sat down beside her, holding her hand. Once again a wild rush of agony came upon her. But now there was pleasure mingled with the pain, an expectation of fulfillment. As yet she had not the right fierce and festive words for it, but she was certain she would find them. Through Jephta's mind meanwhile there swirled many horrible and many strangely sweet thoughts, but all remained cloudy and formless; he would never be able to convey them.

After a while Ja'ala said: "Now tell me, my father, I beg of you."

And as best he could, Jephta told her of the battle, of how it had begun as a victory and then turned into defeat and desperation, and how he had made his vow and Yahweh had accepted it, and the god had come rushing forth from his Ark, inspiring him and his men with tenfold strength and draining the strength out of their enemy's bones.

Ja'ala listened attentively. Several times she nodded, thoughtfully, ponderingly, approvingly, understandingly. Something festive, some marvelous joy, lit up her face, and she said: "With all my being I praise Yahweh. How much grace he has bestowed on me because he delights in you and because I am of your flesh and blood!"

And she confided in her father fully, revealing to him what had hitherto been concealed in her breast. Jemin was a good friend to her; the god had sent him that time to save her. But he wanted her on his mat; if he did not say so in words, at least he did so with his eyes and his whole manner. And from this she shrank. For her the loftiest and the loveliest thing was to give utterance to what she felt in her heart; in good hours she could do it. She herself was nothing, but when she thus found expression in song she lived and felt something of her father's being. Yet if she were to lie down with a man on his mat, if she were to feed some man's pleasure with her breath and life, then —she knew for certain—she would lose her gift. And now Yahweh in his grace had sent her release from that fear. He permitted her to be united with him, the god, so her blood would be his and serve to strengthen him.

Broodingly, accusingly, Jephta said: "Yahweh has breathed it into you to move men with the sight of you and the sound of your voice, and now he wants to have you for himself and to rob me of you. And he refuses you what is every woman's right and every woman's pleasure."

"I do not wish it," Ja'ala said. "I was afraid of it. I am glad and proud to take part in your victory, my father. Do with me according to the words that issued from your mouth."

They stayed there together for a long time. Jephta felt that he loved this child more than any other woman, and differently; he was jealous of Yahweh and greatly downcast. But wild, sweet thoughts went through Ja'ala's breast. She saw the stone on which she would lie, she saw Yahweh's knife, and she shuddered. Yet at the same time she felt great pride and joy; for the thing at which she shuddered held the highest happiness, true happiness, the only one that was right for her. Already in anticipation she felt her union with Yahweh, and her father and Yahweh merged into one for her, and she was at peace.

The men of Ephraim had gone to Shiloh, avid for vengeance against the murderer of their brothers. But when news came of Jephta's sacrifice, they grew thoughtful. Yahweh had stepped between them and Jephta. The god himself had wrought vengeance and absolved him; they would be provoking the god if they fought against such a man.

Then a new and frightful menace loomed up, reducing the last cries for vengeance to dead silence. The Israelite tribes had been able to hold their ground west of Jordan, only because the Kana'anite kings of the ancient fortified cities were at odds with one another. But now that irreparable discord had arisen between the Hebrews of the east and those of the west, these war-experienced kings formed an alliance to attack the Israelite invaders and wipe them out. Never since the days of Barak and Deborah had western Israel been in such jeopardy.

Only one man could help, and that was the victor of the Nahal-Gad, the man who by his sacrifice had bound the god Yahweh to give his unfailing aid. That man was Jephta.

Among the tribes of western Israel, Ephraim was the most important. Thus the judges of the other tribes went to Tahan, the captain of the Ephraimite hosts, and asked him to appeal to Jephta for aid. Furiously, he refused. Then they turned to Elead, the high priest.

Elead declared his readiness to go to Mizpah. But he did it reluctantly, for he was by temperament best fitted for sitting in the stillness of his Tent of Yahweh in Shiloh, reflecting on events in Israel, discussing them with his pupils, chronicling them and interpreting them. He did not like to intervene in the direction of Israel's affairs, preferring to give quiet counsel, and he felt ill at ease at the thought of arguing with this Jephta who raged so mightily up and down the land. But it could not be avoided; without Jephta's help Israel could not be saved.

He set out. It was early summer, the weather was beautiful, the journey was pleasant, and yet he felt bitter. It depended on the persuasiveness of his words, whether Israel would survive or perish—and would he find the right words to convince Jephta?

He was in the habit of musing about people, and he had often reflected on Jephta's character and deeds. However unwelcome the encounter was, he was eager to see the man and speak to him.

He wondered what his attitude should be. The Gileadites had not been dwelling long enough in towns and villages; law and order still irked them like a garment that was too tight. They were still sons of the *tohu,* the wilderness, and clearly this man Jephta was beyond all the others of his tribe a man of the desert and the wilderness. Furthermore, he had doubtless grown arrogant from success and fame, and then his bloody vow must have deranged him utterly. How difficult it must be to make him listen to arguments and remonstrations! The high priest Elead resolved that all during their interview he would remain patient, adapt himself to the man's mood, and watch for the favorable moment.

When it was announced to Jephta that the high priest of Ephraim was

asking to see him, he felt a faint stirring of his old conceit. This priest of
Shiloh had the reputation of being very wise; the Ephraimites had sent their
shrewdest man to win him over. But strong armor had grown up around his
heart and there was no priest for whom he did not feel himself a match.

He was greatly tempted to stay on his side of the Jordan and watch how
the Ephraimites showed their mettle in extremity. But he would keep an
open mind. Perhaps he would deign to show them generosity and save them.
He would act according to whatever whim occurred to him in conversation
with the priest.

Elead came. This man from Shiloh looked different from what Jephta
had imagined. He was unassuming in appearance and gesture. His pale face
with the veiled, intelligent eyes was framed by a very short beard. He was
young for his office, probably under fifty. His robe was plain brown in color,
but of the best stuff and well suited to his somewhat stout figure. Jephta
would never have taken him for one of Yahweh's priests, they were generally
unkempt and violent of gesture. This man from Shiloh reminded him rather
of the well-groomed lord from Babel, of Prince Gudea, who had once been his
prisoner.

For a short while they stood in silence, scrutinizing each other. Then
Elead bowed and greeted him: "Peace be with you." But he pronounced the
word *shalom* with the lisping 's' of the Ephraimites. And then something
happened that had not happened for a long time: Jephta laughed. He laughed
boisterously. He thought of the jokes he had heard all his life about the
Ephraimites' droll accent, he thought of the Ephraimites at the Jordan ford
and their "*sibboleth,*" and he could not stop roaring with laughter.

The high priest Elead had been prepared to find Jephta neither gracious
nor dignified; but he had not expected this reception. For an instant he was
offended. But then he thought of his resolve never to forget that Israel's
salvation depended on help from this man Jephta. Besides, he realized that
this wild laughter was not directed against the tribe of Ephraim and himself,
Elead, but sprang from one of those wild, bloody, ludicrous memories that
the man had. And so Elead bore with Jephta's laughter and calmly waited for
it to cease.

And when he had taken a grip on himself Jephta did in fact say: "Forgive
me. Nothing is further from my mind than to offend my guest." He went up
to him and greeted him with the conventional embrace and kiss, and invited
him to seat himself on the mat.

"I can imagine," he began, "that you have not come to me without
reluctance after all that has befallen your people on this side of Jordan. Your
need must be very great."

"It is very great," Elead confessed straightforwardly. "For this first time
since the age of Deborah the kings and cities of Kana'an have united against
us. They have superior numbers and superior arms. Nor can it be to your
liking if Kana'an destroys western Israel, for then you will have enemies not
only in the east but also in the west."

Calmly, almost casually, Jephta replied: "I had enemies in the north and in the south and in my own house as well, as you must be aware. I was a match for them all."

Elead surveyed him thoughtfully and said: "You fought in Yahweh's service. Yahweh is not only Gilead's god, he is the god of all Israel. I come to you as to the captain of Yahweh's hosts."

"Then you have come to the wrong man," Jephta answered. "My debts to Yahweh are paid in full. I am no longer in his service and need not wage any further wars for his sake. We are quits, Yahweh and I."

Elead would have liked to answer these uncouth words with courteous mockery; but he must not provoke this man. He was silent, rubbing the palm of one hand with the fingers of the other—strong fingers, skilled in a scribe's work—and meditated his answer. He scrutinized Jephta's face. For all its harshness it was a tired face. The flesh was shrunken; the underlying bones of the dead skull were beginning to show through the face of the living man. The man had fought with his god, he was exhausted, he wanted to abandon the struggle, but he could not break free from Yahweh.

"I think, Jephta," the priest said at last, "you are mistaken. Between you and Yahweh it is not a matter of service, obligation and debts. You can never be quits with your god. You are a part of him."

A shock swept through Jephta. No one had known that he and Yahweh had one face, none among the living had known it, only Ja'ala. How did this stranger know it?

Elead saw that his words had moved the other man. Cautiously, almost casually, and yet firmly, he went on in his soft, pliant voice: "If there is any man in Israel, then it is you who are a hero and thus one-third a god. We who chronicle the ways of Yahweh know that. You participate in Yahweh's being more than we others do, and any who attack the god attack you."

Trying to shake off his confusion, Jephta sneered: "Do not exhaust yourself, lord high priest of Ephraim, with praising and exalting me. I am not a bear to be snared with honey."

Elead realized that Jephta was full of defiance, but intelligent and able to think, and his, Elead's, words had already broken through the hard crust. Elead took hope; he abandoned his plan and tried to lure Jephta with certain bold, precarious truths that might have seemed blasphemous to other men.

"It does not astonish me," he said, "that you deny the real, proud share you have in Yahweh. You are a soldier, and your task is to act, to fight. Musing and meditating about the god is not your function: that is what we priests are for. We in Shiloh have reflected long and intensively concerning the god, and, we believe, not without results. I tell you, and I know: you *are* a part of Yahweh, whether you wish it or no. Yahweh lives in you, and you live in him. The *baalim* of alien peoples live in trees, stones, springs, and images, and for the simple people among ourselves even our Yahweh is visible and tangible only in such things. But the true Yahweh, your Yahweh and mine, lives in the deeds of Israel."

It disconcerted Jephta that the priest should again have uttered so plainly and clearly what he himself had sometimes vaguely sensed to be the

meaning behind certain obscure utterances of Ja'ala's. The almost outrageous
words, savoring of blasphemy, both attracted and angered him. "Do I understand you rightly?" he asked, almost mockingly. "Do you seriously assert that
Yahweh lives also in my deeds?"

"It is as you say," Elead replied.

Challengingly, Jephta pressed him further. "So if I do great wrong, it is
also Yahweh who does great wrong?"

Courteously the other corrected him: "Not entirely so. If you commit a
wrong, Yahweh is weakened. Yahweh becomes less when Jephta does wrong."

There was a short silence, then Jephta said forbiddingly: "I am a soldier.
You have yourself said so. I am not the man to understand your subtle,
tortuous words."

Elead replied with unusual emphasis: "Of course you understand me,
even though you try not to."

He paused. He recollected his resolve to conduct this discussion only to
gain one end. Jephta was now sufficiently softened; the time had come to use
strong words and press him hard to take part in the war.

But Elead's breast was full of his new and precarious truth, and there
were only very few men to whom he could reveal it. This wild, extraordinary
man Jephta—he could read it in his face—had the imagination to comprehend his doctrine and to be excited by it. Instead of pressing him further
he moved nearer to Jephta and spoke to him urgently, confidentially as to a
close friend: "You know it is so. Yahweh was born with Israel. Israel's
struggles are his struggles. He lives more strongly when Israel is stronger, he
fades when Israel is weak. He dies if Israel dies. He is what we have been and
are and will be."

Elead's words entered into Jephta's breast; slowly, against his own will,
he turned them over. Surely this priest's god was not his. His, Jephta's, was a
god of war, breathing forth fire, roaring in the storm. But Jephta realized that
Yahweh also had other faces, many faces, and this man Elead had undoubtedly seen faces of the god that would forever remain unseen by him. Nevertheless he, Jephta, was far from being one of those simple people who comprehended no more of the god than they could see with their eyes and touch
with their hands. And now for the second time since Elead had entered the
tent something happened to Jephta that had not happened to him for a long
time: he took hold of the other man's thoughts and clutched them to himself, made them is own, took them into his own breast so that they grew there.
Yahweh was not of ordinary human stuff, then neither were his needs ordinary
human needs. And suddenly, in terrifying clarity, Jephta saw what lay at the
far end of Elead's thoughts. The little green lights of anger flared up in his
eyes, and his voice hoarse with suppressed fury, he challenged the other: "Go
on, say more, O arch priest, arch speculator, archscribe, say it to my face:
you think my sacrifice was vain. You think there was no need for it."

Now it was Elead who experienced a shock. He was startled by this
sudden onslaught, and by the intelligence of this rough warrior who so
quickly fathomed what he had scarcely dared to admit to himself.

He collected himself. For an instant he was tempted to contradict the other in courteous, devious phrases. But then he was overwhelmed by the realization that this coarse-grained man of war, to whom so much action, conquest, plundering, and killing had left no time for thinking, this man who could not read the tablets, saw things as clearly and distinctly as himself, perhaps in his simplicity even more deeply; and for the first time in his life Elead was ashamed of his pride as a priest and as a man of learning. He could not lie to this man. He said: "You may be right insofar as after another seven or twice seven generations, Yahweh may no longer require sacrifices such as yours. Yet deeds of courage and of devotion, such as you have performed, are something he will always need."

All that Jephta heard in the priest's words was confirmation that indeed his own agonizing act had been mere futility and madness. He rose from the mat and paced up and down. Locked in his thoughts, he rushed back and forth between the walls of the narrow tent, an animal in a cage.

In his heart of hearts he had long suspected that his vow and his sacrifice had been futile; the doubt had loomed up in him as soon as the deed was done, when he had gone away and hidden in the bush. And so there were others who suspected it—who *knew* it. At least this one man here knew it. So it was not merely fumes of fancy, it *was* so: he, Jephta, had made his terrible vow in order to buy the support of a god who did not exist. He had shed his best blood, his own blood, for a god that did not exist. Jephta the hero, Jephta the fool! No god had aided him: it was Ephraim that had helped him. And it was for that that he had slain his daughter, the beloved, the lovely one. He had spilt the best and reddest blood of his body for nothing.

The words the priest had spoken came back to him: first the sound of them, then their meaning. "Acts such as you have done are something the god needs, something Israel needs." And suddenly he realized that all he now was and all he stood for was linked with his great and senseless act. What made his enemies small and afraid, what protected him more than arms and fortifications, was the awe that his deed had conjured up around him. For an instant the complex, cruelly tangled consequences of the sacrifice were brilliantly clear to him in all their grim absurdity, in their imbecile grandeur.

The priest had also risen. Jephta gazed at him, at first blankly, then with seeing eyes. So this man had found it out—the utter senselessness of the sacrifice and the tremendous consequences. That was what he was here for—to make use of the great awe that emanated from the deed. That awe offered protection against Kana'an too, if only he, Jephta, would cross the Jordan. This man here before him saw the connections and had meant to conceal them from him. But he, Jephta, had wrung the truth from him.

He was filled with savage, malicious satisfaction. "Did I finally manage to drag your true opinion out of your throat, lord high priest of Shiloh?" he asked. "My deeds!" he jeered. "My deeds! How cleverly you spin your phrases, O arch speculator and archscribe, to make them sound soft and caressing even while they break a man's skull!" His bitter merriment increased.

"And to think," he said, "that it is men like you who form the picture later men will have of me!"

Elead was silent. He did not know how Jephta's outburst would end. He had not foreseen that Jephta would guess the real meaning of his words. Perhaps he had forfeited everything by the untimely revelation of his doctrine, and Jephta would mockingly send him back across the Jordan.

As for Jephta, he was still quivering with fury. But in the midst of that fury, and beyond it, the very presence of the priest made him think and ponder. He had no reason to be angry with this priest; he ought to be grateful to him. This was a shrewd, wise priest, very different from Abijam, who was vain and ambitious. Now that he, Jephta, had done such a great and mad thing, the priest wished to turn it to account—and was he not right? The blood should not simply trickle away into earth, wood and fire; the priest wanted to give meaning to the great awe that had grown up out of the blood— and was he not right?

Jephta made a resolve. The resolve took hold of him. He stood before Elead, thrust his head forward and asked with ferocious mockery: "Tell me this, O wise and clever priest! Give me counsel: how shall I contrive it that the stories you tell of me will not ring to badly in the ears of later generations? Shall I send you as many hundreds as you sent me? There were, I think, thirteen of them?"

Elead drew a deep breath of relief. There was joy, warmth, and respect in his voice as he answered: "The mere news that Jephta is taking part in the campaign will frighten Kana'an off. And if you send us even one single squad of seven, you will have aided us."

But now something had been set free in Jephta and he found he could get on with this man, he could talk to him as once he had talked with friends. He began to jest. "I have negotiated with King Abir of Bashan, who is a shrewd man at a bargain, and with King Nahash, who is the cunningest quibbler and word-twister among the princes of the Jordan lands. But you, lord high priest of Ephraim, are even more skilled at worming your way, with sly words, into the breast of a man who should be your enemy."

"Do not say you should be my enemy, Jephta," Elead replied. "We are wayfarers on one and the same road. It was granted to my words to touch you, and now with a few answering words you have done more to save Israel than anyone else could do with armed thousands and the sharp blades of swords."

He prepared to leave. But Jephta said: "One favor you must do me, high priest Elead, before you return to your own land of Ephraim, and do not take offense. Do not avoid the word, but say it once more—*shalom.*"

22 Samson's Strength

Many people have used the stories of the Bible to their own ends, and so it is not surprising that Vladimir Jabotinsky writes of Samson's stealing the gates of Gaza so that the iron could be forged into sword blades, for Jabotinsky led an illegal army which was forbidden arms. A Russian-born writer and publicist, Jabotinsky organized the Jewish Legion which supported the British and Allied cause in the First World War. In 1920, during the anti-Jewish outbreaks in Palestine, he organized and led the Haganah, that small underground army which in time became the foundation of the army of Israel. Three years later he resigned his command and turned to a writing career. But he never abandoned the fight for a free and independent Jewish state. Advocating an immediate declaration of freedom, he called for a state created "by force, if necessary." Jabotinsky died in 1940 near Hunter, New York, before the creation of modern Israel.

And Samson lay til midnight, and arose at midnight, and took the doors of the gate of the city, and the two posts, and went away with them, bar and all, and put them upon his shoulders, and carried them up to the top of an hill that is before Hebron.

JUDGES: XVI, 3

JUDGE AND FOOL
by ALTALENA (Vladimir Jabotinsky)

BEFORE SUNRISE, while it was still dark, he left the house. The streets were empty, but on the wall of the town he could make out the dark figures of sentries armed with bows. He stole along, and peeping round a corner, beheld the gate of the town. The burning torches revealed the usual guard, armed with swords and spears. Their numbers had not even been reinforced. This gate was famous throughout the whole of Philistia, and the people of Gaza trusted in its strength. The doors were of thick iron, ornamented above by a sharp pointed grid.

Then a happy thought occurred to Samson, the happiest of all his heroic years. He set to work on its realization, making use of one of his oldest tricks. From a neighboring street arose the shouts of men, women and children: "Hold him tight! Help! Guards!"

The officer of the watch rushed off in the direction of the outcry, taking his soldiers with him, and leaving only one sentry at the gate. The shouting receded farther and farther away as they followed it. When Samson had decoyed them far enough away, he stopped shouting and ran back to the gate by another route. The sentry was standing in the torchlight, listening. Samson felt in his pouch, took out a flat stone, bent down and threw it. The sentry dropped without a sound.

A minute later, when the officer of the watch was still standing at a street corner, inquiring of a group of sleeply, half-dressed townsmen what had happened, he suddenly heard a shattering concussion and a noise of splintering from the direction of the gate. Rushing back, he came in sight of the gate, and beheld a black gaping space between its huge pillars. The door had been lifted from its hinges; it was gone; the sentry lay on the ground with his head smashed in.

The officer did not lose his nerve. He drew from the circumstances the only conclusion satisfactory to himself. Whipping out his sword, he planted the hilt on a stone and threw himself forward so that the point pierced his breast. Strictly speaking, he should first have sounded the alarm, but there was no time to lose, for he did not wish to die under a rain of blows.

No one ever reckoned how long a time elapsed before the trumpeters sounded their trumpets, other officers came running to the scene, and the horses were led from their stables. Meanwhile it was growing light. The road leading from the gate to the hills was paved and would consequently show no footmarks, but it was obvious that even Samson himself could not have gone far with so terrific a burden. They did not expect to catch Samson, but the gate had to be found and brought back at all costs.

Detachments of mounted men were sent out in all directions. Towards midday they returned: they had found no trace of the gate, nor of Tayish (Samson), not so much as his footsteps in the sand.

The Saran called a council.

"We must search the farmyards of the natives," proposed one of the councilors.

"Why?" asked the Saran.

"Perhaps the gate is hidden somewhere under a haystack—"

"Impossible," answered the commander-in-chief. "There are fields on both sides of the road—there is not even a village. The hillsides are all plowed, and if Tayish had turned aside into a farmyard with that weight on his shoulders, he would have left deep footmarks in the soft ground. Consequently he can't have turned off anywhere, but must have gone straight along the road."

"What?" cried the indignant Saran. "Is it possible for a man to have carried on his back a weight that four oxen could hardly drag here, and to have run so quickly that our horsemen could not overtake him?"

No one answered, but the general declared with a shrug: "Tayish is Tayish!"

The whole of Gaza was in a state of agitation. A stream of people arrived from every part of the tyranny to gaze at the empty gateway. Some swore, others laughed in their care-free Philistine way, though the joke was against themselves. But the natives kept away from the spot where the gate had been, lest they should call attention to themselves. They had been expecting trouble since the previous evening, when Samson had taken down the crucified natives and hung up the soldiers in their place. In the excitement over this new event they had been forgotten, and they took care to keep out of the way. One by one they led their oxen and asses to water at a small pond by the roadside, about five hundred paces from the gateway, and halfway between Gaza and the hills. They came no nearer to the town than that. Their manner showed that they were uneasy. They beat their cattle as they drove them into the pond, and the animals' feet churned up the mud till the water was almost yellow. Thanks to this no one noticed, except the natives, that on the bottom of the pond, three elbow lengths beneath the surface, lay the iron gate of Gaza.

Samson spent the day in hiding with the brother of one of the natives he had rescued from the cross. When night fell he quietly left the homestead, drew the gate out of the pond, lifted it on to his shoulders and carried it away. First he followed the paved road, walking slowly and resting from time to time; then he turned off across the fields and hills. Towards morning he was among the mountains of Judah, near the Hebron road. There he hid his spoil in a cave, and going on to Hebron told the Levites of its whereabouts. Nehushtan and his apprentices spent a whole month forging sword-blades from the gate of Philistine Gaza.

23 Samson's Revenge

Felix Salten, best known for his *Bambi* and other children's books about animals, seems uncomfortable in his *Samson and Delilah,* which follows the trend toward a realistic approach to the Bible. He shifted the story to satisfy probability. Delilah loves her husband, who is betrayed by her sister, Kadita. The reward for Samson's betrayal is marriage to Zemeah, King of Gaza. Ehi and Atargatus, fictional parents of the two girls, are participants in the plot against Samson. According to Salten, Samson was not chained at the well in Gaza, but was allowed his freedom after being blinded. Time after time, in his search for what he believed to be reasonable explanations, Salten violated his source, with the result that Samson loses some of the charming folk hero qualities he has in the Bible. Yet the novel is successful in its own right. Born in 1869 in the old Austro-Hungarian empire, Salten seems entirely unlike his translator, the late Whittaker Chambers, who comes more clearly from our own era. It is curious how the story of Samson, a prototype of Paul Bunyan, has interested such disparate men as Milton, Jabotinsky, Salten and Chambers.

> *But the Philistines took him, and put out his eyes, and brought him down to Gaza, and bound him with fetters of brass; and he did grind in the prison house.*
> *Howbeit the hair of his head began to grow again after he was shaven.*
> *Then the lords of the Philistines gathered them together for to offer a great sacrifice unto Dagon their god, and to rejoice: for they said, Our god hath delivered Samson our enemy into our hand.*
> JUDGES: XVI, 21–23

SAMSON AND DELILAH by FELIX SALTEN

A GREAT FEAST was being prepared in Gaza.

Zemeah was to marry Kadita. She had striven for it, attained it by guile, by stubborn pertinacity. At last she was at the goal. She would be princess, together with Ganna, and Ganna had agreed—after a long and stubborn resistance, after her hard conditions had been fulfilled, and an involved pact drawn up and sworn to.

Before it was concluded, this marriage divided the inhabitants of Gaza into two camps. Ganna's faction was numerous and strong. She was still regarded as the deliverer of the city. In vain did the others, urged on by

233

Zemeah, Kadita and Ehi, contend that it was Kadita who had captured Samson; it availed nothing. In the eyes of the people, Ganna remained the conqueror of their mighty enemy.

She herself was convinced of it. Therefore she had demanded that Samson be brought to the feast. There he was to stand in the assembly hall, high upon the base of the two columns—and sing.

Kadita opposed the idea violently. She did not want to see Samson. She could not endure to look at him or to hear his voice.

Those were difficult days for Zemeah. He wavered back and forth between the two women who, since the day of Samson's downfall, had neither seen nor spoken to each other. He let the savage scenes that Kadita prepared for him go over his head; he endured the cold contempt with which Ganna, from whom he was constantly more estranged, treated him. Kadita screamed, howled, abused, adduced a thousand reasons why it was imperative to leave the prisoner in his tread-mill, not to display him to the people, but to forego his presence, which always brought misfortune. Ganna remained inexorable. Above all, the prisoner must be there! Her prisoner! Especially on the day when she was permitting another princess to ascend the throne beside her, Samson must be displayed to the populace. He must stand on high, between the columns; whether he sang or not would be determined later, but he must be seen by all.

Ganna triumphed by asserting that she was otherwise firmly resolved to absent herself from the marriage. That would be dangerous. Kadita gave in. She proposed a single condition, that Ganna receive her the day before the ceremony. Laughing, Ganna agreed. Kadita's visit to the palace took place with much pomp and ended in humiliation for Kadita. But only the two women themselves knew that, the princess born, who made the girl of the people feel bitterly her lowly origin, and Kadita, who did not succeed in triumphing in her moment of greatness, so bewildered and confused was she.

Thus the marriage ceremony began. The entire populace crowded into the vast assembly hall. They came from Thimnath, had trooped in from the remotest villages, as in the days when everyone came to see the captive Samson. The mid-day sunlight lay clear and hot as the feast began. The mob packed the vast hall tighter and tighter. They devoured the rams and steers that were roasting whole on the fires outside. They grew drunk on the wine that poured from countless skins. They shouted, howled and danced, massed together in one spot, for there was soon no space in which to move freely.

Ehi was again busily employed, again arrogant and held his head high. The marriage made him a wealthy man. For Atargatis received the richly furnished house that her daughter was leaving, as well as all the slaves, male and female, and treasures of gold and precious stones. He, Ehi, received Atargatis. It vexed him that Samson was to stand aloft there between the columns. But that day he had an idea that made him laugh for joy.

He summoned four armed men. "Go into the country of the Hebrews," he commanded. "You know Manoah's house. Take Samson's parents, put ropes around their necks and bring them here! Make haste! by the time the feast is in full swing, you will be back!"

The four men hastened away. When Manoah saw them coming, he ran to meet them, terrified. "Is he dead?" he wailed.

"No," replied the leader, "but you must come with me, you and the old woman!"

Manoah trembled. "Is he dying?"

"Nonsense," growled the man, "he is strong and healthy as far as I know."

Samson's mother stood as motionless as a statue. Only her eloquent eyes, flashing darkly, scrutinized the armed men. "What must we do there?" she asked in a firm voice. "Has he asked for us?"

The leader laughed. "If he did, we wouldn't come for you!"

Samson's mother nodded. "That's what I thought."

"Enough of this chatter," cried the leader. "Forward!"

"What are we to do there?" Samson's mother repeated peremptorily.

"Be there!" the leader shouted in her face. "Be there, when your son adds his bit to our festivities."

The blood left her cheeks.

"It will be more sport if you are there," the leader laughed, "so forward!"

"I won't go," she said with quiet determination, her face pale.

"Hoho! You won't go, old woman?" The leader seized her firmly by the shoulder.

Manoah ran to her. "I beg you, wife," he entreated, "Don't resist. I beseech you. It's useless."

"The rope!" commanded the leader. While the rope was being coiled about the woman's neck Manoah kept talking, with jerky gestures. "We'll see him. What a joy in the midst of all our misery—to see our son again!"

Samson's mother resisted the rope. "I don't want to see him humiliated. I don't want to! I don't want to!"

When the rope was thrown over Manoah's head he was meek. "Why the rope?" he asked. "I am old and weak, and I am going with you obediently."

The armed men laughed. They put on the rope but let the end dangle. "All right, walk along free with us."

"The steer is tame," said one of them, "but the cow is wild." They dragged Samson's mother along.

Manoah came tripping beside her. "Don't resist," he said in a troubled voice. "Listen to me, wife, don't force them to drag you. Don't force me to watch them kill you!"

Samson's mother followed, reluctantly, her head high; the rope between her and the man who led her, was taut.

"We are crushed," said Manoah with infinite sadness, "all of us—crushed."

Samson's mother said nothing.

"Forever and ever the rope will remain about our necks," he continued, "forever and ever will the heavy hands of others treat us as if we were cattle—or offal."

Samson's mother heard him but her lips were sealed.

"Ours is an accursed blessing," Manoah continued, "but it remains a blessing! A glorious blessing!" His thin voice was lowered and deepened as always when inspiration seized him. "We possess the light of the world, and therefore we must suffer as long as it is dark. We possess the wisdom of the world, and therefore must endure mistreatment as long as stupidity rules. We bring liberation to the world and therefore are persecuted as long as there is bondage . . ."

"Ha!" A brief laugh broke from the lips of Samson's mother.

"Wise is the Almighty!" Manoah glanced at her. "Unfathomably wise to lay upon us all these martyrdoms, all these humiliations. Else how great would our pride become!"

"If I could still pray to your good-for-nothing God . . ."

"Wife!" cried Manoah.

"If I had any respect left for Him, I would beseech Him on my bended knees to let me die—me, or Samson!"

"Wife! Wife!" cried Manoah horrified.

"Yes, die! Only, I do not want to see him. Not that way!" Tears flashed in her eyes. She said no more but walked more slowly.

"I cannot wait to see my son," said Manoah softly.

They marched along through the warm, sunny fields and did not speak again.

Ganna's servants came to the tread-mill to fetch Samson.

"What do you want with him?" asked Delilah, terrified.

"Nothing bad," the men answered kindly.

"I am not afraid, beloved," whispered Samson.

The men heard him. He did not utter a word to them. They were used to his not answering. "Come with us, we don't need chains."

Samson smiled.

"The princess wants to see you," they said. "Ganna wants all the people to see you—and she wants you to sing."

Samson groped with his arm. Delilah took it and drew him to her.

"Of course, of course," laughed the man, "she can come!"

He stooped and called the dog, who fawned upon him.

"There'll be room even for your dog," they assured him.

As they passed out the door in the palisade, the tumult of the feast assailed their ears. The wild hubbub of drunken, riotous voices, the shrieking of women, the clear murmur of many harps, the loud blaring of trumpets, and long, resounding crash of beaten cymbals.

At their entrance the tumult in the hall swelled to a deafening thunder.

"Make way for Samson," cried the men who escorted him.

"Room for Samson," everyone shouted. "Samson! Samson!" The hall bellowed and howled. Engulfed by the tremendous uproar, thronged about by the thousands of men and women, amidst the frenzied crashing of the cymbals,

Samson advanced, led by Delilah. The air was heavy with the smell of humans, the odor of spilt wine, of roasted meat, the fragrance of flowers and frankincense. Samson was provoked. His shoulders, his thighs, kept rubbing against people. Hands reached for him, touched him timidly or boldly. His heart began to throb. Delilah felt it and tried to whisper a quieting word to him, but it was impossible. Everyone would hear her. She simply pressed his hand more tightly, and was happy that he responded to her clasp. In this fashion, they made their feelings known to one another a number of times. When the dog, which in terror kept close to his heels, was stepped on and uttered a terrible howl of pain, Samson stopped and glared angrily about him. Then men hastened to appease him. "It's nothing." He groped for the animal, stroked its warm fur and strode on. They let Samson and Delilah mount the base of the columns alone. Only the dog followed them.

At last Samson appeared, standing above the entire populace between the columns.

The hall was perfectly still, as he stood, erect and beautiful, youthful and filled with natural majesty, the expression of his noble features softened by his blindness. Pitiable and terrifying, he towered above them, breathing heavily. The dog had stretched himself at Samson's feet, his tongue was lolling out of his mouth. He wagged his tail and yawned in embarrassed perplexity, excited and tired.

Delilah leaned against Samson's breast. She gazed down at the masses of people. She saw Zemeah on the throne opposite. At his right sat Ganna, her burning eyes fastened on Samson. At Zemeah's left cowered Kadita, her head bowed, shunning her sister's glance.

After a brief silence, several hundred voices shouted, "Ganna! Ganna!" More and more joined in, and the hall resounded with jubilation. "Ganna! Ganna! Our deliverer! Our deliverer!"

Ganna rose, nodded to all sides, inclined her head in acknowledgement and, with a wave of her hand, commanded silence.

By degrees the tumult ebbed.

Then Ganna spoke. "Sing for me, Samson," she said.

The blind man did not answer.

"Do you hear me, Samson?" she said loudly, and there was a quaver of embarrassment in her voice.

Samson nodded his head ever so slightly.

"Sing, Samson! Sing for me. I am Ganna!" As there was no response, she said more softly, "Sing for me!"

Samson remained silent.

But Kadita laughed aloud.

Ganna threw all restraint to the winds. "Sing, Samson, my friend, I love you, sing, you glorious singer!"

"You *will* sing!" cried a shrill voice at the sound of which Samson involuntarily frowned, while the dog started up, barking furiously.

"You *will* sing!" screamed Ehi. "Wait, Manoah is coming, and your mother! They are bringing you your harp. Then you'll sing!"

Their incipient laughter died in their throats at the terrible cry Samson uttered.

"Samson," pleaded Ganna, "I did not command him to do that, believe me."

He did not even hear her. He pressed Delilah to his heart and whispered, "I could not bear that, not that!"

Delilah flung her arms about his neck. "Beloved, you are as strong as ever! Here, these columns support the roof!" She encircled either column with one of his arms.

"Eternal God," he said devoutly, his face lifted upwards, "Eternal God, with Your spirit upon me, let me perish—together with my enemies."

He grasped the columns.

Delilah kissed him. "I will die with you."

Tears started from his blind eyes. "Let me perish with my love," he sobbed. He threw all his strength into the power of his two arms.

Suddenly, in the midst of the tense, expectant mob, Kadita screamed horribly. She was the first to grasp what was about to happen.

But the beams were already cracking, men who had been crouching aloft were hurtling into space. The room plunged down, and a moment later smoke and dust were rising from the heap of ruins under which lay Samson and Delilah—and all the rest. Even the dog.

Manoah and Samson's mother had just reached the city gates when the roar and crash of the collapsing palace made the air tremble and sent up clouds of dust that darkened the sky.

The armed men ran off in terror to the scene of the disaster.

"My son! My son!" Manoah wailed, rending his garments and his hair.

Samson's mother stood quietly, with closed eyes. "I forgive you, God," she said fervently, "I praise You again! You are a deliverer from bondage! Oh, wonderful, rebellious God!"

She took the rope from her neck, cast it far off, and strode homewards.

24 Ruth and Naomi

Irving Fineman took that route so common in the United States today—the English professor turned novelist. Educated at Massachusetts Institute of Technology and Harvard, he has lectured at the University of Illinois and Bennington College. *Ruth*, his second biblical novel, followed one about *Jacob*. In *Ruth*, Fineman uses the original story for a purpose beyond the mere retelling of a Bible story. Following the original faithfully in an amazingly simple and yet highly stylized English, Fineman depicts an intermarriage in which one partner sincerely embraces the faith of the other. The book is a plea for tolerance, going no further than its source, but rather expanding upon what is already there. Fineman has also written novels with contemporary backgrounds, notably *Hear Ye, Sons* and *Dr. Addams*.

Now it came to pass in the days when the judges ruled, that there was a famine in the land. And a certain man of Bethlehem-judah went to sojourn in the country of Moab, he, and his wife, and his two sons.

And the name of the man was Elimelech, and the name of his wife Naomi, and the name of his two sons Mahlon and Chilion, Ephrathites of Bethlehem-judah. And they came into the country of Moab, and continued there.

And Elimelech Naomi's husband died; and she was left, and her two sons.

And they took them wives of the women of Moab; the name of the one was Orpah, and the name of the other Ruth: and they dwelled there about ten years.

And Mahlon and Chilion died also both of them; and the woman was left of her two sons and her husband.

RUTH: I, 1–5

RUTH by IRVING FINEMAN

TOWARD DAWN THEY came to where the highway crossed the River Arnon and there they stopped. And Naomi said to Ruth: "Now think well, my daughter, if it would not be better to leave me here and return to your people and their gods."

And Ruth said, "I dearly loved thy son Mahlon who weaned me away from the ways of my people and their gods. And now that Mahlon is gone I have left only thee, his mother, to love."

239

Naomi kissed her daughter-in-law and she said: "It is a hard journey to Judah; and it is not easy to be a stranger in a strange land. Even though we in Israel have been commanded by Moses to consider the stranger among us, and to treat him justly, still it will not be easy for you there."

Then said Ruth: "Entreat me not to leave thee, and to return from following after thee: For whither thou goest, I will go; and where thou lodgest, I will lodge. Thy people shall be my people, and thy God my God. Where thou diest, there will I die, and there will I be buried: the Lord do so to me, and more also, if aught but death part thee and me."

And when Naomi saw that Ruth was steadfastly minded to go with her she left off speaking, and the two women rode on, Naomi on her dove-grey donkey and Ruth on her milk-white one. And for fear of pursuit by the men of Moab they turned there at the river and left the King's highway. They crossed over the Arnon there at the ford where it was shallow and turned westward following the brawling course of the river as it went plunging down its wild gorge, falling away from the high cool plains of Moab toward the torrid basin of the dead Salt Sea.

As the two donkeys went stepping down the steep ravine, Naomi took out her spinning whorl and her wool and began spinning a long strong thread. And, as they rode downward along the green flowering bank of the river that ran among mossy rocks and rested in cool shining tree-shaded pools, the two women talked, the old and the young, the one garrulously wise and the other eagerly attentive. And much of their talk, as is the way with women, was about the ways of men. Ruth asked many questions and Naomi answered them and counseled her out of the store of her wisdom and her long experience.

"For I must prepare you," she said, "for your life among the men of Judah in Israel." And Naomi, as she rode and talked, steadily turned her spinning whorl; and it was as if, with the long thread she spun, she was spinning out the story not only of her own men—of Elimelech, her husband, and Mahlon and Chilion, her sons—or merely of the men of Israel, but of all mankind since the beginning . . .

"Now my Elimelech was a fine strong young man when I married him, and a hero in Israel. He was among the first to go up against Gibeah in that dreadful civil war against the Benjamites in which Judah was commanded to go ahead of all Israel; and twenty-two thousand of our men were slain the first day and eighteen thousand the second. And it was my Elimelech who devised the trick to lure the men of Benjamin out of their city on the third day and thus turned the tide of the battle for us. And they made him a judge in Judah; for there are no kings in Israel and every man does that which is right in his own eyes, the Israelites being a stiff-necked people and freedom-loving, remembering their bitter bondage under Pharaoh in Egypt from which Moses led them back to Canaan. So instead of kings they have judges to lead them in battle and to judge between them in their own differences, and the judges are chosen from among their heroes; for men, even stiff-necked men, are inclined to exalt their heroes, though heroes are often far from wise, as witness strong Samson, who—" and there Naomi suddenly bethought herself and stopped talking as her withered hands unraveled a knot in the skein of wool.

"And who was this Samson?" asked Ruth, riding close alongside Naomi. "I dearly love to hear tales of strong and heroic men."

But Naomi said no more of Samson. "My Elimelech," she continued, "was both heroic and wise, a strong and a thoughtful man, such as are to be found more often among the Israelites than among the other peoples who prize strength alone and not thoughtfulness."

"I remember," said Ruth, "how my father belittled Mahlon not only for his frailty but because he was thoughtful. And were it not for the high price he paid for me my father would not have considered giving me to Mahlon, though it was his very thoughtfulness, the like of which was unknown to me among the men of Moab, that drew me to Mahlon. And my father was wont to say that all Israelites thought too much. They are too shrewd, he would say."

"The strong mistrust the thoughtful," said Naomi, nodding her head as she spun the whorl, "often, to be sure, with very good reason—as the father of all Israel, shrewd Jacob, proved long ago to Esau his powerful brother, whom he tricked out of his inheritance. But my Elimelech, who was both thoughtful and strong, did not lack the foolish pride of strong men. And when the land of Israel was afflicted by a great famine although the Lord God of Israel had promised us a land flowing with milk and honey, the people, who relied on the wisdom of those heroes and judges who had always risen to save them, came to Elimelech for guidance out of their calamity; and my Elimelech, seeing that he had failed them and remembering how Joseph in Egypt had wisely laid up a store of food in the years of plenty for the years of famine— proud Elimelech, whose mother had well named him 'kingly'—could not face his suffering people nor bear their reproaches, although it was doubtless because of their own backsliding that this calamity had come upon them. So he left the land of Israel and went to Moab; and there he proved our old proverb which says:

Pride goeth before destruction
And a haughty spirit before a fall."

And Ruth saw bitter tears rise to the eyes of Naomi as she spun her whorl faster; and bitterness was on her thin wrinkled lips as the old woman continued speaking: "And had I known then what time has taught me about the stubborn ways of men and the power women have over them, I would have used guile, as the mothers of Israel did when they had to: I would even have deceived my Elimelech, as our mother Rebekah deceived her husband Isaac into giving the blessing to smooth gentle Jacob instead of his wild hairy brother Esau, and as our mother Rachel deceived her own father Laban when she hid his gods and saved her beloved husband Jacob from his anger. I would have prevented Elimelech and my sons from going to Moab."

"But then," said Ruth, "I should never have known thee and thy ways,

Naomi, nor thy son Mahlon, and I should still be a foolish young woman in Moab, sunk in its abominations."

And Naomi looked up from her spinning into the dark eyes of her loyal young daughter-in-law and leaned over to her and kissed her.

"Not that I do not think I have much yet to learn," said Ruth, as their donkeys, the dove-grey and the milk-white one together, went stepping daintily down the deepening and widening gorge of the river whose banks were blue with wild iris. "Especially," said Ruth, "of the ways of men."

Naomi said: "In Israel we have a saying:

> *There be three things too wonderful for me:*
> *Yea, four that I know not:*
> *The way of an eagle in the air;*
> *The way of a serpent upon a rock;*
> *The way of a ship in the midst of the sea;*
> *And the way of a man with a maid."*

And Naomi glanced keenly at Ruth; and then, resuming her spinning, she said, "Indeed you have much yet to learn, my daughter. For you are still young and you were but a child when you married my first-born son whom I named Mahlon because he was so frail, so pale and puling, so sickly even in infancy."

"And you, too, like Rebekah," said Ruth, "you loved Mahlon the frail one better than Chilion the robust one."

"That is so," said Naomi. "And yet when I see how often it happens that the first-born are weaklings it seems not entirely without reason that the thoughtless peoples who worship strength are wont to sacrifice their first-born before their gods. For frail children are apt to grow up into weak and troubled men, too gentle for the struggle of life and too troubled by their own thoughtfulness which wins them the enmity of the strong. And perhaps that is why Jacob, the father of all Israel, on his deathbed in Egypt insisted on giving his first blessing not to the elder but to the younger of Joseph's two sons."

"And was Jacob himself the first-born son of his father?" asked Ruth.

"Well," said Naomi hesitantly, "Jacob and Esau were twins—though it is said that Esau came forth first and Jacob had hold of his brother's heel, which would make him the younger, and he should not have been the weaker—but they were really twins and the rule therefore does not apply to them. But why the first-born should be the weaker of two sons of the same father I cannot tell you, my daughter, only that it is more often so. With my Elimelech who was both strong and thoughtful it was as if he had divided the powers of his flesh and spirit between his two sons. Mahlon, the first-born, got his wise spirit, and Chilion, the second, got his lusty flesh. So much so that while delicate Mahlon reviled the abominations of Moab his hardier brother Chilion was drawn to them."

"And was it for that reason," asked Ruth, "that, when your sons married, Mahlon chose me, and Chilion took Orpah?"

Naomi smiled as she spun. "Now that would be difficult to say, my daughter. You were both very young, you and Orpah, so young that you had not yet been taken up to the rites of spring. Yet even then as a maiden you were gentler, more earnest in spirit than Orpah, and it is possible that Mahlon preferred that in you. But there is no denying that men have a power over women too. So it may well be that—because gentle, thoughtful Mahlon, who feared the violence of the men of Moab and despised their thoughtlessness, married you, while Orpah was taken by lusty Chilion, who, despite the teaching of his father and the laws of his forefathers, went up to the high place—that now you are with me and Orpah remained there in the City of Moab." And Naomi glanced again from her spinning into the dark eyes of Ruth. "Now tell me truly, my daughter, were not you, too, tempted at times by the fierce lustful ways of those princes of Moab?"

And Ruth said: "I cannot deny that the sight of their manly strength sometimes moved me in a way gentle Mahlon never did—so that my flesh fainted in the presence of their lust; but I—" And she stopped speaking.

"But," said Naomi, "even in the little time you lived with my gentle Mahlon you had learned from him what Moses knew and taught the children of Israel—that, untamed in man, his joyous, life-giving lust turns to a dreadful death-dealing thing—which Mahlon saw when his brother Chilion died of the foul disease he had got on the high place." She mused sadly a moment over her spinning. "My Elimelech used to say, *From the forest itself comes the handle of the axe that fells it,* meaning that men have in their hearts the seeds of their own destruction. And man cannot be a mere animal: he is either better than the beast, or he is worse. All the same it is a pity my poor Mahlon had not got a little of his brother's robust lustiness, then he would have been like his father, both wise and strong, and he would have lived to make you as good a husband as Elimelech made me—for all his foolish pride." And Naomi sighed fondly and smiled as she spun. "And is it not curious, my daughter, that a woman can yet love her husband and her sons though she sees plainly all their faults; while it seems that a man, to love a woman, must see no fault in her." And she raised her quavering voice again and sang:

> *Lo thou art all fair, my love;*
> *And there is no blemish in thee.*

"Thus sing the men of Israel. And it is his vision of her, not the real woman, that a man loves. And perhaps that is why, when a good man loves a woman, he has the power to make her a better woman. But however good a man may be he must above all be manly to make a full and happy woman of the maiden he marries. And my frail, thoughtful Mahlon was good but not manly—not much of a mate for you." And her wise old eyes looked again into the dark troubled young ones beside her. "Yes, my daughter, I have known; though Elimelech used to say:

> *The heart knows its own bitterness;*
> *And even with its joy no other can meddle.*"

Ruth said: "It is strange that among the men of Moab I never saw one with the spirit of Mahlon, whom I loved greatly despite his frailty."

And Naomi said: "Perhaps it is because the Moabites sacrifice their first-born sons that there is not to be found among them such men, gentle, thoughtful and frail as my Mahlon was. But look there, the Salt Sea!" cried Naomi, pointing downward.

For as they descended with the River Arnon it had turned to a steaming stream rushing down a hot gulley of stones, naked but for prickly cactus and thorns; and there at the foot of the rocky ravine the river fell into the dead Salt Sea, lying like molten metal under the sun that hung blood red over a maze of mountains on the farther shore.

And then, looking out on that desolate expanse, Naomi told Ruth the old tale of Lot's wife who, because she looked back at Sodom and Gemorrah, was turned to a pillar of salt. It was there, and Naomi pointed southward, at the foot of that very sea which was salt to this day, the old wives in Israel said, because a woman had looked back behind her. "And however that may be," said Naomi to Ruth with her wise old smile, "you, my daughter, must put your life in Moab behind you now, and look back no more."

And Ruth smiled too, though her young heart was heavy with anxiety for the future and longing for the peaceful past with gentle Mahlon, as they turned their sweating donkeys and went northward along the arid shore of the sea. Its leaden waters hardly rippled beneath the hot heavy wind which blew at sunset over that silent uninhabited place of evil-smelling sand, bare burnt hills, and beetling cliffs.

And when the sun sank behind the mountains they stopped by a brook running into the sea and washed and made them a meal of bread and cheese and dried figs; and they gathered dry thorn bushes and made a ring of fire around their resting place to keep away the howling jackals and the yelping foxes which they heard all of the night in their fitful sleep. Once Naomi woke Ruth and pointed with trembling fingers to the shining eyes of some wild beast glaring at them from the darkness beyond the dying fire. And Ruth overcame her own fears and rose up and replenished the fire and fashioned a sling and beat off the beast with stones she slung at it. And she took Naomi in her arms and comforted the terrified old woman until she slept again. . . .

The next day they continued northward along the seashore. And riding her dove-grey donkey in the bright warm daylight Naomi was again of good cheer and resumed her spinning and her talk, laughing at her fears of the night before. . . . "And men like to think," she said, "that we are all and always like that, fearful creatures, dependent on them for our safety. Even my Elimelech who was so strong seemed troubled sometimes by any sign of a strength of spirit I might have learned from him; and he seemed happiest when he was comforting me in my foolish fearfulness as you did last night, my daughter. But you, who might have learned timidity from poor Mahlon, are as courageous as those women of valor whom the men of Israel celebrate in a song I shall teach you some day. For though, like most men, Israelites do not appear to want their own wives to be strong, still do they cherish the memories of those determined mothers in Israel, like Abraham's Sarah and Isaac's Rebekah and Jacob's Rachel and of prophetesses like Miriam the sister of Moses and Zipporah the Midianitess, his wife, who circumcised her own son and saved the life of Moses from the wrath of God. And the men of Israel even sing the praises of valiant women who have won battles for them."

"And was Jael, of whom thou didst speak to the revelers, was she who killed Sisera one of these?" asked Ruth, and her dark eyes shone with new fire which the words of Naomi had kindled, for Ruth had a vision of becoming herself a renowned woman in Israel.

"Yes, Jael, though she was not one of their own women but the wife of a Kenite," said Naomi, ceasing her spinning and proudly raising her head. "And Deborah, too—Deborah the great woman of God!"

"Tell me of them," begged Ruth, "of the valiant women of Israel."

And Naomi said: "When the Israelites, softened in the sixty years since Moses left them and weakened by their backsliding to Baal worship, feared to come forth and fight the gathering hosts of King Jabin of Canaan and his general, Sisera, in the north country, it was valiant Deborah who roused the men of Israel to battle. Princes and shepherds came to her call out of all the tribes. And Deborah called upon the Lord God of Israel for help and he, too, heard her call and it is said that the stars in their courses fought against Sisera and the River Kishon rose up and swept his fallen army away and Sisera fled and sought refuge in the tent of Heber the Kenite."

"But what of Jael?" asked Ruth. "Tell me what Jael did."

"Jael was the wife of Heber, one of the Kenites who were friendly to Israel. And it is told in our Book of Remembrance that she went out to meet Sisera and said to him, *Turn in, my lord, turn in and fear not.* And he went into the tent and lay down and she covered him with a rug. And he said to her, *Give me, I pray thee, a little water to drink; for I am thirsty.* And she opened a skin of milk and gave him to drink. And he said to her, *Stand in the door of the tent and it shall be when any man doth come and inquire of thee and say, Is there any man here? that thou shalt say, No.* Then Jael took a tent pin and she took a hammer in her hand and went softly to him and smote the pin into his temples, and it pierced through into the ground."

Then, seeing the look of horror in the eyes of Ruth, Naomi said, "I tell this to you who are going to be a woman in Israel only to prove that though in the land of Israel as in other lands men are wont to think of women as weak and unreliable, changing in spirit with their time of the month and their years, yet have women in Israel shown themselves firm and strong as any man, sometimes when need be even more determined than their men. And to this day the men of Israel sing of Jael, who like yourself, Ruth, was not one of their women;" and she raised up her old voice and sang:

> *Blessed above women shall Jael be,*
> *Blessed shall she be above women in the tent!*

He asked for water, and she gave him milk;
   She brought him butter in a lordly dish.
She put her hand to the nail,
   And her right hand to the workman's hammer;
And with the hammer she smote Sisera.
She smote through the head,
   Yea, she pierced and struck through the temples.
At her feet he bowed, he fell, he lay:
At her feet he bowed, he fell:
   Where he bowed, there he fell down dead."

And Naomi said: "Now sing it with me."

Then Ruth's young voice joined with Naomi's as she began again:

   Blessed above women shall Jael be....

And the two women sang together, the elder teaching the younger, their voices ringing bravely against the forbidding rocks as they rode northward skirting the rim of the dead and silent sea.

Late that afternoon the narrow track they followed climbed to a shelf on a cliff overhanging the sea, and toward evening the hungry donkeys, picking their way among heaps of rubble in which lay shards of old pottery, stopped to crop the sparse grass springing up on a hillock surmounted by crumbling walls. And there was a well of water and a pair of palm trees; so the two women camped there for the night.

"This is the ruins of an ancient fortified city," said Naomi, preparing a place under the palms for their meal while Ruth laid the fires. "Doubtless the men of Reuben took it from the men of Sihon who dwelt here before the Israelites returned from bondage in Egypt. And this is also odd about the men of Israel: that they are by nature lovers of peace, greeting each other with 'Peace unto you' and 'Unto you peace' so that their more violent and less thoughtful neighbors are wont to consider them slavishly fearful of might. And yet given a just cause and aroused to anger they can be as violent and ruthless as their enemies, though *Thou shalt not murder* is one of the ten commandments which Moses brought them down from Mount Sinai. Thus you will find the men of Israel curiously divided in spirit and often tormented within themselves, especially those who, like my Elimelech, are both strong and thoughtful. The spirit of that Moabite prince who took Orpah up to the high place was not so divided. Like any animal he lives for the satisfaction of his untamed appetites. He is not troubled about his violence and his lust and he would no more think of restraining them than would a wild tiger. Nor do his gods, which are lovers of violence and lust, command him to be otherwise."

"Yet, on the other hand," said Ruth as they sat and ate, "it never seemed to me that my Mahlon was divided in spirit. Though he was troubled by the abominations of Moab and the frailty of his own flesh, a more peaceable man never lived, always gentle and self-restrained."

Naomi said: "You must not judge all the men of Israel by poor Mahlon. It is easy enough for a frail man to be virtuous. If you had lived with a man like my Elimelech you would know what I mean. But you will see for yourself when you come to Judah. And now let us lie down and rest. For I am weary as if I had been wandering forty years in the wilderness like Moses toward the promised land. Tomorrow if all goes well we should reach the River Jordan."

So they laid them down to sleep in the circle of fires Ruth had made; but Naomi roused Ruth again to say that there was not one but a host of yellow-eyed beasts moving all about them, until Ruth showed her that it was but a flock of fireflies rising in the darkness and the rustling of the palm fronds in the night breeze.

And all the next day they followed the narrow track northward along the cliffs above the edge of the silent sea, but because Naomi's donkey, that dove-grey creature with deceptive liquid eyes, got balky as Balaam's ass and would not go on without being beaten, they did not reach the Jordan by sunset and had to make camp again by the way, within sight of a high mountain peak rising up from the plain to the east.

And Ruth said as they lay down to rest: "That is Mount Peor, is it not? I have heard my father tell of it with awe; for it is the home of his gods— Baal-Peor and his wife Ashtar. And I have heard him speak of it in anger, too, as the place where Balaam was brought by our King Balak to curse the Israelites but was moved instead to bless them."

And Naomi said: "It is often so between the Israelites and their enemies who are torn between hate and envy of this peculiar people of whom Balaam said, looking down on them from that mountain:

Lo, it is a people that dwell alone,
And shall not be reckoned among the nations.

But to the children of Israel that is not Mount Peor but Mount Nebo where weary Moses after patiently leading the children of Israel through the desert went up to look out on the land the Lord God of Israel had promised them, but which the Lord had told Moses he would not enter with them."

"And why," asked Ruth, "was Moses denied entry into the promised land after leading his people all that long way through the wilderness? I, who have come only from Moab and now look forward so eagerly to our arrival in Judah, can easily imagine how his heart must have grieved him as Moses stood there on Mount Nebo. Why then did the Lord forbid him to go into the land?"

Naomi said: "Long before, when they had come into the wilderness of Zin where there was no water, the children of Israel cried out against Moses and Aaron, saying, *Wherefore have ye made us to come up out of Egypt, to bring us into this evil place?* And the Lord gave Moses a rod and instructed him to speak to a rock in the name of the Lord and it would give forth water. But Moses in his impatience did not speak to the rock as the Lord had told him; he smote the rock with his rod, twice. And though the water came forth abundantly and the congregation drank, and their cattle, too, yet the Lord said to Moses and Aaron, *Ye shall not bring this assembly into the land which I have given them.*"

And Ruth, lying beside Naomi, said: "But why did the Lord give Moses the rod if he did not wish him to strike the rock, only to speak to it? Is it not strange that God gives a man the means to do wrong and then punishes him for not doing right?"

Naomi said: "Now that is a question which has troubled man since the very beginning when the Lord God of Israel set the tree of the knowledge of good and evil in the Garden of Eden and told Adam and Eve not to eat of it under pain of death. For the Almighty One does not prevent us from doing evil; he lets us have the power to do both good and evil and bids us learn and heed his laws and choose between good and evil. So he gave Moses the rod with which he might strike though he bid him speak to the rock."

"But surely," said Ruth, "the impatience of Moses on that occasion was forgiveable."

"To anyone but the Lord God of Israel," said Naomi. "For the God of Israel, though he is jealous of all other gods and wrathfully chastises his people for their backsliding to Baal worship, demands of his people that each one curb his spirit, submitting faithfully to the instruction of the Almighty One. So Moses, who had in his impatience displayed his own power instead of the power of the word of God, was punished by being kept out of the promised land, the land flowing with milk and honey that he could see plainly from Nebo; and there he died alone, and no one knows where he was buried."

And Ruth said: "Would that Moses were still alive; for surely he, who thought to teach the Israelites forbearance for the stranger while they were yet wandering in the wilderness, would have befriended me—for all that he said a Moabite shall not enter into the congregation of Israel." And she looked up at the mountain whose summit under the darkling sky shone blood red in the last light of the setting sun.

And Naomi said: "Some say he was murdered and his body hidden away by those who hated him for the hardship they suffered in the flight from Egypt and wished he had left them there in bondage instead of bringing them out to serve this jealous God, who is one God yet is everywhere and commands them to such self-restraint as most men can hardly practice. And others say that the grave of Moses was hidden lest it become a shrine where his fellow men whom he had brought to freedom might come and bow down and worship him; and that would be abominable to their jealous God who differs from the gods of other men in that he is singular where they are many and while they are capricious he is lawful—not to be swayed or placated by cruel sacrifices, or celebrated in lewd and beastly rites, but served in learning and obeying his commandments which are the laws of all creation and of life. And it is this search for God's will under leaders like Moses who was concerned not merely with the acts of men but with their desires and their thoughts, it is this that has troubled the spirits of the strong and thoughtful men of Israel. They are torn between the promptings of their flesh and the commandments of their austere God who is the Lord of all creation yet himself has no wife. But a true man needs both. For without his lusty body he is no man and without that knowledge of God he is no more than the brute beast. But the man who has both, I can tell you, is not easy for a woman to live with. Just as he spends a good part of his life learning the laws of God, you must spend a good part of your life learning his laws. And sometimes it seems easier for a woman to learn the laws of God than of man. Consider even Moses, the greatest of them, of whom it is said: *The man Moses was very meek, above all the men which were upon the Earth.* Yet he killed an Egyptian who was smiting a Hebrew slave; and in his impatience he smote the rock for water, as I have just told you; and again in his anger at sight of the Israelites worshiping a golden calf he broke the tablets of the law which he brought down from Sinai. But only with knowledge can we avoid or overcome difficulties and reap rewards in living with such men. And when you know such a man, my daughter, you will surely love him, as I loved my Elimelech. So despite all I have borne and suffered yet do I counsel you to find such a man in Judah and marry him. For our Mahlon is gone forever, and what the Lord God said to Adam: *It is not good that the man should be alone,* is it not equally true of woman?" said Naomi to Ruth.

But to this Ruth made no reply, for she was fast asleep. So Naomi leaned over and kissed her gently, and she covered her well with the warm shaggy quilt of goat's hair and lay down to sleep beside her. . . .

25 David and Goliath

When Elmer Holmes Davis died in 1959, he was internationally known as a political commentator. He had been a news analyst for two radio and television networks and had served the last three years of World War II as the Director of the U.S. Office of War Information. What was forgotten by many was that Davis, a former Rhodes Scholar and student at the Academy in Rome, was an archeologist by training and had spent fourteen years of his life earning his living as a novelist. The best remembered of his novels is *The Giant Killer,* an attempt to find a reasonable interpretation of the story of David and Goliath that "provoked . . . vituperative fan mail." "What aroused the ire of these infuriated pen-in-handers" Davis wrote "was not the novel but the history. They had been taught in Sunday school that David killed Goliath, and anybody who told them otherwise was a lewd fellow of the baser sort." Davis declared his chief interest to be in the personality of David. "Certainly he did not kill Goliath. The report of that affair in II Samuel 21 : 19 (as correctly rendered in the Revised Version) is history, while I Samuel 17 is only later legend. Nevertheless, David left a reputation as the kind of man who might have killed Goliath, and this in spite of certain incidents in the record that showed him in a much less flattering light. What was he really like? And what was Joab like. Joab who appears in the record only as a tough and ruthless fighter. Certainly he was something else beside that (as was Bismarck, whom he so much resembles)." Years after the book was written, Davis gratefully acknowledged that there remained a following "who are less interested in the depiction of individual character than in ideas."

And there went out a champion out of the camp of the Philistines, named Goliath, of Gath, whose height was six cubits and a span.

And he had an helmet of brass upon his head, and he was armed with a coat of mail; and the weight of the coat was five thousand shekels of brass.

And he had greaves of brass upon his legs, and a target of brass between his shoulders.

And the staff of his spear was like a weaver's beam; and his spear's head weighed six hundred shekels of iron: and one bearing a shield went before him.

And he stood and cried unto the armies of Israel, and said unto them, Why are ye come out to set your battle in array? am not I a Philistine, and ye servants to Saul? choose you a man for you, and let him come down to me.

I SAMUEL: XVII, 4–8

"And there was again a battle in Gob with the Philistines, where Elhanan the son of Jaare-oregim, a Bethlehemite, slew the brother of Goliath the Gittite, the staff of whose spear was like a weaver's beam."

II SAMUEL: XXI, 19

GIANT *KILLER* by ELMER DAVIS

I

GOLIATH OF GATH paraded on the hillside beyond the brook, swaggering and bellowing; the tall plume of feathers tossed above his bronze helmet, his sword clanked against bronze shin guards as he stalked and postured on the slope. In the sunset, the burnished scales of his armor shone ruddy and baleful, the broad steel blade of his spear flashed bright and cold. His roarings filled the windless evening; and in all the army of Israel, cowering on the hilltop across the valley, no man dared answer him.

"Come on! Come on! Pick out a man, if there *is* a man in Israel! Pick out a man and send him down to me! If he kills me, we Philistines are your slaves—*if* he kills me!" A derisive cackle went up from the groups of Philistines sprawling on the crest above him. "Come on!" he roared. "Where is he? Saul, King of Israel, send me down a man!"

But there was no answer. Goliath laughed.

"Ho, ho! A man—in Israel! . . . Then send me a woman! I liked your women, when I campaigned in the hill country. Ho, ho! Ask your wives if they remember Goliath!"

He named names, he went into intricate detail of reminiscence, and still no man came down. He spat.

"Call on your god!" he jeered. "Yahweh, god of Israel—your god in a box! Your war god! Where is he? . . . Ho, ho! We took him! We took him in battle, your god and his box too! Israel, Israel! Your god is no god, and your women are anybody's women!"

Still not a sound, not a movement, in the Hebrew lines. And the boy who had been listening from the bushes, on a knoll down the valley, flung himself face downward in the dust and wept.

Only that morning he had left home—a home where nobody appreciated him, in a small town where nothing ever happened—and had gone out into the world to make a name for himself. No one knew that he was setting out on this high quest; he had been sent on an errand, with strict orders for a prompt return. But, once over the hill, he had sung and shouted in pure joy; for now he could prove himself, find some great adventure that would make his fortune.

Here it was—the supreme adventure; he could strike not only for himself but for his people and his god. He could see himself answering the challenge, striding boldly down the hill to meet Goliath while King Saul and the army of Israel cheered him; a bright and glorious picture, that far. But he could see the rest, too, with sickening certainty—the giant's yawn of contempt, then his sudden snarling aggression; the single swift thrust of that broad bright spear. He could see that, and feel it too; as often as the sunlight flashed on the blade his stomach leaped convulsively within him; he shuddered, sick and cold.

He tried to force his arms to thrust aside the screen of shrubbery, he commanded his legs to carry him down the hill; but he could not stir. He reviled himself for a coward, he cursed, he prayed; but at last he lay prone in the dust and wept. He was a failure. His nation was a failure. His god who would not help him, who let himself be blasphemed without reply, was a failure too.

II

He dragged himself up out of the dust at last; the bellowing had ceased; Goliath was climbing the farther slope, going back to supper. Beyond the crest, the smoke of camp fires rose thin against the sunset. In the Hebrew camp, too, across the ravine that flanked the knoll, fires were lighted, dark figures swirled about them. So the obscene farce was over, for today. But tomorrow it would be played again, and the next day—till the giant tired of his sport, and drove Israel before him like frightened sheep. . . . Listlessly the boy picked up the rope of his pack donkey and started down the path toward the ravine. He must do his errand; and then he must slink back home.

But a turn in the trail brought him on a sentry—a gaunt man in the bronze helmet and leather shirt of King Saul's regulars. His bronze-bladed spear pointed at the boy's belly; he snarled a savage "Halt!" And then, as he saw that it was only a boy, he relaxed with a rather sour grin.

"Your name and your tribe and your father's name!" he demanded, in the soft Southern drawl. "And what do you think you're doing here?"

The boy stiffened, in a hot revulsion of pride; but the spear blade was too close for argument.

"My name's Joab," he said sullenly. "My father's dead; I live with my mother and my grandfather Jesse, in Bethlehem of Judah."

"And you've run off to join the army," the sentry concluded. "Better go back home, boy. This is no army to join."

"I'm not running off. I'm only bringing a message to my uncle."

"Your uncle, eh? That would be Eliab?"

"No—my uncle David . . . But how did you know?" The sentry grinned.

"Oh, I come from Bethlehem myself. Elhanan the son of Jair—ever hear of me? No, I reckon not; it's fifteen years since I ran off to join the army. What we thought Saul was going to do, in those days! . . . Your mother's Zeruiah, ain't she? A fine lady like her wouldn't remember me;

but I used to work for your grandfather, at sheep-shearing and harvest time. It wasn't such a bad town, Bethlehem. Slow, but I've seen worse since I been in the army." He leaned on his spear, melancholy and reminiscent. "David. That would be the youngest of the four boys, as I recollect."

"He's only two years older than I am," said Joab, somewhat heartened by this recognition of his standing back home. "We all grew up together, he and I and my brother Abishai."

"And he's in the army now—that little fellow? Well, well!"

"Not David. My uncles Eliab and Abinadab and Shammah went up last spring, when the King called for volunteers; but David had to stay at home to herd the sheep. My mother sent him to the front last week with some home-cooked food for my uncles—they don't like army rations. He wanted to enlist—but the King wouldn't dare take a gentleman's son without his father's permission. And my grandfather has sent me up to tell David to come back home." Elhanan chuckled.

"Well, if the old gentleman says come back, I reckon he'll come. They don't argue much with old Jesse." His eyes strayed to the pack donkey. "What've you got there? I don't like army rations myself." He strode past Joab, inspected the load, and held up a bulging goatskin. "Wine!" he said severely. "Good wine, too, if your grandfather made it."

"You leave that alone!" Joab blazed. The rage and humiliation that Goliath had aroused boiled over on Elhanan; the boy's knife leaped out. But a casual backhand swing of the spear butt knocked it out of his hand.

"Try to knife a sentry, would you? Lucky I know who you are, boy. Anybody else would have stuck a spear through you." Joab's stomach quivered again. "Don't you know it's against the rules to bring wine into camp?" Elhanan demanded. "War is holy unto the Lord and soldiers are consecrated men. Neither wine nor women till the campaign's over—that's a statute and an ordinance in Israel. Judah's not Israel, so you might not know that; but my sergeant's an Ephraimite. If he'd seen this wineskin—! But I'll just hide the evidence; and so long as you don't say anything, nothing will happen to you." And he hid the wineskin away in the bushes.

Only the pride of Jesse's grandson before a soldier who had been Jesse's harvest hand enabled Joab to swallow the lump in his throat. His wrist ached where the spear butt had struck it; his soul ached with the conviction that he was a coward and a weakling, contemptible and absurd.

"Well?" he said bitterly. "Now will you let me go?" Elhanan sat down, laying his spear beside him.

"Oh, I'll let you go. But how will you get by the sentries without the password? . . . My relief comes pretty soon, and maybe I can get leave to go over to camp for the night. If I can, I'll take you with me. So you open up that pack, and we'll have supper while we wait . . . Come along, now!" as Joab stood glowering. "Never mind who you are and who I was back in Bethlehem. This ain't Bethlehem, boy; this is the front. . . . Yes, and just as far front as it'll ever be, in this war."

In slow bitterness Joab undid his pack of bread and dates and cheese. "That's a fine way for a soldier to talk!" he snarled.

"Boy, if you'd sat here and listened to Goliath morning and evening, every day for a week, you'd feel that way, too."

Joab slumped down on the limestone outcrop, hopelessly depressed. "I know," he groaned. "It's sickening. . . . But—" He shuddered. "I don't wonder nobody's dared to fight him. Why, he must be nine feet tall!"

"He may be," said Elhanan. "I never went down there to measure him. That plume of feathers on his helmet makes him look bigger than he is, but he's big enough. There's three or four of these giants down in Gath, I hear. Brothers. Nice family to marry into. . . . Boy, this is good cheese!"

"Why doesn't Saul fight him?" Joab cried. "He stands head and shoulders, they say, above every man in Israel."

"Now, you want to remember Saul's a king. He can't take time off to accommodate everybody that wants a fight. Besides—this kingdom of Israel may not amount to much now, but where would it be if anything happened to Saul? Tell me that."

"Prince Jonathan—" Joab began; but Elhanan cut him off.

"Jonathan! He's as good a soldier as I ever saw, but the King of Israel has got to be a politician too. You don't have to serve long in an army recruited from all the tribes to see that. Jonathan's a soldier and that's all; and the other princes ain't even that much. A lot of people have turned against the King since he had that quarrel with the prophet Samuel; but I tell you we might have a lot worse kings than Saul."

Elhanan returned to his cheese; and Joab discovered with amazement that he too had been eating while the soldier talked. An hour ago he had believed he could never stomach food again; but now that he had absently devoured a loaf of bread, life no longer seemed quite so hopeless.

"The Philistines must be afraid of us, too," he offered in reviving spirits. "Their army hasn't attacked."

"That's no army. Only a frontier guard, to make sure Saul won't come down and burn a few barns while they're getting in the crops. About two thousand of them—and six thousand of us, regulars and volunteers, when we got here last week. I doubt if there's five thousand, now; a lot of volunteers remember they've got work to do back on the farm, after they take a look at Goliath. I don't mean gentlemen like your uncles; they'll stick till the volunteer regiments disband in the fall. But fellows like me, it takes time to learn not to mind the way your stomach turns over, when the sunlight flashes on the spears."

Joab stared at him in abysmal amazement.

"Did your stomach do that, too?" he gasped.

"Did it? Does it yet? Every time I go into a battle."

"Then how—How do you manage to go in at all?"

Elhanan grinned.

"Well, if you're a soldier you're supposed to fight; that's what they pay you for. So you set your teeth and go ahead; and pretty soon you're too busy to think about your stomach." Joab pondered that.

"And do you mean to say everybody feels that way?" he asked.

"Oh, now and then you strike a fighting fool that doesn't; but most people do. Yes, even Philistines."

And the boy who had begun to regain faith in himself was abased once more by the shame of his people.

"Then why can't we ever beat them?" he cried.

"Oh, we beat them—sometimes. You're too young to remember when they had garrisons all over Israel, even in Saul's town of Gibeah. After the battle of Ebenezer Israel was a conquered province till Saul started the rebellion and drove 'em out of the hills. But on the plains—Boy, you wait till you see a squadron of iron chariots drivin' down on you! These giants are showy fellows, but the Philistines would beat us just about as often without 'em. . . . Why shouldn't they beat us? Their swords and spears are steel; ours are bronze, all but the King's and Prince Jonathan's. Only our officers can afford armor; but they're rich, they all wear it. Besides—" He spat. "If we don't win in the first rush we don't win at all; we can tell right off if God is with us, if it's Yahweh's day. But these Philistines don't seem to care whether their gods are with 'em or not. They can get the worst of it all morning and still come back to win, giants or no giants."

"It makes me sick!" Joab groaned. Elhanan laughed cheerlessly.

"It's been makin' some of us sick for years. . . . I was down at Beersheba on leave a couple of years ago, and I met an Egyptian girl, and we had some drinks and so on. 'Soldier,' she says to me, 'what a fine big chest you got!' 'Why, yes,' I says, swelling it out, 'it *is* pretty good.' 'My Philistine friends,' she says, 'have told me a lot about the Hebrew army, but they never told me you had such fine big chests. But then of course they only see your backs,' she says. . . . I clouted the little cat over the ear, but she was pretty near right at that."

He was silent, morosely regarding the stars that were beginning to glimmer. Joab heaved a shuddering sigh.

"Then what's to become of us—Yahweh's chosen people?"

"Don't ask me, boy. They pay me to fight, not to think. . . . But sometimes a man can't help thinking, anyway." Elhanan rose, picked up his spear. "Here comes the relief."

Sandals clopped on the stony trail; the sentry's drawling challenge was answered in the nasal twang of the Ephraimites; a squad of soldiers slouched through a gap in the bushes. Elhanan parleyed with the sergeant in an undertone; then, to Joab—

"Go ahead, boy. I'll be right with you."

He laid down his spear, unbuckled his sword belt, and cautiously drew the wineskin out of hiding. The squad had slouched on, but the sergeant lingered.

"What's that?" he asked. Elhanan gave a groan of resignation.

"That, sergeant? Why, that's a sack of barley that I'm taking over to

some friends of mine in camp. Want to step behind this bush and take a
look at it?" Screened by the shrubbery, the sergeant tilted the wineskin and
drank deep.

"Barley it is," he agreed, smacking his lips as he returned it to Elhanan.
"But be careful nobody sees you. And be back by daylight."

With the wineskin under his cloak, Elhanan followed Joab down the
trail.

III

Between the blazing camp fires the boy from Bethlehem walked in
wide-eyed amazement. Spears were stacked, helmets were off, pots simmered
on the fires; five thousand men, as they ate supper, were abusing each other
for being afraid of Goliath; their gesticulations made a ceaseless shadow-play
in the firelight. Five thousand men, more than Joab had ever seen in his
life; men of every tribe in Israel, from Danites of the distant North, their
speech strange with the idioms of their Philistine neighbors, to a scattering
of Jerahmeelites from the desert's edge, far to the south of Judah.

In Bethlehem they knew the southern clans, Judah and Caleb and
Jerahmeel—wild jealous tribes who might send men to fight for Saul, but
would never acknowledge him as King; they knew the Benjamites, the King's
own tribe, their neighbors to the north. But Joab had hardly ever seen an
Ephraimite and the remoter northern tribes were only names. Now the
northern twang was everywhere; here was the army of all Israel and all
the South as well, from Dan to Beersheba—and not one man who dared to
fight Goliath.

At that blistering reminder the boy hung his head, no longer interested
in this great impotent array; he plodded on, his eyes on Elhanan's heels, till
his guide halted, pointing to a camp fire near the brow of the hill. Beyond
its leaping blaze the feathery foliage of an acacia was bright against the
shadow.

"You'll find your uncles over there," Elhanan grunted; and was gone.

Around the fire lounged half a dozen men, their armor laid aside,
taking their ease in belted tunics and sandals—Joab's three uncles, stocky,
square-jawed, sullen; two or three other Judean officers whom he knew by
sight; and a stranger in a fine blue tunic, with a kindly face. No sign of
David. . . . Joab came forward into the firelight; and Eliab, the eldest of the
uncles, looked up at him and came to his feet with a bound.

"As God lives!" he swore. "You, too? You might as well go right back
home! Nobody wants you here!" He scowled, panting. "I'm sick of it, I
tell you! You boys trying to edge your way into everything—"

"I'm not trying to edge my way into anything," Joab interrupted. The
respect and fear which he felt for his mother and his grandfather dwindled,
when it came to Eliab, to the mere perfunctory deference due the eventual
head of the family. "Your father sent me up," he said, "with a message
for David. Where is he?"

Now Eliab smiled malignly, and his two brothers smiled with him. "David!" he called. "Come out here!"

There was a stir in the shadows beyond the fire. A young man, not quite so tall as Joab, sauntered out with a rather lordly unconcern; the firelight shone on his unkempt tangle of curly red hair, it gleamed in brown eyes, bright and restless, shadowed with a trace of apprehension.

"Hello, Joab!" He tried hard to be casual; but the pretense broke down before the snarling expectant grins of his brothers. Joab felt a rush of pity.

"Come over here," he said. "I've got a message for you—but we needn't disturb the others." But Eliab seized his arm as he turned away.

"Stay here, both of you! We all want to hear this. Though maybe we can guess what it is." He laughed, and his two brothers laughed with him, acrid and mirthless. "We've been trying for a week to tell him that nobody wants him around here."

"Don't discourage him," said the stranger in blue with a cheerless chuckle. "We need all the men we can get."

"We don't need *him,*" Eliab growled.

"You never give me a chance!" said David. "I could be as good a soldier as any of you, if I only had a chance! Why, once when I was herding sheep, a lion came down—" Eliab snorted in disgust.

"A lion? It was a bear, the last time you told it. Next time I suppose it will be a dragon. . . . They sent him up from home with some things to eat," he explained to the stranger. "They thought he'd know enough to come back without being told; I always did, when I was his age. But he's been hanging around ever since, making a nuisance of himself—trying to get a commission, trying to get some officer to take him as armor-bearer, playing his harp, making up songs—He's done about everything, except offer to fight Goliath."

A laugh ran around the circle, but the man in blue only smiled.

"Oh! So he plays the harp and makes up songs?"

"All the time. Especially when there's work to be done. Anything but work, is his motto."

"Why, Eliab, in some countries you'd be proud of such a brother. He's what the Babylonians call an artist."

"Oh, is that what they'd call him? Well, we call him The Pest. Always trying to push in everywhere, get himself noticed—" He turned on Joab. "What did father tell you to tell him?"

"He said to come home and herd the sheep," Joab admitted reluctantly.

"Hah!" Hands on hips, Eliab laughed at David. "I thought so! Who did you leave those sheep with in the wilderness anyway? It's about time you got back to them. . . . You start at daylight, you and Joab, too. And don't let me see you again tonight. I'm sick of you!"

He sat down beside the fire; and Joab, after a moment of hesitation, picked his way around the lounging circle and retired into the shadows. David was sitting against the tree, his head bowed; his harp—the light sickle-shaped harp that fitted into the curved arm—lay beside him.

"That's always the way!" he muttered as Joab flung himself down. "They never give me a chance. . . . Or you either," he added in afterthought.

"What's the difference?" said Joab wearily. "Perhaps we couldn't use a chance if we had one . . . After all, we both had our chance today—the most glorious chance any man could want." And, as David looked puzzled —"Goliath," he explained, David shrugged.

"Oh, well! I meant something reasonable. . . . How's everything at home?"

"Worse than ever. Mother and grandfather are furious at you for not coming back, and as usual they take it out on me and Abishai. Especially me; Abishai does everything they ask him to, now that he's in love and hoping they'll let him get married. But I—" David nodded.

"I know," he said. "They're afraid we'll do something new—something that wasn't done by our ancestors. God knows, it's about time somebody did something in this country." Then, more cheerfully, "Has anybody been asking about me?" Joab grinned.

"Your father. . . . But I suppose you mean some of the girls. Well, they haven't asked me. They wouldn't."

"Girls would look at you," David told him, "if you ever looked at them."

"I haven't time for girls. Not till I've done some of the things I mean to do . . . Or meant to do," Joab amended cheerlessly.

"You're missing something. . . . You haven't seen Rachel, have you?"

"No, I haven't seen her. I let married women alone . . . And you ought to. If your father ever found out about that—" David yawned.

"He won't. Nor her husband, if that's what's worrying you. She's clever."

"Clever?" Joab grunted. "She's common—riffraff! David, I don't see what you can get out of a girl like that." In the light of the distant fire, he could see that David was smiling faintly.

"Every woman has something," he said. "Something no other woman has. I've never been disappointed yet. . . . And neither have they, unless they've lied to me." There was a pause; then—

"Who's the man in blue?" Joab asked.

"His name's Beriah; a volunteer officer, of one of the great families of the hill country of Ephraim. He's traveled—to Tyre, and Babylon. . . . Did you hear what he said about me? The Babylonians would call me an artist! And that's from a man who's seen the world, who hasn't spent his life cooped up in Bethlehem. If only I could get to Babylon—!"

"Babylon's a long way off," said Joab. It seemed ten times as far, somehow, since he had seen Goliath. "Sing me a song, David. I need one of your songs to-night. Any one."

"Eliab won't let me sing, when he's within earshot. He found out that the soldiers liked it too well. If I could only stay a few days longer, the King might hear me—But what's the use?" David finished, his spirits sinking. "Back to Bethlehem in the morning!"

The boys lay silent and disheartened; and after a time they heard voices raised in argument around the fire.

"My dear Eliab," Beriah the Ephraimite was protesting. "I said no such thing. I merely argued that from the viewpoint of a man who has seen other countries, as well as our own little corner of the earth, there's something to be said on the side of the Philistines. I prefer my own side, naturally. But I visited the Philistine cities in the last armistice, and I must say I liked the people. The old aristocracy, that is; the masses are only a mongrel mixture of Canaanites, Amorites, renegade Jews, Egyptians—But the old families, the descendants of the invaders who came in from Crete and conquered the country—they're good people, Eliab. We have to fight them, certainly; but we needn't despise them."

"Good people! Their cities are sinks of luxury and vice!"

"Well—" Beriah smiled thinly. "We have vice in Ephraim, and I suspect it's not unknown in Judah; though certainly we haven't much luxury. But there's more than that in Philistia. A spaciousness, a grandeur, a freedom that we never feel, cooped up in our hills. Those splendid porticoed temples; those domed palaces with their gardens; the caravans you see in Gaza, passing through from Egypt to Babylon; Ashkelon harbor, with ships at the docks from Cyprus and Ionia and Tarshish. . . . I tell you, Eliab, it makes Judah and Ephraim seem rather provincial."

"I'm not ashamed of being provincial!" Eliab shouted. "Or of being poor either! We Jews are producers—farmers and sheep ranchers. The Philistines are only middlemen, parasites! They buy and sell, and charge commissions, and lend money at interest. They crowd together in cities, and build themselves palaces, and take hot baths in marble tubs. They load their women with jewels—short-haired, insolent women, who think they are as good as men, women unfit to be named with our mothers in Israel! They stay up late at night, drinking wine out of golden cups while they listen to sensuous music. God hates them!" he summarized.

"I don't doubt that Yahweh hates them," Beriah conceded with a yawn. "Yahweh, we might as well admit, is a rather provincial god. A good enough god for our ancestors in the desert; but it's time we outgrew that old narrow intolerance if we ever expect to amount to anything. I'm glad to see our women taking up the worship of Ashtaroth. Some of them carry it a little too far; that's usually the way with a new fashion. But Ashtaroth is a strong goddess, the goddess of great nations. Under one name or another they worship her in Philistia, in Phoenicia, in Assyria, in Babylon—"

"You are an assimilationist!" Eliab flung at him.

"Calling names isn't argument. . . . And I'm not an assimilationist!" said Beriah with unexpected earnestness. "I'm all for what Saul is trying to do— unite our weak clans into a nation and make the Philistines keep their hands off of us, give us a chance. But I don't see that patriotism need make us hostile to everything that makes life worth living. Surely we can fight our War of Liberation against Philistine militarism without abusing Philistine culture and Philistine music. Let's try to see both sides."

"You can't afford to see both sides in war time!" Eliab shouted. "And there is only one side, anyway! Our god is better than their gods—"

"Is he? Yahweh is a war god first of all, the Lord of the hosts of Israel. Fifty years ago the Philistines beat us at Ebenezer and captured the Ark of God. They hold it still—on neutral territory, to be sure, if you can call Kirjath-Jearim neutral; practically it's a Philistine dependency. At any rate, the Ark of God is there, and we don't dare try to recover it. I must say, Eliab, a god who can do no better than that—"

"The Ark of God is an Ephraimite superstition!" said Eliab angrily. "God lives on Mount Sinai, not in a box."

"You Southerners take your religion so literally!" Beriah sighed. "You see no beauty in symbolism. . . . At any rate, if Yahweh were such a strong god the Philistines wouldn't beat us continually. Their gods are better than our god—or they are better men than we."

"You are a defeatist!" cried Eliab's brother Shammah. Beriah looked at him coldly.

"I think my military record will bear inspection. I haven't gone down to fight Goliath—but I might, if I had as much faith in Yahweh as you men of Judah. Why don't you go down and fight him? Why does no one at all go down, day after day? Because we've lost faith—faith in ourselves and in our god. We can't change ourselves; but perhaps if we changed gods—"

"I won't change gods!" Eliab cried. "I will have only our old Hebrew god, who brought us up out of the land of Egypt and gave us this Promised Land!" But his fierce heat cooled before the Ephraimite's acid smile.

"The Promised Land!" said Beriah softly. "Yes, our god gave it to us —if we could take it. We drove out the inhabitants of the hill country; but even with his help we can't drive out the inhabitants of the plain. They have chariots of iron. We even lost our hill country once, and if the Philistines ever put forth their strength—as they may do some of these days—we're likely to lose it again, to be conquered and enslaved.

"And meanwhile we cling to our barren hills, grubbing a bare living out of the rocky soil, and swear that this is a land of milk and honey! Poor and ignorant and provincial, we soothe our sense of inferiority by shouting that the things we can't get are not worth having, that they're wicked, hateful to God. Touchy and suspicious and narrow, we make up wonderful tales of the greatness of our ancestors to forget what we are now. . . . The Promised Land! A land of poverty and pettiness, of envy and jealousy and spite that we vent on each other, because we're too weak to turn it on the Philistines! As God lives! Could we, a rural people with a rural god, suspicious of everything that makes life worth living, ever build a Promised Land? Why, any civilized observer—from Babylon, for instance—would say that the best thing that could happen to us would be absorption in a cultured nation like the Philistines!"

Now men sprang up around the fire. "Treason!" they cried. Beriah, lounging on his elbow, only laughed at them.

"Treason? You know it's true. You wouldn't be so hot, if you didn't know it. . . . Tell the King I'm a traitor, if you like; or the General. Saul and Abner know me; they know I'm the only nobleman of Ephraim who still brings his men down for every campaign, year after year. I'm for Saul till the end; but you know as well as I do Eliab, what the end must be.

"It's not a question of one god or another. I think we weaken ourselves by depending on our outworn god of the desert; but it's more than that. They talk in Babylon—the philosophers at the great temples—of a Law that is above all gods, a great unalterable law that controls the sun and stars in their motions, and writes the fate of men and nations in the stars; a law that brings one nation up and another down in some inexorable succession. . . . I'm afraid, Eliab, that law is on the side of the Philistines."

"The Babylonians are ignorant idolaters!" Eliab screamed. "Our god is stronger than their silly law. With his help we can—"

"Kill Goliath?" Beriah suggested; and Eliab choked, with an uncontrollable shudder. Beriah laughed wearily.

"Oh, I'd like to believe you," he said, "to believe that we are the greatest nation on earth, and our god the strongest god. But there's an argument against that, that none of us has answered. . . . Goliath."

In the great silence that fell about the camp fire, Joab could hear David moving nervously, with sullen mutterings.

"Our god *is* the strongest god!" he growled. "This Ephraimite is a blasphemer!" But Joab hung his head in impotent despair.

"He's right!" he groaned. "He's right. Say what you like—always, at the end, there's Goliath. . . . What can we do, David? What can anyone do?"

He lay down and buried his face in his cloak. But David still sat brooding; and presently he began to strum softly on his harp.

IV

King Saul strode up and down in his tent, his scarlet cloak flapping about long hairy legs, his black beard clutched despairingly in both hands. By the table where an oil lamp flickered sat a stocky grizzled man in a bronze corselet, his eyes uneasily following the King.

"Abner!" Saul halted, his eyes lurid. "I can't stand this any longer! Tomorrow morning I go down to fight Goliath."

"You must think of the kingdom," the Commander-in-chief reminded him. "If anything happened to you, which may God forbid—"

"If anything happened! Could anything be worse than sitting here day after day and listening to that man? You know what it is doing to the morale of the army! . . . Yes, and to my morale, too!"

"If you would approve my plan for a flank movement—" Abner began. But the King cut him off with an impatient sweep of the arm.

"A flank movement, around Goliath? Our people are too imaginative for that. They'd be wondering what he was doing behind them; one flight of arrows from a thicket would rout them. . . . No, I must fight him. After all, God was with me once, before I quarreled with Samuel—" He broke off, uncertain.

"God is with you still," said Abner. "Samuel is against you because he made you King; he has never forgiven you for being King, a greater man than he. But—"

"Samuel is still strong, Abner! The country people believe in him. When I do anything, he talks it over with his cronies, and sneers at me—and they go out from Ramah to spread the poison over the whole country, saying that God has forsaken me." He tugged savagely at his beard. "I wonder if God does prefer Samuel!" he muttered. "He never answers me any more, when I inquire at His oracle; His prophets are silent; He never sends me dreams—" His dark eyes burned in torment. "Abner, are we going to fail after all?"

"No!" cried the General. Then, reflectively—"It may not be too late for a reconciliation with Samuel, even yet. He's jealous and conceited; but he is an Ephraimite—and he was a priest at the old temple of Shiloh, serving the Ark of God before the Philistines took it. If we could only recover the Ark, we might recover Samuel too." The King threw up his hands.

"Impossible! The Ark is on neutral territory."

"Yes, the Canaanite cities are neutral," Abner agreed drily. "But they pay tribute to the Philistines, they keep the Ark for the Philistines. . . . Neutral! Saul, if we made a sudden raid on Kirjath-Jearim, after the Philistines have gone into winter quarters—"

"No!" Saul thundered. "You military men have no respect for the sanctity of treaties! Our ancestors guaranteed the neutrality of the Canaanite cities, swearing a solemn oath before the Lord—"

"And ever since," the General finished, "the Canaanite cities have been a wedge driven into the heart of our country, cutting off Judah from Ephraim. If we held them we could bring Judah into the kingdom too. Must we be bound forever by the diplomatic mistakes of our ancestors, when considerations of imperative strategic necessity—"

"No, no!" said the King uneasily. "It wouldn't do. If I broke that oath, God would certainly forsake me. . . . Besides, that wouldn't dispose of Goliath. Tomorrow morning I am going down!"

The General pondered, stroking his curly grizzled beard; then he rose and held out his hand.

"Well, Saul, if you must! My cousin—my oldest friend—may the Lord go with you!"

But the King drew away from the offered hand; his eyes were troubled.

"So you're willing to let me go at last! . . . Abner, if anything should happen, swear to me that you will establish my son Jonathan on the throne!"

"Jonathan? But of course! He is the heir—" Saul laughed harshly.

"The heir! What does that mean, in Israel? Our monarchy is new, and less popular every year. The other tribes are jealous of Benjamin; Samuel and his friends are always talking me down, saying that Israel needed no King, that it should serve only God—and Samuel! If I die without some great success, Israel may abolish the monarchy. Or, even if they will still have a King, they may say that my successor should be elected, as I was. But I choose my successor! I choose my son!"

"And I will elect him!" Abner promised. Saul stared at him darkly.

"You!" His voice was a hoarse whisper. "You will elect him! Yes, I might have seen it. . . . Oh, I know Jonathan! A good soldier, but no politician. If he succeeds me you will be the true King—yes, as half the time you are King now!" His anger rose gustily. "I give the orders, I bear the complaints of the people; but the ideas are yours—"

"My lord!" the General protested; but the King stormed on.

"Oh, I know you, Abner!" Saul's hand hovered about his sword. "You could never make yourself king; you aren't showy, you lack imagination. It needs a man who has imagination, and who can catch the imagination of the people, to be King in Israel. This unruly nation admires Jonathan the soldier; but you would stand behind him, think his thoughts, move his hands—"

The sword flashed out, swung up—Then, shuddering, Saul lowered it slowly, thrust it back into the scabbard.

"I'm sorry, Abner. These sudden rages come over me—I wonder if God sends them! He knows I have enemies enough, without turning on my best friend. . . . No, I won't fight Goliath. You and Jonathan together might do better than I, but I must try a little longer. If Jonathan only had more insight —or if you could only catch the imagination—I could do that, once."

Through the open tent flap he stared out at the stars. Abruptly he turned back.

"Send word throughout the army," he commanded, "that the man who kills Goliath can marry my daughter."

"The Princess Michal?" Abner asked, his brows lifting. "It is not the custom to give the younger daughter before the firstborn. Public opinion—"

"That's true. . . . Well, then—Merab!" Abner stroked his beard.

"Dare we do that, Saul? We've practically promised her to Ariel. His family is powerful beyond the Jordan. If we offended them—"

"Could anything be worse than this? Offend anybody, if only we can get rid of Goliath! Proclaim it throughout the camp—the Princess Merab is the prize for the man who kills Goliath!"

"Any man? Officer or private?"

"Any man! We can't stand on class distinctions now. . . . That's all for to-night," he finished. "I'm going for a walk."

The fires were dying now; through the sleeping camp the King strode, his hands clasped behind his back, his face haggard and tormented.

Perhaps he ought to fight Goliath, after all. It would be suicide; he felt that with utter certainty. But it would be a gesture that would catch the imagination of Israel, that would tinge the nation's memory of its first King with an ineradicable respect . . . He shook his head angrily. Thinking of himself! Never mind that; would the gesture help the kingdom? It might establish his dynasty, if he died for the people; it might give Jonathan the prestige that would enable him to keep Abner in his place. . . . Or it might hopelessly discredit Jonathan; this peculiar people might think of him only as the son of the man who had failed to kill Goliath.

To die bravely was not enough; Israel needed more than a moral victory. For Abner was shrewd; he knew his limitations; he was patient and unwearying. Dangerous to Jonathan, if he were a secret overlord; but he could be a useful servant. Jonathan was obtuse, credulous, easy-going; but, if his father avoided Goliath and lived to train him, he might yet become the King that Saul had meant to be—glorious and victorious, the father of his people; schooling them to forget quarrels and pettiness and jealousy, to act and think together—a great nation, fit to build, at last, the Promised Land. Saul had seen that vision, had set his hand to the work; and then the endless wars, victory followed by defeat, and that fatal quarrel with Samuel—

The King groaned aloud. Always his thoughts went round and round in a closed circle, back to the same old mistakes, the same bits of undeserved incalculable ill-fortune—things that had happened once for all and could never be mended now. Israel was finished; Israel lay helpless before the giant—and Israel's King, and Israel's God. . . .

Saul lifted his head; down the wind came the music of a harp, a clear tenor voice was raised in song. He found himself moving toward the music; other men were moving, too; around the red-haired boy who was singing, a circle had gathered, and deepened, till it was a hushed, tense crowd. The King paused—and then the vague solace that the music had brought him leaped and blazed into new hope.

For it was a song about Goliath; how he stood forth in his arrogance, defying Israel and Israel's God; how all the army fled from him, dismayed and sore afraid—until a boy came out to meet him, a shepherd lad. "Who is this uncircumcised Philistine, that he should defy the armies of the living God? The Lord that delivered me out of the paw of the lion, He will deliver me out of the hand of the Philistine!"

Now the music was harsh and dissonant; Goliath was mocking the boy, cursing him by his gods. And in crashing, swelling chords came the boy's reply—"You come to me with a sword and a spear, but I come to you in the name of Yahweh Sabaoth, the God of the armies of Israel! This day will the Lord deliver you into my hand, and I will give the carcasses of the host of the Philistines to the fowls of the air and the beasts of the field, that all the earth may know that there is a God in Israel!" Then the singer's voice rose in an ecstasy of triumph: "I smote him; I prevailed over him! I slew him!" And at last King Saul knew that this boy he had never heard of was telling his own story, singing to-night what he would do to-morrow; and he wept with joy as the song rose to the climax: "Blessed be the Lord my rock, who teaches my hands to war, and my fingers to fight; my high tower, and my deliverer; my shield, and He in whom I trust! For lo, thine enemies, O Lord, thine enemies shall perish; all the workers of iniquity shall be scattered! But my horn hast thou exalted like the horn of the wild ox; I am anointed with fresh oil!"

. . . Joab, squatting at David's side, was dimly aware of the crowd that pushed and packed itself in around them, of knees pressing against his shoulders, of the stifled breathing of a great company all about. But that only touched his consciousness and slipped away. He had soared high above the world men lived in, to an empyrean of shimmering magic where boys killed giants, and Israel triumphed over Philistia, and all things ended right. His ecstasy mounted to an unendurable pitch—and then the strings rang in a glorious final chord; the song was ended. . . . And with a crash he came back to the world of reality: a world buried, just now, in a cold oppressive silence through which he sensed a shudder of relaxing tension, the reluctant reawakening of many men to things as they are. His head drooped. After all, it was only a song. . . .

There was a stir behind him; men stepped on him, fell over him, in their haste to get out of the way of a figure thrusting through the crowd—a huge figure in a scarlet cloak, its bronze helmet banded with a circlet of gold. The King! In the firelight his face was bright with exultation; his hands fell on David's shoulders, he drew the bemused boy to his feet.

"At last," Saul thundered, "God has sent me a man! To-morrow morning you will go down and kill Goliath!"

David stared at him; he blinked and shivered; he tried to speak. Joab knew he was trying to explain that it was only a song; and that to-morrow morning he must go back to Bethlehem. But the words would not come. . . . The King broke out in a roar of jovial laughter.

"Don't be afraid of me, lad! Don't think of me as the King; think of me as a father. For when you've killed Goliath you marry my daughter!"

That brought Eliab forward, hastily, his hand raised in salute.

"My lord! Don't take this boy seriously! He's always making up silly songs that don't mean anything!" And as the King glowered at him— "Why, he's no soldier!" said Eliab. "He's only a sheep herder."

David's head flung up; at last he found his voice.

"I am an artist! . . . Temporarily employed as a sheep herder."

"Whatever you are," said the King, "you have faith—in our god, in our people, in yourself. To-morrow morning you will kill Goliath!"

Now all the brothers gathered round, protesting; they knew their father's unacknowledged tenderness for his last-born son; he would hold them responsible. "He didn't mean it!" they clamored. "It was only one of his songs!" And from behind them, Beriah's voice—"The boy is an artist, my lord the King—not a man of action! Artists always see things as they ought to be."

"But," Saul cried furiously, "he said, 'I smote him!' I!"

"With all respect," Beriah offered, "an artist is not responsible for the opinions of his characters, even in a first-person narrative."

Saul shook his head like a tormented bull.

"I don't know anything about art; I've never had time for it. But I thought I had found a man! . . . Boy, did you mean it? Will you fight?"

David cowered away from his lurid eyes; and Joab, watching in an agony almost as keen as David's own, knew that he was afraid—afraid of this infuriated King, this circle of frenzied men, ready to cheer him if he volunteered for certain death, and to hoot him out of the camp if he behaved sensibly. Against that unendurable picture, David closed his eyes.

Now, Joab knew, he could see another picture—a boy armored in faith answering the giant's challenge, striding boldly down the hill while Saul and

the army cheered him. A bright and glorious picture, that far. But after
that—

David's eyes opened; he stiffened proudly, he looked Saul in the face.

"Yes!" he cried in a rush of ecstasy. "I'll fight him! I'll kill him!"

And as the King embraced him, the crowd broke into a tumult of
exultant cheers. So far as they were concerned, Goliath was already slain.

Joab felt that fiery confidence too, above his tremendous awed wonder.
David was going to do it! David! . . . But afterward—when they had planned
the morning's work in a sort of clamorous mass meeting, and the others had
gone away at last, leaving him alone with David, to try to sleep—he found
himself thinking, David is going to try to do it . . .

They were lying at the edge of the hill, where David could see Goliath
as soon as he appeared in the morning. Joab sat up, looking down into the
blackness of the valley. David was going to try to do it. . . . But he was only
a boy, and Goliath a man of war from his youth; his burnished armor shone
so balefully, his spear was so broad and bright—Saul had sent for his own
armor and made David try it on; but they could all see that the bronze corselet
and shin guards would only be in the boy's way. . . .

"David!" Joab whispered. "Are you asleep?"

"No." David sat up; in the starlight, his face was glum.

"David, are you going down to meet him as soon as he comes out?"

"Might as well get it over with."

"Get it over with?" Joab gasped. "You—you're not afraid, are you?"

"No, I'm not afraid. Of course. . . . But—Oh, how did I ever let myself
in for this?" Joab stared at him in cold horror.

"Why, the spirit of the Lord came upon you! A man can do anything
when the spirit of the Lord is upon him!"

"Spirit of the Lord!" David laughed savagely. "It was that harp! I still
had the rhythm in my muscles; I could still hear the echoes of my own music.
. . . I forgot it was only a song."

Only a song. . . . Joab shuddered. It couldn't be only a song; Israel was
lost, unless it were a reality.

"You mustn't worry about this now," he said desperately. "You'll be all
right in the morning." (He *must* be all right in the morning.) "We'll all be
cheering you, praying for you—"

"Yes," said David. "So you said."

"David!" Joab flung himself into high resolve. "If he—if he should kill
you, I'll go down and let him kill me too!"

Uh!" David grunted. "That helps." And as Joab would have persisted
in his reassurances—"Oh, shut up; will you? Go to sleep!"

Joab lay down, shuddering with a great cold apprehension; he knew he
could never close his eyes that night. But he had had a long journey that day,
and an evening of draining excitement. Presently he slept.

But David still sat, wide awake, his heart like a stone within him. His
glance fell on the harp, and lingered, baleful and vindictive. And after a while

he snatched it up and flung it far away down the hillside, in a hopeless frenzy of rage and despair.

V

The morning star hung over the eastward hills when Elhanan the son of Jair said a thick-tongued good night to his friends and started back for his post beyond the ravine. They had heard the King's proclamation throughout the camp, and afterward they had heard distant cheering; but that did not disturb these half-dozen veterans, earnest and appreciative drinkers. Let the others shout, if they had anything worth shouting over; but those who had the rare luck to drink old Jesse's wine could enjoy it in prudent silence. Elhanan had enjoyed it copiously; now he picked his way through the camp with tangled feet, walking in unbalanced rushes, more than once almost treading on sleeping men. It was a relief to come out on the hillside with the ravine below him; if he fell, now, he would fall in the way he was going.

. . . So, he mused, the man that kills Goliath can marry the Princess Merab. Saul better bid higher than that. I've seen her, this Princess Merab. Fat girl—no fire in her. I'd never fight a giant for her, Princess or no Princess. That Egyptian girl, now, at Beersheba—she was a hot little piece, even if she did say that about the Hebrew army. . . . Queer the way the stars swing back and forth; I must be drunk. That's it, sure enough; I'm drunk. Why not? The sergeant'll let me sleep it off and I won't have to listen to Goliath. Uncircumcised dog—says our god's no god and our women are anybody's women. But who's going to shut his mouth? Not Elhanan . . . I make a lot of noise on this hill; the bowlders roll out from under a man's feet. Ah! Here's the bottom at last! Now where's that trail? If only the stars would hold still till I got my bearings—What's that? Water! Wet feet! Huh! Thought this brook had been dry for a month. . . . More water—!

. . . Elhanan stood still, a cold fear crawling over him. Water—the wrong brook. He had lost his way, come out on the wrong side of camp; up the hill to the right were the Philistines. Already dawn was beginning to break; if a sentry saw him now—! Stumbling, panting, he ran down the brook bed; never mind the noise if only he could get around the shoulder of the hill in time. Over this bowlder, around that bush—

A man who had been washing his face and arms in the brook sat up on his haunches, looming big in the dimness.

"What's all the racket about?" he growled. The Philistine accent! . . . Elhanan's teeth chattered; he had left all his weapons on the knoll.

"By Dagon and Atargatic!" the Philistine swore. "Can't a man wash his face without somebody crashing in on him? You've muddied the water, too, just when I was ready to take a drink." He laughed grimly. "I make it a rule never to kill a Jew before breakfast; but just this once—"

He rose—and rose, higher and higher, his monstrous shoulders blocking out the stars, one by one. Elhanan screamed in sudden horror.

"Goliath!"

With a hoarse chuckle the giant came down on him barehanded, his long arms reaching out, his huge taloned fingers groping. Wild with fear, Elhanan ducked under the swinging arms, tried to dive out of reach. His body plunged against the armored shins as Goliath lurched forward with a roar of rage— lurched and stumbled, and fell headlong in a great clatter of metal. His forehead crashed against a sharp corner of the rocky outcrop. He lay still.

Elhanan, pinned down by those mighty legs, waited helplessly for the giant to turn and tear him to pieces. But Goliath lay still. . . . Hesitant, fearful, Elhanan dragged himself out, inch by inch. He stared at the huge inert form. Something was oozing away from the head, a dark trickle across the limestone. Elhanan touched it, tasted it. Blood . . . Goliath was dead.

In a disintegrating rush of ineffable relief, Elhanan collapsed. Face down in the bushes he wept hysterically; he was sick, long and miserably; at last, in utter exhaustion, he slept.

. . . And in that moment David, keeping shivering vigil above the valley, saw across the eastward hills the first red streak of day. The day when he must die. . . . No! Other men die but it can't happen to me! God will not let it happen to me! Goliath will be sick to-day! A snake will bite him! There will be an earthquake—a thunderstorm—an eclipse of the sun—

But as the red streak slowly widened that wild hope grew more tenuous; the truth weighed down on him, insistent; it compassed him about, inexorable, ineluctable. He must die . . . And the artist who had never had to look Necessity in the face, because one refuge was always open, found that refuge closed against him now; his hands groped vainly for the weapon that had always armed him against reality—his harp. The harp that, in haste and anger and folly, he had thrown away, down the hill.

He peered down into the valley; it was still a pool of darkness, no Philistine sentry could see him now. And he couldn't have thrown the harp so very far—

Silently he stepped over the sleeping Joab and crept down the slope.

VI

Elhanan's eyes opened. Daylight. His head was throbbing, his bones ached, his throat was hot and dry; he lay gasping in feeble misery, and vowed that he would never touch a drop of that stuff again as long as he lived.

A recollection edged its way into his consciousness. It was fantastically incredible; he tried to frown it away. But it persisted. Presently he turned his head, still dryly skeptical—and stared in stupefaction at a monstrous form, lying prone and lifeless. So it was true. . . . I've killed Goliath! I've killed Goliath! I'll marry a Princess and live like a King—

He looked again, frowning, and sat up, peering over the hulking shoulders. There lay the giant's sword, all bloody; his neck was a truncated mass of bloody meat; the head was gone . . . That's queer, Elhanan mused. I know I was drunk, but you'd think I'd remember cutting off his head—

He struggled to his feet in wild haste. Up the eastward hill toward the Hebrew camp—far up the hill—a red-haired youth was swiftly climbing.

Something was slung over his shoulder, something he was carrying by a black tangle of hair. . . . The head of Goliath. . . . Elhanan raised a frenzied shout.

"Hey! Come back here! Where you going with that?"

But the red-haired youth—remote, preoccupied, all but out of earshot—only went on climbing. Elhanan shook off his paralyzed horror; he too began to climb, stumbling and wheezing, toward the summit, and the dull murmur of the waking camp. But it was too late; he knew it was too late. Before he was half way up the hill the boy had gained the crest; he stood for an instant silhouetted against the sunrise, his body thrusting upward like a lance, holding high above him the head of the giant . . . And the confused murmur of the camp recoiled and deepened, and then leaped skyward in a mad roar.

"David! David! He's killed Goliath! Forward—for Yahweh and David!"

Before Elhanan, still plodding grimly on, had reached the summit, the first men ran past him—half-armed, in no order at all, but crazed with confidence and fury. Across the valley trumpets sounded in the Philistine camp, but Elhanan the old soldier knew that no troops could stop the Hebrews when in rare incalculable moments they were seized with this raging frenzy. For the spirit of the Lord had come upon them; they knew that it was Yahweh's day.

And now they streamed past him, officers and men intermingled; Saul too, unhelmeted, his sword bare, running like the rest—

"Stop!" Elhanan screamed. "I killed him! Listen—"

They passed him; they were gone. . . . More men and more, an interminable swarming; even boys, now, and camp followers. A dark-eyed boy came leaping down the hill, waving a stolen sword.

"Joab! I killed him! David cut his head off but I killed him! Listen—"

In a single bound Joab was past him; he had not heard him at all. . . . Now the rush was thinning; but the valley below was a mass of men, they swarmed up the farther hill; swords clashed on armor as the first comers flung themselves on the Philistines. Elhanan stood still, sick, dazed, dumbfounded. From across the valley came a ceaseless roar—"David! David!"

In the wake of the army stumbled a single belated camp follower—a Syrian eunuch, fat and puffing. Elhanan seized him by the shoulders.

"I tell you I killed him!" he sobbed. "Not David!"

"Let me go!" the eunuch squealed. "We'll loot the Philistine camp! Their officers wear gold rings, gold amulets! Get out of my way!"

"But I tell you—"

The eunuch gave a frantic heave, a thrusting push—and leaped over the conqueror of Goliath, lying flat in the dust.

"Stop!" Elhanan bleated. "Listen—"

But it began to dawn on him, now, that no one would ever stop and listen.

So presently he too was stumbling down the hill; not the betrothed of a princess, but an old soldier who hoped he would not be too late for the looting. He did not hear the shivering crackle as his blindly plunging feet crushed a forgotten harp.

26 Saul and
the Witch of Endor

Of Shirley Watkins' *The Prophet and the King,* Edmund Fuller has said, "This is the only book dealing with this material worthy to stand beside Gladys Schmitt's *David the King,*" and Louis Untermeyer has called the book, "One of the great novels of the last decade." Others have found such praise exaggerated, but there is no question that *The Prophet and the King* is a fine and carefully researched biblical novel. Miss Watkins claims the book took her thirty-three years to complete. The greatest influence upon her writing, she says, was that of the Russian novelist Turgenyev, "whose simplicity and objectivity baffle me." Making a sympathetic hero of Saul and a villain of the prophet Samuel, Miss Watkins occasionally distorts the biblical story, and it is difficult to understand why some changes were made, but these alone detract from what is otherwise a fascinating book.

> *And the Philistines gathered themselves together, and came and pitched in Shunem: and Saul gathered all Israel together, and they pitched in Gilboa.*
>
> *And when Saul saw the host of the Philistines, he was afraid, and his heart greatly trembled.*
>
> *And when Saul enquired of the Lord, the Lord answered him not, neither by dreams, nor by Urim, nor by prophets.*
>
> *Then said Saul unto his servants, Seek me a woman that hath a familiar spirit, that I may go to her, and enquire of her. And his servants said to him, Behold, there is a woman that hath a familiar spirit at Endor.*
>
> I SAMUEL: XXVIII, 4–7

THE PROPHET AND THE KING by SHIRLEY WATKINS

. . . a random arrow struck Saul in the thigh, and he was forced to stop while Ezra bound the wound lest the King should die from loss of blood. Then the King, weakened by the great pain of the wound, rested for a time. When at last he had recovered his strength sufficiently to continue, he and Ezra presently lost their way in the darkness, and so paused again in the

270

shelter of a great rock, until the fury of the storm should have spent itself, for Saul no longer had the bodily power to contend against it.

Nevertheless he assured Ezra that the arrow had only scratched his flesh and had spent its force against the leather of the saddle, which had repelled it. He was more concerned to know if Ezra had sustained any wounds, and when the young man had convinced him that he had suffered only a few cuts and bruises, he was content.

"If I could find some better shelter than this rock," Ezra said, "it would be well, dear lord, if you would sleep a little. Dawn is not far off, and when the day breaks the wind and rain may lessen. Lie here, while I search, and let me spread your mantle over you."

"It is a question which is the wetter, the mantle or the man," Saul said. "Yet do as you suggest. Already the din of battle is subsiding and I believe that we have taken Shunem . . . But it is not yet full victory, Ezra. When day breaks they may return upon us, and discover that our strength was not what they took it for; nor do I myself know how greatly our own forces are broken or diminished. Even so, it will be best for us to rest a little, and, if you can find a shelter, to build a fire and dry our mantles."

Ezra, noting that his lord was in cheerful and confident spirits, then left him and groped about for a time, yet never daring to wander far from where he had left the King lest he should again lose his way. Presently, however, he saw at no great distance what seemed to be a dim glow as of a fire smoldering, and as he hastened toward it, he saw with astonishment the mouth of a cave in which an old person—whether man or woman he could not tell—was stirring a pot over the fire. At once he turned and went back to the King, and told him what he had seen.

"The old man was alone, lord. There can be no danger. Come with me, therefore—see, put your arm about my shoulder—so, and lean upon me as upon a crutch. Or is the pain too great?"

"No, not too great. It is more likely that my weight upon you will be more than you can bear. But I shall try to lean lightly. A fire, you say? An old man stirring a pot? Perhaps, for a golden chain or a bracelet of gold from my arm he may share his supper with us, or at the least refresh us with a scrap of cheese and a swallow of stale water."

They set forth, moving with slow, difficult steps, and feeling their way through the darkness, until their eyes did indeed catch sight of a murky, jagged opening in a rocky glen. As they came nearer, Saul perceived a lean figure bending above a round black pot, and for a moment he also took it for that of an old man. But when he and Ezra had proceeded still some ten laborious paces, he stopped, and the grip of his hand tightened on the shoulder of his armor-bearer.

"Ezra! It is the Witch! The Witch of Endor!"

They stood still, while the rain beat upon them and the dying wind buffeted them in fitful gusts. Then Saul loosened his mantle, and rewrapped it so that it covered his helmet, and his beard and shoulders, and only the upper part of his face was visible.

"We will go to her," he said, "but do you speak to her, Ezra, telling her that I am wounded and faint from loss from blood. And when you speak to me, do not address me as 'lord,' but simply as 'master,' and if she asks to know my name, tell her that I am called Zophar, son of Enoch. Otherwise, you will fill her heart with fear, for she knows that the King deals harshly with soothsayers, and may work us some harm by her spells and incantations."

Now Ezra was frightened, for the name of the Witch of Endor was one that mothers had used to threaten naughty children with while he was still a child, and even now in his manhood it awakened echoes of dread and wonder in his heart; but the odor of boiling meat and herbs that came to his nostrils weakened his fears so that he went forward staunchly until they were just beyond the entrance to the cave. Then the old woman, without raising or turning her head, inquired:

"Who is there—Philistine or Israelite?"

"Answer her," Saul said softly, and Ezra replied, though mastering his trepidation with difficulty:

"We are two Israelites, good mother, who seek shelter from storm and battle. My master has been wounded and is fainting from hunger and weakness. We mean no evil."

The old woman rose and looked out at them.

"Enter. Whether you mean good or ill is of no matter to me. If you are hungry, feed yourself from this pottage. If you are weary, you may share my bed, which is this bare, beaten earth, softer than rocks, and familiar to soldiers and wayfarers."

So they went into the cave, and Ezra helped Saul to seat himself on the ground by the fire. The woman watched them with her sharp eyes, and presently she asked:

"What are your names?"

"My master is called Zophar, son of Enoch, and I am Ezra, son of Simeon," Ezra responded, as Saul had instructed him; at which the woman smiled slightly, as though something had amused her. But all she said was:

"I will tend to your wound, Zophar. I am a witch—or at least men call me so. I have ointments and herbs that can staunch blood and heal torn flesh and relieve pain and cure many kinds of sickness. It is because I have this knowledge that men look at me askance and say that I am in league with the Evil One. Though how they come to the view that good can come forth from evil, I cannot say. Stretch out your leg, master, and I will wash and bind it."

Ezra was startled to hear her speak with such brusque authority to the King of Israel, and still more to observe how readily Saul obeyed her; then he reminded himself that she did not know to whom she spoke so tersely, and that the King, taking her ignorance into consideration, was merely playing the part he had assumed.

With skillful fingers she unbuckled the leathern straps that held the brass greave in place, and laid the piece of armor aside, not apparently observing the magnificence of its workmanship. She inspected the wound carefully, and pressed the flesh around it, until Saul winced with the pain. Then she said:

"The flesh is healthy and the blood clean. There is much swelling, of course, but there is no fever in the wound, and I do not think that any fever will come."

She went back into the shadows of her cave, and returned presently to the fire, bringing a vessel of water, a roll of old linen cloth, and a small earthen vial, from which rose a strong acrid smell, aromatic, and not disagreeable. When she had washed and anointed the wound, Saul was astonished to feel that the pain of it began to diminish almost at once.

"Now drink this," she said, and poured out two cups of wine, one of which she handed to Saul and the other to Ezra; it was thin and acid, but it quenched their thirst, and refreshed them. Then she looked to Ezra's slight wounds, and washed and anointed them, with the same quick, knowing touch as that with which she had ministered to the King.

"When you have eaten and slept a little, you will both be greatly strengthened," she said. "It will soon be dawn, and the storm is already abating."

They sat around the pot that simmered on the fire, and passed a wooden spoon to one another, each in turn taking a mouthful of the stew, which was hot and of a most excellent flavor. It was necessary for Saul to loosen the mantle that he had wrapped around his head, but he still kept his face in the shadow. The witch, however, showed no great curiosity concerning either of her guests, and seemed rather to avoid looking closely at them than to spy and peer. Presently, then, Saul said:

"If you are indeed a witch, can it be that you are she who is known as the Witch of Endor?"

"I am the same, master."

"I have heard, then, that in addition to possessing the art of healing wounds and curing sickness, you are a soothsayer. Also that you have the power of communicating with the spirits of the dead. Are such reports false?"

"Not wholly. Though they have been foolishly exaggerated. I have the gift of second sight and certain other faculties of a like nature. For this reason, I must live as you find me here, for if the King should know that I live, he would have me slain."

After a brief pause Saul said:

"Certainly the King has made a law against soothsayers and necromancers, saying that they shall not ply their trade in the kingdom upon pain of death. And I hold that it is a righteous and pious law, protecting the people from their own foolish craving to peer into the future—otherwise than by the inspired revelations of true prophets."

"Why, then," said the old woman coolly, "it is within your power to inform the King concerning my hiding place, and to betray me into his hands." As she spoke, she raised her head and looked into his eyes. She was smiling slightly, and the ironic smile lent her strong, gaunt features an odd attractiveness—the same attractiveness that Saul remembered quite vividly.

Again he was struck by the thought that in her youth she had possessed great beauty of a bold and imperative style; even now, when time and danger and hardship had picked her bones and sucked her blood, her face and her tall figure retained a kind of lean handsomeness.

"Surely, I will not return evil for good," Saul said. "Neither I nor my companion will betray you to the King."

"Then you are not loyal to the King," the witch replied, but again she smiled her oddly pleasant smile.

"Indeed I love the King most truly," Saul said, "yet it is true that I am by no means as loyal to him as I should be. And in confessing this, I give you your guaranty that I will not betray you, lest in reprisal you betray me also by my own confession."

At this the witch laughed quite gaily, and Ezra looked from one to the other of the two aging people in the glow and shadows of the fire, wondering at the playfulness of their talk. For himself, he was still frightened of the witch, especially at what the King had said concerning her power of communicating with the dead. And now, as though she read his thoughts, she turned to him and said:

"Yes, that too is true. Or partly so."

"What is true?" Saul asked.

"That sometimes I am in communication with the dead. For that is the question that this young man has been asking himself in his thoughts. But it is certainly not a power that I command at will. On the contrary, I do not command it at all. It commands me. If I attempt of my own will, or at the behest of another, to summon back the spirit of one who has passed through the gate of death, it will not obey me. But there are times when such a spirit, of its own will, makes me its agent. At such times, I feel its presence near me, insistent and imperious, desiring my service."

When she had said this, her face suddenly changed. The smile left it, and the muscles tightened; abruptly she left off speaking, and moved away from the fire. Both Saul and his armor-bearer were startled by this alteration in her manner and appearance, and said nothing, but sat watching her, while the gusts of wind rose and fell, and rain dropped through the smoke hole in the roof of the cave onto the embers of the fire. The witch picked up some fresh faggots and threw them upon the embers, but now she seemed to have forgotten the presence of her guests, and frowned and muttered to herself in a strange fashion, so that Ezra felt a chill pass over his flesh. All at once the witch said in a loud voice:

"I feel such a presence now. There are not three of us here, but four!" And slowly, as though she were falling, she bent down on her knees, with her head bowed, her lean hands tightly clasped together, and her eyes fixed on the fire. Ezra felt the blood in his veins turn to ice, and at the same time sweat sprang out on his forehead and he turned his eyes beseechingly to Saul; his lips went dry with fear, and his breath stopped in his throat. But Saul leaned forward and said softly to the witch:

"Is it Ahinoam?"

She did not answer, and seemed not to have heard him, but continued to stare into the fire with fixed eyes.

The smoke from the fire was growing denser. It curled up thick and gray from the damp faggots, then spread and drifted through the cavern so that the air grew heavier. The flames began to crackle and leap up, but still the air grew thicker as with a fog. And now this fog itself, curling and drifting, seemed to be taking on a misty form, as though invisible hands were working upon it as a sculptor works on clay; there the forehead, there in two shadowy caverns the great eyes, dark and threatening, there the hair, gray and floating, and the beard, flowing and fading into the nebulous shape of a body wrapped in a mantle of gray smoke. This figure, or likeness, wavered, assuming distortions like a reflection in water that has been agitated; but gradually like these agitations subsided. The smoky form, whose nether portions melted into the tongues of the flames out of which the whole figure ascended like that of an ancient god, was clearly perceptible as that of an old man. Ezra would have cried out in the access of his terror at the sight, but his voice was no more than a gasp, and his limbs were heavy and paralyzed as in a nightmare, and he could only close his eyes to shut out the dreadful vision. But Saul gazed at it without flinching, though his eyes were full of melancholy, and he addressed it with respect.

"Samuel, I know thee," he said. "What has brought you here, O mournful shade? Is it to implant some fresh dread in my heart? Is it to instill in me the fear of death, or bitterness toward God, or renewed suspicions against those I love, and so to confuse my thoughts with folly and prompt my hand to evil deeds? Or do you, perhaps, come to me at long last in friendship, to guide and comfort me in this hour of Israel's great agony—to encourage, to support, and strengthen me for the conflict that lies before me and to meet the end of the task to which you called me by God's will?"

Then the shade answered; the sound of the voice was dim and hollow like wind blowing in a cave, and the words were in part the same words that Saul had heard at Gilgal and at Carmel.

"The Lord has departed from thee, and has become thine enemy. He has rent the kingdom out of thy hand and given it to his chosen one, David. And because thou didst not obey the voice of the Lord as he spoke through me, his Prophet, and didst not destroy the Amalekites, as, through me, he commanded thee to do, so he has sent the rains and floods that have hindered Abner the son of Ner, and so he has sent this night the rains and the winds that have destroyed thy hopes. . . . The Lord will deliver Israel and thee into the hand of the Philistines, and tomorrow thou and thy sons, Jonathan and Abinadab and Melchishua shall die and follow me into the land of shades."

When Ezra heard these words he moaned, and covered his ears with his hands so that he would hear no more, but Saul, leaning forward, stretched out his hand to the shade and said:

"So be it then, Prophet of the Lord. Yet these harsh words that you utter no longer weigh down my heart with fear, and if it must be that we meet again tomorrow, can it not be in peace, and forgetfulness of the earthly blindness that separated us? I loved you once and reverenced you as a father, and if I disobeyed you, it was not in pride, but in simple troubled loyalty to the nature God implanted in me, and to the task to which he summoned me. Tomorrow I do not doubt that task may be lifted from me, and I shall go to where God will judge me and punish me as he sees fit. Can you not find it in your heart to forgive me my errors against you—as I have forgiven you?"

But the shade of Samuel drew away from the outstretched hand, and in the silence the ghostly form began to dissolve again into gray, curling smoke. Saul stood alone, with bowed head, and after a little he let his hand fall to his side. Then the witch raised her head slowly, and came to where he stood, and kneeling down before him, she said:

"I knew you, lord, when you first entered this cavern. Had you thought to conceal yourself from me—you who stand taller by head and shoulders than any man in Israel? Now do with me what you will, for I have broken your decrees, though not willfully."

But Saul, gazing down at her, said:

"Peace be with you—have no fear, for you have given succor to your king, the Lord's anointed." He then took the heavy golden bracelet from his arm and the chain of linked gold from his neck and gave them to her saying:

"Keep these in memory of me. Or, if your need grows great, exchange them for what you will after the battle passes. They are not marked as mine, therefore no man will question you as to how they came into your hands. So now farewell."

He gave her his hand, and she touched it lightly to her dry lips, and said:

"I shall be ever the richer in keeping these memorials of Saul than in any goods for which I could exchange them. Farewell, lord, and God goes with you."

Then Saul put his hand on Ezra's shoulder and roused him, and comforted him, and together they went out of the cave, for the wind had sunk and the rain fell now only in light drops and in the east the curtain of night had lifted to show the first gray streaks of coming day.

"See to it, Ezra," the King said, "that you confide to no man what you have seen and heard in the witch's cave."

But the young man was still so affected by the astounding apparition of the Prophet, and the terrible words that it had uttered, that he was dumb with fear and dread and grief for the fate of his country and his dear master. Then Saul said to him:

"Be comforted, Ezra. In times past, the great Prophet filled my heart, too, with terror, so that my sinews grew weak, and all hope ebbed from me, and I asked myself why I should live, since God had turned his face from me, and no act of mine, nor thought, nor word, could bear fruit for good either to Israel or to myself. Nevertheless, because God had called me to my task, and because he showed no readiness to set forth that other whom he had chosen in my place, I lived on, continuing with such strength as he permitted me, to do what I felt he required me to do. Deprived as I was of confidence in his guidance, divided and blind in spirit, I have been guilty of much evil and great follies, and have suffered very greatly. Yet, as I have lived, I have grown to perceive that though Samuel was certainly, a prophet of very great powers, nevertheless he was not a god but a man, with a man's inclination to corruption through love of power; and though he did indeed have the gift of seeing future happenings, yet his vision was not always exact, nor was his insight into God's will by any means entire. I lived because I had a task to accomplish—well or ill, as God ordained it—and in living I have grown, through very excess of fear, to surmount fear; through acquaintance with treachery, to surmount suspicion, through acceptance of guilt and doom, to have become inured to the burdens of guilt and doom, and through a tenacious love of God I have regained a confidence in him that asks nothing and expects nothing, but is content that his will is infinitely wise and desires nothing evil.

"I have not enslaved my people, I have not taken from them their vineyards and their olive groves, nor their daughters to be cooks and confectionaries and bakers, and though I have led them often into war, yet I have fought with them and for them, to maintain them as a nation among the nations. Even so I am heavy with much guilt, and if it is God's decree that tomorrow or in another day I must die, I shall meet death humbly. The Prophet has said that the Israelites shall, for their sins, be given into the hands of the Philistines, but I do not take those words to my heart. I do not believe them, Ezra. Though tomorrow's battle may be lost, nevertheless Israel will survive and triumph. This I tell you, Ezra, and you may believe me, for there is a moment when any man may rise to true prophecy. The house of Saul will live on in David, who is not my enemy but my son, and from his seed will rise a king who will rule the world."

When Ezra heard these words, he felt his courage rise again; and so they made their way on over the rough ground, and back into all the devastation of the battlefield. Here, already, living men were moving among the debris, searching for plunder even while they attempted to recognize and salvage the bodies of the dead. But for the time there was a lull in the fury of war, and two of Saul's officers, recognizing him, came toward him with pale, smoke-streaked, but smiling faces. When they had bowed down before him they said with one voice:

"Shunem is again ours, lord!"

"Where is the Lord Jonathan and the other princes?"

"At Shunem, lord."

"All are there? Are there any wounded?"

"No one of the princes is wounded. But the Lord Phalti, alas—"

"The Lord Phalti! He is wounded? Dead?"

"Whether dead or wounded is not yet known, lord. It may be that he has been taken prisoner. He is missing."

"Bring us horses," said the King, and when the animals were brought, he mounted, and, followed by Ezra, rode on toward the fire-blackened walls of the citadel. There he was met by his sons and by many of his officers, who were all full of rejoicing over the victory, but the Prince Phalti was not among them, and Saul knew in his heart that the Prince was among the dead, and that in this way God had once again made Michal a widow, to be won again by David when his designs were fulfilled.

All through that day teams of men were busy bringing in the wounded from the battlefield and laying them in the deserted buildings of the city; the dead were stretched in rows outside the walls, and soldiers gathered together whatever fuel they could find in order to burn the bodies with as little delay as possible. And at last the body of Prince Phalti was brought into the city; a javelin had pierced him through the neck, and the expression of his handsome dead face was calm, without fear, anguish, or surprise.

Near the south gate of the city there was a temple, with an open altar standing in the forecourt, and other buildings designed to contain the temple treasures and the dwellings of the priest and his ministrants. But now an image of the Philistine god, Dagon, stood under the columns and looked out disdainfully with cruel stone eyes over the altar of God.

Saul ordered that this heavy image should be cast down and shattered and its fragments left on the stones of the court where the ignominy of the false god could be viewed by the soldiers. When this had been done the body of the Prince Phalti, washed and anointed and wrapped in cerements of white linen, was laid on a bier before the altar, and in the evening of that same day Saul offered up sacrifices in gratitude to the Lord of Israel, and in memory of the dead. After this the body of Prince Phalti was laid in a shallow grave in the plain to the east of the city, and the bodies of the fallen soldiers whom he had commanded were buried around him in a circle.

Now, although Saul had not slept for many hours, he took counsel with his sons and generals as to what was to be done; for he knew that the Philistines would return to dispute his victory. Moreover his losses in dead and wounded had been very great, so that, unless Abner were near or the forces that had been promised by Jabesh-gilead came soon to his support, he was in danger of suffering terrible reverses. But after a time the runners brought in good news: the forces of Jabesh-gilead were within a half day's march from Shunem and were in the vanguard of Abner's army, which had already reached the foothills to the south of Mount Gilboa. At the same time other runners came in to inform the King that the Philistines were again massing their forces in the plain of Esdraelon ready for a renewed assault upon the stronghold at Jezreel, and that they might strike at any moment.

When he had heard this, Saul decided that instead of waiting for this assault he would again go forward to meet it, at a point between the two citadels that were for the time being, at least, once more in the hands of the Israelites. And he sent runners to inform both Abner and the captains of the Jabesh-gileadites of his designs. If the Philistines, he said, should drive him back before the reinforcements reached him, he would withdraw southward to meet Abner's army as it advanced from Mount Gilboa, thereby inducing the Philistines to follow him in the same direction while the forces of the Jabesh-gileadites came in to strengthen the garrison at Shunem. When he had dispatched these plans to his approaching allies, he ordered his officers to see that the men were sufficiently informed of his designs, and that they took some needful sleep and food, after the great exertions of the past thirty-six hours.

Then, early on the next morning, he drew up his lines in full battle array between Shunem and Jezreel and facing the plain of Esdraelon. Although greatly reduced in numbers, the strength of his little army was now somewhat fortified by the acquisition of a few war chariots that the Philistines had abandoned in their retreat from Shunem and Jezreel, and a sufficient number of horses, in good condition, to mount a small company of cavalry which would serve well as the spearhead of his attack. He knew that he was assuming great risks, but his mind was clear, and the bearing of his gray head so full of resolute courage that Ezra, mounting with him the gilded battle car that he had taken to lead the advance, was amazed at his strength, and at his forgetfulness of the dark prophecies to which he had listened in the witch's cave.

"Truly, I serve a great king," the young man thought.

Jonathan, with Phineas beside him, rode a second war chariot next to his father, and Abinadab, with his own armor-bearer, and splendid in newly polished armor, drove a third. But the Prince Melchishua, both on account of his youth and his inexperience, had been sent back to a position of minor princely authority, but mounted on a fine horse, black-maned and chestnut-bodied, which lent him a dignity suitable to his rank.

The broad plain of Esdraelon was golden in the light of the morning sun, the sky high and blue with only a few thin veils of clouds trailing across it, and the air was fresh and balmy after the rain. The two armies, each visible to the other, with flying pennants and flashing arms and with bright colors of blue and scarlet distinguishing their leaders, had the appearance of armies in peacetime engaged in gay maneuvers for the pleasure of kings. Then, seeing that the Philistines had begun to advance, Saul shouted the command for the charge.

The two forces met at a point a little to the southwest of Shunem and at the same distance to the northwest of Jezreel; with a kind of glancing shock, each seeming to penetrate the other. Saul's chariot and that of Jonathan drove deeply into the enemy lines, and the deadly knives fixed to the spokes of the wheels cut through the legs of those who tried to waylay them. But the enemy chariots cut into Saul's forces in the same way, and where the Philistines fell back on their side, the Israelites fell back on that. Now, too, the air was thick with flying arrows and with javelins darting like streaks of fiery rain, and the din of shouts and clashing arms and the groans and outcries of wounded and dying rose up to the mild blue heavens. Then Saul heard a voice calling to him, "Father! Father!" and, turning, saw his son Abinadab being dragged from his chariot by three Philistines, while his armor-bearer hung dead over the brazen apron of the battle car. Even as he pressed furiously toward the youth, he saw the sword pierce his son's bare throat, and the young blood spurt forth; and Abinadab's head lolled backward as he sank down under the trampling feet of his enemies.

Now Saul leapt from his battle car, and with his great sword cutting and thrusting with terrible strength, hewed down those who tried to hold him off, and so reached the place where his son's body lay; the Philistines who stood above it fell back in dread of his giant fury, and so he raised the dead Prince in his arms, and carried him out of the battle. Yet he did not stay then to mourn, but returned again to the bloody struggle, aflame now with such lust for vengeance that the enemy soldiers fled from him as from a god whose strength was such that he could destroy them singlehanded. Yet for a time there was no great advantage gained by either army, but the two swayed back and forth on the plain, like wrestlers, alternately giving and regaining ground. And still there was no sign of Abner's approach.

Then gradually and cunningly Saul's forces began their planned retreat toward the south, sometimes breaking and seeming to flee before the Philistines, then standing and fighting fiercely lest the enemy guess that they were being led into the fulfillment of a deliberate plan on the part of the Israelites, or that their opponents were expecting reinforcements from another quarter.

So through the bright morning and golden, pleasant afternoon the bloody struggle continued. Now the two armies had passed south of Jezreel, the Philistines seeming to force the Israelites slowly but irresistibly. Behind the Israelites the blue shapes of the foothills of Mount Gilboa were gradually losing their blueness; their ancient slopes changed to tawny hues, blotched with the green of wild olive clusters. And still there were no tokens of Abner's coming.

As Saul stood on a rise the better to survey the field and to coordinate and direct the movements of his men, he saw four soldiers approaching carrying a body that had been covered with its mantle. When they came to where Saul was standing, they laid it gently on the ground before him, and without speaking drew the mantle away from the face. And Saul saw that it was Melchishua. The young man had been killed by an arrow which had pierced his right eye and penetrated the brain; there was no other wound on him, and only a little blood had flowed, streaking his cheek and chin. His round, sunburned arms and thighs were not yet pale, only his face was white with the bluish pallor of death. Saul gazed again on the face of a dead son, but he showed no sign of grief or of any other emotion, and after a little time he made a gesture, indicating that the body should be taken away.

"He shall be buried at Mount Gilboa," he said. And the men lifted the body and moved slowly away from the King's presence.

Now, as the sun sank into the west, its long beams slanted across the plain and painted the battlefield with a rosy light, the planned retreat of Saul's forces began to weaken in control of its moves; the onslaughts of the Philistines became stronger and more furious, until at last Saul's army broke, and scurrying figures sped across the plain and into the hills, pursued by the Philistines, who shouted with senseless hate and triumph as they ran.

As the waves of the sea, breaking upon a rocky coast, send streams of water seething among the crannies of the rocks, so the army of the Philistines broke over and penetrated the foothills of Mount Gilboa where the Israelites sought refuge. Those who stood and fought against them were cut down.

"Where is Saul? Give us Saul and we will spare you!" they cried.

But wherever they came close upon Saul in the folds of the hills, where the shades of evening were gathering, he eluded them, or else he turned and met them with such fierceness that they fled before him. Now Jonathan fought at his side, and also Ezra. They hid in ambush behind the rocks or in the thickets of wild olive and cedar trees that grew on the hillsides, and when they saw the figures of Philistine soldiers creeping over the slopes, they fell upon them from above, and when their pursuers were dead, they took from them their weapons and so replenished their own stock. From hidden places the Israelites shot their arrows, or hurled stones and javelins, and Saul, with a more deadly aim than any, again and again saw his living target fall as he had seen Abinadab fall before his eyes. There was no longer any plan to the battle; each man had to fight for himself, and kill in order not to be killed or to be taken captive for insults, torture, and slavery. In the lengthening shadows the hills were strewn with the bodies of dead young men, and the roots of trees and of the trampled wild flowers innocently drank their blood.

Then at last, there came a lull, and from where Saul lay in hiding it appeared that for the moment all was still. He crouched behind a great boulder near the edge of a sharp declivity in the hills, and he knew that Ezra and Jonathan were hidden not far away behind other rocks from which small citadels they, like himself, had been shooting their arrows down upon the swarthy Philistines as they attempted to climb the slopes. Now many bodies pierced by arrows and javelins lay scattered in the gully below them, but the shouting and cries and clashing of arms had faded out into silence, or came only from distant places. And after a little Saul called softly to Ezra and Jonathan.

"I am here, lord," Ezra answered softly, and moved out from behind his rock and came quietly through the dusk. But Jonathan did not answer.

"It is growing dusk," Saul said. "If we move cunningly, we can glide back over these hills to the place of our old encampment, where soon Abner will join us." And again he called to Jonathan. But again there was no reply.

"No doubt he has anticipated our purpose," Saul said, "and has seized his advantage when he saw it." But the cold sweat sprang out on his forehead as he strode to the boulder that had been Jonathan's fortress. And there he found the third of his sons, and the dearest, lying face downward on the ground with the feathered shaft of an arrow standing upright between his shoulders.

Now at last Saul's heart broke in two and his strength went out of him. But he made no loud sound of sorrow. He knelt down beside the still body, softly calling his son's name as if to awaken him lovingly from his too deep slumber. Then he seized the shaft of the arrow and wrenched it from the wound. Only a little dark blood oozed forth, and Jonathan uttered no sound of pain. Saul gathered the body against his breast, and stroked the hair back from the pale forehead; the eyes gazed sightlessly into his, and with trembling fingers he softly closed them. Then the tears fell like rain down his cheeks, and his great shoulders shook and heaved with soundless weeping.

"Oh, Ezra, Ezra, look on this! He is dead, Ezra. Jonathan is dead." And Ezra, gazing on the pitiful sight, wept too. And thus they mourned together.

But presently the sounds of battle that for a little while had faded drew closer, and the soldier's instinct roused Saul from the deep indulgence of his sorrow. Gently he laid the body of his son on the earth, and, rising to his feet, listened, turning his head first to this side and then to that.

"They are drawing in upon us, Ezra."

He glanced up at the pale sky where now the first stars were glinting; then he picked up the armored body of his son, and, carrying it in his arms as lightly as another man would carry a little child, he started to move along the slope of the hill in the southerly direction. But after a few paces he stopped, and again laid his burden on the earth.

"No, Ezra. The tale of Saul is told. Leave me now, my well-beloved comrade. He travels safest and swiftest who travels alone, and if you make shrewd use of these gathering veils of twilight, you may still win your way to Abner's army. Yet one last act of love I pray of you."

He drew his sword from its sheath, and holding it by the blade, proffered the hilt of it to his armor-bearer.

"Hold it, comrade, and hold it firm. Oh, hold it, I implore you!" he cried as Ezra, divining his purpose, shrank in horror. "What! Would you have the Philistines take your king as they took Samson—put out his eyes, harness him like a beast of burden, whip him through the streets of their cities, and debase all Israel in his person?"

"Lord, lord—I cannot! Oh, I cannot!"

After a little silence Saul said gently:

"Forgive me, Ezra. I shall not thrust such cruel guilt upon you. Surely it is for Saul to fulfill his destiny and die by his own, not another's act." As he spoke, he unlaced his corselet and drove the blade deep into his own body. He caught at Ezra's shoulder to break his fall; then he went down slowly, clenching his hands and panting a little as the blood began to gush from the great wound. As Ezra held him, supporting him against his breast, he again summoned up his strength and pulled the blade forth from the wound so that his lifeblood could flow forth more freely.

"Go, lad. Go now. All is not lost," he whispered, and then as Ezra wiped the sweat from his cold forehead, he lifted his hand and touched the young man's cheek. "Israel has not died with Saul, nor shall it—They see in part, and they prophesy in part—ah, Samuel—"

His hand fell, he shuddered once, and then he was still.

Then Ezra kissed him on the brow, and, seeing that he was dead, took the sword that lay near his hand, and thrust the blade with all his strength into his own body. It was the first time that he had ever disobeyed his lord.

The next day at dawn two Philistine soldiers, hunting for the bodies of dead Israelites to plunder them, came upon these three who lay on the slope above the ravine, and recognized the face and crowned helmet of King Saul.

They cried out in astonishment and exultation, and when other of their comrades came running in answer to their shouts, they took up the bodies, and carried them back in triumph to Shunem, from which, once again, the Israelites had been driven. There they nailed them all three in their armor against the wall of the temple, where the fragments of the god Dagon still lay on the cobblestones of the forecourt; and all through that day the soldiers and generals of Achish came to gaze at the great figure of Saul, hanging in its armor with outstretched arms, between his son and his faithful servant, and his crowned head fallen on his breast. But even while they stared, and mocked and wondered. Abner's army was marching upon Shunem from the south, and the forces of Jabesh-gilead were marching upon Shunem from the east; in Israel fresh thousands were rising, and in the far south, David, with his fierce band of followers, was moving northward against the Philistines.

But it was the men of Jabesh-gilead who first broke into Shunem, and sacked it; and when they came to the temple, and saw the bodies transfixed upon the wall, they reverently took them down, and washed and anointed them, and laid them before the altar of God. Later they carried them to the city of Jabesh-gilead, where they buried them in kingly honor, and built a temple over them to the glory of God and to the memory of his servant Saul.

27 David and Bathsheba

Louis de Wohl wrote his religious novels as a matter of devotion. A professional author from the age of twenty-one, he completed over sixty books before his death in 1960. The last of these was *David of Jerusalem,* his only novel based upon an Old Testament source. A Catholic, born in Hungary, de Wohl became a prominent German writer in the pre-Hitler years and moved to Great Britain before the Second World War, during which he served as head of the Department of Psychological Warfare. In 1947, he began a series of books representing what might be considered a new literary genre—hagiography in fictional form. In novel after novel, he told simply and effectively the stories of the saints of the Catholic Church. His backgrounds were carefully researched, his stories interesting, his religious intention obvious but never cloying. The Catholic Literary Foundation, The Catholic Family Book Club and the Thomas More Book Club all distributed his works to a wide and appreciative audience. In 1958, he was promoted to the rank of Grand Officer of the Holy Sepulchre, and the next year Pope John XXIII bestowed on him the rank of Knight Commander of the Order of Saint Gregory the Great. As one of the leading Catholic authors of his generation, de Wohl approached the Bible with respect. He did not tamper with the story line. He did not seek a new way to explain miracles. He tried only to breathe life into the biblical characters and more fully to explain what he accepted in faith.

And it came to pass, after the year was expired, at the time when kings go forth to battle, that David sent Joab, and his servants with him, and all Israel; and they destroyed the children of Ammon, and besieged Rabbah. But David tarried still at Jerusalem.

And it came to pass in an eveningtide, that David arose from off his bed, and walked upon the roof of the king's house: and from the roof he saw a woman washing herself; and the woman was very beautiful to look upon.

II SAMUEL: XI, 1–2

DAVID OF JERUSALEM by LOUIS DE WOHL

SOFT CARPETS covered the flat roof of the palace, where a broad canopy, shielding the king's couch from the rays of the midday sun, cast its shadow over a little table of marvelously wrought bronze on which stood the golden fruit bowl, the wine pitcher, and the king's gold cup. Here the king rested

284

during the heat of the day. And here he drew up many of his plans. It was almost the only place where he was certain not to be disturbed. The servants had strict orders not to let anyone up the little stairs, not even his closest councilors or his highest ranking officials. For two hours, often even three, David was alone here every day, as alone as he had been on the sheep pasture, before the Lord, through Samuel, had wrought such changes in his life. He had never lost his love for solitude; it was a necessity for him even today—and perhaps today more than ever before. To get away from all of them—clever councilors, clanking army captains, suave ambassadors, servile courtiers, and the ever sweet, ever loving world of the women's quarters. Up here on the roof things looked different to him; he was not harassed by the cupidity of men who expected from the king praise, honor, recognition, and above all, power and riches. Here not only could he rest, he could also think—and there was so much to think about.

The kingdom had become a vast realm, feared and respected, independent of aid from outside, owing nothing to any other land. War with the Ammonites, the only war that was still going on, had dwindled down to the siege of one city. To be sure, Joab still had much hard work ahead; Rabbah was strong and well fortified. But its fall was really only a question of time. It was good not to have to think about these things for awhile. Strange how one became indifferent to so many things which earlier one had found highly exciting! Was that a sign of age? Day before yesterday he had discovered the first white hairs in his beard. The servant had wanted to take them out. What nonsense! "There will soon be many others. You can't pull them all out. Shall I end by being bald and beardless merely because I would deny the silver of old age?"

The silver of old age—he had said that so carelessly, never thinking that perhaps it was really on the way! One sign of old age was that people to whom you had become accustomed died. Jacob, his former enemy, had died, at the last a puzzled old man, content to be left unmolested. But Jacob had been twenty years older than he. Michol had died—just as the news came from Joab of the end of the Edomite war. But she had been very ill for a long time, no physician knew the cause. She had grown very thin; at the last she had been not much more than a skeleton covered with a brownish skin, and she had suffered great pains in her body that had once been so beautiful—and yet had never brought forth a child. Michol—she had long been a stranger to him. And the only one who mourned her was her slave—now what was her name?—Nossu, a black horror of a woman. She had thrown herself out of the palace window. Well, there had been at least one person who loved Saul's cold, haughty daughter to the end of her life! Even kind Chusai, who had once loved her so deeply, had become estranged. Only Nossu had not been able to live without her—and David had given orders to have her buried at the foot of her mistress's grave.

Suddenly a thought came to him, a harsh, provocative, thought: Would there be anyone who would refuse to outlive King David's death? He made himself consider the question objectively, without any illusions. The women?

Achinoam was no longer the romantic little dreamer of Ceila; since the birth of Prince Amnon and her two daughters, she had grown fat and indifferent. She comforted herself with raisin cakes and with the new Syrian pastry made of almonds, eggs, milk, and honey, a lot of honey. Even Abigail had not retained her beauty, though she had not lost her dignity. To be sure, her gaiety had vanished since the death of her son. Maacha was completely absorbed in her children: Thamar was really a beautiful girl and Absalom—ah, Absalom was a great joy, constantly renewed, a gifted boy, clever and warmhearted. Another year and the hearts of all the girls would be his for the asking; he had only to smile at them! Jonathan must have looked like that when he was a boy. And Absalom adored his father. But follow him in death? It was foolish to think of such a thing—and wrong. The young wanted to have their own life and they had a right to it. Haggith—she would mourn long and sincerely, and Abital would weep too—she wept easily anyway. But she and Egla would soon hope that his successor would take an interest in them. The concubines—how many were there? All specially chosen beauties, highly honored if the king visited them once, but for the rest of the time sunk in apathetic boredom. No woman would take her life when David died.

And the men? Joab—sometimes it seemed as though he were already looking around to select the prince with whom he should curry favor. Abisai thought only of soldiers and war. Neither of the two brothers knew what love was. True, they had been beside themselves over Asael's death, but not so much on Asael's account as because he was their brother, a member of their clan, and therefore part of themselves. They avenged themselves by avenging Asael. Chusai—yes, he would mourn, in his own dry, cool fashion. As Chusai was cool, so was Achitophel hotheaded; where Chusai was witty, Achitophel was malicious. The man was a brain and nothing more. To Nathan the king was a servant of God to whom one brought messages now and then. To the soldiers, a leader who had never been defeated. Many of them would be ready to die to win a battle for the king, to protect the king. But not one of them would follow him in death—certainly none of the court officials and courtiers. With all her arrogance, Michol had had her Nossu, thought David, and he smiled ironically. "Would I be richer if I had someone? And I myself—is there any human being whom, for love, I would follow in death?"

That whole line of thinking suddenly struck him as unworthy. Perhaps one had to be an individual without rank and without attainments, and moreover grotesquely ugly, to do what Nossu had done—an individual who, like a parasite, shared the life of a popular hero. He shrugged his shoulders, poured out a beaker of wine, and drank. How did he happen on such thoughts anyway? Because life on the throne was lonely. And it was not the loneliness of the pasture, in which you were one with earth, air, sheep, and sun. It was an isolation, a cold solitude, that left much unfulfilled. A king bore the sorrows of all, he made the decisions for all. But he himself could go only to the Lord, to the black and white yes or no of the Urim and Thummim stones, or the guidance of dreams and the faces of prophets. There were moments in which he could understand how Saul could not endure the terrible loneliness of sovereignty. But that was the way it was and so it would remain, until old age came and after that—death. He drained the beaker to the last drop and was about to set it down on the little table when his eye fell on the roof of the next house, which lay somewhat below his eyrie; he paused with his hand suspended in air.

A young woman was standing there alone, and she was in the act of taking a ritual cleansing bath. She had apparently no suspicion that she could be seen from the palace roof. Her skin was milky white and when she loosened the two large combs that held her hair, it fell in a reddish-brown wavy flood over her shoulders and back. Her figure and movements were so wonderfully beautiful in their natural comeliness and high dignity—how was it he had never seen her before? He tried to recognize her features, but the distance was too great. She was like a remote, unattainable dream.

Slowly David set the beaker down on the table. Then he struck a bronze tray with a little hammer. A servant appeared from the staircase leading to the terrace.

"The woman down there," said David casually, "do you know who she is?"

The servant looked down. "No, lord."

"Then find out and tell me."

The man disappeared again. That she could only be a woman of some rank was revealed not only by her appearance but by the house in which she lived. Now she had finished her bath and was trying to pin up her hair again, but she could not manage it. Perhaps she was accustomed to the help of a maid, whom she had not brought with her. Laughing, she shook back the reddish-brown flood and picked up a light wrap; it was as though she had wrapped herself in a cloud. The cloud glided toward the stairs and disappeared.

The servant came back. "Lord, the woman is Bathsheba, the daughter of Eliam. Her husband is Urias, the Hittite."

Eliam—the commander of thousands and brother of Achitophel! Urias? A leader of hundreds. Both were at the front under Joab. A king must have a good memory. Nothing makes him more popular with the army than for him to remember the names and deeds of his officers. Bathsheba! Was she alone in the house?

"Who else lives over there?"

"Only a servant, lord."

She was alone. "Go over there," David commanded. "Say that the king wishes to receive her in audience."

"Yes, lord. On which day?"

"Today, you fool," said David angrily. "Now. And here!"

The man, very much flustered, withdrew. David bit his lip. It was unwise to hold the audience here. It was unwise to receive the woman anyway: She was married and the niece of Achitophel. But he was not Esbaal, who countermanded his own orders.

She came a few minutes later, tall and slender and so beautiful that

David had difficulty in hiding his admiration before the servant who had brought her up to the roof. But the finely cut face was pale and fear shone in the large, dark eyes. She threw herself down before the king as custom demanded, and he forced himself to speak calmly as he gave her permission to rise. At a motion from the king, the servant withdrew.

"Forgive your handmaiden, lord," she begged, "but if you have bad news to tell me, do not keep me waiting longer. Has my father Eliam fallen, or my husband?"

"Neither one," he replied. "Do not worry, I have no bad news for you."

She drew a deep breath. But the sudden relief after the tension was too much for her and she swayed. Immediately he was beside her, supporting her.

"My king," she said softly, "I must beg your forgiveness, but I was so greatly afraid . . ."

He led her to the couch. "Sit down," he commanded. He filled the beaker. "Here—to give you strength." She hesitated, but he held the beaker to her lips and she sipped a little. He sat down beside her. "It is not fitting that I should sit in the presence of the king," she murmured, and she made a move to rise. He held her back, kindly but firmly. "It is fitting when it is my will," he said. "Do you feel better?"

"Yes, lord. You are very kind to me."

"Am I?" he asked half to himself.

A shimmer of fear came into her eyes again, but curiosity shone there too and—he recognized it at once—admiration.

"You were worried about your father and your husband," he remarked casually, "and you mentioned your father first. Are you not happy with Urias?"

"Oh, yes, lord." The answer came promptly but without much warmth, and David's heart beat faster.

"Have you been married long?"

"No, lord. He had to go to the front soon afterward. But he was glad to go, he is happy to be a soldier. That is what my father liked so much about him. Since then, I have not seen him for almost a year."

"Drink a little more wine," David urged and, with a shy smile, she obeyed. "What are you thinking?" he asked suddenly, and he watched with delight as a light red flushed the delicate white face.

"I'm thinking how strange it can seem when a wish is fulfilled," she replied hesitantly.

"What do you mean by that?"

The flush deepened. "I have so often wished to be allowed to meet the king," she said softly. "My father stood before you twice and I made him tell me about it again and again. How could I ever think then that one day I would be permitted to sit beside the king and speak with him as I do now! You the ruler over Israel and Judah and so many other lands, the victor over all our enemies—Urias says there is no king in all the world to compare with you."

David frowned. Then he laughed.

"It is unbelievable," she continued. "The hand that slew Goliath has held the cup to my lips."

"For the king, too, this hours means the fulfillment of a wish," said David. "I wanted to see the most beautiful woman in my kingdom."

"The king mocks his handmaiden," she murmured. At that he seized both her hands.

"Do you really think I am mocking you?" he asked softly. The man who held her prisoner was the king, the all-powerful, of whom the people sang songs, the hero who had made his people great. How could she withstand him, whom the strongest could not withstand? Her lips opened under his kiss and her whole being surrendered to him.

The news was brought to him by a slave of Bathsheba's—only a few words scratched on a clay disk. David's face was stony as he read them. He dismissed the messenger, a very young girl who certainly could not read, and lost himself in angry and gloomy reflections. Urias was at the front; he had not seen his wife for a year. And the punishment for adultery was stoning. Stones flung by brutal hands on the most beautiful body among women, her face—that magical work of Nature—bruised, crushed, a mass of bleeding flesh and broken bones. No, no! It must not be! And what of him? Was there a woman who would not call out the name of her lover when she looked death in the face? "It was the king himself, the king!" But him they could not stone. They could not even call him to account, no, not him. He laughed maliciously. He was the supreme judge in the land, he had to provide for justice. He! They could do nothing to him except the worst, the double sorrow: to let him suffer under the terrible fate of his beloved, and under the realization that they knew of his guilt. No! It must not be.

He wrote to Joab. His letter was very short.

"Send Urias, the Hittite, to me."

Six days later the man was there and the king received him alone. A big, strongly-built man with rough-hewn features as if carved out of wood. No Israelite, no man of Judah—a Hittite. He held himself like a soldier; he moved like a soldier. Not a talented man, a little clumsy, inept. Not too bright either —but a man.

David began to question him. "How is my commander-in-chief, Joab?"

"He is in good health, lord, and confident."

"His brother Abisai?"

"He is well, lord."

"And the troops?"

"They are in good health, lord."

"No sickness in camp?"

"Only a few cases of fever, lord."

"Our losses in the last four weeks?"

"Up to the day I left the army, thirty-four dead, one hundred and twenty wounded, and about half of them are well again."

"So, then, no attack was made in the last weeks?"

"No, lord, we are working our way slowly into the City of Waters."

David nodded. The City of Waters was the original Rabbah which lay on the river, a tributary of the Jabbok. Behind it lay the citadel. "How much longer does Joab think it will take?"

"It may take quite a long time, lord. Nine months, perhaps a little less, the commander thinks."

"And what do you yourself think?"

"The captain of a hundred has the same opinion as his commander," replied Urias with unshaken earnestness.

Again David nodded. A good man, but stupid, he thought. It will work. Aloud he said. "I thank you for your report. Now go and visit your wife."

Urias hesitated a second. Then he saluted and strode clanking from the audience chamber.

David clapped his hands. "I shall attend the banquet today," he told the servant who entered. It was the first time for days that the king had not dined alone. To his table companions—all high officials and officers—he appeared to be unusually talkative, but nervous. He went to bed early, but for a long time he could not sleep. He thought of Urias, who now, only a stone's throw away, was spending the night with his wife. Of course he was her husband. But how did this good dolt ever manage to get such a wife? Not till the early morning hours did he fall asleep. A few hours later he was up again, making the rounds through the palace. When he came to the guards at the main gate, he stopped suddenly. He had recognized Urias.

"What is that man doing here?" he asked the commander of the guards. "Has he just come?"

"No, lord, he was here with my men all night long. Four hours he stood guard and four hours he slept like the rest of us."

David went up to Urias. "You have had a long journey," he said in as kindly a tone as he could muster. "Why did you not go home?"

Urias smiled, embarrassed. "I couldn't bring myself to, lord," he said apologetically. "The holy Ark of the Covenant lives in a tent. My commander Joab and my comrades sleep in the open fields. And should I go to my house and lie with my wife? By your blessed life, lord, I could not do it."

"You are a good man," said David in a husky voice. "Stay here today. Tomorrow you can go back to your comrades."

"As the king commands," said Urias and struck his spear against his shield in salute.

David turned away. The clumsy fool, he thought angrily. The good, honorable, seven times cursed fool! He ordered Urias to attend the banquet that day, and at the table plied him with wine. The man drank just as obediently as he had stood guard or fought. David watched sharply to see how the wine affected him, and when the right moment had come, he nodded to him: "You are excused, Urias. Now go home to your wife."

Urias saluted respectfully and awkwardly, strode stiffly from the banquet hall—and lay down again with the guards at the main gate.

That night David did not sleep at all. In the morning he sent for Urias. "I am giving you this letter to my commander Joab," he said, and he did not look at the man. "See to it that it does not fall into other hands. It is important."

"I shall die before I let anyone take it from me," replied Urias calmly. Then, taking the letter, he saluted respectfully and awkwardly and went away.

David smiled bitterly. "Before?" he said to himself. "No. But certainly very shortly after."

Two weeks later a young officer in command of a hundred, by the name of Zettur, stood before the king. "Your commander Joab reports: 'The enemy tried to attack us and we repulsed them, though the Ammonites far outnumbered us. We pushed them back as far as the east gate of the city. This brought us within range of the archers on the wall and we lost sixty-one men.'" Zettur paused.

"Is that all?" asked the king hoarsely.

"All, lord, except for one thing; among the dead was Urias, the Hittite."

The sun shone brightly through the huge palace windows. In the silence that followed ghosts walked through the room.

"It is well," said the king. "Have them give you food and take a rest. When you go back, say to Joab: 'Let not this thing discourage you, for indiscriminate are the events of war and sometimes one, sometimes another is consumed by the sword. Fight on. Conquer!'"

"Yes, lord." Zettur saluted and left the room. His step was light and lithe, not clumsy.

David sent for Achitophel. "I have just received word that a relative of yours has met an honorable death in the battle for Rabbah," he said. "It is the son-in-law of your brother, Eliam. Urias was his name. I knew him only slightly. Will you inform his widow?"

"Urias was no Israelite, but he believed in the Lord," said Achitophel. "I will go to my niece." He spoke, as always, without any trace of emotion. Not a man but a brain, and a good one.

"Present my compliments to her and my sympathy," commanded David. "And inform her that the king will receive her in the royal women's palace as soon as the seven days of mourning are over."

"The king pays my niece great honor," replied Achitophel. Was that the same cool tone as usual, or was there a hint of reserved hostility in it? It was probably only the king's imagination.

"That is all, Achitophel."

"I thank the king."

Saved, thought David when the gaunt man had left. She was saved. She was the widow of an honorable officer who had fallen in battle. No one could point the finger of scorn at her. The child, too, was saved. Two lives for one, the one a brave but very mediocre man. It was the only possible solution.

Immediately after Bathsheba had been brought into his palace, one week later, David went in to her and she lay in his arms happy, released—and unsuspecting.

Seven months later word was brought to the king that Bathsheba had borne him a son. To be sure, the birth was premature, but the child seemed to be very strong. David went to her immediately. She was pale and exhausted and strangely sad. The child was beautiful and full of life.

When he returned to the palace, the visit of Nathan the seer was announced. He had not sent for him—that meant it was something important. Nathan, tall and gaunt, the first white strands in his tangled black hair, entered silently. "Lord, I come to invoke the king's justice," he said.

"I promise you now, you shall have it," replied David.

"It is a case which only the king can settle," Nathan began. "There were two men in the same city, the one very rich and powerful, the other poor. The rich man had exceeding many sheep and oxen. But the poor man had nothing at all but one little ewe lamb, which he had bought and nourished up and which had grown up in his house eating of his bread and drinking of his cup, and sleeping in his bosom; and it was unto him as a daughter. And when a certain stranger was come to the rich man, he spared to take of his own sheep and oxen, to make a feast for the stranger . . . but took the poor man's ewe and dressed it."

Outraged, David leaped to his feet. "As the Lord liveth, the man that has done this is a child of death! And he shall restore the ewe fourfold."

Then Nathan looked him square in the eye. "Thou art the man," he said.

The king was speechless. Nathan's simple tale had taken him back to the days when he was a shepherd. The greedy rich man who would rather rob the poor man of his last possession than sacrifice the smallest portion of his own property—the poor man's grief—all that had so carried him away that it had never occurred to him to connect the story with himself. And now he had pronounced his own sentence. Suddenly his wrath boiled over. "You misled me!" he cried.

"Your passion misled you," replied Nathan. "Do not try to take that attitude toward one who speaks to you in the name of the Lord. Thus saith the Lord: 'I anointed thee king over Israel and I delivered thee from the hand of Saul. And gave thee thy master's house and thy master's wives into thy bosom, and gave thee the house of Israel and Judah, and I shall add far greater things unto thee. Thou hast despised the word of the Lord. . . . Because thou has killed Urias with the sword, therefore the sword shall never depart from thy house . . . Behold, I will raise up evil against thee out of thy own house, and I will take thy own wives and give them to thy neighbor. . . . For thou didst it secretly; but I will do this thing in the sight of all Israel, and in the sight of the sun.' "

And as suddenly as it had come, so David's anger fell from him. He hid his face in his hands. "I have sinned against the Lord," he groaned.

The prophet's fixed eyes softened. "The Lord has forgiven your sin. Your judgment was more severe than his. You will not die. But the child born to you shall surely die."

When the king managed at last to look up, the prophet had gone, silently as he had come. Then the curtain rustled and Jehiel, the head guard of the women's quarters, entered. "Lord, Bathsheba sends word that your son is ill with a high fever."

David fasted. He slept on the ground instead of in his bed. In vain his people tried to persuade him to take a little nourishment, to allow himself a cushion and a cover. And this went on for seven days.

On the eighth day toward noon Jehiel came again. Chusai received him, took his report, and whispered it to the other high officials. No one dared to tell the king. But when David saw them whispering he asked in a weak voice: "Is the child dead."

Chusai gave a great sigh. "Yes, lord, it is dead."

But the terrible cry of sorrow they expected from the father did not follow. David rose, went into the bath, let them give him clean clothes, and went to the holy tent to pray. When he came back, he asked for food. Reading bewilderment on every face, he said, "While the child was yet alive, I fasted and wept, hoping the Lord would take pity on me and the child would live. Now he is dead. Fasting and weeping will not bring him back. One day I shall go where my son is, but he will not return to me." After he had taken food, David went to Bathsheba.

A message came from Joab: "Rejoice, lord, we have taken the City of Waters. Now come with fresh troops and lead us to victory over the citadel, that the name of the king may be shouted throughout the city, rather than the name of your servant, Joab." This sign of loyalty from his commander-in-chief was the first joy the king had had for a long time. He called up his body-guards, marched on Rabbah, and stormed the citadel at the head of his troops. The garrison offered desperate resistance, but after a battle of five hours David's elite troops forced their way in. King Hanon of Ammon was quickly killed and Abisai brought the royal crown out of the treasure house; it was made of heavy gold and set with innumerable precious stones. David put it on, and with that act Ammon ceased to exist. The male population of Rabbah was led away and sent to the king's mines and brick kilns. Then, at last, the army returned home.

Even before the year was out, Bathsheba bore another son. According to custom she should have chosen a name for him, but she begged the king: "Do it for me. It will bring him luck."

"Israel has no hostile neighbors left," said David. "He shall be called Solomon—rich in peace."

28 David and Absalom

No Old Testament novel written by an American has been better received or more respectfully treated than *David the King* by Gladys Schmitt. A professional author and professor of English at the Carnegie Institute of Technology in Pittsburgh, Miss Schmitt has been writing ever since she was a child. Several times she has turned to history for her material—in *David the King;* in *Confessors of the Name,* a novel of early Christian Rome; and in a fictional biography of Rembrandt. In each book her scholarship has been meticulous and her story-telling of the first rank. Her David is a man in search of his soul. There is no fuzzy minded mystic here, but rather a full-blooded seeker able to win and to lose, to be just and to err. The novel is fully fleshed out; hardly any aspects of the story are avoided, and there are no major departures from the Bible itself. In the selection which follows, Miss Schmitt tells with great sensitivity what was probably David's worst trial—the story of Absalom.

And the king commanded Joab and Abishai and Ittai, saying, Deal gently for my sake with the young man, even with Absalom. And all the people heard when the king gave all the captains charge concerning Absalom.

And so the people went out into the field against Israel: and the battle was in the wood of Ephraim;

II SAMUEL: XVIII, 5, 6

DAVID THE KING by GLADYS SCHMITT

YET THE King of Israel did not lift up his hand to do either good or evil in his own house or in the land. When, on the evening of the new moon, some counselor, more audacious than his fellows, would raise his voice to speak of the matter, the King would bid him hold his tongue. Perhaps, he thought, there is treason. Ahitophel no longer shows his face in the palace; the wife and child of Absalom still tarry in Geshur; Amasa lives on my son's bounty; and my son has a baleful, beautiful, treacherous face. Yet if I smite those that I suspect of treason, I may well shed the blood of the innocent; and even if I smite only the guilty, how shall I smite them all? Shall I send the host of God north and south to put every young man who is weary of me to the edge of the sword? The world is black and rotten to the core, and whatsoever a man does is doomed to be evil in such a world. Therefore it is best to wait, to do nothing, to sit still. . . .

"Stand watch for us yet this one night," said Absalom to the steward of his house. "Sit at the garden gate, and throw a great stone into the pool before the window if any man should so much as linger at the garden wall. Watch well for my sake and for your own, for you will not go without your reward in the good days that are to come."

"And if Amasa the Ishmaelite should come?" said the steward, folding the napkins and laying them upon the board.

The son of Maacah smiled and shook his head. "Amasa will not come. He is not in Jerusalem. He will tarry behind in Hebron until the deed is done."

The steward stepped back and surveyed the table. He had been told to deck it as for a festal occasion, and he was proud of the pyramids of figs and grapes, the vase filled with fresh green oak leaves, the copper plates and bowls which his lord had brought back from Geshur, newly polished and gleaming in the light of the setting sun.

"Now take yourself off to the garden gate," said Absalom, "and admit no man save Ahitophel."

And now that he was alone, he walked round and round the table, lightly, swiftly. He lifted his arms and stretched them toward the ceiling. This is the day, he thought, this is the hour. . . . And then, because he was a son of the desert and therefore superstitious, he reproached himself for exulting over an unfinished matter and thereby tempting the wrath of God. A thousand stones may yet be hurled in my path, he told himself. Ahitophel may return out of Hebron with evil news. At the last moment, the hearts of the Judahites may have turned cold. The men of the King's bodyguard may have been sent to fall upon the old counselor on the highway. For all I know, he may at this moment be lying at the King's feet, telling the whole tale from beginning to end in order to save himself. . . .

But even as he let these thoughts flow through his mind to forestall evil, he lay down on a couch and stretched and yawned and smiled. He knew that Judah was in the palm of his hand. He knew that the king knew nothing. And he knew that he could as easily doubt himself as he could doubt Ahitophel.

The old man had his own reasons for sedition—if it could be called sedition to unseat an incapable king and place his rightful heir upon the throne. In spite of his early loyalties to the House of Kish, Ahitophel had come to Jerusalem with only one purpose: to serve the House of Jesse well. But he had no sooner established himself than he found himself shut out—a woman had come between him and his lord. A quiet niece of his, so undistinguished that the family had seen fit to marry her to a Hittite, had been lifted out of her obscurity and set at the side of the King of Israel. Slowly, carefully, with sidewise disparaging looks and casual insinuations and little smiles, she had avenged herself upon the uncle who had held himself aloof from her and her Hittite husband, the man who had failed to visit her in her somber palace. It was Hushai whom she chose to be the teacher of her child and the other children. Ahitophel had the barren title of chief counselor, but Hushai had Bath-sheba's favor.

It was impossible to make open war against her. All that she did she did with subtle urbanity. How gently she had dealt with him when he came to the palace to ask for release from those negligible duties which her malice had left to him! How she had commiserated with him over his palsied hands and his weak eyes! How lyrically she had spoken of the pleasures of retirement—the blessed quietness of the little towns of Benjamin! But even after the King had granted him the relief that he did not desire, he tarried in the capital, waiting, hoping to be called back. It had been this period of waiting—this, and the sacrifice of the last survivors of his beloved House of Kish—that had finally driven him to conspire with Absalom.

"Ahitophel is the oak and I am the vine," the son of Maacah had told him over and over. "Let Ahitophel live for a hundred years, for if he should perish, I would be trampled into the earth."

"Let the son of Maacah set his heart at peace. There are more years left in me than Bath-sheba cares to think. The Lord will let me live until I have seen Absalom seated upon his father's throne."

And it was the old counselor who had drawn together into one outcry the desultory complaints which had been raised against the son of Jesse in the scattered towns of Israel. It was Ahitophel who had ridden east and west, north and south, to nourish grievances and foment rebellion. He and he alone had thought of pointing out to the Judahites that their grain rotted in the storehouses because the King of Israel chose to feed his army upon Philistine wheat; he and he alone had taught young men to assemble in caves and forests and curtained rooms, whispering together of the days when old men would no longer direct all the King's business and hold all the captaincies in the ranks of God. It was he who had led the son of Maacah down to show him to the Calebites and the Kenites; it was he would had sent men to say at every shrine and in every market, "The young man Absalom—he is such a one as should reign over Israel and Judah." From the first hour to this hour of consummation, when everything was in readiness and waited only for the signal—the beacon fire on the hilltop, the blast of the trumpet, the unfurling of the standard in Hebron—the conspiracy had been the handiwork of Ahitophel.

The son of Maacah rose and went to the window. His guest was late, but he remained serene. And it was only a few minutes until the steward coughed discreetly and stirred the foliage near the gate; it was his manner of informing the master of the house that the awaited one had come.

Ahitophel came up the garden path and lifted his shaking hand in greeting. His garments were festal garments, white crossed by deep, rich bands of blue; his meager, wispy hair and beard had been washed and anointed; to behold him was to know that he had found Hebron panting after the hour. "God is with the son of Maacah," he said, crossing the threshold and embracing his host. "Nothing is needful now save that we go down into Hebron and take the ripe fruit in our hands." His slight, dry body trembled with excitement; his shortsighted eyes were filled with tears.

"How shall I ever reward the labors of my friend? How shall I find words to tell him—"

"Come now and feed me well, for I have not broken bread these last six hours."

It was fortunate that the steward of the house was not by to behold them. They set aside his vase of oak leaves so that it might not stand between their faces; they toppled the pyramid of grapes and figs; they did not see the polished plates on which they laid their cakes of bread and their slices of meat. They ate swiftly, like men who are engaged in a prospering enterprise. They talked incessantly, caring not in the least that their mouths were full. Everything was well, everything was in readiness—the elders of Judah and Caleb and the land of the Kenites would assemble within three days in Hebron to await the arrival of their new lord. The moment he showed his face within the gates of the city, the trumpet would sound and all the children of Hebron would run forth into the streets, shouting, "God save Absalom, King over Judah and Israel!" And within the same hour, as soon as beacon fires could be lighted on a hundred hills, the same shout would go up in a hundred cities, and all the discontented youth of the land would march down to swell the ranks of that very creditable host which was already gathered on the hills above Hebron.

"And the elders of Judah—have they named the day to Ahitophel?"

"They have accepted the day which we thought best—the Feast of the First Fruits."

"Good, good, that is very good—that leaves but seven days of waiting before we two set out together. Now tell me, shall I go forth without a word to the son of Jesse, or shall I beg his leave to go down?"

"I have been pondering that matter," Ahitophel said, "and it seems to me that you will incur greater danger if you depart without a word. Go up to him and tell him that you have promised God to make a sacrifice in Hebron, the city of your birth. He will not think of it a second time, save to regret that you will be absent from his table for the Feast of the First Fruits."

The young man stared at his plate. Even at such a moment, when he was ready to sound the trumpet of rebellion across the length and breadth of the land, he felt an inward ache at any remembrance of the King's tenderness. There was a time, he said in his heart, when we made a great occasion of the feast at home. I remember well how he came to the board in his splendid robes and took the knife in his fine long hands and carved the meat. It is true that once he gave my brother Amnon a corselet of bronze to mark the occasion, and that my gift was a lesser one—a belt of tooled leather such as they make in his native town of Bethlehem. But it was a fair belt, with curious leaves and scrolls upon it. Where is it now? Have I lost it? I have not worn it these many years. . . .

"Amasa has bidden me say to Absalom that his host numbers four thousand and grows from hour to hour."

"No, now, truly?"

"Four thousand at the least, and five hundred are expected to ride in out of Caleb this very night."

"Inasmuch as we are speaking of my father—" He blushed, knowing that they had ceased to speak of his father some moments since. "Inasmuch as we are speaking of my father," he said, taking an oak leaf from the vase and tearing it apart, "I trust that Ahitophel will not cling stubbornly to that decision which he revealed to me when the two of us last broke bread."

The old counselor sighed and rested his cheek upon his hand. "What can I say to Absalom? He has asked me to consider the matter these three days. Well, I have considered it. I have also laid it before Amasa and before the elders of Judah in Hebron. They know as well as I that there is no peace while two kings are alive in a single land. While Saul and David both drew breath, Israel was an armed camp, and no man knew at what hour his fields might be trampled by marching feet."

"But they were vigorous men—the Star of Bethlehem and the Lion of Benjamin. And he who sits upon the throne this day in Jerusalem—he is no longer concerned with the matters of the world. His hands are loosened so that he cannot hold that which he has—how then should he take back that which is wrested from him? I hold with Ahitophel that the sons of David must be slain. Their hearts and the hearts of their mothers are after the throne. But an old man who is exceedingly weary, whose face is already turned away from the earth—"

"What, then, would the son of Maacah have us do with the son of Jesse?"

Absalom shrugged and covered his face with his hands. "Nothing. Give him Mahanaim, where the host of Ishbaal dwelt in other days. Leave him alone with his woman and his lute. . . ."

"No, now, he is not so depleted as Absalom thinks. He will grow strong on the bitter meat of exile. He is as changeable as the moon—I have seen him wane and wax before."

"I cannot set my seal upon the order for his death."

"I cannot leave an ulcer in the flesh of Israel."

For the space of a heartbeat their eyes blazed. Then the young man reached across the board and laid his hand gently upon the old man's hand.

"Consider it yet a little longer, Ahitophel. There is no need to settle it tonight. Lay it by, and we will speak of it again when we have established ourselves in Hebron."

"I have been considering it since I first thought that the son of Maacah might sit upon his father's throne."

The captain of the host presented himself very early at the door of the palace on the day of the feast. His brother stood behind him on the threshold, dressed in a particularly ridiculous festal garment of sky-blue linen and looking more than ever like a plump infant who had miraclously grown big and old. No one had asked them to come up to the King's palace; it had been Abishai who had thought that the King might be in need of company during the procession to the high place. For how could he put from his mind the thought of happier feast days, when Tamar had walked before him with a basket of flowers, when Amnon had toiled along at his right with a load of pomegranates, and Absalom had walked buoyantly at his left with a splendid sheaf of wheat? Now one tarried forever with her mother in Geshur, and one was dead, and the third had chosen this day of all days to go down into Hebron.

The door creaked on its hinges and swung back upon the long, dim, almost empty vista of the common room. No, now, are half of them still abed? Joab asked himself. Then he counted heads—at the table, near the window, beside the pillars—and knew that the King's entire household was before his eyes, and grieved to find it so small.

Close to one of the columns near the door, Bath-sheba was kneeling in front of Solomon. She could not offer more than a nod to the visitors because there were pins between her lips; she was busy making some change in the hem of her son's robe—furiously busy, although the procession would not set out until an hour before noon. Seeing her in morning disarray, with the puffiness of sleep still upon her face, the son of Zeruiah wondered again how it was that his lord found her so fair. She is a Benjamite matron, he thought, like a thousand others. . . . And he turned his glance upon Solomon. That fourteen-year-old shoot of the House of Jesse was rubbing his back against the pillar and casting imploring glances in the direction of the ceiling. God teach me patience with women, said his eyes. He was slender, but so soft and pale of arm and throat and face that there was something vaguely womanish in his slenderness. His face was like his mother's, delicate and clear, with milky cheeks and straight brown brows. But his mouth was troubling; it was over-ripe, and it still retained a childish pout. "I would gladly escape and fling myself into the arms of my uncles," he said in a drawling voice. "But I am driven against a pillar and hemmed in with pins. I cannot move."

"God walk with the sons of Zeruiah," said Haggith, rising from the couch where she had been sitting with Adonijah. "Have you broken your fast? Can I bring you a little curds and bread?" She was dressed in a garment of pleated white linen, and her graying hair was bound into a coronet above her placid brow. She gave her hand first to Joab and then to Abishai. Behold, her serene countenance informed the world, I am not such a one as is ruffled by early rising, or by uneven hems in garments. . . .

"God walk with Haggith. She is very gracious, but we have broken our fast an hour since," Joab said.

Adonijah had already risen from the couch and was advancing toward them, his hands outstretched, his mild face made doubly pleasant by a cordial smile. "You have come up to walk with us to the high place," he said, passing his arm through Abishai's, "and that was more than kind, seeing that my father will remember other feast days, when he had a longer train than that which follows him now."

The captain looked down the length of the room in search of the King of Israel. Two servants were standing near the table, laying pomegranates in a wicker basket; a third was washing clusters of grapes in a brazen basin, and a serving-maid was making garlands out of almond blossoms and wheat. The old counselor Hushai was eating curds. But the King of Israel was nowhere to be seen.

"The King will be with us in an hour or so," Haggith said. "According to the word of his armor-bearer, he scarcely closed his eyes last night, and we did not have the heart to rouse him up at the break of day."

"Take a little fruit and curds," Adonijah said, drawing both his visitors toward the table. "We will not sit at the board again until we have returned from the high place."

The captain suddenly became aware that Adonijah, unlike his younger brother, who was still squirming against the pillar, was attired in simple white linen. It was almost as if he wished to proclaim to the sons and daughters of Jerusalem: "I have put aside any thought of drawing your eyes upon me. I have an elder brother, and while he lives, I will not bear myself like a fool who fancies that one day he will be King of Israel." And yet, thought the son of Zeruiah, permitting the young man to cut him a slice of melon, I would be far more at ease for Israel's sake if he, rather than the son of the desert or the chattering little parakeet, were to sit after his father upon the throne . . .

Bath-sheba rose from her knees at last. "There, now," she said, "it is perfect. Come out of the shadow of the pillar, my son, so that we may see."

Solomon stepped into a patch of sun and preened himself. Abishai and Adonijah nodded in his direction, but neither of them could bring himself to utter a commending word. As for Haggith, she had been staring at the empty doorway, and she continued to stare at it with insulting placidity. The old counselor Hushai, diverted from his bowl of curds by the length of the silence, started up from his chair. "Beautiful—my lady Bath-sheba has made him beautiful," he said quickly.

"Let Hushai find another word," said Solomon. "The word 'beautiful' is proper only when one refers to a maid."

Suddenly it became plain to all of them that in their zeal to be prepared for the festival in good time, they had risen too early and made too much haste. The young men—and they alone of all the King's household were to accompany their father to the high place—were washed and anointed and clothed to perfection. The morning meal had been eaten. The last pomegranate had been laid in the wicker basket, and the last garland had been put aside complete. Now they found themselves with two dull hours on their hands. What was there to do but stroll up and down the room in uncomfortable finery, growing more ill-tempered by the moment? Hushai and Haggith had a difference over the arrangement of the pomegranates. Adonijah informed Solomon that it would be well if he did not spoil all the garlands in the process of seeking out the best one for himself. Bath-sheba said with some asperity that if the maidservant had made the garlands well, they would not have fallen apart. The maid took umbrage. The garlands, she said, had been made to be worn on the head and not to be tossed about. Her insolence was such that it roused even the dreaming Hushai, who bade her honor her mistress and hold her tongue. The captain of the host, annoyed by the general ill-humor took himself off to a shadowy corner where he could wait in peace for the King.

It was almost noon when the son of Jesse entered the common room. Seeing him in the full light of the early summer sun, Joab wondered how so worn and withdrawn a spirit could present so convincing an aspect of vigor and authority. Within the last three or four years, the King's beard and hair had gone entirely white; but that luxuriant whiteness only lent additional dignity to his spare and solemn face. He wore a long, trailing garment of yellow cloth, ornamented with diagonal stripes of white and gold; his right arm was almost covered by six golden bracelets, and a circlet of gold shone upon his head.

He came forward and embraced the sons of Zeruiah. He looked at the young Solomon, opened his mouth to utter praise, thought better of it, and turned to the table to take up one of the wicker baskets. "Since my armorbearer has decked me out in gold and yellow, I may as well complete his intention and carry wheat," he said. "Adonijah will bear grapes. Solomon will carry flowers." He paused and set his basket of grain back on the table, for the steward had come in from the garden, plainly in a state of consternation.

"My lord—" said the steward.

"Well, then, what is it? We are in haste, we must meet the priests, we—"

"My lord, there is a runner in the garden. He comes with strange news out of Judah. Will you walk to the spring and speak with him, my lord?"

After the King's departure, an awed silence fell upon the little company. The captain of the host turned slowly in the direction of the doorway. He could see only a maze of sunlit hedges; he could hear only low, indistinguishable talk and the trickling of the spring. But suddenly he knew with absolute certainty what tidings the messenger had brought out of Judah—Absalom had revolted in Hebron. Without a word, he crossed the threshold, thinking that it was not good for his lord to be alone.

He waited on the path until the voices in the garden had ceased, and then waited yet a little longer, so that the King might have time to compose himself. Then he walked to the spring and looked about him. The grass was bent on one side—here the bringer of evil news had fallen on his face. But the bench was empty, and, in all the green expanse of the garden, he could see no sign of the runner or the steward or the King of Israel.

Near the brazen gate, there was another bench beneath a palm tree. He hastened toward it and saw, through an opening in the hedges, the ceremonial robe of yellow and gold. The King was alone, standing with his face to the tree. He was resting his forehead against the trunk, and his hands hung loose and open at his sides. "Is it the captain of the host?" he said, without stirring.

"Even he, my lord."

"Absalom has unfurled his standard in Hebron. It is so, I must teach myself that it is so. Absalom has stirred up Judah and Caleb and the Kenites against me. He could not wait for the day of my death—my son Absalom."

The captain stared at the motionless figure leaning against the palm tree.

Caleb, Judah, the Kenites, he thought. Five thousand warriors at the least will be upon us. We must lose no time, we must man the walls. . . ."

"I knew there was much that he could not forgive me. But I never dreamed he would ride armed against me out of the south. . . ."

"In God's name, rouse yourself! Where is the runner? Where is the steward of the house?"

The King did not move. "I have sent them both forth," he said. "They are gone to carry the tidings to the priests on the high place. Ah, God, who would have thought that he would choose to do it on the day of the feast? Go in now and say to my household that they must lay aside their ceremonial garments and put on sackcloth. I will come in to them in a little while. Only, for the moment, let no man come near me. Go in and leave me alone."

Five thousand at least, thought Joab, and Amasa the Ishmaelite at the head of the host, and everything well conducted according to the plans of Ahitophel. . . . And suddenly the sight of the flaccid, motionless back prodded him into fury. "What am I that my lord should send me in to comfort wailing women?" he shouted. "Am I not the captain of his host? I will not depart from David save to carry the commands of David to the ranks. If the son of Maacah can muster five thousand against us, yet have we six thousand, armed and ready to meet him in the plains below Jerusalem, waiting only for the King's word. Cease now to stand like an ailing child, leaning against a tree and bemoaning yourself. Turn and tell me, shall we go out to meet the rebels, or tarry in the city and let them dash themselves to pieces against the walls?"

Very slowly he lifted up his head and turned from the palm tree. The heart of the son of Zeruiah stood still within him when he beheld the King's face. It was gray and sagging above the folds of the gaudy garment. The mouth was open, and the eyes were dazed.

"Go in and rest," said Joab. "Lay it in my hands, I will do all that is needful. For the moment it is nothing—it is a matter of manning the walls."

"No, now, wait a little. . . ." David sat on the bench and bowed his face upon his hands. "It is in no wise my desire that the city should be defended. Any man who defends the city and sheds the blood of the children of Jerusalem does it against my will. If they will have the city, let them take the city; I give it freely into their hands. . . ."

"Surely the son of Jesse knows not whereof he speaks. Surely tomorrow he will awaken and say to himself, Yesterday I was mad."

"Today, tomorrow, and forever, I will not defend Jerusalem. I would swear it before God, but I have ceased to take oaths before Him. He hears, but He does not hearken. He looks upon us, but He does not see. Let Joab lay this to his heart: I will not remain. I will flee northward out of Jerusalem and leave it to Absalom."

Mahanaim, that crumbling fortress town east of the Jordan, had harbored a royal household once before. Here, more than twenty years ago, Ishbaal had filled his empty hours with eating and gardening and wrestling matches, until that day when the sons of Rimmon smothered him in his bed. Here Abner and Rizpah also had made a garden. Both of them had departed into Sheol now, leaving neither sons nor daughters, but it was possible that some of the vines that wandered over the brown bricks of Mahanaim had been planted by their hands.

It was a drowsy town, mellow and aimless; its very name was a sleepy murmur upon the lips. The fields and orchards beyond it yielded a sufficiency of grain and fruit; the meadowland along the river nourished sleek flocks and herds; and the men of Ishbaal had brought the vine into the midst of the city, so that a man had only to thrust his hand forth from his window to take the wherewithal for his raisins and his wine. The bees, drunken with plenty, reeled over the meadows and the orchards with a continuous, slumbrous sound. Honey stood in the comb for the taking, and golden drops of honey oozed from the wax as slowly as the hours.

It was, thought the son of Zeruiah in the first days of his sojourn there, such a town as would tempt the exiled King of Israel to fall into that same daze which had brought him to such a sorry pass in Jerusalem. When the ranks of David entered the brown gates, it was made plain that the host would be cared for. A storehouse had been set aside for them, and the sons and daughters of Mahanaim had already begun to fill it when the King of Ammon anticipated their generosity by sending up a month's supply of oil and wine and flour. Two wealthy elders of the land of Gilead—Barzillai of Rogelim and Machir of Lo-debar—brought beds and basins and earthen vessels, wheat and barley and parched grain, beans and pulse and lentils, honey and butter and cheese of the herd. "These are for David and for the people that are with him," they said. "For the people are hungry and thirsty and weary after their sojourn in the wilderness, and it is only fitting that they should eat and drink and rest."

The captain of the host was glad that Machir at least departed along with the donkeys that had carried his bounty. But Barzillai tarried in Mahanaim, and for three full days the son of Jesse did nothing but talk with his guest in his little garden. God of Hosts, thought the son of Zeruiah, passing the two of them on his way to the encampment, while they sit, the host of Absalom has grown to thirty thousand, and we are but six thousand behind crumbling walls. . . . And on the evening of the third day he could bear it no longer. "If my lord the King wishes to live out another moon," he said at supper, "let him bestir himself and think of the battle that is to come." The son of Jesse pushed his plate aside. "I have been thinking of it," he said. "It might be well to meet the host of Absalom in the forest of Ephraim. Let us go down and look upon that same forest tomorrow before noon."

From that moment forth, the Star of Bethlehem was all that his captain could require—a man of war, a brilliant strategist, sage in council and vigorous in his dealings with the host. That he should have chosen the forest of Ephraim as the place of battle was in itself a proof of his genius; here and only here six thousand might be able to confound thirty thousand, with the help of God. The uneven ground, the slippery, winding paths, the low, interlacing boughs of the wild olives and the terebinths, would be a salvation to those who knew them well and a snare to those who knew them not. Now he dragged the unwilling Barzillai along with him on the business of war. When he was not examining the forest, he sat at the gates of the city, reviewing his ranks and instructing his captains over hundreds and captains over thousands. The fame of his army was spread through the land, so that three thousand farmers came to him out of Gilead. And the town of Mahanaim was roused out of its long sleep and resounded with the ring of the anvil day and night.

"A great change has come upon my uncle," said the son of Zeruiah to the King of Israel one afternoon when they were wandering unattended in the forest of Ephraim.

The son of Jesse stopped beneath the boughs of a terebinth and turned a thoughtful face upon him. "Change? What change?" he said.

"Surely my lord the King remembers how it was with him not long since —how he said that he would not lift up his hand to save himself or his throne."

The King smiled. "And does the captain of the host believe than an angel of God has come to me by night and restored to my heart the desire for life and the wish for a throne? Do not deceive yourself. As I was in Jerusalem, so I am in Mahanaim. If I go out to make war in the forest, it is not for the sake of my life or for the sake of the throne."

"I have lived in the presence of David nigh unto fifty years," said Joab. "Yet I cannot say that I have known him. There is much in David that I cannot understand."

"No, now, it is a simple matter. Behold, when I came up to Mahanaim, I thought to tarry here even as Ishbaal tarried, until such a time as those about me grew weary of me and sent up a strong man to smother me also in my bed. This I said to Barzillai, who is very old and somewhat foolish, but he made me a good answer. He said to me, 'Are you not a shepherd? What of the sheep?' And I thought then—no, now, what does it matter what I thought? Let it pass. . . ."

"Am I less than Barzillai in the eyes of my lord, that he should tell a stranger what is in his heart and straightway turn his back upon me, saying, 'Let it pass'?"

The long pale hand of David—dry and veined and withered now— reached out through the greenish light and rested gently upon Joab's hand. "It was only that it was a strange thought, and I did not wish to burden the ears of the captain of the host. Long ago, in the hills above Bethlehem, I made a mighty name for myself because I killed a young lion that came to harry my father's sheep. It was not for the sake of the lambs and the ewes that I killed the lion—it was for the glory that the slaying of a lion would bring upon my own head. But now, being utterly weary of the world and of myself, having had all things and yearning after nothing more, I still cannot lie down to sleep while the flock is left to be ravaged in the open field. I will go back to Jerusalem for the sake of the children of Jerusalem, who wept to see me depart. Before I take unto myself my everlasting rest, I will kill one lion for the sake of the sheep."

And as the weeks of waiting were drawn out to three moons, Joab saw that the Star of Bethlehem was truly willing to do far more for his flock than for himself. He dwelt in a black tent in the encampment. He seldom showed his face to Bath-sheba and the others of his household, but pored over the battle plans far into the night. He went with small bands of warriors into the forest of Ephraim and explored the face of the land until he knew every alley, every grove, every network of branches. He insisted that he would march forth with them on the day of the battle, and would not be dissuaded until they made it plain to him that he would be a charge to them in the midst of the fight. It is with him now, thought the captain of the host, as it was in the days of his glory. Even though I should die in the forest of Ephraim, yet would I die with a high heart, for I have been the first servant of the greatest warrior who ever fought in Israel. Not Saul, not Abner, not Joshua, not Barak, could be likened unto my lord . . . And when they brought him the news that the ranks of Absalom were marching northward thirty thousand strong along the western bank of the Jordan, Joab was not afraid. "When we depart for the forest tomorrow," he said to David, "stand at the gate of the city and wish us well, for the men of Israel are bound flesh and spirit to David, and their souls will be strengthened by the sight of his face."

At sunrise Joab brought the host of David out by the gate of the city, and the King stood at the gate smiling upon them. They came forth in three divisions, because they were to be stationed at three different points in the forest—a third of them with Joab and a third with Abishai and a third with Ittai of Gath. Then the King put forth his hand and blessed them, and they made ready to depart. But even as they turned their faces toward the distant green forest, David called Ittai and the sons of Zeruiah back, as though he had forgotten some final command. In a loud voice, so that the host might hear, he charged the three of them, saying, "Deal gently for my sake with the young man Absalom." And they swore before the God of Hosts that they would obey the King's command.

It was pale morning, gray and misty, when the men of David took up their stations in the woods. The plan of battle had been drawn around a certain grove which the Canaanites had cleared generations since in the center of the forest for the worship of Baal and Astarte—a place of uneven ground covered with lush, high weeds that concealed the stumps of felled trees and the remains of ancient altars. This grove, roughly triangular in shape, was bounded on all sides by the interlacing boughs of wild olives and terebinths. Joab and the flower of David's host were stationed at the northernmost point. The captain and the first three hundred of his men stood in the clearing, their banners spread to catch the eye of the advancing enemy and tempt him forth into the midst of the grove, where his cavalry might come to grief among the slippery weeds and the hidden stumps and stones. But the men of Abishai and the men of Ittai stood far to the south, on opposite points

of the triangle, screened by the thick trees at the eastern and western tips of
the grove, motionless, holding their shields and swords beneath their cloaks
so that they would not shine in the first rays of the sun. For it had been
determined in council that the men of Abishai and Ittai would not give battle
until the ranks of Joab had engaged the warriors of Absalom. Then, at the
sound of Joab's trumpet, they would fall upon the rebels from left and right,
and smite them and drive them forth out of the glade into the winding alleys of
the forest, where, with the help of God, they could be taken in small numbers
and slain.

Their wait was long. The host of Absalom, which had crossed the Jordan
and advanced toward the forest during the night, tarried on the western fringes
until midmorning; and even when they plunged into the green shadow at last,
their advance was slow. Plainly the rebels were at odds with the forest: they
were coming up at a snail's pace; there were calls and curses, commands and
countercommands. The men in the ranks of Ittai peered through the network
of leaves and twigs, eager to catch a glimpse of Absalom. That same morning,
on the march down to the forest, their captain had promised ten pieces of
silver to any warrior who would bring him the son of Maacah untouched.
"For," he had said, "I also have sons in Gath, and I would behold the old
King's face when the eldest of his house is restored to him."

It was Amasa who was the first to break through the screen of trees at
the southern border of the grove. He was mounted on a dappled horse and
clothed in a scarlet tunic. On either side of him, the foremost ranks of the rebel
cavalry issued into the clearing, drew rein, and looked about them. The archers
of Abishai, seeing the magnificent figure of the melancholy Ishmaelite through
the interlacing boughs, were hard put to it to contain themselves. As one man,
they drew a long, deep breath. Afterward no man could say how it had come
to pass—whether it was that long inward gasp of zeal or the will of the Lord
that made the rebel captain blind to Joab's flying banners and drew his eyes
to Abishai's hidden host. But from that moment there was no longer a plan
of battle. Amasa, who was to have fallen upon Joab, straightway wheeled his
ranks around and rushed at the men of Abishai, and the matter was given into
the hand of God.

The ranks of Joab and the mercenaries under the command of Ittai
surged forward in complete disorder to the aid of their comrades. They
were intercepted—and their line of advance was shattered—by the innumerable and impetuous troops of Absalom. From the third hour of the morning
until the sun hung hot and high above the clearing, there were confused
commands, clashes between isolated groups of horsemen, aimless showers of
arrows, swift assaults and retreats. Then, very slowly, the battle moved out of
the confines of the grove and was drawn through the winding pathways into
every part of the wood. The boughs of the terebinths and the wild olives were
snapped by the passage of terrified riders. The alleys of the forest echoed
with the screams of the dying; the greenish light was sifted down upon the
open hands and wondering faces of the dead. And the men of David saw
that God had done for them that which the plan of battle had failed to do;

for the host of Absalom was divided and disorganized, fighting on unknown ground, with slippery weeds and roots beneath their feet and vines and leaves before their faces. Then their courage waxed great within them, and they called to each other among the trees, saying, "Take heart, for the day is ours!" They stood firm among the growing heaps of the slain, and the men of Absalom grew sore afraid, so that they gave way by fifties and by hundreds, and turned and took to flight. And there was a great slaughter of twenty thousand men that day in the forest Ephraim, and the forest devoured more of the sons of Jahveh than the sword devoured.

Since the beginning of the encounter, the son of Zeruiah had twice ridden the width of the forest of Ephraim. Ten young horsemen had been with him from the start. They had made it their purpose to seek out the rebel captains; and, although they had not once caught sight of Amasa or the son of Maacah, they had slain some fifty of the flower of Absalom's host. Now, finding themselves in a secluded glade with the noise of battle far from them, they knew themselves to be greatly in need of rest.

"Let us stop and bind up our wounds," said Joab. He himself had twice been grazed by arrows, once on the shoulder and once on the knee. "Go and care for each other," he told the little crowd of solicitous youths who gathered around him as he dismounted. "I am well enough. If I am gray in the face, it is only with weariness, and you will cure that most swiftly by leaving me to myself."

He tethered his horse to the twisted trunk of an olive tree. Even though shouts and the clatter of arms still sounded in certain distant reaches of the forest, the battle was over. Those among the ranks of Absalom who had survived would soon be in full flight toward the Jordan—he knew it as certainly as a mariner knows that the day will be fine. Well done, he said to himself; and he sat down in utter weariness in the shadow of a tree.

He looked at the wounds on his knee and shoulder; they ached, but they were nothing; they were already well covered with dried blood. He was resting his head against the trunk of the wild olive when he heard footfalls behind him. A Judahite warrior, one of his own men, squat and stolid and shining with the sweat of battle, came up and stood before him. "Not fifty paces from this place I have seen a strange sight," the warrior said. "Absalom, the son of our lord the King—he is hanging in a terebinth, and his life is yet whole within him."

The captain started up and clutched the Judahite's shoulder. "What? What is this?" he said.

"The son of Maacah was riding upon his mule in flight before the men of David, and the mule went under the thick boughs of a great terebinth, and the king's son was taken up by the boughs between heaven and earth, and the mule that was under him went on."

"You saw him and smote him not? I would have given you ten pieces of silver and a fine girdle if you had told me, 'I struck him down.'"

The Judahite stared somberly into the captain's face. "Though a thousand pieces of silver should be laid in my palm," he said, "yet would

I not put forth my hand against the King's son; for in our hearing the King charged you and Abishai and Ittai, saying, "Have a care, whosoever you be, that you do not touch the young man Absalom.' Had I taken his life, the King would have known as much, for nothing is hidden from the King our lord. And as for you—you also would have set yourself against me and punished me before the host for David's sake."

He is not so stupid as he looks, thought Joab. Nevertheless . . A quiver filled with darts hung round the Judahite's waist, and Joab thrust his hand into it and drew forth three darts and tested their sharpness against his palm.

"Inasmuch as the King our lord has charged us expressly—" said the warrior.

"No, now, I cannot tarry here in speech with you," said the captain, and he turned and went from the glade, following the trail of trodden grass that had been left by the Judahite.

God keep the mercenaries of Ittai away from the spot! he said to himself. For the sake of ten pieces of silver any one of them would take him down, so that he might yet live to murder his father in his bed. . . . But all about him the forest was empty. Even the last sounds of battle had ceased, and the place was oppressively still. Suddenly he stopped, and his heart beat violently, for he saw the tree and that which hung upon it—the fair body in its tunic of white linen writhing against the green—the chin caught in the fork of a branch, the long hair spread out among the leaves.

Because the Judahite had told him that Absalom was hanging between heaven and earth, the son of Zeruiah had expected to find him high in the midst of the tree. He saw now that the young man had been taken up by the lowest of the boughs; his toes, not more than three handbreadths above the ground, grazed the tips of the tall grass. Then it will be a small matter to smite him while he is yet in the tree, he told himself . . . And he drew close to the terebinth, holding the darts in his hand. Absalom's face, thrust backward by the prongs of the branch, was blue and distorted. His eyes were two watery, colorless slits beneath his swollen lids, yet the captain felt that those eyes were fastened upon him. Is it possible that he can see? he asked himself. . . . He did not pause until his face was level with the taut neck. Then, with his left arm, he clasped the young man and held him still. "Traitor, rebel, fratricide!" he said. And he thrust the darts into Absalom's heart.

Yet the son of Maacah lived, struggling and twisting. And terror seized upon Joab, so that he sprang backward. Behold what I have done, he said in his heart. I have taken the son of my lord helpless, and I have thrust at him with shaking hands, so that he suffers and will not die. For this my lord will surely hate me and utterly turn from me. . . . There was no other weapon upon him—he had left his sword beneath the olive tree. In his horror he called aloud after the ten young men who had accompanied him to the glade. They came swiftly, thinking that some evil had befallen him, then stopped and stared in consternation at the writhing body in the tree. "Smite him now," said Joab, "for he is in great anguish." And they compassed Absalom about and slew him with many wounds, with spears and swords. And because his comely face was swollen beyond recognition and his fair body was torn by twenty wounds, they did not dare to bear him back to Mahanaim to his father, but cast him into a pit in the forest and raised over him a great mound of stones.

While they labored over the monument, the son of Zeruiah sounded the trumpet to bring the host of David together. Among the first to come out of the midst of the wood was a certain Ahimaaz, the youngest of the sons of Zadok, who had come up to Mahanaim with messages for David and had tarried in the ranks of God. "Come, now," he said, lifting his dark and winsome face to Joab's, "let me bring the news to the King. I am a swift runner, and all the news that I have carried before this day has been evil news, and I desire for once to take our lord such news as will delight his heart." But the son of Zeruiah pushed the youth aside and chose from those who were gathering around the terebinth an Ethiopian slave, a servant of Ittai's, to bear the tidings to the gates. When he had instructed the slave and sent him on his way, he wandered apart from the others and sat down on a knoll with his back to the terebinth and covered his face with his hands. His body had begun to shake so violently that he did not wish any man to look upon him. For they will say among themselves that I am old and outworn, he thought, pressing his palms against his quaking jaw. . . .

Ahimaaz, the son of Zadok, came and flung himself down at his captain's feet. "Even though you have sent the Ethiopian to Mahanaim, yet let me run also," he said.

"Bear tidings another day. This day you will bear no tidings, inasmuch as the King's son is dead."

"Nevertheless, whatever has come to pass, let me run after the Ethiopian."

"Wherefore would you run, my son? I tell you, you will get no thanks for the news from the King of Israel."

"Nevertheless, I beg you—"

Why should I trouble my mind over what will befall this young fool? the son of Zeruiah thought. . . . And he shrugged and thrust at the lad with his foot. "Go then. Run," he said.

It was late afternoon before all the host of God was assembled. Their delight in the victory was clouded by the knowledge that they had left more than three thousand of their comrades among the slain. Abishai had come forth unscathed out of the engagement; but Ittai of Gath could scarcely sit upon his steed alone. He had been thrown from his saddle and trampled; his arm was mangled; there could be no cure save to lop it off, the surgeons said. During the long wait in the forest, one warrior after another walked round the great gray mound of stones. They stared at it and whispered together. "God help that man who laid the son of Maacah low!" they said. "For did the King our lord not charge all of us expressly, saying 'Deal gently for my sake with the young man Absalom'?" And their hearts were heavy when they departed out of the forest of Ephraim.

From the first hours of the morning until late afternoon, the King of Israel sat upon the ground before the gates of Mahanaim. He had made it plain to those who remained within the city that he wanted no company. I am an old man now, he told himself, and I have waited many times—in the Valley of the Rocks, in the plains of Sharon, in Ziklag, in the high house in Jerusalem—and this at least I have learned in the passage of the years: that no man can fully share another's exigency. . . . The meadowland before the gates of the town stretched out for miles before him; far off the trees of the forest of Ephraim stood dark against the sky. The world upon which he gazed was as empty as though the race of men had departed from it, for no herdsman had led his beasts into the fields and no farmer had gone out to gather the grain.

He did not lift up his voice to God that day, but he spoke very earnestly to the dead. "Look, now, my father," he said, turning his face toward the purple hills of Moab, "at long last I have remembered the sheep." He conjured up a vision of Noi going down the hall with a lamp toward the room of a sick servant. "See, now," he told her, "should we meet in Sheol I would blush the less, inasmuch as I also have risen from my bed by night to tend the wounds of Israel." To the Lion of Benjamin he said, "They strive now in the forest of Ephraim so that all which you brought to pass at Michmash and Ephes-Dammim and Jabesh-Gilead shall not have been in vain." And to Jonathan, "Though I should die while the land is broken in twain, yet have I endeavored to mend it, nor will I cease while the breath is yet in me, believe me, beloved."

High above him, in the tower room in the right-hand pylon of the gate, a single watchman had been stationed. The King of Israel had not seen the face of the watchman; he was no more than a voice raised against the utter silence, for the city was hushed with waiting and no sound of battle could carry across the broad fields. Now and again the son of Jesse would lift up his voice and call to the watchman, "What do you see?" And all through the morning and the early afternoon the answer was "Nothing, my lord."

Nothing, nothing—the agony among the trees was so small as to be invisible in the magnitude of the earth; the dark, uneven line of the wood remained solid, imperturbable; a thousand died, and not one of the upper branches stirred. . . . And then at last, when the sun had begun to decline, the watchman called from his tower, saying to the King, "Behold, a man has come forth out of the forest land and is running across the fields alone."

"If he is alone," said David, "then he is not fleeing out of the battle. Surely there are tidings in his mouth." And he rose up and stood against the gate.

In a moment the watchman called again. "Behold, there is another man, and he also is running alone."

"Then he also brings tidings."

"I think the running of the foremost is like the running of Ahimaaz, the son of Zadok."

And the King said, "He is a good man and will bring us good news."

Now, over the curve of the sunlit meadow, he also could see the first of the runners—Ahimaaz, the son of Zadok, who had outrun the Ethiopian in his zeal to tell good tidings to the King of Israel. Far off—so far that his voice was scarcely audible even in the complete silence—he stopped and made a trumpet of his hands and shouted, "All is well!" And he came and flung himself down at David's feet, and said, "Blessed be Jahveh your God, who has delivered up the men who lifted up their hands against my lord the King."

Then at least it was well with the sheep. But the heart of the son of Jesse was not lifted up within him. He stared at the bowed, glistening shoulders of the runner and said, "Is it well with the young man Absalom?"

The stripling did not raise his head. "When Joab sent me forth out of the battle, I saw a great tumult, but I knew not what it was—"

And David was sore afraid, for there was uneasiness in the lad's voice; and when the King raised him up from the earth, he turned aside and could not bring himself to look into the King's eyes. "Well, then," David said, "stand with me here against the gate until the second runner also has told us his news."

"Behold," called the voice from the watchtower, "he that comes now is an Ethiopian, a servant unto Ittai of Gath."

The second runner, black and sleek as a wild beast out of the mountains, came in long strides across the grass. For one moment he stood erect before the son of Jesse, smiling, his teeth and eyeballs white in the glistening blackness of his face. Then he flung himself, still smiling, upon the ground, and took the hem of David's robe in his hand.

"Tidings for my lord the King," he said. "Jahveh has brought the vengeance this day upon all those who rose up against you."

The King said to the Ethiopian also, "Is it well with the young man Absalom?"

Then the Ethiopian answered, saying, "All the enemies of my lord the King, and all those who rise up to do him hurt, may they be as that young man is."

And the King was much moved, and went up to the watchtower above the gate, and wept as he went saying, "O Absalom, my son, my son Absalom! Would I had died for you, O Absalom, my son, my son!"

Would I had died on that night when I sent them forth to bring him out of Geshur, for I have long been old and unfit to reign, and he might have reigned in my place and loved me still. . . . The watchman, departing in haste lest he should look upon the King's sorrow, brushed against him and begged forgiveness. But David neither saw nor heard; he knelt and laid his head upon the sill and wept. Far away, at the margin of the forest, the men of Jahveh issued into the plain. They will come singing over the meadows, he said to himself; they will light torches and make a great noise of rejoicing in the streets because they have taken my enemy and laid him low. To them he was the lion that came upon the flock by night. I also said amongst them, "He has torn Israel, and therefore he must be taken." But he was my little one, the child of my bowels, flesh of my flesh, blood of my blood. . . .

He heard the thud of hoofs on the dry earth below him. Ahimaaz, mounted now, was riding out toward the advancing host. He has gone to them to hush their singing, David thought; he will charge them, saying, "Put off your garlands now, for the King is in the watchtower, mourning for Absalom." And it is not right that they should be denied their songs and their garlands, inasmuch as they have fought nine thousand against thirty thousand all this day, and they have done it for my sake. If only they had brought him living out of the forest, if only I might have taken his face between my hands and kissed him upon the brow! . . . And he saw that face, vital and beautiful, the dark cheeks washed by tears of reconciliation. He knew then that it was utterly lost to him—blank, unbreathing, blind. And he covered his face with his hands and cried out again in a loud voice, "O my son Absalom, O Absalom, my son, my son."

And that day the victory was changed into mourning for all the people. Those who were within the gates and those who returned out of the battle whispered to each other, saying, "The King of Israel is grieving for his son." And the host of God broke ranks in the field and put aside their garlands and lowered their banners. By twos and threes, stealthily, like those who steal away from the field of defeat, they crept through the gates of the city; and no man came forth to meet them or to bless them or to give thanks unto them for their valor, nor was there any shouting in the streets.

At about the hour of moonrise, when the King was utterly worn with grieving, he heard footfalls on the stair of the watchtower. Darkness had begun to settle upon the little chamber, and David's eyes were weak with weeping, so that he stared long before he could be certain that it was the son of Zeruiah who stood before him. Now I must rise up, he told himself, and give thanks to him who has delivered me. . . . And he rose, leaning heavily upon the sill, and opened his mouth to speak graciously to the captain of the host.

But Joab stood motionless on the threshold. "This day," he said, "you have shamed the faces of all your servants who have saved your life and the lives of your sons and the lives of your wives and the lives of all those who have followed after your uncertain cause. This day you have made it plain that you hate them who love you and love them who hate you. You have shown before all Israel that the princes and the servants who fight for you are nothing in your eyes. I see now that if Absalom had lived and all we who bled for you this day had died in the forest, it would have pleased you well. Arise, then, go forth and speak comfortably to your servants, for I swear before Jahveh that if you go not forth to thank them, not one man among them will tarry with you through this night, and what comes to pass tomorrow will be worse for you than all the evil that has befallen you from the days of your youth until now."

The King rose then and took water in a basin and washed his face. Leaning upon Joab's arm, he went down and sat between the gates of the city. And it was spread about among the people that the King had come forth to give thanks to them and bless them; and they kindled torches and gathered from all parts of the city and came before him, wearing garlands and singing his praise. And he spoke fair words to them, saying that they had saved the flock. He went also among the wounded and laid hands upon them; and he found Ittai where he lay dying, and embraced him and kissed him upon the lips. All things that were fitting he did, even though he did them late. But his spirit was not with his people. His spirit had gone forth from them to stand in the forest of Ephraim, where they had buried Absalom.

29 Solomon's Loves

It would be difficult to find a less likely person to have written of the personality and love life of Solomon than Alexandre Kuprin, the Russian novelist and short story writer. In his *Sulamith, A Prose Poem of Antiquity,* he speaks as the historian of Solomon's court. The description is rich, sensuous and detailed. Accepting the Song of Songs as Solomon's, Kuprin gives us a fictional woman for whom such a poem might have been written. When one remembers that Kuprin was the writer whose major works, written in the Gorki manner, include *The Pit,* a naturalistic description of the life of Russian prostitutes, *Sulamith* seems even more incredible. Kuprin fled his homeland at the time of the Revolution, but returned the year before his death in 1938.

But king Solomon loved many strange women, together with the daughter of Pharaoh, women of the Moabites, Ammonites, Edomites, Zidonians, and Hittites;

Of the nations concerning which the Lord said unto the children of Israel, Ye shall not go in to them, neither shall they come in unto you: for surely they will turn away your heart after their gods: Solomon clave unto these in love.

And he had seven hundred wives, princesses, and three hundred concubines: and his wives turned away his heart.

I KINGS: XI, 1–3

SULAMITH

A Prose Poem of Antiquity

by ALEXANDRE KUPRIN

WHATSOEVER THE EYES of the king might desire, he kept not from them; and withheld not his heart from any joy. Seven hundred wives had the king, and three hundred concubines, without counting slaves and dancers. And all of them did Solomon charm with his love, for God had endowed him with such an inexhaustible strength of passion as was not given to ordinary men. He loved the white-faced, black-eyed, red-lipped Hittites for their vivid but momentary beauty, that bursts into blossom just as early and enchantingly, and fades just as rapidly as the flower of the narcissus; the swarthy, tall, vehement Philistines, with wiry, curly locks, who wore golden, tinkling armlets upon their wrists, golden hoops upon their shoulders, and broad

314

anklets, joined by a thin little chain, upon both ankles; gentle, diminutive, lithe Ammorites formed without a blemish, whose faithfulness and sub- missiveness in love had passed into a proverb; women out of Assyria, who put their eyes in painting to make them seem more elongated, and who ate out with acid blue stars upon their foreheads and cheeks; well-schooled, gay and witty daughters of Sidon, who knew well how to sing and dance, as well as to play upon harps, lutes and flutes, to the accompaniment of tabours; xanthochroous women of Egypt, indefatigable in love and insane in jealousy; voluptuous Babylonians, whose entire body underneath their raiment was as smooth as marble, because they eradicated the hair upon it with a special paste; virgins of Baktria, who stained their nails and hair a fiery-red colour, and wore wide, loose trousers; silent, bashful Moabites, whose magnificent breasts were cool on the sultriest nights of summer; care-free and profligate Ammonites, with fiery hair, and flesh of such whiteness that it glowed in the dark; frail, blue-eyed women with flaxen hair, and skin of a delicate fragrance, who were brought from the north, through Baalbec, and whose tongue was incomprehensible to all the dwellers in Palestine. The king loved many daughters of Judea and Israel besides.

Also shared he his couch with Balkis-Makkedah, the Queen of Sheba, who had surpassed all women on earth in beauty, wisdom, riches, and her diversified art in passion; and with Abishag the Shunamite, who had warmed the old age of David—a kindly, quiet beauty, for whose sake Solomon had put to death his elder brother Adonijah, at the hands of Benaiah, the son of Jehoiada.

And also with the poor maiden of the vineyard, by the name of Sulamith, whom alone among all women the king had loved with all his heart.

Solomon made himself a litter of the best cedar wood, with pillars of silver, with arm-rests of gold in the form of recumbent lions, with a covering of purple Tyrian stuff, while the entire inner side of the covering was orna- mented with gold embroidery and with precious stones—love-gifts of the women and virgins of Jerusalem. And when well-built black slaves bore Solomon among his people on grand festal days, truly was the king glorious, like the lilies that are in the Valley of Sharon!

Pale was his face; his lips like unto a vivid thread of scarlet; his wavy locks of bluish black, and in them—the adornment of wisdom—gleamed gray hairs, like to the silver threads of mountain streams, falling down from the dark crags of Hermon; gray hairs glistened in his dark beard also, curled, after the custom of the kings of Assyria, in regular, small rows.

As for the eyes of the king, they were dark, like the darkest agate, like the heavens on a moonless night in summer; while his eye-lashes, that spread upward and downward like arrows, resembled dark rays around dark stars. And there was no man in all the universe who could bear the gaze of Solomon without casting down his eyes. And the lightnings of wrath in the eyes of the king would prostrate people to the earth.

But there were moments of heartfelt merriment, when the king would grow intoxicated with love, or wine, or the delight of power, or when he

rejoiced over words of wisdom or beauty, fitly spoken. Then his lashes would
be softly half-lowered, casting blue shadows upon his radiant face, and in
the king's eyes would kindle the warm flames of a kindly, tender laughter,
just like the play of black diamonds; and whosoever might behold his smile
was ready to yield up body and soul for it—so indescribably beautiful was it.
The mere name of King Solomon, uttered aloud, stirred the hearts of women,
like the fragrance of spilt myrrh that recalls nights of love.

The king's hands were soft, white, warm and beautiful, like a woman's;
but they held such an excess of life energy that, by the laying on of his palms
upon the temples of the sick, the king cured headaches, convulsions, black
melancholy, and demoniacal possession. Upon the index finger of his left
hand the king wore a gem of blood-red asteria that emitted six pearl-coloured
rays. Many centuries did this ring number, and upon the reverse side of its
stone was graven an inscription, in the tongue of an ancient, vanished
people: "All things pass away."

And so great was the sway of Solomon's soul that even beasts sub-
mitted to it; lions and tigers crawled at the feet of the king, rubbing their
muzzles against his knees, and licking his hands with their rough tongues,
whenever he entered their quarters. And he, whose heart found joy in the
dazzling play of precious stones, in the fragrance of sweet-smelling Egyptian
resins, in the soft touch of light stuffs, in sweet music, in the exquisite taste
of red, sparkling wine playing in a chased Ninuanian chalice—he also loved
to stroke the coarse manes of lions, the velvety backs of black panthers, and
the tender paws of young, speckled leopards; loved to hear the roar of wild
beasts, to see their powerful and superb movements, and to feel the hot
feral odour of their breath.

Thus did Jehoshaphat, the son of Ahilud, the historian of his days,
depict King Solomon.

30 Solomon and
the Queen of Sheba

Solomon ranks high among the Bible characters who have both intrigued and eluded novelists, no fewer than nine of whom have attempted to tell his story. Among them are John Erskine, the great Hebrew poet Chaim Bialik, Alexandre Kuprin, and Vardis Fisher, who along with many lesser novelists saw primarily lurid sex set against a biblical background. Generally these books have been little better than the motion pictures based upon Bible stories. It is unquestionably difficult for any novelist to draw back from the fact that Solomon had seven hundred wives, and therein lies the pitfall. However, Jay Williams has handled the problem with more restraint than others. Making the central thread of his novel Solomon's romance with Balkis, Queen of Sheba, he entwines this with the conflict between Solomon and his elder brother Adonijah. In the selection which follows, Williams, who has written children's books as well as historical novels of various periods, faces squarely the problem of dealing with an exotic and mysterious woman from an exotic and mysterious place.

And when the queen of Sheba heard of the fame of Solomon concerning the name of the Lord, she came to prove him with hard questions.

And she came to Jerusalem with a very great train, with camels that bare spices, and very much gold, and precious stones: and when she was come to Solomon, she communed with him of all that was in her heart.

I KINGS: X, 1–2

SOLOMON AND SHEBA by JAY WILLIAMS

SOLOMON WAS PREPARED for Balkis to be lovely, to be gracious, charming and intelligent: all those things Sittar had told him of. But he was not prepared for her to be a queen. All the lands which fringed the borders of Israel were ruled by men, and he had never seen a woman who was herself the receptacle of a goddess, who stood between her people and their Deity as he with his.

He received her in his throne room, seated upon his throne of ivory.

This throne stood upon a dais with six steps, and its arms were golden lions, and pairs of golden lions stood on each step with their mouths open as if roaring the glory of the king. On either side of him were ranked his counselors, bearded and grave, Benaiah and his captains, and the princes his brothers. Joel the son of Abner stood at the foot of the dais with a drawn sword, and about the walls were guardsmen, in whose golden shields the whole room was reflected, blurred as if seen through a morning mist.

Trumpets sounded Balkis' arrival, and the double doors of the throne room were opened. The king's steward, Ahushai the son of Asaph, struck the floor with his staff and said, "Behold the queen of Sheba, Mesha, and Sephar, the daughter of Merisamis."

There entered first a double file of Sheban soldiers in brazen helmets and straight tunics, girdled with belts of brass, that fell to their knees. Behind them came lines of veiled women dressed in rich robes, surrounding a litter borne by six brawny men. The bearers set the litter down before the throne and stood aside. Sittar came forward and knelt, and Balkis placed her hand on his shoulder; thus aided, she stepped from the litter. She stood perfectly still, her hands to her sides, and on her face a look of such utter detachment that she seemed no more than an image made of ivory, enamel, and precious stones. Her eyes were painted so that they appeared larger; her dark hair was covered with a veil of golden gauze sewn with pearls. From neck to ankles she was covered with a close-fitting robe of blue linen heavily worked with silver thread in leaves and flowers, and over it a mantle of blue samite encrusted with golden suns. On her head was a tall golden crown made like a sun-disk, horned, and set with gems. Beneath this heavy crown she neither swayed nor trembled, holding her head erect as if unconscious of any weight, and this added to her majesty and to the quality of unreality that clothed her.

Solomon sitting as rigidly, with his hands resting on his thighs, caught his breath. He was not conscious of her beauty but of her strangeness: she was unnatural, like a work of art. Through his mind flashed the phrase: "You shall not pay homage to a graven image. . . ."

He glanced sideways, quickly, at Sittar, who still knelt with his face upturned and a small smile on his lips. The strangeness was dispelled, a little, and he thought, She is after all no more than a woman in royal garb, his sister, as my sister Tamar was to me.

Then, to do her honor, he rose and slowly descended the six steps to stand before her. "The queen of Sheba is welcome in Israel," he said.

In a low, musical voice, she replied, "The son of David is gracious."

He became aware that the painted eyes were full of curiosity; that behind the composed mask of red-dyed lips and powdered cheeks, she was examining him with the caution of an adversary who looks out of ambush. He was at once amused by this, and looked more closely at her. He could see now that she was younger than he had thought, and that her features were delicate and perfect, although the steady stare of her eyes repelled him a little. As he watched, he could see that her chin shook with a tiny tremor, and he realized then the effort that it cost her to hold her head so still.

He said, "Will the queen sit?"

He did not wait for her answer, but motioned with his hand. A servant brought two folding chairs of olivewood, and opened them, placing cushions on each.

With an almost inaudible sigh, Balkis sat. Solomon then seated himself facing her. She said, "Let King Solomon accept the few small gifts I have brought him out of Sheba."

She lifted her hand, and porters, who had been waiting outside the doors of the throne room, now entered. They set before the dais bales of spices and herbs so that at once the whole room was filled with a sweet, savory odor; carvings of ivory, and sandalwood also, as well as goldwork, weapons with jeweled hilts, and bundles of fine cloth they placed beside the king.

Solomon nodded, smiling. "Rich are the gifts and blessed be the giver. They are accepted," he said. "My own gifts are poor indeed beside them."

At his gesture, Ahushai led out servants of the king, who placed beside the queen dishes of gold to the weight of a hundred talents, with cunningly wrought jewelry on every dish, and besides, parcels of sea-cloth from Philistia, deep purple dye from Tyre, and goblets of precious glass artfully colored.

After this ceremonial exchange, he said, "A house has been made ready for the queen. And we will dine together at sunset. But before she retires to rest and prepare herself let her make known to me what further may be done to add to her welcome."

Balkis replied, "The King has opened his hand to me so that nothing remains for me to desire, save this: let me go up to your chief temple, the fame of which I heard when I was yet two days' journey from Jerusalem, so that I may make a sacrifice there before your gods in token of the friendship between our two countries."

Solomon heard behind him a gasp from many throats. He regarded the queen impassively. He fancied that he detected a note of challenge in her voice; now that he thought of it, certainly Sittar must have told her of the God of Israel. Was it possible she asked this favor merely to place him in a quandary? For certainly it was no easy problem she set him: however he answered, he might give offense either to her or to his own people.

He said, at last, "What the queen asks is impossible. For Yahweh, our God, is a jealous god and he has forbidden women to minister to his altars or to appear before him. It is from caution that I deny the queen's request, for Yahweh might send down fire from heaven upon her, and while the queen's own goddess would doubtless protect her, surely the wrath of Yahweh would be upon me and my people."

In answering thus, he made her responsible for the safety of his own land, so that she had no recourse but to agree.

"However," he went on, "let the queen Balkis go up on the slopes of Olivet, to En-rogel to the Stone of the Serpent. There I will send her whatever beasts are necessary and there she may sacrifice to her own gods."

He heard a rustle of movement, and murmurings among his counselors. He turned his head to eye them, and said, "Let not the honored elders mutter behind their hands. If any would speak, speak now that I may hear him."

Chimham the son of Barzillai, clearing his throat and fumbling with his curly lamb's-wool beard, said, "May the king live forever. Your servant only fears that this may be an insult in the eyes of Israel and Judah as they keep the Feast of Booths, to see the smoke of a foreign sacrifice go up in the sight of the House of the Lord. Further . . . hm, hm . . . a sacrifice to a woman's god . . . "

Solomon looked from him to the others. Some were scowling, some shook their heads, and even Benaiah had an unhappy expression on his broad face.

Then the king said, "The son of Barzillai is wise and experienced. Does he speak for himself alone, or for all?"

"For all, lord," said one, Azariah the son of Zadok, and the rest nodded their heads.

"Very well. Now let the son of Barzillai tell me: if the House of the Lord were destroyed, would the God of Israel also be destroyed?"

Chimham looked shocked. "My lord—" he began.

"Then," Solomon continued, "the House of God is not God. And although our God dwells among us in the Temple, yet tell me, does he see only Jerusalem or does he see all Israel?"

"He sees all Israel, blessed be his name."

"And does he see also into the land of Moab, and even into the land of Egypt?"

Chimham said, in puzzlement, "He who made the earth sees to the uttermost corners of the earth, my lord."

"This is so. Yet, although he sees the altars of Ashtarte in Tyre, and the altars of Ra and Osiris in Egypt, he does not smite the Phoenicians nor the Egyptians. Why is this, son of Barzillai?"

"I—truly I do not know, my lord," Chimham stammered.

"Why, wherein is it written that we are to forbid to other peoples their own worship or their own gods? Only to us, his people, is it commanded, 'You shall have no other gods beside me.' It is we, alone, who are chosen of the Lord. Or is this not so, son of Barzillai?"

"It is so, my lord," said Chimham submissively.

"And does the son of Barzillai—do the rest of you—imagine that to the Lord Yahweh the distance from his Temple to Tyre or to Egypt is greater than the distance to En-rogel? All the earth is but a pebble in the hand of the Lord."

He bit in the corner of his mouth to keep from smiling, for it was clear that they could not answer him. "Therefore," he said, "let all be done as I have commanded, unless—" He turned back to Balkis, and now he allowed the smile to creep out. "Unless the queen have a further objection?"

He saw her mouth twitch. She rose, and said, "Happy are these your servants who stand before you continually and hear your wisdom, son of

David. I am satisfied with your decision. I will go up to this place you have named and offer a sacrifice to Shams—and invoke her blessing on your head."

At this, there came a positive groan of terror from some of the old men. But Solomon ignored them. He stood, and said, "If it will please the queen, let it be so."

He watched her seat herself within the litter, swinging herself in with practiced ease despite the heavy crown and tight-fitting robes. Her women assisted her, setting her mantle straight and placing cushions at her back. The bearers slung the straps about their shoulders, set the loops over the ends of the poles and heaved up the litter. At that moment, she looked sidelong at him with a slow smile.

"Until dinner, son of David," she said, and it was as if she granted him a brief truce.

But at dinner, she was another woman. She had washed the pale, ceremonial paint from her cheeks so that her skin glowed with its own honey color. Her hair was braided in tresses, and about it, over her veil, she wore a wreath of little flowers made most cunningly of copper and silver. Her dress was cut full in the sleeves and skirt, with three flounces all embroidered in colored thread; the women of Solomon's household who were at the table gazed at it from the corners of their eyes. There was nothing of the cold and distant queen about her any longer; she was gay and winning, full of jests and ready to laugh, bending now toward Solomon, now toward Sittar who sat upon her other side, and eating with relish of the many delicacies with which the table was covered.

Solomon was utterly charmed, so that he could not look at her enough. He took opportunity to say, as they were washing their hands after the roast meats had been cleared away, "It is my hope that the queen will make her visit a long one."

"Oh," she replied, "the king must first say what beauties there are in his land for him to show me."

"Little to match that which has come to me out of Sheba," he answered. "Nevertheless, this is a fair land which our God has given us. There are here both high and low places, snowy peaks and fertile valleys. I will show the queen the wonder of the Sea of Salt and the chalk plains above it, whiter than the moon. And there is winding Jordan, which flows down from the Lake of the Harp between green meadows, woodlands, and desolate cliffs. There are dark forests of oaks, wide grasslands flowing like a sea, vineyards where a single bunch of grapes is a load for two men . . ."

She smiled, and said, "Rich indeed is this land in the love of its king. Well, you may show me what you will."

She watched him covertly as he took up an orange and began to peel it. He rested his elbows on the table, his head bent and a little inclined to one side, intent upon his task; his long musician's fingers, strong and nervous, stripped off the rind, which threw golden lights upon his brown skin. A worthy antagonist, she thought to herself. Sittar was right, he is a man and a king. This is not such a one as Hadad to be led on a halter . . . better for me if he were put down and another, easier to deal with, in his place.

She glanced at Adonijah, who sat halfway down the board. He was eating grapes, two and three at a mouthful, and spitting the seeds on the cloth before him. Beside him, Nebat the son of Ahijah lounged, yawning languidly and toying with a cup. The two together put her in mind of some great shaggy hunting dog companioned with a lazy leopard; but who, she wondered, was their master—the king, some other, or were they masterless? Looking about, her attention was caught by Joab, who was seated opposite Adonijah eating very frugally, no more than a mouthful of bread and cheese. The heavy-lidded Bedouin eyes were upon the prince and there was a half-smile, almost of contempt, on Joab's face. As she watched him, his eyes flickered toward her, cold and dangerous, appraising, even scornful. She had been introduced to him earlier; she knew the name, not only from Hadad's tales, but from Sittar's account of the conflict between the king and his brother. This was one to watch, one who, if she was not wary, might upset all plans for the sake of his own ends.

The servants brought honey-cakes and sesame-cakes, and poured a rich, dark, sweet wine. Benaiah was telling the tale of how he had gone down into the pit to slay the lion, speaking in his slow, modest way; the story was well known to most of those present, but he had been urged to tell it again for the sake of the Egyptian and Syrian envoys. At the other end of the table, Abishag chatted with Solomon's two wives, the Egyptian princess, Tuosri, daughter of Psusennes, and Mahalath the Sidonitess, the niece of Hiram of Tyre. Bathsheba sat there also, watching her son and the queen of Sheba with a confusion of emotions: pride that he was sought after by so great a monarch, and resentment that he should pay so close a court to a foreign woman. As if, she thought, we had not enough foreigners already in the house. And she turned, and over her shoulder spoke sharply to one of the servants, who moved too slowly with the wine jar.

Solomon had fallen into a reverie, resting his chin upon the fork of thumb and forefinger, looking at Balkis and her brother as they conversed together beside him. In both faces the same liveliness showed, the same spark of amusement at life itself, her fine and tawny profile against his darker, rounder face, like amber upon sandalwood. Absently, the king hummed to himself, a snatch of melody that wound into his mind; he touched his finger to the table and heard in his imagination the answering sound of a chord. It was long since he had composed a song, and suddenly, with the profile of Balkis before him, words fitted together to follow the gentle weaving of the melody:

> *Rise, my love; my beautiful one come away.*
> *Let me see your form, let me hear your voice,*
> *For your voice is sweet and your form is comely.*

Balkis turned to him abruptly. "What said the son of David?"

He started. He had unconsciously spoken the last few words aloud.

"Nothing," he said. "A sudden, passing thought." And then he smiled, sitting straighter and reaching for the dish of fruit. "I will tell it you one day, perhaps," he said.

One day, Solomon and Balkis rode out along the Vale of Kidron, northward toward the high mountain village of Ramah, where Solomon had a summer house. It was a cool morning with a fresh breeze that puffed feathers of cloud across the sky and set the plumes of their horses' caparisons nodding and snapping. Solomon's spirits were high, and as they rode he sang aloud a mountaineers' song: "Turn, turn, O maiden, turn that we may gaze on you."

"The heart of my friend is merry today," said Balkis.

"Wherefore not?" he replied, laughing. "Is it not blithe to ride free as a bird, to be winged, to smell the mountain wind and have no cares?"

"Is it so? Has the king no cares, then?"

"Call me not 'king' this morning, I pray you," he said. "I have set aside that heavy mantle for these few days. I will not think of cares; there will be time enough for that when . . ." He paused. And when she looked at him, he went on, "When my sister, Balkis, feels that she must return to her own place. I would that day might be put off forever."

"We need not think of that now," she said. "I, too, have put away my cares. Tell me, rather, what that great rock is that looms above us where the road climbs?"

He said, "It is called the Stone of Meeting, for at it this northern road meets those which come from Gibeah and Gibeon. At its summit there is a hill track branching off; we will leave the road and take it."

"Let us make haste, then," she said, "lest those cares we seek to escape catch us up. *Hai!* my little Orab is restless, she is athirst and looks for the mountain streams."

With that, she clapped her heels into the mare and urged her forward. The flat, round cap she wore blew off, and her hair streamed out like the wings of a raven. With a shout, Solomon galloped after her, and bending far over from the saddle scooped up her cap and bore it with him.

They dashed up the road, the dust rising behind them in a great cloud. The road bent round the foot of the steep, ribbed face of rock which towered on their right hand, bleak and gray. Balkis looked over her shoulder at Solomon, laughing, and then suddenly her mare checked, reared up neighing, and almost fell. From behind the angle of the rock a tall old man had stepped directly into her path, holding out a knotty staff to bar her way. With some difficulty, Balkis kept her seat, reined in her mount and gentled it, and then looked fiercely at the intruder.

He was burnt almost black from the sun, hard and dry as a mummy, his flesh shriveled to cords, his white hair hanging below his bent shoulders and tangling in his coarse beard. But his eyes glared into hers with such wildness that for a moment she was deprived of speech. In that moment, Solomon joined her.

He said, "Long is it since I have beheld Nathan the prophet. Yet it would be better for him to come to me in my palace, rather than to stop me like a highwayman by the roadside."

Nathan leaned on his staff, and retorted, "Little have I to do with palaces, O king. I come and I go where Yahweh sends me. Nor will the son of David escape the eye of the Lord either within his palace or upon the roadside. For the Lord God will come upon you unawares, like a highwayman, to call on you to stand and deliver over to him your charge, the care of Israel. How will you answer him, son of David?"

Solomon answered, quietly, "That is between my God and myself."

"Pride, pride!" cried the prophet, in a ringing voice. "Be not deceived in yourself, man of Judah. Solomon is not above the Law of God, given to our fathers upon Sinai. 'If anyone entices you, saying, "Let us go and serve alien gods," you must not yield to him nor heed him; you must not show him mercy, nor spare him—your own hand must be first against him to put him to death!' So says the Law. Woe to you, O king, if you break the covenant you and your father made with the Lord God, to follow his commandments and to walk in his ways."

Solomon listened patiently, although Nathan filled him with annoyance, and he thought, Never does he open his mouth save to croak warnings of doom. Has my mother perhaps incited him to follow me here and cry out against Balkis, also, in her jealousy?

Balkis said sternly, "Why do you permit this madman to speak thus to you? Ride him down, and let us go."

Nathan's eyes blazed at her. "Woman of Sheba," he said, "be silent. Thus has it come to pass in Israel that an alien speaks before the face of the Lord's anointed." He turned his hot gaze on Solomon. "Beware, son of David. Go not whoring after strangers and their abominations. The voice of God speaks through me, saying, 'I put before you a blessing and a curse; a blessing if you heed my commands, and a curse if you do not heed them but run after alien gods.' "

"I have heard all that Nathan has said," Solomon replied, putting his hand on the bridle of Balkis' mare, to hold her still. "Be assured I will take careful thought of it. Let him also remember that it is the queen of Sheba of whom he speaks; unwise and discourteous is he who offends a guest. Now let us pass."

Nathan paused, looking up at Solomon's calm face. Then he raised his staff above his head. "Israel from your hand, O king!" he cried. He swung away from them and strode up over the crest of the hill and soon was lost to view, going down upon the left side toward Gibeon.

Solomon took his hand from the mare's bridle, and began to walk his horse, Balkis riding beside him. They came up to the meeting of the roads in silence, and he departed from the road, taking the narrow track along the hill crest. Then she said, "The customs of Israel are very strange to me. In my own land, any who spoke thus to me would be put to death. I have seen Solomon give judgment, and behave as a king should, yet he bowed his head before a ragged and dirty beggar."

"His admonitions may be divinely inspired," said Solomon, gravely. "In any case, such a man acts as the conscience of the king."

"Conscience?" She lifted her eyebrows. "What need has a sovereign for such a commodity? What is right and what is wrong come from the queen who is the flesh of the Goddess—or so it is among us. And that man said that Solomon was not above the law. But is the king himself not the lawgiver? And is not he who gives able also to take away? Is not the giver greater than the gift?"

Solomon said nothing for a time, smoothing absently with one hand the neck of his steed. At last he said, "We do not think that the king is God. I am a man, Balkis, anointed of God. No man can set himself in the place of the Almighty. Our Law is greater than any man for it was the covenant made between our forefathers and Yahweh, when the Lord brought us out of bondage in Egypt and led us through the desert into this land promised us by him. We are the people of his choice, governed by his Law."

"You are a stubborn people," Balkis murmured, "stubborn and conceited. In all the lands where I have journeyed, or all that I ever heard of, the gods of the land permit temples of other gods, and the worship of other gods. But your Yahweh will permit his people none but himself. Jealous is he indeed! All other nations know that their gods are kin to those of other nations, call them by what name you will. Your own temple is built upon the Jebusite altar to Khepa, I am told. And Shapash is the name the Cananites give to our goddess, Shams, whom the Moabites call Chemosh, worshipping her as a man since, among them, inheritance and rule was through the fathers of tribes. So, too, the Egyptians worship Ra, the Horned Sun; and their Isis, the Great Mother, is but another name for Babylonian Ishtar and Astarte of the Phoenicians, to whom we also sacrifice as Ashtar, the Lady of the Morning Star. What does your god fear—that he will not receive his full due of burnt meats?"

"Our God neither fears, nor feels pride," said Solomon. "Yet what Balkis says may have a germ of truth in it: that all gods, are, indeed, aspects of One. For what is the sun? It is a globe of fire nourishing the world. Like the moon, it is a lamp. It is neither eternal nor unchanging, but was made and set in the heavens—by whom? By One greater than moon or sun or morning star, the maker of all things, the Eternal. He cannot be expressed in an image and yet he is reflected everywhere in his works—in these hills, the blades of grass, the clouds above us, and . . . in us. An image may be carved of the Sun Queen or the Moon King, but how shall we carve an image of the whole world with all its creatures?"

The moon, slanting through the branches of fig and almond trees, dappled the ground with moving silver and cast a sparkle upon the still surface of the cistern. A little owl called softly and sweetly once, and tiny chirps and creaks from among the foliage hardly disturbed the silence of the night.

Like a thief moving among the shadows came the king of Israel. The gate stood a trifle ajar; he entered and closed it behind him. He stood motionless, striving to pierce the confusion of leaf shadows and moonlight. Then, with uncertain steps, he went to the cistern. All was silent.

He had brought his lyre, wrapped in a piece of dark cloth. He drew it out and softly, lest he waken anyone, tuned it. Was she asleep? Had she forgotten? Or had it been a jest, spoken hastily, nothing but mockery? As he waited, he drew the plectrum lightly across the strings, dropping from note to note. He began to hum in accompaniment; then, allowing his verses to fill his mind, he began, very softly, to sing:

> *Rise, my love*
> > *my beautiful one, come away;*
> *For see, the winter is past,*
> > *the rain is over and gone;*
> *The flowers have appeared on the earth,*
> > *the time of song has come,*
> *And the call of the turtle dove*
> > *is heard in our land;*
> *The fig tree is putting forth its figs,*
> > *and the blossoming vines are fragrant.*
> *Rise, my love,*
> > *my beautiful one, come away.*
> *O my dove in the clefts of the rocks*
> > *in the recesses of the cliffs,*
> *Let me see your form,*
> > *let me hear your voice;*
> *For your voice is sweet*
> > *and your form is comely.*

There was a rustle, and from between the fig trees, holding their broad, round leaves away from her face, came Balkis. She passed from the darkness into the light, seeming to float upon the film of her draperies. The low moon shone over her shoulder, through the curve of waist and arm, silvering her dark hair and the pointed tips of her breasts.

Solomon's fingers stilled on the lyre. He sat motionless. All that was lovely in womankind, all that was softness and sweetness came toward him with light steps, on arching feet. Her garments flowed over her thighs like smooth water over stones; her hair was a dark waterfall upon her shoulders. His music was forgotten. He whispered, "Ah, you are beautiful, my love, you are beautiful. Your eyes are doves behind your veil, your hair is like a flock of goats streaming down from Gilead . . . your lips are a thread of scarlet; your two breasts are like two fawns that pasture among the hyacinths . . ."

"I am here," she said. "I have heard. I listened to your voice on the hilltop, I held you when you climbed on the cliffside, I heard your voice singing in the garden and it called me."

He held out his hand to receive hers, to draw her close.

"My dove," he said. "My perfect one."

She came to his arms as a swallow returns to its nest, cleaving to him as one flesh, her lips upon his like honey and milk.

The lyre slipped to the ground, and its strings sounded a single cry, and died away.

Solomon and the Queen of Sheba 327

She came to his arms as a swallow returns to its nest, nestling in his
second flesh, her lips upon his like honey and milk.

The bird slipped to the ground, and its strings sounded a single cry, and
died away.

31 Elijah and

the Priests of Baal

Of the ten novelists who tried to tell the story of Ahab and Jezebel, only Dorothy Clarke Wilson and Louis Paul succeeded in coping with the lurid aspects. In *Dara, the Cypriot,* Paul, a seasoned novelist who has also published short stories in most major American magazines, tells his tale through the eyes of a non-biblical adventurer, a Cypriot who marries a Hebrew girl and settles among her people. Dara the Cypriot has witnessed the trial between Jezebel's four hundred and fifty priests of Baal and the Prophet Elijah, who speaks for the people being taxed to support the extravagant alien queen and her priests. Dara gives his account as though to set the record straight for history. With the skill of a professional novelist, Paul leads his readers movingly through the trial. Both the tone and the detail give a feeling of authenticity.

And it came to pass, when Ahab saw Elijah that Ahab said unto him, Art thou he that troubleth Israel?

And he answered, I have not troubled Israel; but thou, and thy father's house, in that ye have forsaken the commandments of the Lord, and thou hast followed Baalim.

Now therefore send, and gather to me all Israel unto mount Carmel, and the prophets of Baal four hundred and fifty, and the prophets of the groves four hundred, which eat at Jezebel's table.

I KINGS: XVIII, 17–19

DARA THE CYPRIOT by LOUIS PAUL

NOW CERTAIN EVENTS occurred which proved I had estimated rightly. Elijah's drought was no mere action designed to provide a temporary embarrassment for the Crown; rather, the prophet intended to use it as an instrument of force to compel king Ahab to do his bidding. Apparently this God-driven man had managed to produce a situation which made it possible for him to stand as an equal opponent to a ruling monarch.

I have shown you how Elijah and Obadiah met at the house of Naboth. As ordered, the king's servant set out to relay Elijah's message to Ahab. It seemed the monarch was somewhere in the vicinity with a band of troops who rifled farmhouses and storage sheds for the little grain that might still be hidden there. At day's end Obadiah returned, and it was found that Ahab was excited at the news of Elijah's presence in the land and had arranged a place of meeting for the morrow at the Well of Harod, a place of a few palms a little distance from Jezreel.

Meanwhile Joelah had received my message and arrived during the night, and he had covered that distance in good time, starting with the sun halfway overhead and arriving in the second watch of night. By morning there was much buzzing and gossip, as it had somehow leaked out that a meeting was to take place between Elijah and Ahab. Certainly I had no intention of being absent from it. Though Joelah had barely closed his eyes, I shook him awake, and we set out for the Well of Harod soon after sunrise.

Arriving, I was astonished at how that tiny way station had filled up with citizens of every sort, camped and munching hard cakes and seeing if it were possible to buy a sip of water. A seedy creature with skins hanging from crossbars across his shoulders finally appeared, and what he had was pure mud, but people gladly paid his usurious price and drained it through a fine cloth. I, along with Joelah, went with face half covered, as I wished to be a witness to rather than a participant of the occurrences here.

At last, when the sun was risen high enough to produce a noticeable heat, the king came up, surrounded by armsmen, and Elijah appeared to stand beside a well now dry and overcoated with a film of powdery dust. The monarch's eyes rolled at the sight of Elijah, and his temples bulged with barely controllable rage. "So it is you again," cried the king. "You who have brought nothing but trouble to Israel!"

"My lord, you delude yourself," observed the prophet calmly. "The cause of Israel's trouble is Ahab and his blasphemous house. Having forsaken the God of Israel and gone whoring after foreign baals, would you expect to have prosperity in the land?"

"I have listened to this same monotonous speech before," said the king. "I hear it repeated until it sickens me. Indeed, I am sick to death of you and your insane theology. Now say something to provide my ears with more than harsh noises and jibberings, or be on your way."

"I am sorry, my lord. I did not appear in Israel merely to exchange words with you, but also to address my countrymen. Your fate was sealed long ago. These others may still be saved by common reason." Turning to the multitude gathered about, he cried, "How long will you people hobble on crutches, taking neither one direction nor the other?"

The crowd could hardly mistake the meaning of this figure of speech, seeing how many there are in the country who limp from diseases of the limbs. "You cannot worship Yahweh and love Melkart at the same time. If the Lord is God, then worship him. If Baal is God, worship him. Choose and choose now, one or the other!"

Elijah then turned and looked squarely at the enraged monarch. "Listen well, my lord," he said. "In Israel Jezebel has her temples, and four hundred and fifty priests to minister to them, while I am the last prophet of Yahweh remaining in the land. Now go and gather these foreign devils, and all her other priestly attendants, and before your eyes I will show you what power there is in my God."

"Why," demanded Ahab, "should I go and gather these priests of Melkart according to some whim of yours? I do not take but give orders in Israel."

Elijah's lids were narrowed as he looked hard at the king. "If so, my lord," he said coolly, "look up to heaven and order the rain to fall. And when we stand drenched in this downpour, I shall bow and say, 'Ahab commands in Israel.' But as I believe only I and my God can do it, circumstances leave you no choice but to please me in this whim."

So it was shown how cunningly Elijah had planned to make the drought his weapon in commanding obedience from the king. Said Ahab, "And, having Jezebel's priests in a body before you, what action do you propose?"

"I propose to show these doubting people, citizens you have perverted to a false belief, that Yahweh and not Melkart is supreme in Israel. Gather your priests, and the citizenry of the land, in Harosheth of Carmel, for that is fair country. And let us see what we shall see."

"Then let it be done," said the king. Turning to a captain, he said, "Take whatever detachment is needed, and say you act under my orders. Bring the baal priests of Jezebel to Harosheth. Do so without noise, as the queen has small understanding of mad Hebrew prophets and can only add confusion to the matter. Notify the populace, and say tomorrow they will see Elijah, the man responsible for their misery, confounded."

"As you command, my lord."

I said to Joelah, "Let us go, for tomorrow may be an interesting day in our lives. The prophet uses this drought as a dread thing to compel obedience. But will he employ it overcunningly? He promises to pass some manner of miracle, pitting himself alone against the combined priesthood of Jezebel. And whose magic is stronger, we shall soon discover."

"All matters of theology make my head swim," said Joelah. "If people would just have a god, without some forcing others to their beliefs, we wouldn't need theology at all but could go in peace and contentment."

"If," I said. "If it were not for little foxes, we should all eat larger grapes."

We then went back to our inn, and the next day, along with many others of the curious, journeyed to Harosheth, no particular distance. This was an unwalled place also having dried-up wells. In good times it was rolling meadows, noble terebinth trees, and dancing brooks, the country rising gently and leading to the promontory of Mount Carmel. Now it was sear and brown.

When the time had come to gather, Elijah asked for two young bulls, one to be placed on a pile of wood atop an altar built by him, the other in this same manner by the priesthood of Jezebel. The king acted servile to all his commands, but there was a certain light beneath his expression, as though he thought Elijah had finally gone too far and was about to ruin himself.

When the animals at last had been procured and the altars raised, Elijah stood and challenged those gathered prophets to bring their pile to flame without human aid!

Hearing this, I too thought the man of Tishbeh had exceeded himself. Nevertheless, the contest began. The baal priests did everything in their religion to invoke a spontaneous fire—praying and moaning, dancing and leaping about, all morning.

Elijah stood with arms folded and called out mocking words. "Go ahead," he taunted. "Groan. Shout. Cry your heads off. After all, Baal is your god. He may be wrapped up in conversation. Perhaps he's taken a journey somewhere. Or maybe he's just asleep and needs to be awakened."

The priests set up bloodcurdling cries, working themselves into a frenzy, as I knew their custom to be, whipping out knives and cutting their heads so that their faces were splotched with crimson and the blood ran down to stain their priestly robes. But evening came and still their altar remained unlighted.

Finally Elijah stood up and addressed the crowd. "Have you not had enough of this howling nonsense? Then attend to me."

His altar was constructed of stones such as his ancestors had used from time immemorial. Digging a trench around these, he called for water to be spilled in it. In addition, he ordered the wood drenched with water from the skins of the water-peddlers three times in succession. Then he turned his face to heaven, "Hear me, O Lord, that this people may know that thou art the Lord God and that thou hast turned their heart back again!"

Suddenly a fire broke out in the wood of Elijah's pyre, and the animal was sacrificed. Now I will say that if this act was done by trickery, it seems a harder trickery than real miracles are. Certainly the great multitude thought otherwise, as they fell on their faces and proclaimed in a loud voice, "The Lord, he is God. The Lord, he is God!"

Gravely the prophet turned to the king, whose eyes were wide with fear and wonder. Said Elijah, "Consider well what has happened here today, my lord. I bid you Shalom. Go, drink and eat. For as the God of Israel has promised me rain, so will it come in full measure soon."

He now turned to face the awe-filled crowd. Pointing to the priests of Jezebel, he said, "Will you leave these false prophets alive in the land?"

"No. No!" shouted the mob.

Elijah's expression was hard. "Then those of you who carry swords surround them."

We were now to witness the planned sequel to Elijah's miracle, a bloody massacre of horrifying proportions. As you may know, there is a brook that flows from Carmel and waters in its proper season the plain of Esdraelon. The brook Kishon runs through green meadows and sweet willows only a short way from Harosheth.

Today, if you go to that field of bloodshed, you can see no stains on it. It is a place of wooded aspect, swept by soft sea breezes, full of charming glens and dotted with wildflowers. Beyond its high peak spread the waters of the Great Sea, sparkling blue in the brilliant sunshine. Certainly Carmel might well have been that first Paradise, celebrated in song and story, where the lion lay down with the lamb, and there was perfect harmony in nature.

32 Elisha and
the Shunamite's Son

Probably no writer has ranged through more fields of literature than Robert Graves, the English poet, novelist, critic, translator, historian, essayist, biographer, and folklorist. In the past seventy years he has written several volumes of poetry, which he considers his most important work, and numerous historical novels, among them the classic *I, Claudius, Claudius, the God,* and the undervalued *Count Belisarius.* He has commented perceptively on the Greek myths and has probed the source of folk concepts in his brilliant *White Goddess.* He has written a history of his own time in *Goodbye to All That,* analyzed the techniques of prose writing in his perceptive *Reader Over Your Shoulder,* enlarged in fictional form the diaries of *Sergeant Lamb* who fought in the American Revolution, translated Latin American classics for the United Nations, sought to discover *The Real David Copperfield,* and edited *T. E. Lawrence to His Biographer.* In short,

Robert Graves is a maker of books, a man of profound learning who has ranged over much of Western history and myth. He has written two biblical novels, *King Jesus* and *My Head! My Head!.* With the help of the biblical scholar and anthropologist Raphael Patai, Graves has most recently published an interesting interpretation, *Hebrew Myths: The Book of Genesis.* Dedicated to T. E. Lawrence, *My Head! My Head!* was one of his first literary prose efforts. In this slight and curious volume, Graves attempts to isolate the mythical aspects of Elisha. This pattern of seeking the rational in every story, in every scrap of history, in every legend and myth, is interesting in its revelation of both Elisha and Graves. The book is sub-titled: Being the History of Elisha and the Shunamite Woman; with the History of Moses as Elisha Related it, and her Questions Put to Him.

*And it fell on a day, that Elisha passed to Shunem, where was
a great woman; and she constrained him to eat bread. And so it was,
that as oft as he passed by, he turned in thither to eat bread.*

II KINGS: IV, 8

MY HEAD! MY HEAD! by ROBERT GRAVES

WHEN ELISHA CAME to Shunem, staff in hand, by way of Jezreel and Chesulloth, the day was hot. Gehazi came wearily behind carrying a cooking pot and flints and the box in which Elisha kept samples and magical tools. This Gehazi was a tall youth who loved his master and was already after a two years' ministry well skilled in divination and in the properties of herbs and metals. Elisha had chosen him from the College of the Sons of the Prophets, twisting his staff and throwing it in the air; where it fell there it had pointed to Gehazi. The chief prophet of the College had said: "What are his stars?" The priest had said: "Good and indifferent, and again good. Indifferent is to say; in that middle time between good and good, he will sin if his master sins or refrain if his master refrains." Elisha had said: "Jah be with us both. Come then, Gehazi."

Now it had been revealed to Elisha that he should lodge that night at the house of a rich Shunamite; but he did not know the man's name. As he passed up the street, Gehazi following at a little distance, they saw a great house standing across the way: Elisha knew that this was the lodging intended, for the vision was no obscure one; yet over the lintel of the door which he saw in the vision were written in Egyptian writing the words: "My head! My head!" and on the house to which he came there was no writing at all. But the fig-tree at the gate was the same fig-tree and the lattice of the roof was the lattice of the vision. So he prayed "Jah with me," then entered without so much as knocking; and he sat down.

Gehazi came up stumbling and stood by the door under the fig-tree. A sparrow muted upon his head, so that he said: "My head! My head! I am unclean. There is evil on me from this house." So he could not enter in, but continued outside under the tree. Elisha hearing Gehazi's cry said: " 'My head! My head!' was written over the door of this house in my vision. You should have made a prayer as I did when you came to the door; for I told you of my vision. Now no harm shall come to me while I am within the walls of this house, but you are unclean until tomorrow, and must continue where you are."

Jochebed the Shunamite heard Elisha come into the room where she sat; she did not look up at him or see him, but speaking as one who had foreknowledge of his coming said to her maid Zibiah: "Bring water for this prophet; he has walked from Jezreel today." Then she said to Elisha: "Let my lord excuse me." With that she went to an inner room and Elisha did not see her again until the morning. Zibiah drew water from the well in the courtyard and Elisha drank. Then Zibiah went out to Gehazi with the cup, but Gehazi said: "A sparrow has defiled me. Set the cup upon the ground and I shall drink: tomorrow I shall purify the cup and give it to you again." She did as he said.

It seemed strange to Elisha that the mistress of the house had knowledge of his coming through a dream or a vision, yet used him with so little reverence. He called the maid and said: "Who are you, and who is your mistress?"

She answered: "My mistress is Jochebed, the wife of Issachar, son of Dodo, and I am Zibiah, daughter of Izri, Issachar's steward."

Elisha asked her: "Does your mistress treat all strangers in this manner? Does she offer them no food when they come?"

Zibiah said: "My mistress gives the thirsty to drink, so much custom requires of her: and sometimes more, for she is not a niggardly woman. But she has fancies."

Gehazi could not prepare a meal for his master: his cooking pot and the food he carried were unclean until the next day because of the sparrow. But Elisha said: "Fasting is good," so they fasted and slept, Elisha in the house but Gehazi in the street. In the morning early Elisha went to take leave of Jochebed, for Issachar her husband was not with her, being upon a journey. He saluted her courteously, and thanking her for the water and for the lodging, said: "We are going on our road again."

She answered: "Would you go fasting? Yet if there were more prophets who could fast so contentedly, Israel would be a cleaner land. Of the many prophets who come to this house from time to time the greater number have the eyes of drunkards and the lips of gluttons. And when they go from this house in the morning they speak no courteous words as you have spoken, but shower reproaches; for to try them I always give them water but no food. You, I perceive, are a holy man, and your servant has done well: he has kept from defiling this house. Therefore" (with that she clapped her hands), "Zibiah, bring that banquet which we have prepared. Set before this prophet, and when he has eaten let the servant eat also." So Elisha sat down and thanked her, and ate; Jochebed poured the drink for him.

When Elisha had eaten and washed his hands, Jochebed said: "Man of God, I have a question to ask you." Then she said: "Zibiah, take this food out to the servant." So Zibiah went, and when she had gone, Jochebed asked Elisha: "This is my question, a plain one expecting a plain answer: 'How, truly, did Moses die?' "

Elisha said: "It is written in the fifth book of Moses, the last verses of the book."

Jochebed answered: "Yes, but in riddles."

He said: "How, in riddles?"

Jochebed said: "It is written plainly for fools, but for men and women of wit, of whom I am one, obscurely, unless an honest prophet should first expound the history. For the book says that Jah, our God, buried his servant Moses in a valley of Moab, after he had died on Pisgah according to the word of Jah, but that no man knows to this day where the sepulchre lies. But is Jah a man that he buries his prophets in a hole dug with a mattock? Jah is a spirit and His ministers a flaming fire. Either Moses was translated to Heaven as were our father Enoch and your master Elijah, or else, as it seems to me, some man buried him. Tell me then, for I am no fool, how did Moses die or who buried him in the valley?"

Elisha wondered that a woman should ask such a question, for he had never before encountered a woman of wit, unless it was Jezebel, the wife of Ahab: but Jezebel was a princess of Sidon, a city of learning and merriment where all the notable women have wit. So he inquired from her: "Who taught you to ask this question? Was it Issachar, the son of Dodo, your husband? Or was it an Amorite slave or a Baalite stranger mocking at our traditions?"

She told him plainly: "No, Issachar is also one of the fools, though he is my husband and most dear to me of all men. Nor do I learn questions from slaves or strangers. I ask this question from my own heart."

Elisha then promised Jochebed: "The story of Moses, his birth, his death and all that came between I shall tell you when I come again: for you have used me well, and it is clear that you have understanding above most men."

Zibiah had reclined herself upon the floor and was now sleeping, but Jochebed did not see that she slept, for she was troubled with other things. She said to Elisha: "My heart is bitter as the heart of Moses was bitter when Aaron put the curse upon him that he should not see the promised land."

Elisha asked her: "How so?"

She answered: "From childhood we women are instructed in our blessedness that we shall have children to cherish; all the life of a woman is ruled by this one thought. The suckling of children is our promised land of milk and honey. I have no children, and my heart is bitter."

Elisha said: "Are you cursed with barrenness from Jah?" She answered: "No, I do not think so, but my husband is old and therefore I have no children. It is a grief both to him and to me, but especially to me. His line is not lost, for his sons' sons are living, and he occupies himself with the work of the fields and with his trafficking. But I am here in the house, and the servants are many and the steward a trusty man. I have nothing to do but to trouble my head with questions and my heart with longing for a child. And Jah forbid that I should wittingly dishonour my husband, for he loves me and is jealous both of my honour and of his own."

Elisha heard her speak this word "wittingly"; he looked strangely at her and he said: "What if Jah should speak through me and say you shall bear a child to Issachar? Would Issachar give it credence?" Jochebed answered: "He would believe it if the prophecy came from your lips, for he knows you for a holy man and a worker of miracles."

Elisha said: "You shall bear a child." She answered: "Is this a true prophecy?" He said: "Do you know the penalty of false prophecy in the name of our God? If anything spoken in Jah's name by a prophet does not come to pass, that prophet dies. It is the Law." Then her eyelid winked so that she knew that it was true: she was astonished, and thanked him and fell on the floor at his feet. And deep sleep came upon her and Elisha took her up and laid her upon the bed.

Zibiah awoke and saw that Jochebed was upon the bed. She said: "Mistress, you have fallen asleep." Jochebed, still half-dreaming, said: "No, I did not sleep, but for pain I laid me here." Zibiah said: "Where is the pain?" Jochebed answered: "My head, it was my head, but now the pain is gone." Jochebed said this not knowing what she said, and Zibiah believed it.

In due season a child was born to Jochebed and she called it Caleb, for she said: "Let him live without offence." And also she said to Issachar: "See, he has red hair; red is a holy colour and by the holiness of God he was given to us." Yet often she pondered what Elisha had meant when he spoke of mother-right in Egypt and said: "They did not know in those days what even fools know now, that a child is not born to his mother except because of a man."

She wondered: "Is this child then an appearance like those appearances which Moses showed in the desert?" But the child was firm to handle, and healthy, and loved his mother and Issachar. So she was happy and thought no more of it. Yet she longed for Elisha to come: she would show him the child, and the colour of his hair, and Elisha would bless him. Issachar boasted to his friends of the miracle and had great honour from it, for Elisha was beloved by the people and in favour with the King. Yet Issachar did not love the child with a great love and this grieved Jochebed.

One morning early, when the child Caleb was twelve years old, he said to his mother: "Mother, I am tired of playing about the house. Let me go out to the great field where my father is: he is watching the reapers at work." She said: "Go, child," and gave him food and water, and he went out and talked to Issachar; as he talked he ate the food of which his mother had given him overmuch. When he had eaten he lay in the shade of a terebinth tree and slept, and Issachar went again to the reapers. The shadow of the tree moved and the sun shone full upon the child's head. He awoke vomiting, and called his father, who came to him from among the reapers: the day was very hot.

Issachar asked him: "What ails you, child?" He answered: "My head! My head!" Issachar said to a big lad: "Carry him in quickly to his mother." So he was taken in, and Jochebed took him and sat on a chair with the child on her knees, and he complained again of his head, and at noon he breathed no more.

Jochebed did not weep when she saw that the breath was gone from him, but she remembered her childlessness of former days and said bitterly: "Would to God he had never been born, for then I should not now be weeping." Then she grew angry and said: "Elisha has deceived me; this is another of the illusions of magic. He knowingly deceived me and for that reason he has not come to the house since that day. He is a lie-monger, like all the other prophets. Is this a repayment of my hospitality to him?" So she took the child and laid him upon the bed in Elisha's room, for the room had been left always ready for him throughout the thirteen years; then she shut the door and went out.

She went out to Issachar in the cornfield and said: "My husband, let me have an ass saddled and one of your men to run along with me because I intend to see Elisha the Man of God." He said chidingly: "Now, of all the fanciful notions that you women entertain! First it was that you must send young Caleb here to vex us with his chatter, and next it was that he ate greedily and so vomited and I was constrained foolishly to send a lad to carry him home to you. Now you come to me and ask for another reaper to take you out riding on an ass. Tell me, why do you want to see Elisha? He has not been near us these thirteen years. Do you even know where he may be found?"

She said: "He is on Mount Carmel: It is not a long journey and I shall return at once."

Issachar smiled and said: "Dear wife, what can you want of Elisha? This is not a Sabbath nor a new moon. Do you want him to come and tell you stories as he did in your days of childlessness?"

Jochebed did not tell him that the child was dead. She came nearer and kissed him and said: "This is a secret; I beg you not to press me about it now. In good time you shall know."

Issachar said: "Well, take the ass. But do not trouble us again until the harvest is over, for we are behind our time already with this reaping."

She thanked him and went with one of the reapers, who also had charge of the asses. Issachar called out as she went: "See that you do not speed the ass too fast, or it will be the second ass you have killed in pursuit of these fanciful notions." For once in the days before Elisha came she had ridden to consult a wise woman, and a fly had stung the ass and the ass had died. The anger that she had for Issachar at this speech kept her from overmuch grief and it was with dry eyes that she came to Mount Carmel where Elisha was.

When Elisha saw her coming he said to himself: "My sin has found me out, my sin has found me out! Issachar has cast his wife off and she has come to kill me, for knowledge has come to her of my misdeed." But he said aloud to Gehazi, for this was before Gehazi's leprosy came on him: "Here comes that Shunamite at whose house we once lodged. Go and meet her, saying: 'Is all well with you and with your husband?' Then if she does not answer 'All is well' come back quickly, for I fear she means to kill me."

Gehazi ran and asked her: "Is all well with you and with your husband?" She answered: "All is well." So he came back with her. Then she alighted from the ass and came running towards Elisha, but Gehazi ran between them with his staff, for he thought she would kill him with a hidden dagger. But Elisha saw that she had no murder in her eyes, and he said: "Stand aside, Gehazi, my servant."

So the Shunamite caught Elisha about the feet and there wept. Elisha said: "She is vexed with great grief, but I cannot read her thoughts. Jah has hidden this matter from me."

He said to her: "What ails you, wife of Issachar?" and he asked her this knowing that the answer must be to his great hurt, for he could not read her thoughts. When a prophet cannot read the thoughts of woman or man, he is in sin towards that person.

She answered: "Did you not swear when you foretold the birth of my child that you were not deceiving me. Did I not ask: 'Is this an appearance like those appearances which Moses showed in the desert?' And you said: 'No!' "

Elisha said: "Is the child then dead?" She did not answer; to confess the child dead was to set him beyond rescue. This she knew, for Elisha had told her of it; and for that reason she had hidden the child's death from her husband. When Elisha saw that she would not answer, he said in his heart: "Then here at last is punishment for my lust; my life for the life that I engendered." And he was calm with that calm of Moses when he knew that the death foretold by Aaron was upon him.

He said to the woman: "It shall be well with him." Then he said to Gehazi: "Run on, quickly, and if you meet any man do not greet him or make any pause by the way until you come to Shunem. Then lay this staff of mine upon the child, lay it in a line between his mouth and his thighs." And he said to the Shunamite: "Go with my servant, riding upon your ass, lest Issachar meet with Gehazi at the house and ask him: 'What do you here?' " She said: "I will not leave you," for she did not trust him.

Gehazi, girding up his robe, ran forward and did not pause until he had laid the staff on the child, but the child did not move. Gehazi ran back to meet them and said: "The child has not yet awaked." When Elisha heard that, he knew that the breath was out of the child, that he was not in a trance. Now his own life was indeed required of him. He went into the room and shut the door upon Gehazi and Jochebed, and prayed to Jah, saying: "Jah, heal this child."

Then he climbed upon the bed and, taking away the staff, lay upon the child, setting his mouth upon the child's mouth, his eyes against the child's eyes, his hands upon the child's hands. But he could not bring himself to utter the spell.

He got up and laid the staff again upon the child, and walked to and fro in agony, for a sudden dread of death came upon him. Then he heard the Shunamite's voice outside; he saw the child upon the bed and the child's hair red like his own above the whiteness of his face: and in horror he remembered his sin. He prayed to Jah and said: "Between my sin and the birth of this child there was a space of nine months. Now between this miracle which shall be done through me, and my death which is the penalty, grant, I beseech You, that same space of nine months." His eyelid winked at that and he knew that his prayer was answered. So again he lay upon the child as he had done before and spoke the spell. "In Jah's name I redeem your life with my own."

The dead child stirred, his heart knocked against Elisha's. He sat up and sneezed seven times, and opened his eyes.

Then Elisha called Gehazi and said: "Bring the Shunamite in." She came in fearfully and saw her son sitting upon the bed where she had seen him dead. Running, she embraced him and kissed him, and called him loving names, and lifted him up. When she turned to thank Elisha, he was gone.

And after nine months he was dead: his death came in the sixteenth year of the reign of Jehoahaz, the King of Israel, and in the thirty-ninth year of the reign of Joash, the King of Judah.

33 Zedekiah's Rebellion

and Punishment

Laurene Chinn has written two Old Testament novels, *The Unanointed,* in 1959, and *The Voice of the Lord* in 1961. Both are well written, with imaginative characterizations, and something more—vivid depictions of politics and life in the Holy Land in ancient times. *The Voice of the Lord* covers the lifetime of the prophet Jeremiah, when Israel was caught in the center between mighty Egypt and mightier Assyria. Mrs. Chinn tells the story of the siege of Jerusalem and the destruction of the temple through the eyes of Baruch, who was secretary to Jeremiah, and of Baruch's wife, Miriam, a fictional character. Her approach is realistic, but she follows the Bible with care. Her Jeremiah is an aristocrat, intelligent and perceptive rather than a mystic. Focal to the work is the pledge of fealty made by the young Hebrew king Zedekiah to Nebuchadnezzar and the siege which follows the breaking of that pledge.

> *Zedekiah was one and twenty years old when he began to reign, and reigned eleven years in Jerusalem.*
>
> *And he did that which was evil in the sight of the Lord his God, and humbled not himself before Jeremiah the prophet speaking from the mouth of the Lord.*
>
> *And he also rebelled against king Nebuchadnezzar, who had made him swear by God: but he stiffened his neck, and hardened his heart from turning unto the Lord God of Israel.*
>
> II CHRONICLES: XXXVI, 11–13

VOICE OF THE LORD by LAURENE CHINN

JEREMIAH CAME TO the throne room at the hour Nebuchadnezzar had appointed. He found Zedekiah on his knees before the beardless youth who was called Master of the World. They are just lads, both of them, thought Jeremiah.

Zedekiah repeated wearily, "May my eyes be darkened. May my right hand wither. May leprosy rot my flesh. May my seed be cut off from the earth if I forswear my oath of allegiance to the Master of the World."

340

Nebuchadnezzar said harshly, "Ashpenazer! Is it enough?"

The Ethiopian who was Nebuchadnezzar's body servant and also his most intimate counselor appeared from behind the throne. He wore a robe and a great, fluffy turban of brilliant yellow. "My lord, it is enough. The lad has been your friend these many years, bringing the tribute. He is moreover the son of Josiah and the brother of Ahaz, and has more reason to hate Egypt than you yourself."

Nebuchadnezzar said fiercely to Zedekiah, "Remember this then: I do not desire to waste my substance or my troops or my time besieging this city again. You are young, Zedekiah of Judah. If you reign for seventy years, will you still be loyal to me?"

"Aye, my lord." Then, because Zedekiah could not resist the mischievous impulse, "That is, if *you* reign for seventy years more, my lord."

Ashpenazer lifted a spear. "Do not jest with the Master of the World!" Seeing Jeremiah in the entry, the eunuch said, "My lord, this is the diviner for whom you sent, Jeremiah, called prophet by the Jews."

Nebuchadnezzar looked Jeremiah up and down. "Can this youth be trusted to keep a promise?" he asked.

"You take every counselor from him. Who can tell what will happen in a land where nobody remains who is competent to advise the ruler?"

"You are to advise him. This merchant, Baruch, will also advise him."

"Give him Gideon also—the king's secretary. There is not another man in Jerusalem as experienced in government as Gideon, son of Shaphan."

"Ashpenazer, see that Gideon is set free to remain as advisor to this youth who will rule Judah for us."

Zedekiah rose, rubbing his knees as though he had been kneeling for a long time. "Thank you, sire." He seemed shaken by his recent ordeal.

Ashpenazer hustled Zedekiah out. Nebuchadnezzar beckoned Jeremiah closer, and now Jeremiah saw that the Master of the World was not as young as he assumed at first glance. He appeared young because he wore no beard. His brow was high, his nose long, and his mouth seemed crowded between the long nose and the firm, jutting chin. In his eyes was a brilliance which Jeremiah recognized as driving determination plus incisive intelligence. So this, he thought, is the scourge God has sent to chasten His people.

"You are the diviner of Judah," said Nebuchadnezzar. "What! You do not kneel to me?"

"In our nation, sire, prophets do not kneel to any save only God. Tell me, why do men pursue power? The kingdom you build will be dissipated by your sons. What profit is there in shedding the blood of uncounted thousands?"

Nebuchadnezzar exclaimed, "I brought you here to question you, seer of Judah. I will send you away if you prove troublesome."

For two weeks Yokin with his mother and his wives, together with the people who were to go captive with him to Babylon, had been herded together in the Temple court with their bundles and their baggage, drenched, depressed, guarded by Chaldean soldiers. In caves and ravines outside the city, soldiers searched for escapees, while the City of David sheltered the people who were to remain in Jerusalem after the captives departed. The homes in the Zion and Mishne quarters had been taken over to house the victorious army of Babylon.

Nebuchadnezzar said, "I brought with me two diviners. They have scanned the heavens night after night, seeking in vain through the overcast some indication of which day will be most auspicious for the journey of the captives to begin. These captives are gifted and useful, the best of the Jews. I want them to reach Babylon alive. I am impatient to be gone, for I have seen enough of this poor, plain city, which was built with little artifice and no art. You Jews have no talent for architecture."

Jeremiah was astonished to hear his beloved city so described. He waited, while Nebuchadnezzar paced as if he found the council chamber too small.

"One thing only have I seen that I would like to take home," he said. "It is too heavy and too bulky to be carried to Babylon without first being chopped into pieces. That is the copper basin on twelve brazen bulls. The artist who made those bulls was gifted."

"He was Phoenician," said Jeremiah indifferently. He had always hated those bulls, for such figures had no place in the worship of the Lord God. "You are not impressed by our Temple," he remarked.

"We have twenty finer ones in Babylon. Your little temple of plain stone could be set down within the arching vaults of several of ours. Our tower——"

"I have heard about your tower. Is Marduk so hard to find that you must climb up to the sky to reach him?"

Nebuchadnezzar laughed aloud. "The penalty of being Master of the World is only this—I find few men who will dispute with me. I wish you would come to Babylon. No, no, I do not insist. You are free to do anything you like. My diviners have lost their power here in the land where your god rules, and I suppose you would lose your powers of divination in Babylon." He paused in his quick pacing. Coming close to Jeremiah, he said, "You are the diviner who dared predict my success even when your king had an alliance with Egypt." A smile touched the sensitive, pouted mouth. "The scourge your god chose to punish a disobedient people. Now let me explain. Marduk blessed my father, and Marduk has blessed me. My trust is in Marduk. Yet I have found satisfaction in knowing that the gods of other peoples have also marked me for success. How did you reach your conclusions?"

Jeremiah was feeling a little overborne. Kings he had known, but not this masterful, incisive, ruthless variety. You shall stand before kings, came a soft echo within him, and he straightened. "I have had a dream, recurring many times——"

"Ah, a dream." Nebuchadnezzar nodded. "We divine dreams also. We read the pattern formed when oil is dropped on water. We study the entrails of sacrificial animals. We read the stars—our astrologers are kings among diviners, as diviners are kings among priests. But among diviners no method of piercing the dark curtain of the future is so well beloved as the interpretation of dreams. To lie down beside some holy shrine and there to dream—surely the gods are very favorable toward men they guide by means of dreams."

Nebuchadnezzar rubbed his hands together with satisfaction, then wheeled and came very close to Jeremiah. "I will tell you something I have told no one else, holy man. You must not suppose I credit all the mumbo jumbo of Babylonian lore. That is for the credulous, the ignorant. God the creator is one God. Each nation gives to Him its own name, together with attributes it values. Bel-Marduk was a minor divinity, a god of the spring-time, until Babylon became great. Babylon's chosen god became supreme with Babylon's supremacy. Which is to say that we then began to call God the Creator by a name already known to us. And shall I tell you when I came to understand this truth?"

Jeremiah nodded. He had read this theory in the works of various prophets, and it stirred him to hear this youth who commanded armies, destroyed nations, and ruled an empire speak so earnestly on such a subject.

"An agent of Babylon reported to my father that a certain schoolmaster in the palace at Jerusalem was teaching that Babylon was the scourge God would send to punish those who had broken the covenant. I had long known that I was the scourge God would use against Assyria for their savage brutalities, and against Egypt for their worship of death. But when I learned that a diviner in Jerusalem had heard from his God this same message which I had learned from diviners in Babylon, I knew both gods were one God."

Jeremiah would have replied, but Nebuchadnezzar was too preoccupied with his subject to listen.

"You asked why I embarked on conquest. By God's will I do what must be done, for as all gods are one God, so God will make of all the earth one nation. Babylon will rule it, by divine right, since Babylon is the most beautiful city on earth, and no other city has a temple which compares with our tower of towers, which rises into the heavens, the dwelling place of God."

Jeremiah said sternly, "God made you a scourge to chasten the nations. But nothing lasts forever. Another man will arise to chasten Babylon when the cup of God's wrath against the arrogance and evil of Babylon is full."

Nebuchadnezzar smiled. "An honest man. I meet one so rarely. But in this you are wrong, diviner of Judah. I have built a city so strong, with walls so strong, that no invader can ever break through to destroy us."

"What cannot be destroyed by the enemy from without can be destroyed by the worm which bores within," said Jeremiah. "Now I say to you, Master of the World, that if you are bent on taking the cream of Judah captive to Babylon, go quickly, for the people waste away, penned as they are, and the sooner you go the more captives will survive to reach Babylon."

"Good! The diviner of Judah has spoken. Moreover, you said what I wanted to hear. We will leave tomorrow. Ashpenazer! Go to the Temple! Say to the captain that the people are to move out with their baggage today, and form a line along the road. Tonight they will camp beside the road. Tomorrow the march begins."

Miriam waited outside the door until the bolt thudded into place. The girls would be safe alone for the little while she would be away. So apathetic we grow, she thought, leaning in her weakness against the cold stone. And no wonder, fed on this stuff which passes for bread—which is all we can buy with the gold Baruch laid by for such a time. So much gold for so little bread, and that containing as much clay as flour. So apathetic have I been that until today I could not make up my mind to leave the girls alone for longer than it takes to make the daily journey to the street of the bakers.

She raised her face to the spring warmth. Spring remains the same, she thought. Spring brought me courage to undertake an errand not concerned with physical survival, an errand made for love alone. Dear Jeremiah, she thought, you will find me changed. You too will be different, having been for a full year a prisoner. I must prepare my mind for the alteration in you. Baruch, the girls—they change day by day as the siege goes endlessly on, the vicious, savage, senseless siege Jeremiah described in terms I thought exaggerated and impossible.

Miriam came out into the High Street, passing by houses allotted to high army officers or turned into barracks for men serving in the army, men who ate the king's bread. She wore only her oldest homespun. Men murdered to obtain a whole garment of wool. Consequently Miriam never wore a decent coat on the street. She kept her eyes down, kept her homespun mantle wrapped close about her face. She did not want to see the devastation of this city after a year and three months of siege. She was accustomed to what she saw in the lower city when she went daily to the street of bakers—the thinning of the population, as people deserted to the besiegers or died of hunger or disease. The deserters could at least hope to be fed, if they served on the rams. The lucky ones were permitted to farm the land and keep enough of their produce to stay alive.

We were scandalized, she thought, when Jeremiah begged us to go to the farm. He was right—it must be dreadful to be always right. This war should not have been fought, and if we had refused, every one of us, it could not have been fought. Now the city will be destroyed, and those of us who survive famine and pestilence will go captive, and those of us who do not go captive will farm the land, and the city we could not abandon will be dead because we could not see truth when Jeremiah spoke truth, but had to have it hammered in by Nebuzaradan's rams.

All animal life had vanished. During the past winter, small children also had disappeared—at least, if any were left they were never seen in the streets. There were few corpses for the carts any more. Miriam's mind shuddered away from thoughts of horror more dreadful than death. We at least have had gold to buy what passes for bread. Those who have had no gold and who did not eat the king's bread have become animals preying upon one another. Thus the people are destroyed in horrible ways, even before the city is demolished.

She passed through the sheep gate into the Temple court. The sheep pens had long ago been ripped away, their wood and stone needed elsewhere.

When she passed around to the front of the Temple she stood at the steps and looked into the sanctuary and beyond, into the inner shrine.

You let this happen, she told the Presence whose habitation this was. Curse You, she said, but silently, for the court was continually filled with praying people. Praying? Praying for what? Curse You.

With this blasphemy she turned away, unable to endure the unaltered interior of sanctuary and shrine. The city and the people suffered unnamable horrors, yet God's habitation remained unchanged. Still, the blasphemy had not eased the hard core of pain she had carried ever since Bobo . . .

She hurried through the priest gate and south toward the palace. She supposed she would need permission from Zedekiah to visit Jeremiah. She shrank from the prospect of seeing Zedekiah, who had once been dear to her as a younger brother, but who had fumbled his way into these present horrors through sheer ineptitude. Perhaps Jedida would take care of it for her.

Miriam had not seen her mother for a long time. Well, she thought, if she does not want to visit us that is her affair. I only told her not to come at mealtime, since she eats the king's bread and we have not enough for our own needs. She ought never to have forced me to say something so obvious.

Miriam recalled with a stab of unbearable pain the queenly serenity of Jedida. I wanted my daughters to be like her, she remembered. I wanted them to see more of her, because my fretting upset and unsettled them. How far away such considerations seemed. For it had come to this, that Miriam wanted only to keep the girls alive until the siege reached an end. Keren had lost most of her teeth. She would never recover her beauty, whether in Babylon or Anathoth, or wherever they went when their father's house no longer stood, strong and comfortable in the midst of Jerusalem. Ketura's legs were hopelessly crooked. Still, thought Miriam, they live. They live.

She felt the earth shake beneath her feet and heard the nearby crash of the ram against the north wall. Baruch had said that Jews now carried the huge logs, running full tilt down the ramp, fifty or more on each side, gripping the ropes on which the ram rested. So many Jews served the logs that there were now three complete shifts for each ram. These men ate bread from grain raised by other Jews on the good land of Judah. And the Jews upon the walls looked down upon the Jews who bore the battering rams, and hatred for their own people was a poison eating into their will to defend their own city.

Baruch was one of the men who continually shifted stone to reinforce the walls, separating newly cracked blocks from good stone, giving the cracked and broken pieces to the defenders to be used as weapons.

As Miriam came within sight of the palace, she encountered Ebed-melech. He was carrying something wrapped in a napkin. By its smell she knew it was bread of a kind she had not tasted since Pashur stopped paying his men in grain and began giving them loaves to be eaten at work. Death was now the penalty for any man who carried his own bread home to be fed to nonworkers. Miriam's belly knotted at the smell of this bread.

Ebed halted, looking down upon her with gentle compassion. Miriam had not seen her own face, but she had seen the faces of her daughters and knew what he saw. In the palace they had real grain in their bread. Jeremiah, in prison, also ate the king's bread.

Ebed said, "My lady Miriam. Ah, my lady Miriam." Then, having controlled his emotion, he said, "I have not seen any of your household for many months, except Baruch now and then. How do they do?"

"They live. My daughters live. And I. And Baruch, who still eats the king's bread." She spoke with bitterness, though Baruch could do nothing about the situation. If he stopped eating the king's bread, he would become one more mouth to feed with the stuff they bought with gold from the vault.

"Have you come to visit the lady Jedida?"

"I came to get Zedekiah's permission to visit Jeremiah."

"Come with me. I go each day to the prison with a loaf for the prophet. He will take joy in seeing you, my lady. After many months in the prison, he yearns for those he loves."

"I do not need Zedekiah's permission?"

"Come. You will see."

The prison doorkeeper had a withered arm and a stump where one foot had been. How fortunate you are, thought Miriam, to eat the king's bread in return for this trifling service. Then she saw Jeremiah sitting on the cistern rim, and within her something fluttered where she had thought no feeling remained. She ran to him and threw herself down and laid her face in his hands and wept. She had not wept in many months.

She dried her face on her mantle at last and looked up into Jeremiah's face. "They took my little boy, my little Bobo," she said. "One morning when I went for bread he followed me into the street. I heard him scream. I ran. I ran, I ran, but I could not catch them."

"I know, my child."

"How do you know? Nobody knew but me, and I have not spoken of it —not to a single soul."

"Baruch came and told me. That was many months ago. Why did you stay away from me, my daughter? I have watched and waited for you, but you did not come."

Miriam said wonderingly, "Baruch told you? But he did not know! I could not speak of it until today. I told Baruch he sickened suddenly and died, while he was at the wall. I said I buried him at once because—because now that those who do not eat the king's bread, and who have no gold to buy . . . and there are no more animals in the city they can use for food . . ."

"Do not speak of these horrors, my daughter. Baruch knew of it through Keren. She opened the door when she saw that Bobo was gone. She saw and she heard, and she has blamed herself all these months for failing to keep Bobo safe."

Miriam exclaimed, "Why didn't she tell me? She did not speak to me for days after it happened, and I did not speak to her. I thought she was careless, that she had not missed him, or noticed that he was gone. I thought she did not care—about her little brother. Why did she talk to Baruch about it, and not to me?"

Jeremiah sat silent upon the cistern rim. Suddenly Miriam noticed the transparency of the flesh upon his skeleton face. The once heavy, russet beard was white as snow and sparse as the beard of an old, old man. Jeremiah could not sit erect, for one shoulder was drawn down and forward. She took the long, thin hands and laid them against her checks.

"Why does God let these evils come upon us? Especially upon you, dearest teacher? You kept the covenant, all your life. What good is there in doing right, keeping the laws of Moses, serving God, when evils come anyway? Jeremiah, I have learned to—hate God. I cursed God as I came past the Temple."

Ebed had been standing silently by, holding the loaf in its napkin. Now he said softly, "Though He slay me, yet will I trust in Him."

Miriam jerked to her feet. "Though He slay *me*—oh yes, that would be easy. But to slay my children, and deform and disfigure them, while I am helpless to prevent—" She stopped. "Bobo did not live long enough to do evil."

She looked up into the dark compassionate face of Ebed and remembered that his children had been slain unborn. She knelt again and gripped Jeremiah's hands. "Tell me *why!*"

He answered softly, "Long ago I shouted my challenge to God, when Ahaz went into exile in Egypt. Why do the wicked prosper? Why do the righteous suffer?" He rose, and Miriam rose with him, still clinging to the bony hands. Jeremiah looked into her face with deep tenderness. "I can only give you the answer which satisfied me, my child. I hope it will have some meaning for you.

"God made us in a wondrous image, which seems to us so good that we have called it God's image. God endowed us with wondrous gifts—intelligence, affection, appreciation, curiosity. God set us in a world which might well be called an Eden. But this was not enough. Because it was not enough, God gave us the power to choose. 'See, I have set before you life and death, good and evil, blessing and curse.' If we could not choose evil, we would not be able to choose good. There would be no such thing as nobility, righteousness, honor.

"We can choose evil. And evil brings pain and terror and anguish and death. But evil comes not only upon those who make the choice; for no man is wholly self-sufficient, but all of us depend upon one another. Zedekiah and Pashur made choices whose results have extended on and on. War came, and we who chose to remain in Jerusalem, out of love for Judah and our own dear city—we suffer with them for the evils resulting from their evil choice.

"Submit to pain, Miriam. Submit to loss and grief. Accept, knowing that God loves this people even now, and never more than in this extremity of our suffering.

" 'Is Ephraim my dear son?
Is he my darling child?

For as often as I speak against him
I remember him still . . .' says the Lord."

Miriam murmured, "As I loved and pitied Bobo, so God loves Judah. Oh, Jeremiah, that is very hard to believe. I could never stand by and do nothing while my children suffered."

"Every child who learns to walk risks walking into danger, as Bobo did. Yet we rejoice when an infant begins to walk. No mother would maim her child to keep him safe by the fire in his own court. Nor will God maim us, taking away the power of choice which lifts us above the level of the angels. God looked upon His work, and it was good. It was good. It *is* good. And God is good, though kingdoms rise and fall. You have seen the worst that men can do. Yet these things will pass away, but God's love is eternal. Believe this, Miriam. God's love will not pass away."

Shortly before sundown the wall was breached. To aid the defenders, priests had laid great torchfires in the capitals of Jachin and Boaz, and on the north wall of the court torches waited, ready to be set afire and held aloft by old men and women to brighten the scene.

Again and again during the day stones from catapults had landed in the threatened area. Whenever this occurred, the wounded and the dead were removed and others crowded to replace them. Stripped to their loincloths, they were a scarecrow lot. Their movements were slow and listless, the movements of men already defeated by hunger. Aware that they could not win against the well-fed thousands beyond the wall, they were yet stirred by the mysterious courage which keeps men struggling on after they know the battle is lost.

Ebed prowled about the Temple roof all through the afternoon. From there he saw people on housetops, Baruch with his family among others, waiting for the wall to yield to the many months of pounding, waiting for the climax which would end the interminable siege.

"I have never entered your Temple until today," Ebed told Jeremiah. "To me it has seemed very strange that a eunuch is forbidden by your law to come here to worship the Lord God, though on midsummer night eunuch priests come into the court to serve Astarte."

The first warning that the breach had been made came with the screams of those in line with the moving rock, men caught and crushed. Soldiers were crowded so thickly about the area that people on walls and roofs could see nothing though they heard the spine-chilling screams.

Then began the slow toppling of stone, with battlements falling outward to crash down upon the roof above the ramp. This was followed by the outward pitch of more and more blocks from the upper wall, while beneath the blocks that fell, other stone was settling. The avalanche of these great rocks upon the structure crushed it, catching men who had delayed too long in getting away from inevitable destruction, perhaps because they were befuddled into thinking the ram must be drawn back in the routine way. The destruction of these victims too was heard but not seen.

From the Temple roof scores were watching as the first formation of Chaldeans ran forward to clamber up over the tumble of massive blocks of stone. Their shields formed a wall before them and they bristled with spears. On the wall west of the muster gate, the famished army of Jerusalem stood, armed with lances, with arrows, with stones, while the targets they had so long awaited came jogging toward them in solid formation.

Suddenly a score of chariots came swinging around to the right of the advancing army, speeding toward this section of the wall. The chariots were crammed with archers. They thundered forward, two abreast, and as each chariot let fly a stream of arrows, it swung around to the right and away, while the chariots behind came pelting forward. As fast as Jews fell from the walls, other scarecrows in loincloths scrambled up the piled stones to replace them.

Now the foremost Chaldean foot soldiers reached the breach and began the difficult labor of clambering over the massive blocks while fully armed, and attempting at the same time to protect themselves from the rain of stones, arrows, and lances from the wall above and from soldiers who waited beyond the breach. As those who went first fell, their bodies smoothed the path for soldiers who followed.

From the Temple roof, Jeremiah and Ebed and many others watched the epic of courage which began at dusk and continued by torchlight, the unequal struggle of the naked, scarecrow bodies of starved men who matched their weakness against the thick, vigorous bodies of the invaders. Many fell, and many more, but the tide of the invaders welled into the breach in wave after wave while the ranks of the defenders thinned.

The first objective of Chaldeans who got past the defenders was to reach and open the Ephraim gate. It happened all too soon. Those on houses and walls saw what the defenders at the breach could not see, for the river of advancing soldiers had found a new channel, and came pouring through the gate and down the street to attack the defenders from the rear. After that the battle for the breach ended quickly; those few defenders who remained, though they raised their weapons above their heads in token of surrender, were slaughtered where they stood.

Before the end of the second watch the chariots of Nebuzaradan and his chief officers had whirled in through the Ephraim gate, down Wall Street to where it was clogged with bodies and stones. Dismounting, Nebuzaradan entered through the Astarte gate into the court. Standing upon the Temple platform, he cupped his hands and shouted, "Bring me the diviner called Jeremiah!"

On the fifth day, as midday was ending, Jeremiah sat with Jedida near the golden gate, where Nebuzaradan with Gideon still gave judgment, since every day more people, and more, were brought into Jerusalem by the Chaldean patrols. They heard a stir of excitement along the street where people were lined up awaiting judgment. "The king! They have taken the king!" The news ran like fire down the line, leaping from person to person.

Jedida covered her face and rocked with grief. "Poor lad, poor Zedekiah." Hamital came hurrying, and Jedida rose and they stood together, waiting for Zedekiah to appear. Within the court the murmur passed along and necks craned for a view of this new captive.

Presently Zedekiah appeared, and with him Pashur. Each carried a small child in his manacled hands. Behind them stood the two young queens, faces swollen with weeping and blistered by the sun.

The captain who had them in charge passed across to Nebuzaradan half a score or more sacks of gold which he had taken from the prisoners. There were also some small bags containing jewels. "These they carried instead of water bottles or spare sandals," the captain remarked to Nebuzaradan with a contemptuous smile.

Jeremiah looked upon Zedekiah with his infant son in his arms, but could see only a little lad with no aptitude for scholarship, who often brawled in the schoolroom with the lad Seri.

Pashur had not been taken easily. Dirt and blood and wisps of his homespun coat obscured much, but his right shoulder was cut deep, and his right arm was bound tightly against his body, useless. The child he held was supported by his left arm, and slept with its face buried in Pashur's wild beard. The old scar was obliterated by dirt and blood. Remembering how Pashur doted on cleanliness, Jeremiah knew that his longing to bathe must have added its peculiar anguish to this hour.

Upon Zedekiah were only minor wounds, but his dazed and despairing expression and his tight grip on his son betrayed his emotions.

The guards cleared a space so the two men could stand alone before Nebuzaradan. Even the two queens were drawn back amongst other prisoners. It was then that Jeremiah noticed that Tavi was wearing sandals which must have belonged to Pashur. She seemed preoccupied with trying to make her bedraggled skirts cover the ungainly objects.

Nebuzaradan spoke clearly and sternly. "Zedekiah, you were set upon your throne by the Master of the World. You knelt before him and swore an oath to be his loyal servant, faithful to him as long as you lived. 'May my tongue be cut out, may my eyes be darkened, may my right hand wither, may my seed be cut off from the earth and my memory blotted out, if I forswear my oath.' Tell me, Zedekiah, what ought to be done with a man who forswears such an oath?"

Zedekiah stood silent, eyes fixed on Nebuzaradan as a child might look into the face of an angry father.

"Pashur, son of Immer," said Nebuzaradan, "you also bound yourself by an oath while you were in Babylon. 'I swear by my life,' you said. 'I swear by my God, the God of my fathers.' "

Pashur was swaying with pain and exhaustion. He looked past the officer, making no reply. Suddenly his eyes caught Jeremiah's and a spasm crossed the wounded face.

"You make no defense?"

Pashur made no sound. Zedekiah looked upon Jeremiah and seemed to draw strength from him. He straightened. "I am your prisoner," he said.

"Your punishment was determined by the Master of the World. Now I will stand in your Temple door while I pronounce sentence upon you."

Zedekiah turned to give the child in his arms to Tavi, but Nebuzaradan said, "Bring your sons also into the place of judgment, Zedekiah of Judah."

Nebuzaradan arose and crossed the court, and the crowding people moved back before the soldiers of Babylon, opening a path from the golden gate to the door of the sanctuary. Prodded by soldiers, Zedekiah and Pashur followed Nebuzaradan. Jeremiah walked beside the captive king.

Zedekiah murmured brokenly, "What will he do to my boys, teacher?"

"You are a man, Zedekiah. You know what will be done."

Pashur spoke for the first time. His voice was harsh, but to Jeremiah it seemed the harshness of exhaustion rather than hatred. "How did you know Egypt would lose and Babylon win? How did you *know?*"

"Pashur, the contest between us is over, and we have both lost, and all Judah has lost."

The dark eyes were fixed on Jeremiah without hatred for the first time since they were boys in Anathoth. "Can it be that you were a true prophet all along?"

"Does it matter to you now?"

"I have spent my life fighting in a bad cause. Certainly it matters."

Zedekiah burst out, "If I had listened to you, teacher, instead of—" He paused. "You are right. A king lives by the decisions he makes. He must not blame others if he chooses to heed the wrong advice. My father chose you to be my mentor when I was very young. I turned from the path on which my father set my feet."

"Cease dwelling upon what is finished. Set your thoughts upon the Lord your God, who loved you and sought to draw you to Himself from the day you were born."

"Silence!" roared the officer who had them in charge. "Hear the sentence which is to be pronounced upon you."

Nebuzaradan stood upon the Temple platform. "If you find the sentences stern, let it be remembered by all men here present that the Master of the World does not seek vengeance, but to warn all who serve him that he will render kindness for kindness, but for betrayal no punishment is too severe. Let the sentences he has pronounced against the renegade king of Judah and the renegade commander of Judah's armies—both offices held by Nebuchadnezzar's appointment—remind all who dwell where the banner of Babylon has been planted that the Master of the World intends that his subjects shall serve him and make no alliances with his enemies.

"Pashur, son of Immer, by your life and by your god you vowed loyalty to Nebuchadnezzar. As you swore so shall you be punished. You will die upon the altar of your god, and your carcass will be left within the sanctuary of your god."

A muted cry went up from all over the court.

"Zedekiah, son of Josiah, king of Judah," continued Nebuzaradan, "you swore by many things to be faithful to the Master of the World. He does not take from you all that you swore by. He takes only your seed and your sight."

The outcry was not quelled until soldiers with whips appeared among the people. Then a burly Chaldean seized the infant Pashur held and dashed out its brains against the altar's ramp.

In the horrified silence the older boy suddenly wakened. Clasping his arms tightly about Zedekiah's neck, little Josiah began to wail. The Chaldean tore him from his father's arms and killed him in mid-scream. Now indeed the people could no longer be silenced, for all over the court rose sounds of lamentation.

Above all other sounds came Zedekiah's cry, "Kill me also!"

The executioner threw Pashur down upon the ancient altar which had once been a threshing floor. With an ax he severed his head from his body, and his blood flowed into the channels made for the blood of sacrifices in the reign of King David.

Zedekiah broke from the soldiers who held him and ran up the steps to kneel upon the platform before Nebuzaradan. "Kill me also!"

Jeremiah knelt beside Zedekiah and took the manacled hands in his. "Your people need your courage, my son. You are the last king of Judah. One gift remains which you can give your people, your courage."

Nebuzaradan took a spear, tested the point and found it sharp. "Look upon me, Zedekiah," he commanded.

Zedekiah raised his face. Then Nebuzaradan put out his eyes with a touch, first the right eye, then the left. And when it was done, Jedida came with Hamital, and led him away.

34 Queen Esther and Haman's Plot

The year before Norah Lofts published her *Esther*, she wrote in another slight and intriguing book called *Women In the Old Testament*, that "It is impossible to read the Book of Esther and avoid the thought that here is one of the most perfect historical novels in the world. Few stories are so rich in romance and drama, so full of colour and movement and tension. Against an exotic and voluptuous background the vital and comprehensible characters shape the story; and that story includes love—on the 'Cophetua and the Beggar Maid' theme—intrigue, revenge and hatred—and even holds within its scope the foreshadowing of events which were to stir the story of nations, for in the Book of Esther we see the beginning of anti-Semitism, of the ghettoes and pogroms of a later day." With this insight she wrote her novel, never varying from the original in any detail and utilizing every detail with sensitivity and understanding. Part of the reason for her success may be that not only is Mrs. Lofts an exceptionally skilled writer, but she also has respect for her subject. She writes that "The Bible stories were the first I ever heard; I learned to read from a Bible."

After these things, when the wrath of king Ahasuerus was appeased, he remembered Vashti, and what she had done, and what was decreed against her.

Then said the king's servants that ministered unto him, Let there be fair young virgins sought for the king:

And let the king appoint officers in all the provinces of his kingdom, that they may gather together all the fair young virgins unto Shushan the palace, to the house of the women, unto the custody of Hege the king's chamberlain, keeper of the women; and let their things for purification be given them:

And let the maiden which pleaseth the king be queen instead of Vashti, And the thing pleased the king; and he did so.

ESTHER: II, 1–4

ESTHER by NORAH LOFTS

IN THIS SMALL AND HUMBLE HOUSE, overgrown and yet in a measure supported by the ancient vine which covered it, lived the old Jew whom Artaxerxes had casually mentioned to Vashti—he who had burst into tears and rent his clothes at the sight of Jehovah's sacred vessels being used as kitchenware. With him lived his niece, the daughter of his younger brother, an orphan whom he had brought up to the age of fifteen years. They were very happy together because they were very much alike. Their neighbours regarded them as oddities. Mordecai was a scholar; in the old days, in their own city of Jerusalem he would have been honoured and revered, lifted high above the common rut of men; even here, in this place where the Jews were merely people conquered by the people whom the Persians in turn had conquered, he could have made a comfortable place for himself had he been so minded. A good number of the cleverer Jews had succeeded in finding places for themselves as scribes, or accountants or stewards. Mordecai took no trouble at all; unlike most scholars he was clever with his hands and did not despise manual labour. He would work as carpenter, bricklayer, potter or cobbler, doing whatever job offered itself. He would write or read letters for the illiterate, taking payment, generally in kind, if he thought his client could afford it. He would work out, with great diligence, the family tree of any Jew who feared that, in the captivity, his pedigree might be lost and his chance of fore-fathering the promised Messiah be obscured; he would explain any point of law or correct procedure to those who were in danger of forgetting. He was, naturally, very poor. Occasionally, when jobs were scarce and hunger threatened the household, Esther, who shared his manual ability, would engage herself to some wealthy household as seamstress or embroiderer, or in a humbler sphere, do the baking, housekeeping, baby-tending for a woman temporarily indisposed.

They kept themselves alive and that was all, but in all Shushan there was no couple less concerned with material wellbeing than Mordecai and Esther; and when, as sometimes happened, there was food in the house for two days ahead they would both settle down happily to read and study and feel themselves completely independent of the world. Motherly women had, at various times during the last year, ventured to remind Mordecai that he had a duty to his niece—she should soon be betrothed to some orthodox Jew; and it was time, they said, tactfully, that she had some other clothes than the simple, much mended, snuff-coloured garment which she wore in cold weather, or the equally old white linen robe which was her summer wear. They said that she would ruin her eyes and round her shoulders with reading. Mordecai, who had great innocence in worldly matters, was a little troubled by these admonitions and sometimes felt guilty because he had reared this girl, Esther, exactly as he would have reared a boy. But when he reported such a con-

versation to Esther she only laughed; and very soon Mordecai forgot so
trivial a matter and their happy life continued smoothly. The house was very
clean, for Esther had a curious fastidiousness in some matters; but it was
very untidy, littered with scrolls and the tools of their various trades and an
assortment of treasures which Mordecai, as a trusted man, had taken into his
keeping for other Jews who had never succeeded in finding a settled home in
Persia, and quite a few heirlooms awaiting the arrival of some known, but un-
located heir, lost in the Dispersion.

To this house Mordecai returned on the mid-day after Artaxerxes' decree
had been posted in the market place at Shushan. It was a very hot morning
and for a moment after his arrival Esther wondered whether he was suffering
from a touch of sunstroke. There was a curious, suppressed excitement about
him and as soon as he entered the shady house he led her to the window and
said, "Esther, let me look at you." Holding her by the shoulders he stared
into her face and then stepped back, considering her as a whole until Esther
felt her face redden and her whole pose stiffen into awkwardness. Then he
turned away, as though deeply satisfied and, dropping down to the bench
near the door, said, "Esther, I believe we have a chance!"

"Of what, Uncle?"

"Of gaining a powerful representative of our race at court."

"You?" she asked, delight in her voice. Perhaps his qualities as an
historian and scribe had been recognised at last.

"Not I, my dear. You!"

That confirmed her worst fears. "You have been smitten by the sun,"
she said; and hastened away to get a wet rag for his head. She knew how he
would stand at any corner to give advice or argue a point.

Mordecai accepted the rag gratefully, though with scorn.

"My head can do with cooling," he admitted, "though it is not the sun
that has set it awhirl. It is the notice in the marketplace. . . ."

"He isn't . . . sending us . . . home?" Esther asked breathlessly voicing
the dearest, the foremost hope of every Jew in Persia.

"Not yet. Though even that . . . even that might result."

"Oh, what are you talking about?" she asked impatiently. These broken,
hesitating, inconclusive sentences were so unlike his usual concise and
scholarly way of talking.

Briefly he told her.

"It is the sun—or else you are out of your mind," she said. "I'm pretty
enough; but all the loveliest, all the really beautiful women in the Empire will
be displaying themselves and how should I compare? Besides I wouldn't
dream of doing anything so silly. He must be crazy to think of such a way of
choosing a wife. As bad as a blind auction!"

"Eliezer, sent out to choose a wife for our forefather, Isaac, selected
Rebekah by equally blind chance," said Mordecai, solemnly. "One must, you
know, my dear, make a *little* allowance for the hand and the will of God!"

"Take then the most fantastic view, Uncle, and imagine that out of all this horde of women I should be the one chosen. How would *that* work in with the will of God? Who would be benefited, except possibly, me?"

"Our whole race, my child." The old man brooded deeply for a moment. "*If* you were chosen . . . I am not suggesting that any immediate difference would be felt or seen; influence grows slowly. But the influence which a good, loyal, attractive wife can wield is in the end practically infinite. If you could marry Artaxerxes, Esther, we Jews should always have, in the very heart of Persia, a most powerful ambassador. Not an agent, not an agitator, I am not thinking of that, but a voice to speak the right word at the right time. There are stormy times ahead for us, you know. With every day that passes and that sees us adhering to our own old faith, our own old customs, we grow more unpopular. We are an unassimilable people. And that which cannot be absorbed is always hated. The time is coming when a friend at court will be badly needed."

"And before that time comes," Esther said calmly, "God will provide it without help from me, Uncle. *He* knows that I have no desire to marry any-one. I want to stay here with you and lead this life which suits us both; and if, when you are gathered to your fathers the idea of getting married does arise in my mind I shall choose a man of my own race and of my own kind, a scholarly man. In fact, a man as like you as possible! There, doesn't that flatter you?"

"On the contrary, it distresses me beyond measure. It shows me how right Martha was when she said I was rearing you badly. *You* don't want to get married, *you* want to stay here, *you* will choose when you should marry and whom. Esther, that is no way for a well-bred Jewess to talk."

"I am sorry to have distressed you," Esther said, with conventional politeness. "It may be your fault for having reared me to respect the truth. And I might well retort that you have distressed me too. You speak of us Jews being unassimilable—and is it not a fact that that is largely due to our avoidance of mixed marriages. Since our race began Jew has married Jew; and if you are honest you will admit that had any man of another race asked for my hand you would have been the first to object and express repugnance."

"That is true, Esther. But there are times when the law is superseded by the direct will of God. It is against the law to kill one's child—yet Abraham was prepared to slay Isaac in obedience to God's command. It is forbidden to sell one's brother into slavery—yet the slavery of Joseph was the means of preserving all our people."

"Doing ill that good may come of it. That is a dangerous doctrine, Uncle. For the ill can be seen, here and now, the good remains hidden. And how can a simple person distinguish between the ill that is mere ill and the ill which brings forth good?"

"There is one safe rule," Mordecai said gravely. "And that is to obey one's elders." That sentence was so unlike him that she looked up quickly to see whether he were really teasing her; but there was no twinkle in his eye at all.

"You mean," she said, slowly, "that it is my duty to obey you in this and enter myself for this undignified . . . beauty competition? That is what it is. Vulgar, undignified . . . a cock fight!"

"Our father Jacob was vulgar and undignified when he cheated Laban over the spotted lambs, Esther; but he thereby laid the foundation of all the herds of Israel. You will excuse me for saying this, I trust, but the minds of women are limited and apt to be over-literal—and yours shares the fault of your sex."

"Oh," said Esther and closed her mouth against the sharp retort that rose. In one half hour she had been told, for the first time in her life that blind obedience to one's elder was a duty; and that women had inferior minds. She went away to think these things over.

It was some little time before the subject was mentioned again. The old happy life flowed on and Esther had begun to hope that Mordecai had either forgotten, or changed his mind. And then one evening as they sat at their simple supper of bread, milk and ripe fruit, her uncle said abruptly, "Esther, tomorrow is the day when the first tests for this part of the city take place. I need hardly tell you, need I, that there is nothing further from my thought than the desire to force my will on you. You should know by now that I value your love above all things and that you are the very heart of my heart and have been since, long ago, you came into my care. I do not wish to force you to enter this contest, or to enter it unwillingly, but I wish most fervently that you would do so, for the sake of your own people, and to please me."

"You make it very difficult for me to refuse without seeming ungrateful, disobedient, disloyal and churlish," Esther said. "I wish you would answer me one question, honestly."

"I have always endeavoured to answer all your questions—honestly," said Mordecai, remembering some most awkward ones she had asked him in the past.

"If I refused, Uncle, would you compel me?"

Mordecai stared at her gravely for a moment and then said:

"Yes. With regret, Esther; but in the conviction that I was acting rightly."

"I am glad to know that," she said. "Because that takes the decision out of my hands. If I agree, I go, and if I refuse, I go. Very well, then, I go. And after tomorrow it will be in other hands than yours and mine—the decision, I mean."

"It is always in other hands. God's hands, my dear. Tomorrow two of the palace officials appointed to the office will stand in the covered part of the Corn Market—which has been transformed, by the way, into a place of palatial splendour—and they will select those virgins they think fit for the King's inspection. But they are only instruments. Jehovah knows at this moment upon whom the final choice will fall."

"That, in general, is a profound and very disturbing thought," Esther said. "But at the moment it is comforting. It means that I need do nothing."

"What nonsense," Mordecai said. "The will of God is above us, but it works *through* us. In every trade there are good tools and bad tools; the bad are discarded, the good are cherished. And it lies within our choice to be good tools or bad."

"Then the judges tomorrow will be tools of a sort; how can they be good or bad?"

"By judging fairly or unfairly. Suppose, for the sake of argument, one of them favoured a candidate who was obviously unworthy; he might advance her claims; he would thus be acting against his orders, against his better judgment, against the will of God. He would thus be a bad tool and finally he would be discarded. It is all very simple."

"Then tomorrow I put on my best white robe—having washed myself thoroughly—smooth out what Martha calls my scholar's scowl and straighten my shoulders and then I shall be a good tool. Is that so?"

"Precisely," Mordecai said, with relief and pleasure in his voice. "And now since you have decided to take this sensible view I will tell you something that I have heard today in the city. Something that has a connection with the first conversation we ever held on this subject. There is a young man called Haman; he is the son of Hammdatha, an Amalekite—you know what that means for *us*—the bitterest enemy in the world. He entered the King's service as a menial, but he attracted notice and courted favour and for some little time now has been granted special treatment. Lately a few well-born courtiers ventured to—well, one doesn't *complain* exactly to the Lord of Persia—but they pointed out that the situation was slightly irregular; and yesterday Arta-xerxes answered them by making him a noble. He is now Lord of the Western Gate, is entitled to wear scarlet and fur, and draws revenue from all the area between the city boundary and the brickyard; and he will go further. He is—naturally, for he was so born—a confirmed Jew-hater and I tell you frankly, my child, that were it not for the hope and trust which I repose in *you,* I should have the very gloomiest thoughts about our future as a race."

Esther was silent for a moment. Then she leaned across the table and said seriously, "Uncle Mordecai, I do love you and I do respect you and I am grateful to you for all you have done for me . . . but I must say this. You set too high a value on me. You don't know anything about women; you've never been married; you've never had any dealings with any woman except old Martha and me. You don't *know* how lovely, how dazzlingly beautiful women can be. Tomorrow we shall go to the Corn Market and you will see. You'll see women who could murder their mothers and fathers, their husbands and fifteen children—and have the sympathy of every man who looked on them, because of their beauty. I'm saying this because I don't want you to be disappointed tomorrow when I come home, rejected."

"But Esther, you are very beautiful. Lately I have thought that God gave you this beauty that it might be used, *now.*"

"Uncle Mordecai, I am not *beautiful.* I am merely pretty. My hair is nice; and I have the eyes you say Hadassah, my grandmother had, which do make rather a startling contrast to the black hair; but my top lip is too short and my lower one too full and my nose isn't absolutely straight. But there, you will see tomorrow . . ."

"I shall see," Mordecai said. "So long as you present yourself in good will I am content to leave the rest to God."

"And so am I," said Esther, falling back on the thought that if Jehovah had really intended to make her Queen of Persia He would have devised some method a little more certain than this. If the test had been one for scholarship she would have been more confident of her chances—and more frightened lest she should pass. As it was, though she dutifully washed and then oiled her long black hair and made a few other innocent little preparations, she faced the morrow's ordeal in a spirit of lighthearted cynicism. There would be so many more beautiful women. . . .

Mordecai and Esther walked to the Corn Market at ten o'clock the next morning. It was a hot and rather breathless day and Esther let her veil fall loosely. Before they had left the Street of Camels where their little house stood they could see, in the bigger street beyond, an unwonted amount of traffic; litters and palanquins, mules, donkeys and horses and camels were carrying girls and their attendants towards the Corn Market. The air was thick and yellow with stirred-up dust. Mordecai paused in his stride and said:

"I should have thought of that. I should have hired a litter. Go you back, Esther, and wait and I will run and ask Joab for the litter in which his mother-in-law goes to the synagogue. If I carry one end and he the other he can hardly charge me more than three copper pieces."

"You would waste your errand," said Esther. "Miriam, the baker's daughter, bespoke that litter a fortnight ago."

"You should have thought of it yourself," said Mordecai, a little irritably. "You should have known that it was essential to arrive looking fresh and unfatigued." The peevishness in his voice betrayed to Esther the importance he attached to this excursion. He began to walk on again. "At least," he said, "draw your veil closer. . . . Your hair looked so beautiful, it would be a pity if the dust dulled it."

Oh dear, Esther thought, obediently drawing the veil closer, he is going to be so miserable, so disappointed, so downcast, when we walk home again; blame me for not thinking of the litter; blame himself. . . .

They reached the Corn Market where the candidates for the first test were ushered into a great waiting room where there was every convenience for the repair of beauty; scented water in porcelain bowls, soft towels, silver mirrors, brushes, cosmetics, pins. Outside this door Mordecai was halted and bidden wait, and Esther, entering the place alone, realised that she was the only girl unaccompanied by a female relative. Many had three. Every woman seemed to be excited, arranging a gown's fold, pinning in a flower, adjusting a jewel, arranging a curl. "Smile, Nana, do remember to smile, your teeth are your best feature," one woman was whispering, over and over again. "Your gown is creased; I *told* your father to bring Chinese silk. Oh dear, oh dear, the fool said the clothes did not matter. He's ruined us. . . ." "Darling I am not quite sure about that rose . . . it is brighter than your lips and that is bad. Let me pin it here, lower down. There, now it does not detract. . . ."

Gabble, gabble, gabble, Esther thought, waiting her turn at the mirror and when it came leaning close to see if the dust *had* dulled her hair. It hadn't and, with hands which seemed cold and clumsy suddenly, she threw the veil back into its original position and stood aside. She remembered a sentence in a book by an obscure philosopher called Baalas, "The trouble with women is that their minds are so easily distracted from great matters to trivialities. And yet why should I say 'trouble' since this attention to small things does in great measure contribute to man's comfort?" Well, she thought, probably all this attention to detail will, in the end, contribute to Artaxerxes' comfort. But there was no other detail to which she could attend; so she left the place of preparation and went out and stood quietly by Mordecai who at least did not now admonish or advise her and waited until her name was called.

The ordeal, when it came was horribly like being exposed in the Slave Market. (They should have held the contest there, Esther thought, irrelevantly.) Two men, with bored expressions asked her to open her mouth and studied her teeth; looked at her hands, paying attention to her nails. They came close, as Mordecai had done, and studied her face and then moved away, as he had done, and looked at her figure. Loathing it all, but patient, she turned this way and that, walked, stood, as they directed and was finally handed a little red seal of stamped wax attached to a piece of purple ribbon. She said, "Thank you," as she said it when Elias the fishmonger handed her the piece of salt fish for which she had bargained and then, dismissed, went through another door and into a corridor where to her relief she found her uncle waiting.

"They gave me this," she said, holding out the little seal, unaware of its significance.

"God be praised," said Mordecai. He saw the lack of understanding on her face and added, "It is the sign of the chosen. It means, my dear child, that I must leave you here. You will be taken up to the palace and wait your turn with the other chosen for the King to approve of you."

Three evenings after he had decided upon his plan, after three days of waiting an apt opportunity, Haman was supping with the King and everything was going merrily when a dish of artichokes was set on the table, each a little green island floating in a yellow sea of spiced and melted butter. They were the first of the season and the King set to with a will. But Haman's appetite and his spirit seemed to have suffered a decline. He left his artichokes untasted and sat looking thoughtfully.

"Don't you like the dish?" asked Artaxerxes, plunging his buttery fingers into the rose-scented water and wiping them on the fringed napkin.

"Who? Me?" Haman asked, using one of his deliberately endearing little tricks of speech. There was no one else at the table.

"Yes, you. What's the matter with you?"

"An association of ideas. Jerusalem artichokes they call these. Jerusalem set me thinking about the Jews and that took away my appetite."

He pushed the plate from him, set his elbows on the table and his chin in his hands and so sat, looking very solemn indeed.

"They had the most magnificent funeral today," Artaxerxes said, conversationally, helping himself to what artichokes remained in the dish. "I watched it for half an hour. They are very peculiar people."

"I suppose one could call the odour of an open sewer *peculiar* if one strained tolerance to the point of insanity. But dangerous is a better word to use."

"Haman, Haman, we are supping," cried Artaxerxes. "I've noticed before that you are a little—shall we say prejudiced—against Jews. But surely that is no reason for losing your appetite and then trying to spoil mine by talking about open sewers."

Haman did not alter by the movement of a muscle the glowering expression of his face; but he directed his brooding stare at the King and said:

"You like my company because I make you laugh; and you have done me signal honour for which I am most abjectly grateful. But I can't go on playing the fool forever. I can laugh and joke, but I can also see as far into a brick wall as the next man, and at the risk of incurring your displeasure I am now asking your permission to speak seriously on one of the subjects that seems to me worth being serious about."

He had gained his first point, which was to arouse Artaxerxes' interest and curiosity.

"My dear Haman, since when had you been obliged to ask permission to speak on any subject?"

"Since the Jews were mentioned," Haman said. "They happen to be a subject concerning which your good sense fails you. You're like that unfortunate Lady of Tyremis who was given a lion cub for a pet and never noticed how much it had grown until one day it ate her for its noonday snack. Don't you remember the poem about it:

> She said it loved her. And in fact the old sinner
> Said, "I do love a lady between breakfast and dinner!"

"My dear Haman," Artaxerxes said again, "what are you talking about? Remember I'm just a plain man; all this talk of open sewers and brick walls and lion cubs and poems is confusing my mind. Are you trying to be very tactful and tell me some bad news?"

"You could call it that," said Haman, deciding to come to the point. "You would agree, wouldn't you, that in a scattered, loosely knit mixture of nationalities such as compose your Empire, the most essential thing is to impose some sort of unity and overhead loyalty?"

"And isn't that done? Isn't every decree I issue carried into every one of the provinces as fast as a horse can gallop, and posted there and obeyed as though it were Shushan itself."

"To the outward eye. It might surprise you to know that no Jew pays your rules more than lip-service; that you have in every part of your Empire a group of people who hate and despise you and will go on doing so until they have brought you down. If you think they are a humble, harmless subject people you are at liberty of course to go on thinking that. But you think wrongly. Many are poor and engaged in humble trades, but many more are bankers, and pawnbrokers and money-lenders; they hold a far greater proportion of the wealth in the kingdom than any other single group, and far more than their numbers justify. And at any given moment they are likely to band together and say, 'Who is this Artaxerxes, merely a man? We Jews obey only Jehovah.' Jehovah is the name of their outlandish God and He speaks direct to men, called prophets, who of course can tell the people that He has told them just what they want the people to believe. They do hold entertaining funerals . . . but they're very dangerous and they have been responsible for at least one immensely important funeral." He paused dramatically.

"And that was?"

"The funeral of their own Kingdom. David and Solomon had set that on firm and apparently unshakable foundations; nobody outside could have touched it if the Jews could have been loyal to their own King; but they couldn't; Solomon's son wasn't Jehovah-fearing enough for them, so they split up and made two silly little states, quite easily overcome; and even when they were fighting for their lives their prophets were foretelling disaster because the petty kings under whom they were fighting weren't holy enough. A people who can't obey even their own Kings can't very well be expected to obey anybody else's. And to me it is an ominous sign that in almost every country which we have conquered lately, the Jews had previously been favoured and protected and in some cases shown honour."

"That was very true of Babylon," said Artaxerxes, thoughtfully, when Haman, who had been speaking vehemently, paused for breath.

"I am anxious that it shouldn't be true of Persia," Haman said. "I may be alone of your counsellors to hold this opinion; but they are the worm in the bud, the thorn in the foot, the loose nail in the horseshoe that brings the whole thing down."

"I never regarded them of the slightest importance," said Artaxerxes.

"They count on that. Who cares or notices that they won't eat any save their own specially prepared food; that they won't give even lip service to the gods of the country in which they live; that they won't marry a person of another race; that on feast days their shops are open, but always closed on the Sabbath as they call it. They have preserved themselves, an alien and potentially dangerous group in our very midst . . . and you think they have entertaining funerals."

"I will issue orders," said Artaxerxes; "I will send out special orders that on this Sabbath day every Jewish shop is to be open and every Jew about his business. I will say that every Jew is to attend the next sacrifice in the groves of Astoreth. I will make them conform."

"Lots of people have tried that," Haman said, elaborately casual now that he had started Artaxerxes' rancour. "It is useless; they would die first."

"Then they must die," Artaxerxes said crossly.

"It would mean a massacre," said Haman craftily.

"Then it must be a massacre. Better a massacre than an enemy in our midst. Not that I like or approve of massacres—but they are necessary at times, as in the case of Mirimah."

"The Jews are a thousand times more dangerous than Mirimah ever was."

"Then they must be treated in the same way."

"It disgusts you, doesn't it?" Haman asked in a voice of sympathetic indulgence. "I always said that if you have one quality which is dangerous and unsuitable in your position it is the quality of mercy. It is intensely endearing—if I may say so . . . but . . . Look, would you like to leave this entirely to me? Give me your seal and I'll attend to the orders and everything. You need have absolutely nothing to do with it. I saw the danger and I dealt with it in the only possible way. Leave it to me."

Something that was squeamish and sentimentalist in Artaxerxes had reared its head when he had spoken the word "massacre." It was with intense relief that he took the ring with the Great Seal from his finger and handed it over to Haman the Amalekite. Haman went out with the power of life and death in his hands.

Before Esther's feast had lasted ten minutes Haman was wondering why he had imagined that Artaxerxes was displeased with him. Nothing had changed. It was just like last evening. The food and the wine were exquisite; the King in high good humour; the Queen looked brilliantly beautiful and was both easy to amuse and extremely amusing. Haman decided that he had been a fool to take Mordecai's honour as an insult to himself—after all, Artaxerxes hadn't known that Mordecai was his special enemy, he had merely wanted to do honour, belatedly, to the man who had saved his life. And Mordecai would not have long to enjoy his promotion; in the general massacre it would be easy to see to it that he was killed. Everything was all right, Haman thought, and set himself out to be amusing. And Esther, watching him, carried out the plan upon which she had determined. She revealed a hitherto unsuspected talent for mimicry, kinder than Haman's but no less funny; she capped his wildest flights of fancy, she replied to every one of his funny stories with a funny story of her own. Artaxerxes, who asked nothing better than that the company in which he found himself should be congenial and entertaining, enjoyed himself thoroughly, and at last, turning to Esther, said, "Last night I told you that half my kingdom was yours for the asking and you asked only that I should come and enjoy myself here tonight. Now, if I repeat my offer, will you repeat your invitation?"

This was the moment.

"No, my Lord. I shall give no more feasts . . ." her voice, suddenly sombre, banished the gaiety. "You see, my Lord, I am going to die!"

There, even Haman had never equalled that for unexpectedness and melodramatic utterance!

"Die?" Artaxerxes repeated, half rising and taking her by the shoulder.

"What do you mean? Are you ill . . . have the physicians . . ." some secret, deadly disease he thought, borne in brave silence . . . he thought of the quarrel, the month during which they had not spoken, and the bitter anguish of despair and remorse, a physical thing which could be tasted in the mouth, rose within him. "Esther," he breathed.

"No, I am in perfect health, but I have been sentenced to death, together with thousands of others of your subjects."

"Sentenced to death? . . . Esther, you're joking," he faltered, thinking that, even for a joke, even at a feast this was carrying things a *little* far.

"Do I look as though I were joking? Death is no matter for jesting, my Lord. No, the decree has gone out; I and all my race have been sentenced to death by our old enemy."

"Decree? What are you babbling about? Old enemy—who can be the enemy of the Queen of Persia? Who, in the name of madness, has the power to sentence *my wife* to death?"

Esther raised one hand. It was a beautiful hand, white and slender, tipped with henna, sparkling with jewels. It pointed across the table.

"There he sits," she said simply.

Artaxerxes stared stupidly at Haman, and Haman stared stupidly back; his mouth opened and closed and opened and closed, but no sound emerged. Suddenly Artaxerxes felt as though he were strangling; he struggled to his feet and hurried out through the curtained archway into the garden. Anyone observing him might have imagined that he was escaping from a threatened danger, he walked so fast, seemed so intent upon putting a distance between himself and that lighted room. Three thoughts beat like a hammer in his head —Esther, whom he loved was Jewish; all Jews were doomed to death: Haman had arranged it! Under each blow of the hammer his brain shuddered.

Within doors, across the glittering table the glittering favourite faced the glittering Queen. Haman's face, even to the lips, was grey and the sweat of terror stood on his brow. Presently the grey lips moved.

"I did not know," he said, "believe me, I did not know. I meant you no harm."

"No. No more than you meant to harm thousands of innocent people of whose very names you are ignorant," Esther said coldly. She must, she told herself, remember that Haman had brought this upon himself. Otherwise she might even find herself pitying him, suddenly so miserably abject after being so arrogant.

"What shall I do?" he whimpered, sensing the strength in her and instinctively seeking its shelter. "Your Majesty, if you will help, support, protect me now I will be your most humble and faithful servant to the end of my days."

"You are a stranger to humility and faith, Haman. I have seen your service. You are a servant who wishes to rule. I would not choose such a one. And why bargain with *me?* The King at this moment decides between us. He may choose you."

"He is displeased with me," Haman moaned. "My Lady, unless you take pity and speak for me, I am doomed."

"I am doomed already. And many with me. How can I speak for another when I am one of those whose doom is written up in the marketplace? I am a Jew. With what are *you* charged, Haman?"

The mockery in her voice struck like a blow and he gave a low wailing cry such as an animal in pain might utter. Rising from his place and reeling like a man struck with mortal sickness, he came to the end of the table where Esther was. There he flung himself on his knees. "I beg you, my Lady; pity me. Speak for me to the King when he returns. Say you forgive me and understand that I meant you no harm?"

"And why should I lie thus, for you?" Her dislike for him increased as the scent of the heavy perfume with which he had drenched himself reached her, together with another odour, the strong unmistakable smell of the sweat of fear. She leaned towards the other end of her couch and said, "Control yourself, Haman. The King has not yet decided between us. I might as well grovel to you!"

"No . . . no," he gasped out. "Your star is rising; mine sinks. I made a mistake this morning. . . ." The memory of his confidence and assurance, his nearness to the realisation of a cherished dream, his bitter disappointment at hearing Mordecai's name, came over him, and he began to sob. Past words, he began to claw at Esther with pleading hands, as a favourite dog will paw its master, seeking indulgence or notice. Blubbering and sweating and pawing at her he was utterly repulsive; she pushed his hands away and again leaned away from him saying sharply, "Have you no pride at all?"

Meanwhile Artaxerxes' rapid progress had brought him to the end of the garden, to the place where the three fountains played into marble basins surrounded by small dark cypresses; a sickle moon hung low in the sky and a million stars seeded the night. The silence was broken only by the gentle tinkling splash of the water. Artaxerxes stopped; the quiet beauty of the time and place touched him with a great peace; the hammers ceased their beating on his brain. He began to think.

With an utter lack of any personal feeling, without shame, or anger, or surprise, he realised that he was a foolish, weak man. In a rapid, frank survey of his whole life—accomplished in a second of thought-time—he saw that, although he was King of Persia, the most revered and awesome figure in the whole of the world, he had hitherto been nothing but a gaily dressed puppet figure whose strings had always been pulled by somebody else. Even when he had, on rare occasions, made a decision of his own he had invariably been prompted by temper or pride, the desire for amusement, or the prod of a passing mood. Thinking thus frankly, he found that he could credit himself with only one virtue; and that was physical courage; he was, he knew, a fine soldier, completely fearless, and in action, decisive and shrewd and resourceful; but life couldn't be all fighting and in the ordinary matter of living he was a prey to anyone who set out to get the better of him. Courtiers, politicians, favourites, women . . . Only a moment ago, faced with the painful business of deciding between Esther and Haman, what had he done? Run into the garden, as though by absenting himself he could escape from the need of making up his mind.

Well, he would now make up for it, calmly, decisively. Take Haman first. Haman had a talent for being amusing and entertaining; he said flattering things, and he said them differently. But on how many occasions had one deliberately shut one's eyes to the fact that Haman was coarse-minded, cruel, unscrupulous, not even fastidiously clean? And this morning Haman had revealed the full extent of his ambition. Haman's self-love was boundless.

Of Esther it was almost impossible to think so detachedly. The memory of the pang that had struck him when she had said, "You see, I am going to die," would intrude itself, bringing with it the sense of loss and panic and despair. He had realised at that moment how much he loved her, how very much she meant to him. But *now,* now he was thinking, not feeling; he wasn't giving way to emotion. So he forced himself to consider Esther coolly, detachedly. And the thing that stood out most clearly was that she had never attempted to exploit him . . . she was, in fact, the only person in all his experience who had treated him as an equal, as a human being with rights, and dignity . . . paying respect to his position, but at the same time looking upon him as a man. Artaxerxes saw, in one mental flash, that if he were ever to rule his Empire as successfully as he had led his army the one person whose help and support would be valuable, was Esther. To everyone else he was King of Persia, a puppet figure to be pushed around, a giver of favours, a source of wealth, a subject of mockery (as with Haman) or even a matter of contempt (as with Vashti). To the others he himself, Artaxerxes, the man, didn't exist at all. To Esther the man was all important; look how she had lain in his arms and kissed him and never, never once sought any favour for her family or her subject race. Esther, in fact, was a person, not a Jewess, or Queen of Persia, or one of a family, or one of a race, but a person, remote and detached, in her own right; and she treated him as such a person.

In a great calm Artaxerxes turned and began to walk back to the Queen's apartment. He meant, from this moment, to begin to rule his kingdom, with Esther's help. And he would say quite calmly, to Haman, that he disapproved of his behaviour, distrusted his ambition; and that as soon as all these iniquitous plans against the people of Esther and Mordecai had been withdrawn, Haman might himself withdraw from the Court. A modest estate, perhaps, and a small pension. After that, no more favourites, no more pullers-of-strings; just Esther and he, two people who loved and trusted and respected each other, working together.

Victim—though he didn't know it—of yet another mood, but a mood which might eventually harden into character, Artaxerxes walked calmly back through the garden. The grassy lawn stopped short some twenty feet off the palace and gave way to marble pavement. As he stepped onto it the sound was audible within the room. Haman gave a kind of screaming moan and threw himself upon Esther in a paroxysm of terror. He took the upper part of her arms in his hands and shook her, trying by violence to command pity.

"He comes, speak for me, speak for me!" Esther tried to stand up, but he was kneeling upon the skirts of her robe and for a second she was pinned down. She had no notion of what decision Artaxerxes had made; she was aware of the full danger of her own position. She had offended him by attacking his favourite, and now she had made the deadly admission and the challenging accusation. It was quite possible that Artaxerxes might have decided in Haman's favour and, if so, she wanted to meet her fate, the fate of all the Jews in Persia, with some measure of dignity. So she put her hands on Haman's shoulders and braced herself, pushing him away and making a more determined effort to free her robe and stand up. The gauze of her robe split and gave way with a thin shrill sound just as Artaxerxes pushed the curtains aside and stepped back into the room. Haman, quite maddened by fear, grabbed at her knees and again she struck his hands away.

Artaxerxes, suddenly arriving, might be forgiven for misunderstanding the situation.

"You devil!" he shouted, seizing Haman by his jewelled collar and jerking him backwards. "Would you lay hands on your Queen?"

It was a very simple, natural question, but it told both Haman and Esther what decision Artaxerxes had taken. She was "Queen," Haman "You devil." Haman fell, incoherent, almost insensible, upon the floor, and Esther, freed at last, stood up, gathering the torn folds of her robe together in her hands. Artaxerxes, master of the situation shouted, "Harbonah," and the chamberlain who had been taking supper in the ante-room hurried in.

"Take this away and hang it," said Artaxerxes, indicating the prostrate body of Haman.

35 Jeremiah's Last Vision

Franz Werfel was born in Prague in 1890 and died fifty-five years later in Beverly Hills, California, an internationally famous novelist. His *Forty Days of Musa Dagh* and *Song of Bernadette* were among the most popular novels of their time. *Hearken Unto the Voice*, less well known, is a strange work about a twentieth-century man who, in seeking his own salvation, is taken back into history and who finds himself by identifying with the Prophet Jeremiah. Except for the beginning and end, the book is entirely biblical. Unlike Laurene Chinn, who also wrote of Jeremiah, Werfel focuses his attention on the character and personality of the prophet, quoting the visions set forth in the Bible and attempting their interpretation. His Jeremiah is a man dazed by the revelations thrust upon him. Werfel brought to this work the sensitivity and depth of compassion of a man profoundly involved in religious thought.

The word that came to Jeremiah from the Lord, after that Nebuzaradan the captain of the guard had let him go from Ramah, when he had taken him being bound in chains among all that were carried away captive of Jerusalem and Judah, which were carried away captive unto Babylon.

And the captain of the guard took Jeremiah, and said unto him, The Lord thy God hath pronounced this evil upon this place.

Now the Lord hath wrought it, and done according as he hath said: because ye have sinned against the Lord, and have not obeyed his voice, therefore this thing is come upon you.

And now, behold, I loose thee this day from the chains which were upon thine hand. If it seem good unto thee to come with me to Babylon, come; and I will look well unto thee: but if it seem ill unto thee to come with me to Babylon, forbear: behold, all the land is before thee: whither it seemeth good and convenient for thee to go, thither go.

Now while he was not yet gone back, he said, Go back also to Gedaliah the son of Ahikam the son of Shaphan, whom the king of Babylon hath made governor over the cities of Judah, and dwell with him among the people: or go wheresoever it seemeth convenient unto thee to go. So the captain of the guard gave him victuals and a reward, and let him go.

Then went Jeremiah unto Gedaliah the son of Ahikam to Mizpah; and dwelt with him among the people that were left in the land.

JEREMIAH: XL, 1–6

HEARKEN UNTO THE VOICE by FRANZ WERFEL

EVERYTHING CAME TO PASS as had been predicted. The almond blossoms of
Jeremiah's first vision had changed to crackling flames. The seething pot in
the north had spilled over and spurted glowing streams that scalded the whole
land. When they returned home the prophet and his companions found on
their way not a single hamlet or house that remained intact, only smoking
ruins. In the fields lay those who had been massacred where they stood or
whose bodies had been cast there that the roads might be clear. The air was
tainted with a pestilential stench that grew more pervading the closer they
approached to Jerusalem; and the clouds of birds that darkened the sky
screeched their pleasure at the full table which Nergal had provided for them.

When Jeremiah raised his burning eyes to the familiar hills and mountains, it seemed to him as if the mountains swayed and the hills were in
motion. Were the heights of Judah and the mountain ranges of Israel about
to leave the land and wander with their children into exile? What was there
left for them at home? Should they sing dirges for the empty pastures and the
desolate orchards? There was no more reaping of corn or gathering of fruit;
the pressing of the vine and shearing of sheep were at an end. The Lord had
rolled up His land as a shepherd rolled up his woollen cloak. Or did Jeremiah's tortured eyes deceive him? Were the mountains and the hills rejoicing
that they had been freed from this stubborn people who had dwelt upon them
for countless generations? Once more they would see men like those who had
lived there before Abraham, Isaac, and Jacob; men who were dull, silent,
and pious, to whom God spoke but little and who spoke but little to God;
men who lived easily and died easily and were such as the earth welcomed.

In terrible contrast to the emptiness of the countryside with its smoking
ruins were the crowded roads and paths. Though several weeks had passed
since the ninth day of Ab and the overwhelming of Jerusalem, there was still
no end to the cruel processions of captives who were being driven to Babylon.
Nergal Nebuzaradan was himself supervising the great migration. Unlike the
earlier occasion when the Babylonians carried away their prisoners from
Judah after the death of Jehoiakim and the fall of Coniah, the dignitaries
had to leave their rank behind them and the wealthy their possessions. Everything of value, whether in money or chattels, fell into the hands of the victors;
no distinction was made among princes, priests, and bondservants. All who
came under the decree of expulsion were regarded as being in bondage.
Marduk had no intention of burdening his land with a mob of distinguished
idlers, with scribes, soothsayers, scholars, lazy dreamers, crafty money-
changers, dealers in jewels, or other merchants. He had more than enough
of that kind in Babylon already. But some ten myriads of slaves to bake
bricks, cut weeds, drain swamps, irrigate steppes, and work at the hundreds
of places where he was building under the sign of the Ram—these constituted

369

a considerable enrichment of his country and a fitting payment for the war. Both high and low therefore had to become accustomed from the very start to the ruthless misery that awaited them, so that they might regard even the hardest labour at the end of their journey as pleasant and refreshing by comparison. Whoever found the effort beyond his strength could die by the wayside. What did it matter if a few thousand remained lying there? The exodus acted as an excellent sieve for the slaves. Marduk could use only strong arms in his work of construction. Nergal Nebuzaradan had prepared a central camp for the captives in the little town of Ramah in Benjamin; here were collected all those whom the Babylonian patrols managed to hunt out from the more remote villages, caverns, and mountain gorges after the great levies of the first days subsequent to the fall of Jerusalem. Only the old, the sick, the crippled, and the blind were allowed to remain in addition to the poorest of the peasants. The latter class is always unaffected by the course of historic events. Like cats who are attached to a house and not to the people who dwell in it, the poorer type of peasant belongs less to the nation than to the soil. Therefore, however numerous they are, they never constitute a danger for a conqueror. From his central camp in Ramah, Nebuzaradan sent the processions of exiles at suitable intervals to Babylon. And there was no end to them.

With unexpected generosity Marduk had permitted Maacha and her companions to obtain good riding-animals and to take with them an adequate number of attendants. Even so, they could proceed only step by step along the crowded roads. Every hour they encountered a new procession of wretched prisoners, consisting generally of a hundred men with their wives and children stumbling after them in little groups. The men were chained together in pairs or in gangs, and in accordance with ancient military custom they bore heavy yokes on their bowed necks, so that they panted along under the burning sun with sweat pouring down their faces to mingle with their tears. The chafing yokes and chains soon wore through their thin garments, with the result that most of them had to journey into lifelong captivity in rags, and many of them were virtually naked. They were not allowed a moment's pause to breathe freely or any rest other than the regulation halts. The troop of horsemen who accompanied each of the processions struck at the men with their whips or the flats of their swords if there was any stoppage, if one of them refused or was unable to continue, or if anybody was overcome by the desire to lie down at the edge of the road to die. To increase their sufferings and lessen the opportunity to plan revolt, families and neighbours had been divided up and kept strictly apart, so that the men chained together all came from different parts of the country and were of various ages. The Lord was mingling His people like a mixed draught stirred in a cup.

The sight of the women was even more tragic than that of the men. The latter had to carry their yokes and chains, but they had no other burden. The women were loaded with all the immediate necessities of life that the Babylonians allowed them to take. Many a one was to be seen staggering along with an enormous sack on her back, a child on each arm, and a couple of older children wailing and stumbling at her side. In the pitiless rays of the sun the light skin of the young women, girls, and children blistered painfully, and their feet gradually turned to bleeding, shapeless lumps. If any of the women were good-looking and happened to stir the desire of their captors, then lots were cast to decide who should have them. When their piercing shrieks rang through the desolate countryside, the fettered men were unable to rush to their rescue and avenge them as the Law demanded. The Babylonians even took delight in giving their prisoners unclean food and filthy water at which they themselves shuddered in horror. On one occasion Jeremiah saw some Chaldean bowmen shoot down a number of carrion fowl and roast them. But the men and women of Judah refused to eat the forbidden flesh. Only one or two, beside themselves with despair or overcome by hunger, stretched out their hands to receive the abomination. The others sat still as death, closed their eyes, and let their heads sink lower and lower till they touched their knees. Meanwhile their conquerors unstrapped the wine jars from their saddle-horses and passed them from hand to hand, drinking amid laughter and uproarious singing in front of their parched prisoners. Even the women were too proud to betray their suffering; they pressed their moaning children more firmly to their breasts that their tormentors might not hear the cries of the little ones and rejoice still more.

Of the ten thousand terrible scenes that met the eyes of Jeremiah and his companions on their return home, this was but one. Again and again the prophet took Maacha's hand to draw her attention to some heart-rending sight, that she might realize that she was truly not alone in her affliction. In spite of the scorching sun, her hand was as cold as ice. Her whole being seemed to have frozen. She sat erect on the ass she was riding as if she belonged to another world. Since the judgment of Riblah she had not spoken, even to ask Jeremiah about the blinded King and his last leave-taking. Baruch and Ebed-melech thought that grief had stricken her dumb. When the others felt as if they would perish from the heat, she was attacked by a violent fit of shivering and her teeth chattered. When they stopped to rest, or at night, she was unable to get warm. Heated stones and all the blankets they could provide were of no help. It was as if her grief had dried up her blood. She lay shuddering under the awning, and the two maids whom Marduk had permitted to accompany her took turns during the night in rubbing her little white feet. But though they never ceased their ministrations, her feet remained stiff and cold, like those of a dead person. Yet when Jeremiah wanted to order a longer rest than usual because of her condition, she shook her head vehemently and her face became distorted with an expression of anger.

The goal of their journey was the little city of Mizpah, which lay not far from Anathoth on the borders of Judah and Benjamin. This was where the Remnant of Jacob had gathered, consisting of all the men of rank and wealth, together with their households, who had been allowed for various reasons and by favour of the King of Babylon to remain in their native land. Among them were the deserters and their families, the landowners and priests who had been hostile to Zedekiah and had openly gone over to the Babylonians during the war, but also some men who were pure of heart and, like the sons of Shaphan, had tried until the eleventh hour to avert the complete downfall of Jerusalem. Gedaliah had been appointed governor over the Remnant by Nebuchadnezzar and he ruled over them in Mizpah. His reputation had spread throughout the devasted land. People came even from Ephraim and Manasseh, from Issachar and Zebulun, tribes which had long been estranged from Judah, to gather round him. He had several thousands of families under his charge, and the number of souls was by no means insignificant. Wise preparations were being made to divide the country afresh, and Baruch did not conceal from Jeremiah his hopes that even the total destruction of Jerusalem and other cities was a wound that might be healed within a few generations. Jeremiah did not throw cold water on his optimism, for which, indeed, grounds were not lacking. Gedaliah was vigorous and energetic, and he was working day and night at the sacred task that had been entrusted to him. His less sturdy brother had already succumbed to his strenuous exertions. With iron resolution and courage the Governor overcame every obstacle; he had even succeeded in ensuring the partial preservation of the vintage and the olive harvest despite fire, massacre, and expulsion. In obedience to the wish of their dying father the sons of Ahikam had prepared the fold, and it was to this fold that Jeremiah and his companions were journeying. It was the duty of the new ruler of the people to take the wife of Zedekiah under his care.

One evening, while they were still on their way, they came to an ancient burial place not far from Ramah. Twelve great stones rose above a weather-worn tomb that had sunk deep into the earth, and there was no inscription to show which of the notable figures of antiquity was interred there. The travellers rested in the open, for their hearts were too heavy to enter Ramah, the headquarters of Nergal Nebuzaradan where he had established his camp for those who were being carried into captivity. Maacha, however, suddenly stood up, walked with solemn steps towards the tomb, and seated herself on one of the grey stones. For the first time since the judgment of Riblah she opened her mouth to speak.

"This is the grave of Rachel, our ancestress," she said to Jeremiah, and there was a strangely stubborn note in her voice as if she expected him to contradict her.

"The Queen is mistaken," he corrected her gently. "This is not the grave of Rachel who bore Joseph and Benjamin. Rachel lies buried in the Valley of Rephaim, near Bethlehem."

Maacha surveyed him contemptuously from head to foot.

"What words are these, impious man! Surely I may know my own grave, to which I am returning after so much affliction?"

Jeremiah looked at her wide-eyed, whereupon she turned from him with a haughty gesture of rebuke. After a while she began to speak again, this time to herself:

"They have slain my two sons . . . Joseph and Benjamin . . . They have slain all my children . . . Yet it was not easy for me to bear my sons. . . . The wailing women are carrying my dead children in their arms to Baylon, my

Adajah and Ichiel. . . . Lord, why hast Thou done this thing to Rachel's sons? . . . Thou who hast made it so difficult for mothers to bear children, why hast Thou done this thing? . . ."

She ceased to speak. Tears streamed down her sorrowful face, which might have been that of Rachel for whom Jacob served fourteen years. But there was no healing power in her tears and they brought her no relief. Jeremiah tried tenderly to persuade her to rise from the tomb, but she would not. She protested that her place was there, where she would at last be able to sleep again and be warm in death, as she had not been for so long. He had to let her have her way and she spent the night sitting motionless on the stone like a statue of Rachel. Towards morning she slipped to the ground and fell asleep. Jeremiah took Ebed-melech aside and said to him:

"You must never oppose your mistress, but always do what she wishes so far as lies within your power. Be gentle and humour her. Perhaps the Lord will heal her, perhaps He will not; but stay with her wherever she may be and for as long as she wishes. You are well protected. When she is prepared to go on, then go with her to Mizpah, whither Baruch and I will precede you."

"My teacher may go with a tranquil mind," nodded the Ethiopian, "for my mistress is now my master."

Jeremiah bade the tall Ebed-melech bend his curly head, and he stretched out his hand to bless him.

"The Lord of hosts," he murmured, "who has given so many of the King's servants into the hand of death, all of them sons of Jacob, has spared you, a man from a strange land. And even more. Because of your faithfulness, you have been received among those who are most faithful."

"Received?" asked the Ethiopian sadly, as if he could not believe Jeremiah's words. "If I had children they would not be children of Jacob, but strangers, dark-skinned, unmarked by the hand of God."

Before he went, Jeremiah comforted him with the promise:

"The deeds of our hearts too, Ebed-melech, are not without their progeny."

As soon as they passed through the gate of Mizpah they heard the dreadful news of what had happened during the previous night. The house of the Governor was besieged by a wailing, cursing throng, but as Jeremiah and Baruch were recognized by the guards they were allowed to enter the court of the palace. In the centre of a muttering group of men they saw a body, wrapped in a blood-stained sheet, lying on the stone pavement. It was Gedaliah, whom the prophet had seen in his vision pierced by four swords. In reality it was not four, but ten swords that had lacerated the back and breast of Gedaliah. The worst aspect of this unutterable crime was the fact that it had been committed at a time when Marduk had decided to show favour to Judah and had sent special orders to Nergal Nebuzaradan putting an end to further expulsions. The central camp at Ramah was to be broken up without delay and the prisoners released without regard to rank or past conduct. At the same time an amnesty had been decreed throughout the country which affected all the fugitives who had gone into hiding either within or beyond the frontiers. There were no exceptions mentioned in the amnesty, not even the old warrior Elnathan or Prince Ishmael. Thus it had been possible for Ishmael, in whose veins flowed some drops of David's blood, to appear unexpectedly and unpunished in Mizpah a few days before. Accompanied by a number of his closest friends, he had come to pay homage to Gedaliah.

Among the grief-stricken mourners who surrounded the bloody corpse was a young man whom Jeremiah and Baruch had seen once or twice in Shaphan's room in the Temple. His name was Johanan, son of Kareah. In the confusion he seemed to have become the spokesman and leader. From him Jeremiah learned how the crime had been perpetrated that had destroyed the hope of the last Remnant.

It was less than three days before, said Johanan, that Gedaliah had gathered the people and the men of rank (including Ishmael and his friends) around him and had exhorted them to take no heed of the soldiers of Babylon, but to live quietly in the land and gird their hearts with patience. He himself would stay to govern them and further their cause with careful planning until the crushed nation should rise up again. Meanwhile they should all go in peace, fill their vessels with wine and oil and fruit and resume the cultivation of their fields. Gedaliah had proffered this wise advice and the people had listened to him. But he intended to do more than persuade his enemies with prudent words. He wanted to bind them to his side with firm bonds, and to this end he had prepared a festive banquet to take place two days later. To this banquet he had invited Ishmael and nine of his companions, the Tartan whom Nebuzaradan had put in authority over the town of Mizpah, and some of his own chief collaborators. Though Johanan had warned the Governor of his danger, the latter had persisted in his plan. The young man repeated to Jeremiah the words he had spoken in Gedaliah's ear:

"I beseech you to forgo this banquet! Are you not aware that these men are plotting against you? Ishmael hates you and will try to take his revenge. He cannot forget that you deserted to the Babylonians and have been raised up by the enemy. His new master, Baalis, King of Ammon, has spurred him on to do you evil."

But Gedaliah had only laughed and replied scoffingly that he would have to abandon his belief in the supreme gifts of God, in reason and logical deduction, before he could believe that such a thing was possible. What grounds could Ishmael have for hating the man who had enabled him to return home unpunished and offered him the hope of again entering into possession of his estates? In any case he knew from Ishmael's own lips how strongly the prince approved of his present activities. Johanan recapitulated every argument that he had employed to persuade Gedaliah, who had brought the interview to an end by forbidding him to appear at the banquet lest his malice should envenom the joyous feast of reconciliation. When the night of the banquet arrived, everything happened as he had foreseen. After the wine had apparently warmed their hearts towards each other, Ishmael and his companions had suddenly drawn their swords and fallen upon Gedaliah like wild beasts. The other guests, too, had been slain, including the Babylonian Tartan.

Jeremiah gazed silently at the shrouded body in its blood-stained sheet. The last prop that supported the house had fallen. The noble mind and loyal friend had been overtaken by his end when he thought he was making a new beginning, just as he was hoping to ward off from the Remnant some of the evil effects of God's judgment. In his mind's eye Jeremiah saw the astute twins as they defended him with their shrewd arguments before Meshullam and the tribunal. Suddenly he was wrenched from his thoughts by an hubbub of agitated voices. The men assembled in the courtyard were shouting to him. He did not yet know the whole extent of Ishmael's crime. This dreadful murder had been only the beginning. Before the night was over, Ishmael, together with a band of ruthless fanatics like himself who had remained in concealment, had engaged in a savage massacre of unarmed men. Not only a number of the most important leaders among the Remnant had fallen victims to his vengeance, but also a company of innocent pilgrims from Ephraim who had been journeying on a pilgrimage to the ruins of the Temple. Towards morning they had been able to collect sufficient men and weapons to resist Ishmael's onslaught and drive the murderous crew towards the city of Gibeon. A message had just arrived to say that the Remnant of Judah were now in the throes of a bloody battle before the jeering eyes of Babylon. Johanan interrupted the incoherent cries and laments with the proud gesture of a newly appointed leader.

"We have now," he said to Jeremiah, "told you, though with much confusion, the whole terror which has befallen us from which we are not yet free. What will be the outcome? Are we to flee? Or are we to stay? One of the Tartans and several others of the men of Babylon have been slain. The King of Babylon will not let this go unavenged, but will kill us all. Of that there can be no doubt. It is therefore my advice that we should go to Egypt without waiting until Nebuzaradan has reported this matter to Babylon. But as others among us have put forward different suggestions, we beseech you to let our supplication be accepted before you." The son of Kareah spoke with an affectation of subservience. "Pray for us unto the Lord your God for all this Remnant, for we are left but a few of many, as your eyes do behold us, that the Lord your God may show us the way wherein we may walk and the thing that we may do."

Through half-closed eyes Jeremiah observed the agitated men as they ran to and fro, plucked at their beards, beat their bodies, and argued angrily with one another. There was a bitter taste in his mouth as he thought of the blinded King and the processions of miserable captives on their way to Babylon, whether he himself had been forbidden by the Lord to journey. Yet it was in a very calm voice that he spoke to Johanan and the other men assembled in the courtyard where the murdered Gedaliah was lying.

"I have heard you; behold, I will pray unto the Lord your God, according to your words, and it shall come to pass that whatsoever thing the Lord shall answer you, I will declare it unto you. I will keep nothing back from you."

After having spoken thus he looked down once more at the bloody form of the man whom all his wisdom and generosity and hopefulness had not helped to rule a stiff-necked people. Giving loud voice to their praise and gratitude the men escorted him into Gedaliah's house, where he was to lodge with his disciple. That evening, while the lamp was still burning, Baruch seated himself beside Jeremiah's couch and tempted him.

"Of what use is it to pray so much," he asked, "and beseech the Lord with your pleading, since we both know what is best and what alone is to the advantage of this Remnant? Let them abide in the land, that this people may not wholly disappear. The King of Babylon will not change his mind because of Gedaliah. He has had enough of us and more than enough, and he wants but one thing—to hear no more of us. Let Jeremiah go to them in the morning and say: 'Abide in the land!' "

Jeremiah had sat up and was regarding Baruch with an intense look, half in anger and half in mockery.

"O shrewd Baruch!" he said. "You still have much to learn. How vividly you remind me now of the day when you stood among the sons of Ahikam in the Temple and were ashamed of my yoke, being so vain of your own wisdom! That is what distinguished me from you, from you and the sons of Shaphan. You always knew what would befall on the morrow. Only I, the prophet, did not know. If I were to send you with a message, would you announce something that I had not said? . . . I see that you understand! . . . Shall I then pretend to these unhappy men that word has come to me, only because I think I know the right way and wish with all my heart that it may be taken? Go to your couch and sleep! But because you have tempted me I will remain awake and entreat advice of the Lord."

For ten days and ten nights Jeremiah took little food and almost completely conquered sleep. He lay on the bare floor and prayed to the Lord as he had promised, beseeching an answer. The Lord held aloof and refused to listen to his supplication, seeming even to take pleasure in probing to the depths the sincerity of the one man on earth who was faithful to Him. Only on the tenth evening, when Jeremiah was at the point of collapse, did he hear the clear voice speaking to him.

When the sun rose again Jeremiah went out to Johanan and the rest of the people in order to communicate to them the words of God. But first he asked them:

"Did you not swear to me that you would obey the voice of the Lord, whether it be good or whether it be evil?"

"We swore it to you and called upon the Lord to be a witness between us!" some of them cried out. Jeremiah looked far over the heads of the crowd as he began to prophesy:

"Thus saith the Lord, the God of Israel! . . . If ye will still abide in this land, then will I build you, and not pull you down, and I will plant you, and not pluck you up. . . . Be not afraid of the King of Babylon, of whom ye are afraid . . . But if ye say, We will not dwell in this land, but we will go into the land of Egypt, where we shall see no war, nor hear the sound of the trumpet, nor have hunger of bread, and there will we dwell: now therefore hear the word of the Lord, O ye Remnant of Judah, go ye not into Egypt! . . . But know that ye dissemble in your hearts if ye first demand to hear the voice of the Lord and then do not obey. . . ."

After these clear words there was an embarrassed silence, which soon changed to an agitated tumult, for during the past ten days the scales had been turned in favour of their journeying to Egypt, the most eager advocate of this course being Johanan. The latter spoke harshly to the prophet, just as the Kings of Judah had done in their time.

"Your ways are difficult, Jeremiah," he reproached him, "for never to this day have you spoken that which you should have spoken. The Lord your God seems to delight in opposing everything which seems to our judgment good to do. What pledge have we that Babylon will give us peace and will not seek vengeance? The word of the Lord your God? It is a word formed by your own lips. If Babylon should seek vengeance, then you have only to plead that you did not hear aright. But in the pleasant House of Bondage we shall be certain of peace."

"You speak falsely!" cried a certain Azariah, another of the spokesmen. "The Lord our God has not sent you to say, Go not into Egypt, to sojourn there. But Baruch, the son of Neriah, sets you on against us, for to deliver us into the hand of the Chaldeans, that they might put us to death, and carry us away captives into Babylon."

Jeremiah stood silent among them as they argued and disputed, as if all this was no concern of his. When the men's wrath had exhausted itself, he said with a strange indifference:

"Remnant of Judah, I will not contend with you, for you do not err against me, but against your own souls. You have decided. Do as seems fitting unto you and prepare for your journey."

Johanan, however, seized Jeremiah firmly with both hands as if he intended to take him prisoner.

"Yes, we shall quickly prepare for our journey," he cried, "but we shall take you with us into the House of Bondage . . . as a pledge of the Lord your God!"

Jeremiah shook him off contemptuously and said very wearily:

"No need is there for you to compel me, since I go with you of my own accord and will lead you. For this is my task. Where you are, there too must I be. But when you are down there in Tahpanhes and in Noph, you will melt away and become shades of the underworld, never to return."

With these words he turned away and left them in their bewilderment. In his heart he felt an unfamiliar and terrifying satisfaction because the Remnant had rejected the Lord's last offer.

36 Daniel and the

Handwriting on the Wall

Using the Bible as a springboard for a romance in the tradition of the Arabian Nights, William Stearns Davis hewed closely to his source, *The Book of Daniel*, weaving it, however, into a larger extra-biblical story of his own creation. A professor of history at the University of Minnesota, and a popular author from the turn of the century until his death in 1930, Davis ranged the whole field of history in his search for story materials suited to romance in the old tradition. He wrote of Caesar's Rome, of Classical Athens, of a medieval barony, of the War of the Roses, and more formally of Europe since Waterloo. His *Belshazzar* is in the tradition of the costume novel, but it unfolds with dash, awe, and wonder. The selection which follows—the moving finger writes—lends itself to just these elements.

> *Belshazzar the king made a great feast to a thousand of his lords, and drank wine before the thousand.*
>
> *Belshazzar, whiles he tasted the wine, commanded to bring the golden and silver vessels which his father Nebuchadnezzar had taken out of the temple which was in Jerusalem; that the king, and his princes, his wives, and his concubines, might drink therein.*
>
> *Then they brought the golden vessels that were taken out of the temple of the house of God which was at Jerusalem; and the king, and his princes, his wives, and his concubines, drank in them.*
>
> *They drank wine, and praised the gods of gold, and of silver, of brass, of iron, of wood, and of stone.*
>
> *In that same hour came forth fingers of a man's hand, and wrote over against the candlestick upon the plaster of the wall of the king's palace: and the king saw the part of the hand that wrote.*
>
> DANIEL: V, 1–5

BELSHAZZAR:

A Tale of the Fall of Babylon

by WILLIAM STEARNS DAVIS

THERE ON THE WALL the letters glowed, right under the torch-holder; glowed like ruddy fire, the whole dread inscription spreading in one long, terrible line under the eyes of king and nobles. While Belshazzar looked, his bronzed cheeks turned ashen. The awful hand had vanished the instant the sentence was written—gone—whither? The lord of the Chaldees gazed upon his servants, and they—back at their master, while none spoke. But the letters did not vanish; their steadfast light burned calmly on. Then came another fearful deed; for Belshazzar caught the golden cup that had fallen from his hand, and dashed it against the wall. A great square of the plaster fell, but lo! the letters were burning still. Then new silence, while every man heard the beatings of his heart and thought on his unholy deeds.

But the stillness could not last forever. Belshazzar broke it. The pallor was still on his face, his knees smote together, his voice quivered; but he was kinglier than the rest, even in his fear—he at least was brave enough for speech.

"Ho! captains of Babylon! Why do we gape like purblind sheep? A notable miracle from the gods! Some new favour, no doubt, vouchsafed by Marduk!"

No one answered; all strength had fled from the stoutest sword-hand. Belshazzar's voice rose to a sterner pitch, as he faced the array of priests.

"What mean these letters? They are not the characters of the Chaldee. Their meaning? Here are learned men, wise in every tongue. Translate to us!"

Still no answer; and the king's wrath now mastered all his fears.

"Fools!" his hand was on his sword-hilt; "Marduk has not added to the miracle by smiting all dumb." He confronted the "chief of the omen-revealers," who stood close to the dais.

"Here, Gamilu, this falls within your duties. Look on the writing. Interpret without delay; or, as Marduk is god, another has your office!"

Gamilu, a venerable pontiff, lifted his head, and stared at the inscription. He mumbled inaudibly, but the royal eye was on him. With vain show of confidence he commenced:—

"Live forever, lord of the Chaldees! A fortunate sign, on a doubly fortunate day! This is the word which Bel, the sovereign god, has sent to his dearly loved son, the ever victorious king, Belshazzar—"

But here he stopped, bravado failing. Thrice he muttered wildly, then grew still. The king's rage was terrible. "Juggler! you shall learn to mock me. Nab destroy me too, if you are living at dawn!"

The luckless man fell on his knees, tearing his beard: his one groan was,

"Mercy." Belshazzar heeded little. "You other priests—you the chief 'demon-ejector'—do you speak! The meaning?"

A second wretch cast himself before the king. "Pity, Ocean of Generosity, pity! I do not know."

The king wasted no curse. "You, Kalduin, 'master of the star-gazers,' who boast to be wisest astrologer in Babylon—look on the writing. I declare that if you, or any other, can read these letters, and make known to me the interpretation, he shall be clothed in scarlet, and a chain of gold put about his neck, and he shall be third ruler of the kingdom, next to Avil and myself."

But Kalduin also fell on his knees, groaning and moaning. Belshazzar turned to Avil-Marduk, who had not spoken since the apparition, and who was still exceedingly pale. "Avil!" the accent of the king was icy chill, "if you are truly the mouthpiece of your god, prove your power. Interpret!"

Then came a wondrous thing, even on that night of wonders. For the chief priest, to whom Babylon had cringed almost as to the king, cowered on the rugs by the royal couch. "Lord! Lord! he moaned in fear, "I know not. I cannot tell. Mercy! Spare!"

Belshazzar shook his kingly head as might a desert lion, he alone steadfast, while a thousand were trembling.

"And is there no man in all Babylon who can read this writing?" was his thunder.

There was a rustling beside him. From her chair the aged queen-mother, Tavat-Hasina, leaned forward. "Your Majesty," she whispered, from pale lips, "live forever. Let not your thoughts trouble you. There *is* a man in your kingdom in whom is the spirit of the holy gods."

"What man?" demanded Belshazzar. Every eye was on the queen, who continued:—

"In the days of your father, light and understanding like the wisdom of the gods were found in him; and King Nebuchadnezzar made him master of the magicians and soothsayers, because an excellent knowledge and interpretation of dreams and dissolving of doubts were found in him."

"Ay! The man! His name!" The king snatched her wrist roughly. Many voices reechoed, "The man! His name! Send for him! Send!"

The queen-mother looked steadily into Belshazzar's eyes.

"The name of the man is Daniel, whom the king called Belteshazzar; now let Daniel be called, and he will show the interpretation."

But the words were like fire thrust into the king's face. He recoiled from her; the ashen gray came back to his cheeks. "Not Daniel! I will never see him! I have sworn it! Not he! Not he!"

So cried the king. But from all the captains rose the clamour:—

"Send for Daniel! He is the only hope. He alone can reveal. Send! Send!"

Avil found courage to rise and whisper in the royal ear, "Let all Babylon burn, ere the king craves one boon of this villainous Jew!"

"Never! I will not send," cried Belshazzar. But as he saw again that burning line, he grew yet paler.

"Daniel! Daniel! We are lost if the writing is longer hid! Send for the Jew!"

The captains were waxing mutinous. Scabbards clattered. Would the feast end in rebellion? Belshazzar addressed Mermaza. "Eunuch, go to the innermost prison and bring Daniel hither without delay."

"Hold!" cried Avil, at the top of his voice; "what god can speak through *his* lips? Is the king of Babylon sunk so low—"

"Read and interpret yourself, priest," bawled an old officer; and from fifty fellows rose the yell: "Away with Avil-Marduk. It is he who angers heaven!"

"Shall I go, lord?" questioned Mermaza, and Belshazzar only nodded his head.

Then there was silence once more, while monarch and servants watched those letters burning on the wall. Presently—after how long!—there were feet heard in the outer court, the clanking of chains; then right into the glare and glitter came Mermaza, followed by two soldiers; and betwixt these an old man, squalid, unkempt, clothed in rags, the fetters still on wrist and ankle. But at sight of him a hundred knelt to worship.

"Help us, noble Jew! Make known the writing, that we may obey heaven, and may not die!" One and all cried it. But Daniel heeded nothing until he stood before the king.

As Belshazzar rose from his couch to speak, a cry broke forth from Ruth. "My father! My father! Help me! Save me!" Almost she would have flown to his arms, but he outstretched a manacled hand, beckoning away.

"Not now, daughter. On another errand have I come." Then to the king, "Your Majesty, I am here."

Belshazzar tried vainly to meet the piercing eye of the Jew. His own voice was metallic, while he groped for words.

"Are you that Daniel, of the captive Hebrews, whom Nebuchadnezzar brought out of Judea?" Where were the king's wits fled, that he asked this of the man so long known and hated? A stately nod was his reply.

"I have heard that the spirit of the gods is in you, and light and understanding and excellent wisdom. And now the wise men and astrologers have been brought to read this writing, and to interpret, but they could not. And I have heard that you can make interpretations and dissolve doubts." The king's voice faltered; he would have given a thousand talents not to be driven to speak the rest. "Now, if you are able to read the writing, and make known the interpretation, you shall be clothed in scarlet, and have a chain of gold about your neck, and be the third ruler of the kingdom."

No response: Daniel looked straight upon Belshazzar, and again Belshazzar strove to shun the captive's gaze.

"Will you not speak?" demanded the king. "Speak! or you are beaten to death!"

Was it triumph or pity that lighted the old Jew's face? "Death? My times are in mightier hands than yours, O king. Answer truly—will you have me speak? For this is not the word of Bel."

All saw Avil leap up, as if in creature fear; but Belshazzar at least faced Daniel steadily, with all save his eyes.

"Answer me truly—be it good or ill. But answer!"

The king stretched forth his hands to the Jew, imploring. The prophecy was fulfilled; Belshazzar the king supplicated Daniel the captive! The old man's form straightened; he swept his gaze around that company, every eye obedient to his. His voice was low, yet in that silence each whisper swelled to loudness.

"Let your gifts be for another, O king; give your rewards to another, but I will read the writing to the king, and make known the interpretation."

Then he told the tale all Babylon knew so well, how when the mighty Nebuchadnezzar hardened his heart in kingly pride, madness smote him, and made him no better than the beasts, till after living seven years thus humbled, he came to himself, and knew that the Most High was above all kings. And by the time the tale was ended the silence was so great, that even the sputtering torches were loud to hear. Daniel stood directly before the dais; the chains rattled as he stretched forth a finger, and pointed into the king's face.

"But you, O Belshazzar, have not humbled your heart, though you knew all this; but have lifted yourself up against the Lord of Heaven; and they have brought the vessels of His house before you, and you, and your lords, and your women have drunk wine in them; and you have praised the gods of silver, of gold, of brass, iron, wood, and stone, which see not, nor hear, nor know; and the God in whose hand your breath is, and whose are all your ways, you have not glorified. Then was the hand sent from Him, and this writing was written."

The finger pointed toward the glowing characters upon the wall. "And this is the writing that was written: '*Mene, Mene, Tekel, Upharsin.*' And this is the interpretation: '*Mene*'—God has numbered your kingdom and finished it. '*Tekel*'—you are weighed in the balances and are found wanting. '*Upharsin*' which is otherwise '*Peres*'—your kingdom is divided and given to the Medes and the Persians." . . .

. . . A fearful cry was rising; captains were on their faces, groaning to Samas, to Istar, to Ramman: "Save! Save from the wrath of Jehovah!" The workings of Belshazzar's features were terrible to behold. Thrice he strove to speak—his lips moved dumbly. Then, as the king looked, lo! another wonder. The fiery words were gone, and only the shattered plaster showed where they had burned. "Woe! Woe!" all were moaning; but the vanishing of the letters gave back to Avil his courage. He leaned over, whispering to the king. In an instant Belshazzar uttered a hideous laugh.

"Good! By Istar, the Jew has me fairly on the hip! Clever jugglery, I swear, to contrive a trick that could chase the blood from the cheeks of the stoutest captains of the Chaldees! Show me the conjurer; I will pardon and reward. A clever jest, my princes, a clever jest."

The shout died away in profound silence. The king grasped a goblet once more. "By Nabu, the jest is so well played, you still wander for wits. Daniel must have reward. Ho! Mermaza; the robe of honour and the chain of gold. Off with these rags and fetters. Behold in Daniel the third prince of the kingdom. Set a new seat on the dais. A health to his Highness!" He drained the cup, then in a darker tone, directly at the Hebrew: "This is the promised reward. But when at midnight I quit the feast, if your prophecy is not fulfilled, you die the perjurer's death, for mocking thus your king."

Daniel answered nothing. The eunuchs pried off his fetters, put on him the robe and the golden chain. They set him in a chair beside Belshazzar, offering a jewelled goblet. He took it, tasting only once. Avil had risen, in vain effort to fuse the company with the same mad merriment affected by himself and the king.

"I congratulate Prince Daniel, my colleague in government! Another health to him, and to our 'ever-to-be-adored' Queen Atossa. Strike up, harpers; raise the triumph hymn to Bel once more."

With reluctant fingers the musicians smote harp and zither, the choir of priests and maidens lifted quavering voices—sang a few measures—the weak notes died away into ghastly stillness. Every eye crept furtively up to the square of shattered plaster. Then, as if in desperation, and bound to hide his mastering fears, a "captain of a hundred" motioned to a eunuch.

"Wine, fellow, wine, heady enough to chase these black imps away! Let us drink ourselves to sleep, and forget the portent by the morning."

"Wine!" echoed all, "more wine! Surely the Jew had lied. Forget him!"

The revels were resumed. The torches flared above the king of the Chaldees and all his lords draining their liquor—beaker on beaker—in one mad, vain hope—to drown out their own dark thoughts. The fiery apparition had vanished from the plaster only to glow before the uncertain vision of each and all. Soon rose drunken laughter, more fearful than any scream or moaning.

Avil at least kept sober. Once he turned to Mermaza.

"What are these flashes? The lamps cast shadow. And this rumbling?"

"A storm approaches, though still far off."

"Foul omen at this season!" answered Avil, and under his breath—scoffer that he was—he muttered a spell against the "rain-fiends."

Atossa sat on her own high seat, watching, waiting, wondering. One can hardly say whether she had hopes or fears. She had not spoken since the miracle. What followed she remembered as she would recall a dim memory of long ago. Daniel was sitting by her side. Once she ventured, despite Belshazzar's frown, to speak to him.

"My father, the spirit of the holy Ahura is on you. Tell me, shall we be saved, you, and Ruth and I, from the power of these 'Lovers of Night'?"

And Daniel, calm, unblenching, sober, amid a hundred gibbering drunkards, answered with a confidence not of this world: "My child, we shall be saved. Doubt it not; but whether we be saved in this body, or depart to see Jehovah's face, He knoweth, not I. But His will is ever good."

The king interrupted boisterously, with unveiled mockery:—

"Give wisdom, noble Daniel. Shall I rebuild the walls of Uruk or spend the money on new canals at Sippar?"

The Hebrew made the king wince once more, as he looked on him.

"Lord of Babylon, think no more on walls and cities. Think of your past deeds. Think of the Just Spirit before whom you must stand."

"Verily, Jew," sneered Avil, "you will play your mad game to the end."

"To the end," was all the answer; but neither king nor pontiff made mock of Daniel again.

Deeper the drinking, madder the revelling. From the outer palace rose the laughter of soldiers and the city folk. The priests of Bel at length gathered courage from their wine. They roared out their hymn, and the dancing girls caught up red torches—brandishing, shrieking, dancing, one lurid whirl of uncaged demons. The officers put forth their hands time and again for the beakers which the eunuchs could not fill too fast. In the reaction after the portent, the scene became an orgy. The king's cheek flushed, his voice was loud and high. Tavat, the queen-mother, quitted the feast; and Atossa would have given all she possessed—how little!—to be suffered to follow. She had hardly tasted the cups pressed on her. She was utterly weary. The gold and jewels on her head seemed an intolerable weight. Oh, to be away—to have that scene blotted out, even by death's long slumber! Her head fell forward. Ahura was kind. Did she sleep? Suddenly Belshazzar's voice aroused her.

"Midnight, the feast ends; and you, O Jew, have lost!"

The king was standing. The lamps were smoking low; the noise of the feasters failing, as the wine accomplished its work. The tipsy priests had quavered out their last triumph song:—

> *"Bel-Marduk, who rulest forever,*
> *Thee, thee we praise!"*

Belshazzar addressed Mermaza. "Eunuch, deliver Daniel the Jew to Khatin for instant death. His mummery turns to his own ruin. *Now* truly let his weak god save!"

Even as he spoke there was a strange clamour rising in the palace without: a headlong gallop, a shouting, not of mirth but of alarm. None yet heeded.

"Your Majesty," Daniel was answering steadily, "suffer me only this: let me embrace my daughter Ruth."

The king nodded. "Be brief, for you have vexed me long!" Then, turning to Atossa: "Ah! lady, Queen—at last! to the harem! you are my wife!"

Atossa knew she was being taken by the hand; she saw all things dimly as through darkened glass. Nearer the gallop without, louder the shouting, and through it and behind a jar and a crashing—not of the elements surely! Daniel had clasped Ruth to his breast. His words were heard only by her and by Another. The king gestured impatiently. "Enough! Away!—" But no more; there was a panic cry at the portal, the howl of fifty voices in dismay; and right into the great hall, over the priceless carpets, through that revelling throng, spurred a rider in armour, two arrows sticking in target, blood on crest, blood streaming from the great wound in the horse's side. Up to the very dais he thundered; and there, in sight of all, the beast staggered, fell, while Igas-Ramman, the captain, struggled from beneath and stood before the king.

"*All is lost, lord of the Chaldees!*" and then he gasped for breath. But already in the outer palace was a fearful shout. "Arms! Rescue! The foe!"

Belshazzar tottered as he stood, caught the arm of his throne. His face was not ashen, but black as the clouds on high. "What is this, fool?" he called. And Igas answered, "O king, Sirusur and Belsandan are traitors. The retreat of Cyrus was a ruse. By night his host has returned. Imbi-Ilu, the exile, has tampered with the priests of Nabu, and they have opened the Borsippa water-gate. Sirusur has withdrawn the garrisons from the chief defences; Bilsandan has released the Persian prisoners and with them over-powered the guard at the Northern Citadel. Prince Darius is speeding to the palace."

"And you, where did you fight?" demanded the king.

"We made shift to defend an inner gate. Treachery is all about. We were attacked in the rear. I fled with the tidings. The Persians carry all before them—hear!" and hear they did; "the foe will come and none to stay!"

"None shall stay? Twenty thousand men of war in Babylon, and Belshazzar be snared as a bird in his own palace?" The king drew his sword, flinging far the scabbard.

"Up, princes of the Chaldees, up!" he trumpeted, above all the shriek-ings all around. "All is not lost! We will still prove the Jew the liar! Who-soever dares, follow me! All Babylon is not turned traitor. We will make our streets the Persian's grave!"

Yet while he cried it a second messenger panted into the great hall.

"The outer defences of the palace are forced, O king! The foe are everywhere!"

But Belshazzar leaped down from the dais, and sped about one lightning glance.

"Here, Khatin, stand by these women and this Jew! See that they do not flee. I will yet live to teach them fear."

A crash without made the casements shiver. Belshazzar sprang forward. "At them, men of Babylon; all is not yet lost!"

And, spurred by his example, the feasters rushed after. The cups lay on the tables, the lamps flickered overhead, the storm wind was shaking the broad canopy, but Atossa knew only one thing—the raging din that ever swelled louder. Then a second crash, mightier than the first; and out of it a shout in her own tongue of Iran.

"For Ahura, for Atossa!"

The battle-cry of the Persians—and Atossa knew that Darius, son of Hystaspes, was not far away.

Oh, the terror, the blind terror, which possessed the guilty, lustful city that night! the stupid guards staggering from their wine-pots; the priests, crazed with the lees, shrieking to Istar, to Bel, to Ramman, their strengthless hands catching at useless weapons. What drunken courage might do then was done. But of what avail? For treachery was everywhere. The citadel was betrayed; Imgur-Bel and Nimitti-Bel betrayed. The giant-built walls frowned down, but the massy gates were wide open—and through them streamed the foe. Right down the length of broad Nana Street, under the shadow of the *ziggurats* and the great warehouses, had charged the Persian cuirassiers, the finest cavalry in all the East. Through the Gate of Istar poured Harpagus and the Median chivalry; through the Gate of the Chaldees swept Hystaspes with the "Immortals," Cyrus's own life-guard, the stoutest spear-men in wide Iran. They met files of tipsy sword-hands, men who fought without order, without commanders. The howls of the slaves and women were on every hand. The light of burning houses brightened the invaders' pathway; and so the Aryan host fought onward, brushing resistance from its way as the torrent sweeps on the pebbles, all ranks straining toward one point, the palace; for the hour of reckoning had come to the "City of the Lie."

37 Hosea's Unfaithful Wife

More modern in tone than most biblical novels, Irene Patai's *The Valley of God* is a plea for the understanding of human frailty. An intimate story of a marriage, the novel is authentic in background and the Prophet Hosea is sympathetically drawn. Mrs. Patai's Hosea does not marry a harlot, as in the biblical account, but rather a woman who takes a lover in her loneliness only after Hosea's long neglect of her in pursuit of his mission. Hosea himself, must, therefore, be considered partly responsible for her wrongdoing. A former high school teacher, Mrs. Patai visited Israel to study the geographical background of her story and to retrace the possible wanderings of Hosea. Her husband, a biblical scholar and anthropologist, assisted her in the research.

> *The beginning of the word of the Lord by Hosea. And the Lord said to Hosea, Go, take unto thee a wife of whoredoms and the children of whoredoms: for the land hath committed great whoredom, departing from the Lord.*
>
> *So he went and took Gomer the daughter of Diblaim; which conceived, and bare him a son.*
>
> HOSEA: I, 2–3

> *Then said the Lord unto me, Go yet, love a woman beloved of her friend, yet an adulteress, according to the love of the Lord toward the children of Israel, who look to other gods, and love flagons of wine.*
>
> HOSEA: III, 1

THE VALLEY OF GOD by IRENE PATAI

HE DREAMED THE NIGHTMARE of his love—the dumb bewilderment, the hurt misery. Why? To go back and forth over time, knowing nothing, understanding nothing, and yet the devastating summing up—the voiceless dying, the ending of one love, the ending of one life, the ending and beginning all fused, drifting by before him like a slowly oozing remnant of a muddy stream. Why? To say why! How many days and nights of saying, how many years of saying, yet to speak and to say nothing. Only the fury of the clenched fist, the hoarse voice, the breath all spent, *I don't understand, I don't understand—* then pain and hate and a voice mocking, *But you do, you do, you do—*

She loved you—yes, she loved you. The rains caress you, the stars look down and greet you, the moon salutes you. But she, she loved you! Surely she loved that day among the green grasses, her head upon your breast, the white heat, the tiny pearls of sweat, the tickling of the ant upon your flesh, the full lips—the pounding heart—the drawing of the breath—Was that not love?

And the night in the vineyards when you searched for her in the lanterned arbor and she came to you from Jonathan's arms. Was that not love? And the marriage day, the scraping dancing feet, the white circle of the moon, the long sharp dagger and your life's blood flowing, flowing—

It was long ago and he yearned for her at Tekoa even while he searched for the dying prophet. Diblayim was there and he took up the flame from his hand and held it in his and vowed his vow to Yahweh and to her. Dear good friend! Did you know, old friend? Did you guess then that my heart's plunder should be her doing, your own flesh and blood? Yes, you knew, and you, Benayahu, and you, Yael, and you, Abiel. You knew but you told me nothing. Why could you not tell me? Were you not all my friends? And You, O Lord, did You not love me? Was I not Your holy man, Your prophet? Was I not pledged to You and You to me? Why did You give her to me?

It would be better to go mad, he thought, stark raving mad, than to face this. Better than that to seek Death. He said, God, what need have You of me—a poor prophet who holds no iron rod but a frail and useless sycamore? Better to let me die, for prophets are stronger dead than alive. Let not the earth cover up my blood till my vengeance is complete but, God, if You love me let me die! He said this and believed still that Yahweh loved him, yet the Lord did not hear him, did not take him, and he saw only her face and did not go mad—

The time came when he could not endure the cliff, for wherever he looked his eyes found the house, and no matter how hard he tried his thoughts turned on her. Once he saw Jonathan walking on the road and was filled with such uncontrollable rage he would have gone down to kill him had he not wrestled with himself. When Jonathan vanished into the hills, he fell upon the ground and beat it with his fists. Afterwards he fed his agony with visions of their bodies fused, asking himself, Was he a better man than I— did he love her more than I? until he reached the point where he knew at last that Yahweh had forsaken him. Why, he cried again impotently—with anger. Did I merit it? Did I not give You my faith and the strength of my body all the days of my years that were sworn to You? My faith and my flesh—even that. What more can You want of me? He was no Abraham—that he knew. While he had been scourged he had not rotted in prison for an entire year, like Abraham, without food, without water, nor had he been burnt at the stake. But if he was no Abraham, neither had Yahweh been to him what He had been to Abraham, first issuing forth clear water through the walls of the cell, then sending His angel to feed him, and at the stake causing the flames to touch him not, but replacing them with a garden of roses. I am no Abraham, he said, but I am Your prophet and You know me not—

At length the anger passed but a dark and fearful torment entered his being, stifling his rage and freeing the cold constraint of reason. Looking straight into the mirror of his soul, he saw there the bitter specter, the wormwood truth and he cried, Must I endure even this, this further trial heaped on the other—Death, Death erase it! It was there and he could hold his breath until the flush of his skin turned blue, but he would have to look at it and see it and there was no penance he could do to make it right because he knew and God knew. He forced himself to say it, hearing the words with the lasting scald of pain. *I have loved her more than I have loved You and I have known it always!*

This shook him to the very marrow of his being. He cried, Mother of Grasses let me sleep, and threw himself upon the earth in a kind of stupor. He lay thus for hours, floating on the ragged edge of somnolence. Submerged, his mind was like a void, but when he drifted back to consciousness he sought the knowledge which had come to him. Remembering pushed him clear across the threshold and he wakened sobbing.

For her I have betrayed You, he said. I have loved her, her flesh and her lips and her woman's breasts, and for these I have abandoned You! Am I better than Jehu into whom You poured the essence of Your will and caused to wipe out the House of Omri? Am I better than Samson whom You set against the Philistines? Or Saul whom You called to bind up the tribes? Behold Your prophet! Like these, a broken vessel which has lost its oil, a scattered heap of potsherds lying in a pool stinking and foaming and settled with dead flies. . . .

He was obsessed with a hatred of himself, of the impulse of his body which had betrayed him. He thought of the holy man of Mizpah who had put out the light of his eyes so that he might not be distracted from his devotions. With a cry of anguish he unsheathed his knife, thinking to put an end to that part of himself which defeated him, which would go on defeating him. He bared his loins. The deep ugly scar where he had drawn blood on his wedding night leaped up at him and a breath of the tenderness, the ecstasy, the exquisite joy of that night swept over him. He wanted to cry. To forswear love, to rip it out of my body so I become a stone, like the futile waters of the sea? How can I go on living? He changed the direction of the knife so that it was pointed squarely at his breast, but his hand trembled, he could not plunge it into his body, and at length the knife fell to the ground. I cannot live and I cannot die! He was imprisoned in a cell, cut off from man and God, the only soul within the universe. He could not bear it. Set me free he said in terror. Since now he could not call on God, he called Diblayim, Diblayim, but there was only silence. . . .

Now he could think only of flight—redemption lay in flight—time and distance. Leave this place, forget her, forget Israel. Seek only peace, only peace—then seek out God again. He ordered Abiel to make ready their asses and then like a wind proceeded out of Dothan with no backward glance and no thought of return.

Their animals laboriously climbed the peaks of the mountain under a bright sky. In the valley everything was in bloom—the polished grape, the olive, the glittering fields. Overhead birds fluted sweetly. The air had a fresh tangy smell as the wind sprayed the rich aroma of blossoming over the hills. Greedily he drank in the sweetness in a desperate effort to rid himself of the gloom which clung to him. But all the loveliness hurt him and set him to thinking with great irony of all this glorious bounty so munificently bestowed, so wantonly consumed. The nakedness beneath these shreds of splendor made it a land of waste and ruin. He said bitterly, Israel is a faithless woman, and turned his back on her.

They had been traveling hardly more than one hour when they heard the sound of hooves and perceived Benayahu on horseback bearing down on them.

"Master, master!" he cried with an anguished air, flinging his huge bulk recklessly off the side of the horse as though he cared not what happened to him. His otherwise expressionless face was contorted with fear, his black hair disheveled by the wind, and he looked altogether half demented.

Hosea regarded him half in dismay, for the sight of him brought back vividly all that he wished to forget. He dreaded the burden of the message. Coldly he said, "Why do you follow me?"

Benayahu threw himself upon the ground. "They fear—" he began hopelessly. His voice broke.

"Come, raise yourself," Hosea spoke harshly.

There were tears in Benayahu's eyes. Dumbly he regarded Hosea. "Pray, sire—"

"For what should I pray?"

"The child will not come—"

"What child?"

"Sire, she will die. Pray, sire."

Then Hosea laughed a hoarse, bitter laugh. "Aye, I will pray. The cracked potsherd will pray. But who will listen? That you must tell me."

"You are a prophet."

"Do you bid God's prophet pray? Hear me then. Hear my prayer, then go your way and follow me no more." He sat astride his beast upon the mountain path drenched in the fullest glory of the sun. With a magnificent gesture he raised his long arms and lifted his beautiful voice which rang out like the drum of thunder. "Give her, O Lord, a miscarrying womb and dry breasts. Give her the withered root, the shriveled fruit. Give her, O Lord, whatsoever You will give—for I hate her, I will drive her out of my house, I will love her no more!"

Benayahu's large body seemed to crumple. Falteringly he whispered, "Forgive me, sire . . . I was thinking of my wife."

For a long time Hosea stared after him. Then he said, "Let us go back."

A sharp cry of pain tore through the night.

He shivered. Her voice so deep, so anguished—a part of her he did not know, the part of her that had to do with suffering. What did he know of her

suffering? He had never been home when she labored. Always he came afterwards when she had rested and restored herself and the child was already a
creature of spirit. This he had missed—her voice crying out in the night
because of his—A sharp twinge of pain contracted his heart. Not his, not
his—She was yours and you cared nothing, knew nothing. She was yours and
you turned your back on her. Yes, even when you took her at the gully, even
when you gashed your thigh upon your wedding night, it was no thought for
her. There was no love on earth which did not spring from the inner selfish-
ness of man. No purity of love. Only God's—

Another cry of pain tore through the night.

What suffering! To live was to suffer. To bring a child into the world,
to lose a friend, to face death—just to be human. No! What suffering was
that? Only a heart that was pure, universally good, could know true suffering.
What did man know of that?

If man's suffering was great, how much greater was God's! If he could
so love such a woman, how much greater must be the love of Yahweh for His
people, how much more infinite His sorrow at their dereliction, at murder and
bloodshed, the Maiden defiled! How enormous His pain! His bride whom He
loved surrendered to others, gone after greed and strife, giving to others that
precious gift which belonged to Him alone! While He lavished His bounty
upon her, rendering her thanks to others!

Let her suffer! Uncover her shame in the sight of her lovers. Cause all
her mirth to cease, her feasts, her moons and her Sabbaths and all her appointed seasons. Lay waste her vines and fig trees whereof she has said,
These are my hire that my lovers have given me. Make them a forest, and
let the beasts of the field eat them, and visit upon her the days of the Baalim
when she offered unto them and decked herself with earrings and jewels and
went after her lovers and forgot You!

For love is what You have wanted from Israel—a love which compasses
all the jewels of the soul. Failing this, countenance no other kind, for it is
better to see her perish than permit her to survive unregenerate. . . .

Another cry of pain tore through the night, penetrating him, calling him
back to her.

He saw her lying on her mat, the dear form torn and racked, the lips
contorted, the sweet breasts veined and swollen. What has come upon you
through man's lust! The whole pattern of their life returned and he saw it all
as one great web from first to last, twined and intertwined, from the buying of
the water lever to the ending on the rocks with the name of Jonathan—and
he saw that the more he struggled to forsake her, the more he cleaved to her
—and he saw in it some purpose—and he saw in it the Hand of God and to
God he now addressed himself, half pleading, half triumphant, for now he
saw that he was no longer damned, for if he saw that purpose, then he could
serve God still.

He said, How can I give her up? Can You renounce her whom You
have loved through so many years? Can You deliver to the vultures her into
whose clay You have blown the spark of life, whose wounds You have bound

up again and again, whom You have led through the desert and succored from her enemies? Even now, when You have reached the limits of Your suffering, can You abandon her who has inspired a love so great, so passionate, so binding?

Behold Your love! Is it not mirrored in the corn and the wine and the oil which You pour out to her, and the silver and the gold which You multiply for her? Was it not manifest in the endless days You spent in wooing her? In the divine patience which restored her to You after bloodshed and trickery? Your love has endured though she were weak and gone astray and it shall yet lift her up and bring her back once more into Your arms . . .

Another cry of pain tore through the night.

He sprang to his feet. "I will ransom her from Sheol, I will redeem her from death. Where are your plagues, O Death? Where your pestilence, Sheol!"

Then Hosea went down to the house and stood above the winnowing basket and gazed upon the boy. He could not tear his eyes away from the little creature, so ugly and misshapen with its mottled skin and wizened features. "From the dust has God made you," he said with tears in his eyes. He took Lo-Ruhamah in his arms and hugged her tightly. Then he went to Gomer and watched her gentle breathing. He saw the fine lines which pain had drawn upon her face and her poor arms daubed with blue spots. The barest smile framed her lips. He waited by her bedside, feeling strangely at peace.

When she woke, she started at the sight of him and her smile faded.

He took both her hands in his and kissed her cheek. And since he wished to please her because she was so white and frail and he was glad that she still lived, and he knew that she sorrowed when he gave the names of Jezreel and Lo-Ruhamah to their children, he said, "The choice is yours. Give the child a name."

She stared at him, not grasping his meaning. Then, in a tight, thin voice, "He is not of your house."

His frame shuddered ever so little. He caught his breath. "Then call the boy Lo-Ami, Not of My People," he said.

He stood before her for a moment. Then taking up his dagger and his sandals and his staff he stood at the threshold. He spoke softly. "Many days shall you wait for me. But you shall not play the harlot and you shall not be any man's nor will I be yours until the day I return to bide with you in this house."

38 The Prophecies of Amos

The Herdsman by Dorothy Clarke Wilson is an almost wholly fictional work because there is so little revealed in the Bible about Amos the prophet. We are told scarcely more about the man than that he carried his message from Judea to Samaria where he forecast the death and destruction which would come from the north. Miss Wilson's Amos is a man with a social conscience, and the contemporary implications of her story are obvious. Amos cried out against the wealthy aristocrats who were selling arms and grain to the Assyrians who were preparing for aggressive war. Like Miss Wilson's four other biblical novels, *The Herdsman* is well written and makes maximum use of the biblical setting against which her story is told.

> *The words of Amos, who was among the herdmen of Tekoa, which he saw concerning Israel in the days of Uzziah king of Judah, and in the days of Jeroboam the son of Joash king of Israel, two years before the earthquake.*
>
> *And he said, The Lord will roar from Zion, and utter his voice from Jerusalem: and the habitations of the shepherds shall mourn, and the top of Carmel shall wither.*
>
> AMOS: I, 1–2

THE HERDSMAN by DOROTHY CLARKE WILSON

SAMARIA WAS IN AN UPROAR. One topic of conversation was on every tongue: the words and actions of a certain tall, bearded stranger who had appeared at intervals in various parts of the city, delivered himself of amazing utterances, and then vanished mysteriously. No one knew who he was or whence he came, but the conjectures were many, varied, and contradictory, as were the general comments:

He was a tall man, at least seven feet high, and when he spoke he stretched visibly, becoming eight or nine and sometimes even ten feet.

He was the god of one of Israel's old enemies—Dagon, perhaps, of Philistia—come in human form to work evil in Israel. In fact one man had proved him to be Dagon by surreptitiously lifting his coat as he passed and ascertaining that his lower extremities were actually the tail of a fish.

He was Elijah the prophet risen from the dead and come to denounce Jeroboam as once he had dared to denounce the great Ahab.

393

He was a creature of evil from the underworld. A child over whom his shadow passed had been shaken by convulsions in its mother's arms.

He was a celestial being sent from above the firmament. A blind man happening to touch his *simlah* had been healed instantly of his infirmity.

He was a wise man—a madman—a second Samuel—a second Goliath —an Edomite—an Egyptian—an Ethiopian—a darkskinned messenger from the far regions of the Indus—

Ben Sered had listened incuriously to all comments and conjectures. He had never seen the man and had not the slightest desire to do so. Until today he had been able to pursue his customary policy of minding his own business —which unfortunately for his peace of mind included that of Jeroboam and all his myriads of subjects—and keeping himself moderately aloof from the whole proceeding. But today at Ben Othni's insistence he had reluctantly agreed to meet with the two other royal commissioners to discuss the whole matter.

And now, as if that were not enough, he had allowed himself to be tricked into this interview with Bilhah. If he had suspected for a moment what she wanted of him—But he had supposed, of course, that she was merely angling for some new trifle, and since the new increase in the tax rate, to meet the expenses of the military campaigns in the north, he had been making so much money he did not know what to do with it. Even another jeweled peacock would furnish not too undiverting an outlet. Besides, he had inadvertently allowed his stores of wine to run low, and he needed a really good stimulant to fortify him for the coming interview with his colleagues. He could always count on his wife to provide the best in refreshment and beverage.

But now, even over a goblet of the finest and most fragrant Lebanon wine, he grimaced distastefully. For Bilhah apparently wanted nothing more than to vent on him her anger and outrage over an event which had taken place at the queen's dinner for royal ladies the preceding evening and which had rendered every one of them almost speechless. What a pity, Ben Sered could not help mumbling into his goblet, that it had not done so entirely!

Bilhah gave him a sharp glance, interpreted the mumbling as an appreciative gurgle, and proceeded with her story. Her great hulk shook so violently with anger that the little jeweled snake heads darted in and out of the crevices of her chins and wrists with startling rapidity.

"There we were lying on our couches in the most sumptuous outdoor banquet hall you can imagine, a courtyard garden planted with vines and pomegranate and apricot trees, all in full bloom, and being served food and wine the like of which was never seen even on King Solomon's table, and who should rush in all at once and begin raving at us but this—this horrible male creature dressed in garments that you wouldn't let your poorest slave wear! And the things he said to us! Calling us—calling us—cows of Bashan—"

"Calling you *what?*" Ben Sered leaned forward suddenly amid his cush-

ions, his upraised eyebrows the first indication of genuine interest which he
had shown.

"*Cows of Bashan.*"

Ben Sered choked over his wine. "Cows of—" He made another choking sound which ended suspiciously like a chuckle. "Go on, my dear. What
else did he say?"

Bilhah shuddered, giving a very able imitation of a mountain in the
throes of an earthquake. "What *else!* What else indeed! He told us the day
was coming when we were going to be—be dragged out with fish hooks
fastened through our noses and our—our buttocks! And—and *thrown out on
the dump heap!*"

"Humph!" Ben Sered drained his goblet. It sent a delightful warmth
coursing through his body. "He said all those things, did he? A—a very
unusual person, to say the least. Cows of Bashan!" He stole a surrepti-
tious glance at the carefully oiled bulk of outraged human flesh which
was Bilhah, pictured the sleek fat beasts which he had seen milling round
and round the narrow enclosures in the market place, and almost choked
again. "Cows of Bashan, indeed!"

"Well?" Bilhah's tone became suddenly militant. "What are you going
to do about it?"

Ben Sered looked startled. "What am I—"

"Certainly. It's up to you, isn't it, you and the other commissioners,
since the king is away? Surely you're not going to let the queen and all the
other noblewomen of Samaria, to say nothing of your wife and daughter, be
insulted by a—a raving maniac!"

"Was Ruhamah there too?"

"Certainly she was. The wife of Ben Othni's son was naturally invited.
Her couch was so close to the—the creature she could have reached out and
touched him."

"And what did she think of this—interloper?"

"I haven't seen her since to talk to. But she was so insulted she got
right up from her couch and left the banquet right after he disappeared. Some
of the women thought it was a joke planned especially for their amusement.
The queen has a rather strange sense of humor. But it was no joke," Bilhah
finished grimly. "I only wish you could have heard him!"

"So do I!" replied Ben Sered heartily. He helped himself to another
goblet of wine. Cows of Bashan, indeed!

Even later, when he sat on his upper housetop and listened to Ben Othni
and Obed Shebna conversing heatedly about this same strange visitant whose
peculiar utterances seemed to be turning the whole city upside down, he found
it difficult to regard the matter seriously.

Suppose the fellow did make a few shocking statements, what difference
did it make? Look at Obed Shebna now, pacing back and forth, back and
forth in the hot sun until the sweat poured in rivulets down his thin, nervous
face; letting himself get all stirred up about a speech this man was supposed

to have made in front of the royal citadel, when a number of soldiers with their military leaders had been on parade! Or look at Ben Othni, so concerned about the importance of the matter that he wouldn't even allow a slave on the housetop to wield a fan, for fear their discussion would be overheard!

Ben Sered suffered his discomfort in silence, thinking with pleasant anticipation of the summer home he had recently built up in the mountains of Lebanon. If Jeroboam would only return to his capital where he belonged instead of traveling all over Iturea and Gilead to visit his conquering armies, his officials might not have to endure the heat much longer. The more wealthy families of Samaria were all moving out of the city now in summer, and many of them had gone to their mountain homes already to escape the heat.

"Imagine the audacity of the fellow!" Obed Shebna's wooden sandals clicked with military precision on the smooth tiles of the floor. "Interrupting the triumphal march of one of our victorious generals straight from his latest conquests in the outposts of Gilead! And saying the things he said!"

"Just what did he say?" demanded Ben Othni, watching his colleague's every movement intently.

"I told you once. He stood there in front of the high citadel and, lifting up his arms, called on the other great nations of the world to attack us. 'Proclaim it in the fortresses of Assyria,' he said, 'and in the citadels of Egypt. Let them muster their armies against Samaria. Let them come and see the bad job Israel has made of herself, for she is full of oppression and injustice and robbery.' Those weren't his exact words, of course. He used a lot of poetic falderol. But that's what he meant."

"Go on," commanded Ben Othni tersely.

"He pretended he was quoting things Yahweh had told him, and he certainly painted a gruesome picture. 'As a herdsman snatches from a lion's mouth' he said, 'two bones or a piece of an ear, so there will be nothing left of the people of Samaria but a bedpost or a piece of silk from a divan. Both the winter house and the summer house will be destroyed, and all the palaces with their inlays of ivory. There will be no more great mansions. For Yahweh has spoken.' "

Ben Sered shivered suddenly. A coldness seemed to have passed over the housetop, yet there was no breeze. He began to understand the restive nervousness of Obed Shebna and the tense concentration of Ben Othni.

"Just what do you know about this man?" he asked.

"Not a thing," said Obed Shebna quickly.

"A good deal," said Ben Othni deliberately. "He made his first appearance at the spring festival at Bethel. After that he turned up in several towns, making speeches and upsetting things generally. He was at Gilgal and Shiloh and Shechem. Since he entered Samaria some two weeks ago I have had spies on his trail constantly."

"Trust you for that!" said Ben Sered to himself grimly. But he listened intently as Ben Othni proceeded.

"He lives in a hole in the wall down on the very edge of the city with a poor scholar named Ephraim ben Esdras. I believe he's a native of a little town in Judah. I thought at first he was one of the *nabis* but there seems to be no connection. The *nabis* are harmless. This man is dangerous. If we let him keep on, people are going to begin to listen to what he says. They're going to ask questions."

"What kind of questions?" Ben Sered was no longer quiet and undisturbed.

"Where their tax money goes, for one thing," said Ben Othni bluntly. "And why you and I live in houses of hewn stone while theirs are made of mud—if they have any. Don't you see that our whole system of living depends on our religion? If the poor of this country ever got the idea into their heads that their poverty wasn't the result of their own sins, that it wasn't according to the will of Yahweh—" Ben Othni bared his large white teeth significantly. "You see?"

"Yes. I—begin to see," said Ben Sered slowly.

"Suppose he's right," injected Obed Shebna suddenly. "From the military standpoint, I mean. Egypt, no. She's fat and lazy and she has everything she needs. Nations that have all they need don't fight. Edom? Philistia? Damascus? No. But—Assyria—"

"Pooh!" Ben Othni pulled his untidy beard impatiently. "Live in the present, Shebna. This isn't a hundred years ago. Assyria's day is over."

"We've let enough munitions and raw materials pass through from Egypt to Assyria to wipe us off the face of the earth."

"Yes, and by doing so made ourselves the richest and most powerful kingdom of our size in the world."

"Of our size, yes," returned Obed Shebna. "But when you begin to compare us with the great nations, like Egypt—*and Assyria*—"

"You see, Simon?" Ben Othni shot his colleague a triumphant glance. "If this crazy fool from the wilderness can hoodwink a brilliant statesman like Obed Shebna—"

The irony was not lost on Ben Sered. He knew that his two colleagues were bitter enemies. Nevertheless he recognized the truth in Ben Othni's double-edged barb. Reluctantly he agreed to see and hear the "crazy fool from the wilderness" if the opportunity presented itself, that he might judge for himself just how dangerous he might be.

The opportunity came sooner than he had expected. Toward evening of the next day, which was the sabbath, a message came from Ben Othni bidding him go at once to the market place.

His religious obligations having been fulfilled early in the day, Ben Sered had yielded himself to rest and to the ministrations of his slaves. His hair was oiled but not curled, the massaging of his body but partially completed. Hastily his slaves bundled him into his clothes. There was no time even to insert the lining of stiffened linen which added height to his headdress and therefore, he flattered himself, to his short, stocky figure.

When finally he reached the market place he felt ill-dressed, deflated, and in a bad humor not only toward Ben Othni but toward the stranger who had occasioned his untimely journey and who obviously had no intention of putting in an appearance. A likely place to find him, indeed, Ben Sered fumed to himself, remembering suddenly that it was the sabbath, when no selling of any kind was permitted. Ben Othni had played a fine trick on him.

The market place was not so deserted, however, as he had expected. Most of the merchants were already in their booths and setting out their wares in preparation for the hour of sunset when the sabbath would be officially over. Prospective buyers were beginning to gather in large numbers. There were advantages in arriving at just this time, Ben Sered soon discovered. A couple of caravans had come into the city just before the sabbath, and he was able to inspect the new wares before they had been all picked over. Half the well-to-do citizens of Samaria were soon following his example. He found several articles which took his fancy—a small cedar chest with gold inlays of lotus flowers, a conch shell of remarkable iridescence, a piece of real Mycenaean pottery—and kept one eye fixed on them and the other on the slowly sinking sun. The leisurely deliberation with which it settled slowly toward the housetops was maddening. And even after it disappeared it would be necessary to wait for the signal from the high place which indicated its disappearance below the true horizon.

To make the time pass more swiftly Ben Sered wandered through the other bazaars. Remembering that he needed a new court robe to wear at the king's reception when his majesty should return from the north, he bethought himself of the fine wool which came from the shoulders of that small, stunted breed of sheep pastured near the wilderness of Judah and went to the farmer's section to see if there was any to be put on sale. There were herdsmen there from Tekoa, but their goods were all in unwrapped bales, not yet on display.

Disappointed, he was about to turn away when a man standing at one side of the booth attracted his attention. Tall, unusually muscular, his skin burned almost as deep a bronze as the rich brown stripes in his *simlah,* he was obviously one of the group of herdsmen yet, strangely, not a part of them. He wore the same plain, coarse garments, so it was not his dress which made him different. Nor did it seem to be his face, though Ben Sered could see only the profile, a strong, definite outline which looked as if it had been cut with bold, overgenerous strokes of a scalpel and then carefully, painstakingly chiseled. It was the way he stood, perhaps, the way he held his tall, magnificent body, with the easy, unconscious grace of perfect self-mastery and co-ordination. Ben Sered had known only one other person who had held himself like that, confidently, unbowed, whether he wore the garments of a slave or stood in the place of honor at a royal table, speaking words which a king's son would not have dared to utter. Hastily, because he shied like a frightened horse from his memories and because he saw the sun was setting, Ben Sered returned to the foreign bazaar to keep his eye on his coveted treasures.

The signal came at last—three clear bugle notes—and almost instantly the market place burst into its customary confusion. Bargaining rose to shrill and rapid crescendos. Salesmen barked their wares. Children and dogs darted underfoot. Pushcarts and ox wagons creaked and groaned. Slaves were hoisted to the auction block and put through their paces. The whole noisy, rumbling, lumbering machine was again in motion.

Ben Sered was able to buy only two of the three things he desired, the conch shell and the pottery. A rival buyer got the chest first. Thinking he might be able to bargain with him, Ben Sered set out after him in hot pursuit. But he could make little headway. The crowds seemed to be surging in one direction, and he was caught in the middle of them. Too small of stature to see what was the disturbance or attraction which drew them, he struggled mightily but to no avail, losing his precious conch shell in the process.

Then suddenly he ceased to struggle, and he forgot his conch shell. For somewhere up in front of the crowd, in the region of the farmers' bazaar, a voice was speaking. It cut through the confusion sharply like a blade, leaving a great swath of silence.

> *"Listen to this!*
> *You who crush the needy*
> *And take bread from the mouths of the poor!*
> *You who mutter, 'When will the feast be over,*
> *That we may sell our grain?*
> *When will the sabbath be past*
> *That we may put our goods on sale?'*
> *You who make your measures small and your*
> *weighing stones large*
> *And cheat by tampering with your scales!*
> *You who sell the very refuse of your grain*
> *To people who are hungry,*
> *Who account a handful of silver*
> *More important than a human being!"*

There was a moment's hush, like a long-drawn breath, then the voice continued:

> *"Yahweh has sworn by the pride of Jacob:*
> *'I never will forget what you have done.*
> *Do I love you any better than the Ethiopians,*
> *You people of Israel?*
> *To be sure, I brought you up out of Egypt;*
> *But I brought the Philistines also from Crete,*
> *And the people of Damascus from Kir.*
> *Listen to me, Israel!*
> *I am keeping my eyes on your sinful kingdom,*
> *I will destroy it from the face of the earth!'"*

Silence hung over the market place like a solid, palpable substance, even after the voice had ceased.

"He's gone!" someone shouted hysterically, and the spell was broken. Gradually the crowd broke its tight, compact unity. Ben Sered moved

through it automatically, oblivious of the excited comments which were bursting about him. The voice still rang in his ears. He had a queer sensation that
he had heard it, not just a few moments previously, but yesterday, perhaps,
or the day before, or even longer, much longer ago; that it had been ringing
in his ears with the same sharp, imperative insistency for a very long, long
time. Was it this impression of timelessness, he wondered, which made it
seem so strangely familiar?

Ben Othni appeared suddenly at his side, smiling. His large white teeth
seemed to have grown in size until they looked oddly like tusks. "You see?"
he demanded triumphantly. "You understand now how dangerous this man
is?"

"Yes," said Ben Sered.

And suddenly he did see and understand, very definitely. The man was
dangerous. He doubted if even Ben Othni understood how very dangerous
he was. For Ben Othni was stolid and unimaginative. He thought only in
terms of shekels and customs duties, of government and *gibborim*. When the
implications of the words he had just heard penetrated Ben Sered's consciousness, as they did now with a startling suddenness, they brought with them a
fear which was like physical sickness.

"What's the matter?" asked Ben Othni, catching him suddenly by the
arm. "Did you stumble over something? Look out! You'll drop that vase.
There! I told you so."

"No matter," said Ben Sered, glancing down casually at the remnants
of the piece of Mycenaean pottery.

"No matter!" exclaimed Obed Shebna, appearing suddenly at his other
shoulder. "You must have paid a fortune for the thing."

Ben Sered walked on up the hill, not bothering to explain that a vase,
however expensive, seemed a trifling thing when one suddenly felt the foundations of society tottering beneath one's feet. For in one swift flash of dis-
cernment he knew vaguely that the voice in the market place, unless abruptly
silenced, would wreak greater havoc than any that had ever spoken. It would
turn not only Israel but the whole world upside down. For its sharp, clean
blade had struck unerringly at the very roots of society itself.

"Did you hear him say that Israel would be destroyed?" demanded Obed
Shebna eagerly. "That's an affront to our national honor. I told you he was a
traitor."

"And a heretic also," put in Ben Othni. "Did you notice that part about
Yahweh having an interest in other nations beside Israel? If that isn't heresy—"

"Yes," said Ben Sered.

He wondered how they could be so blind and stupid, concerning themselves about such small matters as national honor and theological quibblings.
It was not Israel, the nation, which the words of this strange man threatened.
It was the whole structure of society, with its comfortable stabilities of class
and race and privilege. It was their way of life. For the first time in the history
of the world, so far as Ben Sered knew, someone had dared to propound

the possibility of a society in which men would be held responsible for the well-being of their fellows.

"We must stop him!" Ben Sered did not recognize his own voice, it sounded so harsh and unnatural. "He must be seized at once—arrested—"

Over his head Ben Othni and Obed Shebna exchanged a quick glance of triumph.

"It has already been done," the former assured him. "When he left the market place, the *gibborim* were ready to seize him. At this moment, we hope, he is in my house waiting for us."

A considerable crowd of dignitaries was assembled in the inner court-yard of Ben Othni's house. There were seats for the three commissioners among the judges who had been summoned hastily from their positions in the city gate. All had proceeded according to schedule. The arrest had been made quietly, outside the market place, without the knowledge of the rabble, who were disposed to herald the stranger as a divine messenger. He was at the moment in a small anteroom in charge of two burly *gibborim.*

"This is just an informal questioning," Ben Othni told the assembled dignitaries smoothly. "It is not in any sense a legal trial. Hence there need be no witnesses for the defense. If we decide to take action, it will be in effect a royal edict given by the king's deputies in his absence and enforced by his private police force, the *gibborim.*" He gestured curtly to an attendant. "Have the man brought in."

At sight of the tall, straight figure towering at least a handbreadth above the heads of the two burly *gibborim,* Ben Sered started violently. It was the man he had seen standing in the farmers' bazaar beside the booth occupied by the herdsmen of Tekoa. He could see his whole face now, not just the profile. With sudden intentness he studied the arresting features, thrown into bold relief by the flaring lamps in Ben Othni's courtyard: high, broad forehead; straight lips and sensitive nostrils and determined chin; protruding brows and high cheek bones, apparently designed by nature as a protective frame for the wide-spaced, brilliant eyes. Only in one person had he ever seen eyes of that particular brilliance and color, neither brown nor black nor gray—

Ben Sered trembled. The eyes met his, and a flicker of something more than recognition—sympathy, might it be, or perhaps pity?—passed between them. The blood moved in a sudden rushing tide through his body, beating like hammers against his temples. His lips, grown suddenly stiff and cold, silently mouthed one word.

"Amos!"

The inquisition began, conducted by the most venerable of the judges, who took all his cues from Ben Othni and Obed Shebna.

"Treason . . . heresy . . . people have heard him say . . . duty of loyal citizens in the king's absence . . . insults to noblewomen . . . Yahweh's own people . . . city's most respected merchants . . . words and antics of a mad man."

Ben Sered did not listen. Words—fragments of sentences—swept over him, like waves over a motionless rock, but they had no meaning for him. He was being stirred and shaken by emotions which for years he had believed dead. One fact alone possessed reality: Amos. The man he had seen standing in the bazaar was Amos. The voice he had heard in the market place had been Amos' voice. The tall, straight figure quietly facing his accusers here in the courtyard of Ben Othni—

"My son," he said to himself over and over. "Amos, my son, my beloved son."

"Well? What have you to say for yourself?" a voice asked coolly.

The tall, straight figure seemed to straighten itself and become even taller. "Nothing for myself," replied the man quietly, "but much in the name of Yahweh." He leveled an accusing finger at the judges.

> *"You who make a farce of justice,*
> *And interpret the law as your selfishness dictates,*
> *Who hate any man who exposes you*
> *And loathe all those who tell you the truth!*
> *You takers of bribes, who browbeat honest men*
> *And defraud the poor of justice!"*

The dark eyes swept the rows of faces like a flail.

> *"Because you have crushed the poor*
> *And taken bread from the hungry,*
> *Though you build yourselves houses of hewn stone,*
> *You shall not live in them;*
> *Though you plant vineyards for yourselves,*
> *You shall drink no wine from them.*

> *"For thus Yahweh has spoken:*
> *'In all your city squares there shall be moaning,*
> *And cries of anguish in all your streets.*
> *Even the peasants shall mingle their wails*
> *With the dirges of professional mourners,*
> *When I, Yahweh, shall sweep through your midst!' "*

Shrill and penetrating, cutting through the courtyard like a chilling wind, the voice rose and fell in the familiar funereal rhythm of the mourners' dirge.

> *"Fallen, never again to rise,*
> *Is virgin Israel;*
> *Forsaken on her land she lies,*
> *With none to raise her!"*

In the stunned silence which followed his words the tall, straight figure turned and walked quietly, unhurriedly from the courtyard. His accusers sat motionless, staring after him; even the *gibborim* seemed powerless to move. . . .

39 Jonah and the Whale

For the past forty-five years, Robert Nathan has been writing some of the best-wrought, most charming novels of our time. There is a fey quality about his writing, a gentleness of touch which tends to make his work look less important than louder and more bombastic novels, but that look is deceptive. Nathan has reflected his time and reflected it well. As a novelist he rarely strayed far from the path he selected many years ago—the short novel, compassionate and perceptive. Unlike most of his contemporaries, he does not condemn his fellow men, but rather chides them. There is a satiric touch to his writing, but also a kindness that seems to indicate less disapproval than understanding of human frailties. In *Jonah*, Nathan approaches the prophet with tongue in cheek, making of him a sort of buffoon who tries God's patience. The approach, like that of other biblical novelists writing in the mid-twenties, is an attempt to both explain and explain away. But no one can be offended by the author of *Portrait of Jenny*, *Journey of Tapiola*, and *So Love Returns*, because the gentleness of the writer comes through, and there is no malice.

Now the word of the Lord came unto Jonah the son of Amittai, saying,

Arise, go to Nineveh, that great city, and cry against it; for their wickedness is come up before me.

But Jonah rose up to flee unto Tarshish from the presence of the Lord, and went down to Joppa; and he found a ship going to Tarshish: so he paid the fare thereof, and went down into it, to go with them unto Tarshish from the presence of the Lord.

JONAH: I, 1–3

JONAH by ROBERT NATHAN

GOD WENT DOWN to the water. He stood on the shores of the sea and called; like the voice of the storm a name rolled forth from those august lips across the deep. And the deeps trembled. Presently a commotion took place in the waters; wet and black the huge form of Leviathan rose gleaming from the sea, and floated obediently before its God.

The Lord spoke, and the whale listened. After He had explained the situation, God said:

"I foresee that Jonah will not go to Nineveh as I command. He will attempt to flee from Me, and he will choose the sea as the best means of escape. It will not help him. I shall raise a storm upon the waters, and the

403

ignorant sailors will cast him overboard as a sacrifice to the gods of the storm. That is where you can be of assistance to Me, My old friend. As he sinks through the water, I wish you to advance upon him, and swallow him."

"Ak," said the whale; "O my."

"Well," said God impatiently, "what is the matter?"

The great fish blew a misty spray of water into the air. "It is impossible," he declared; "in the first place, I should choke to death."

"You are an ignorant creature," said God; "you have neither faith, nor science. Let Me tell you a few things about yourself in the light of future exegesis. Know then, that you are a cetacean, or whalebone type of whale. Such animals obtain their food by swimming on or near the surface of the water, with their jaws open."

"That is true," said the whale, reverent and amazed.

"The screen of whalebone," continued the Lord, "opens inward, and admits solid objects to the animal's mouth. This screen does not allow the egress of any solid matter, only of water. As the gullet is very small, only the smallest objects can pass down it.

"Jonah will therefore be imprisoned in your mouth. You cannot swallow him; and he cannot get out, because of the screen of whalebone."

"Then he will suffocate," said the whale.

"Nonsense," said God. "Remember that you are an air-breathing, warm-blooded animal, and can only dive because of the reservoir of air in your mouth. When this air becomes unfit to breathe, you must rise to the surface for a fresh supply.

"While you have air to breathe, Jonah will have it also.

"So do not hesitate any longer, but do as you are told."

The whale heaved a deep sigh; his breath groaned through the ocean, causing many smaller fish, terrified, to flee with trembling fins.

"How horrid for me," he exclaimed.

God replied soothingly, "It will assure you a place in history."

So saying, the Lord blessed Leviathan, who sank sadly back to the depths of the sea; and, turning from the shore, the Light of Israel rolled like thunder across the valleys toward Golan.

The night came to meet Him from the east, pouring down over the hills like smoke. In the cold night air God went to look for Jonah.

Poor Jonah, he had not found peace after all. The lonely desert, so calm and quiet in the past, had given no rest to his thoughts. His mind went back over and over again to those days at home; he felt the wonder of the love-night, his heart shrank again with sickness for what followed. And he asked himself for the thousandth time how such things could be. Then he cried out against Judith for her cruelty; yet the next moment he forgave her.

And these thoughts, climbing and falling wearily up and down through his head, kept him awake until long after the desert was asleep. In the morning, when he awoke, it was with regret; he tried to sleep a little longer, to keep his eyes closed, to keep from thinking again . . . why wake at all? he wondered. There was nothing to wake to. Only the hot sun over the desert, only his heavy heart, which grew no lighter as the days went by.

Why wake at all?

God found him sitting wearily upon a rock, his head bowed between his hands. The Lord spoke, and the desert was silent.

"Jonah," said God in a voice like a great wave breaking, slowly, and with the peace of the sea, "Jonah, you have wept enough."

Jonah replied simply, "I have been waiting for You a long while, and I am very tired."

"I had not forgotten you," said God; "I have been thinking."

And He added, "Now I have something for you to do."

Jonah remained seated without looking up. He seemed no longer to care what God had for him to do.

"Arise, Jonah," said God, "and go to Nineveh. Cry out against that great city for its sins."

But Jonah looked more dejected than ever. "What have I to do with Nineveh?" he asked. "Am I prophet to the Assyrians? I am a Jew. Do not mock me, Lord."

"I do not mock you," said God gravely. "Go, then, and do My bidding."

And as Jonah did not reply, he added sadly, "Do you still doubt Me?"

Jonah rose slowly to his feet. His eyes blazed, and his hands were tightly clenched. "Oh," he cried bitterly, all the passion in his heart storming out at last in a torrent of despair, "You . . . what are You God of? Were you God of Israel when a Tyrian stole my love? Was I Your prophet then? Have You power over Tyre, that You let Your servant suffer such anguish? Or are You God of the desert, where the demons mock me night and day, where the very stones cry out against me, and the whole night is noisy with laughter? Nineveh . . . Nineveh . . . in whose name shall I cry out against Nineveh? Do the gods of Assur visit their wrath upon Jerusalem? What power have You in Nineveh? For my youth which I gave You, what have You given me? How have You returned my love, with what sorrow? What have You done to me, Lord? I stand in the darkness, weary, and with a heavy heart. What are You God of? Answer: what are You God of?"

And God answered gently, "I am your God, Jonah, and where you go, there you will find Me."

Jonah sank down upon the rock again. His passion had exhausted him; but he was not convinced. "Well," he said in a whisper, "You are not God in Nineveh, and I will not go."

Then the wrath of the Lord, slow to start, flamed for a moment over the desert, and Jonah cowered to earth while the heavens groaned and the ground shook with fright. And in his hole by the pool in the Land of Tob, the little fox said to himself, "Jonah is talking to God."

But God's anger passed, leaving Him sad and holy.

"Peace unto you, Jonah," He said in tones of divine sweetness; "take up your task, and doubt Me no more."

And He returned to heaven in a cloud. Overcome with weariness, empty of passion, Jonah fell asleep upon the ground.

No jackals laughed that night. Silence brooded over the desert. The stars kept watch without a sound, and Jonah slept with a quiet heart.

But in the morning his doubts returned more strongly than ever. "They will mock me in Nineveh," he told himself. "I shall be made a laughing-stock. What power has the Light of Israel in the land of Marduk, of Dagon, of Istar, of the warrior Ashur? I should count myself lucky if I escaped being stoned to death.

"For how can God destroy Nineveh? I might as well preach to the fish in the sea."

But now he had something to do, at least. He determined to flee from God. "I shall go to Tarshish," he thought, "and begin life over again. There is nothing for me here any longer. The desert will be glad to be rid of me."

And without bothering even to return to his hut, he started south, toward Joppa, where he expected to find a ship bound west for Tarshish.

He traveled swiftly, on other roads from those he had come. Late on the afternoon of the second day he crossed the Brook Kanath, and saw in the distance the white domed roofs of Joppa shining above the sea.

As he came down from the low hills, the sight of ocean rounded like a bowl under the wide arch of the sky, the distant and titanic clouds piled above the unseen shores of Africa, filled his heart for a moment with beauty. But then he thought:

"This is like Tyre. It is by the shore of this same sea that Judith has gone to live."

And he cursed the beauty that hurt him.

It was late when he came to the shore, and night was already moving upon the deep. In profound silence he leaned above the harbor wall and regarded the shadowless water which with the sound of immemorial tides passed under him in the darkness. It was the season when the mists from the ocean blow landward in the evening. In the gray night fog the masts of the vessels at anchor rocked toward one another on the long, low waves; and the mist, salty with sea air, mingled along the quays with the odors of the city.

It was the dark of the moon in the month of Nisan. The moon was gone, and his youth with it. Other moons would rise, fall through the branches of a tree, and cheat a bird to sing. But where would Jonah be? And Judith, in her great house over the terraces of Tyre; she would grow old, soon she would be like Deborah, looking backward over her life . . . What happened to youth, to beauty? Where did they go? They hardly lasted at all.

Night hung black and silent over the sea. The wings of angels leaned upon the wind which moved dark and vast between the earth and sky. The stars paled, and the sun rose like a ball of fire in the east. Then the ocean mist, cold as frost, melted away. The tide turned, and the waves, breaking far out, spoke with their murmur like the sound of wind to the sleeping city on the shore.

In the morning Jonah found a ship bound for Tarshish. The cargo was already loaded; and when he had made his bargain, he went aboard. Bearded and singing, the seamen hoisted the sails, yellow as a slice of moon; with a sly, tranquil motion the ship moved out of the harbor, over the blue sea, sparkling in the sun, past sails stained blue as the sky, or brown as the sands. The white

roofs of Joppa faded behind them in the east, lost in the gradual fog; the sea-
gulls cried above them; and Jonah sat silent, dreaming, gazing at the sea.

He was tired, and listless. "Now," he said to himself. "God has lost me."

And he thought of Deborah with sadness and peace. He remembered
what she had said to him, as she had held him, weeping bitterly, in her arms,
on her breast.

"Jonah," she had said, "when you are dead, or perhaps very old and
ready to die, people will say of you, 'There, he was a great prophet.' And they
will feel honored because they knew you, because their names will be spoken
of with yours. But now . . ." she sighed; she wanted to say, "now you are only
a nuisance."

What she finally said was, "well, people are like that."

But Jonah knew what she wanted to say. And as he sat quietly on the
deck of the ship under the yellow, curled sail, he thought,

"I shall not bother anybody now."

The warmth of the sun, reflected from the sea, entered his mind and
lulled his limbs. Sea-quiet took hold of him; the peace of ocean bathed his
spirit. He grew drowsier and drowsier; he began to doze. And as he fell asleep,
his last thought was that he had got away from God.

All day the sails sang in the wind, under the sun. Jonah slept; his dreams
swept out like homing birds over the calm waters; and in his sleep he wept.

But in the afternoon the wind died away; and ominous haze enveloped
the sky; and the sea grew oily. The sails were hastily drawn in; and the oars
were made ready. Huddled together on the deck, the seamen spoke in low,
anxious voices. All eyes were turned toward the east, which grew darker and
darker. All was still; the air did not stir. Moved by fear, the men trembled;
and as though herself frightened, the ship started to creak in all her timbers.
All at once the sky uttered a moan; high above them the air began to sing;
and the sea rolled in slow, unwilling swells. And then it seemed as if the sky
fell down upon the sea, for the water rose like the hills, and the dark came
down upon it. Unable to move, the ship trembled from bow to stern, lifted
dizzily upon the waves, tilted in the wind, and dropped like a stone into the
trough. The gulls were flattened to the sea, and the air was filled with the
shout of the gale, and the crash of water falling upon itself. It was God's storm,
but Satan also was enjoying it.

Pale with fear, the sailors rushed to lighten the ship by throwing the cargo
overboard. Then, as the tiny vessel dashed about in the water like a cork, they
fell upon their knees and prayed to their gods, to Ramman, the thunderer, to
Dagon, to Enlil, the old god of storms.

Seeing that Jonah still slept, sheltered by the deck which curved above
him, the captain ran to awaken him. "Here," he said, "this is a storm. Well,
see for yourself. You should be more anxious, my friend. Have you a god?
Then pray to him, for we need all the help we can get."

Dazed by the tumult, still half asleep, Jonah gazed in confusion at the
heaving waters. The wind lashed him to the deck; he stared in dismay at the
mighty waves rising above him on every side like mountains. "I will not
pray," he said. And the captain shrank back at the sight of his face.

But the seamen, clinging to the deck, looked anxiously at Jonah, and at the great seas which broke over them without ceasing. "This is no common storm," they told each other; "some great god is angry."

They were good and simple men. Had one of them sinned, to draw down upon them all such wrath? No, it was Jonah, the stranger whose face was like a demon's, dark as the storm itself. They looked at him with terror.

And Jonah looked back at them as frightened as they were. His mind reeled; had he not got away from God after all? Had God come after him—out there on the sea? Was there no way to flee from God?

Why had he tried to run away? What a fool . . . God would never forgive him for it.

And then, in the crash of wind and water, a feeling of disdain came over Jonah, a bitter strength, a final pride. Well, here was the storm . . . here was God still. God had taken everything away from him. What was his life worth to him now? Oh, be done with it, once and for all. "Look . . . if You want it, God . . . it is of no value to me any more . . ."

"It is my fault," he said to the sailors proudly. "I alone am to blame. I am a Jew who has denied his God. It is my life that is wanted. Throw me overboard."

But the sailors were frightened, and they would not touch him. "No," they said, "we will row back to Joppa again. Then your god can do as he likes. If we throw you overboard, you will drown. Then we shall have blood upon our hands."

They tried with all their strength to row against the storm. But the black sea, breaking, splintered their oars, and the wind pressed them backwards.

Then they said humbly, in fear, "This sea belongs to Iaveh, the god of the Jews. We cannot prevail against him any longer."

And seizing Jonah, they cast him overboard, with a prayer. "Do not lay innocent blood upon us," they said, "O god of the Jews. This is your doing, not ours."

So saying they waited, trembling.

At once the sea grew calm, the wind died away, and the sun sank tranquilly down in the clear west. The peace of evening brooded again upon the water. And the ship, with all her sails set for Joppa, fled to the east.

Jonah sank through the waters without complaint. It was the end, and he had no desire to live. But as his breath failed, so his mind brought back to him the blue and shining sky, the sweet odors of the desert, the happy dreams of his youth, of glory, of peace. He began to struggle; his body fought against the sea, his mind shouted against death. "No," he cried to himself, "no, I must live; I must live."

With a groan Leviathan hurled himself through the waves and took the prophet into his mouth.

In the darkness the whale spoke to Jonah. "What a lot of trouble you have made for yourself," he said. And he told Jonah how God had made arrangements.

Jonah was not unhappy. In the whale's mouth he was uncomfortable, but he had a great deal to think about. His mind was filled with wonder.

So it turned out that God was at home everywhere; that He commanded the fish of the sea, as well as the hosts of the air, and the creatures of the land. That was an extraordinary thing.

What an upset to theology.

Jonah asked the whale many questions. And the whale, who had often thought about such things as he rested among the weeds at the bottom of the sea, answered him as best he could.

"Do you deny," said Jonah, "that God created man in His own image?"

"No," replied the whale, "but on the other hand, do you suppose God has only one image? And then it depends, besides, on who is looking; because people do not see things all alike. Well, do you suppose a whale does not also look like God?"

"A whale does not look like God at all," replied Jonah firmly.

"Still," said the whale thoughtfully, "the most beautiful sight in the world, in my opinion, is a female whale. And you must admit I have seen as much of God as you have. So you see what difficulties you make for yourself."

But Jonah would not believe that God looked like a whale. And they discussed other aspects of theology.

The whale swam through the waters green with daylight, or black with night, rising to the surface now and then to breathe. Out of respect for the sanctity of the prophet, he did not attempt to eat any of the small fish which fled in terror from his path. "We will fast together," he said kindly to Jonah.

In his warm, black prison, Jonah slept, and woke, and thought about God. His spirit lifted; he felt peaceful, resigned, and almost happy. Gone was the bitter sense of defeat, the shame of betrayal. What if his heart ached still? he had God again. And what a God, now that he saw Him: the thunder of sea-surges, the holy calm of the desert, all peace, all beauty, were His . . . one need not seek it, it was there, it was everywhere. Jerusalem was His—Tarshish and Tyre . . .

"I am your God, Jonah, and where you go, there you will find Me."

Tyre was His, too. The Master strode through the streets of the city with thunder on His brow, with love and sorrow in His hands. And His prophet walked beside Him, wrapped in glory, like a king.

When they came to Judith's house it was Jonah who blessed it with gently outstretched arms.

"My sister," he said; "my poor, faithless love."

The whale asked Jonah what he was doing. "I was dreaming," said Jonah.

"I think you had better pray," said the whale. So Jonah prayed.

"Lord, I have sinned," he said humbly. "I was unhappy; and I ran away. And for that reason You cast me into the sea; the waves passed over me.

"The waves passed over my soul, Lord.

"I went down to the bottom of the hills; the bars of the earth were about me. But I did not perish. You heard my cry, and You remembered me. I thank You, Lord.

"Look, I am not vain any longer; I do not wish anything for myself. Let me do Your bidding again, with a quiet heart."

And he added with a cry, "Give me peace, Lord."

The whale swam on, past schools of appetizing fish, down through the dim flower-branches of the sea's deep bed, up through sunny foam. Hungry, weary, but hopeful, the great fish waited patiently for God to speak.

On the third day, God spoke. And the whale, lashing the waters with his tail, sped like an eager minnow to the shore, and vomited Jonah forth upon the sand.

Jonah was let out of the whale in the North, near Arvad, not far from Kadesh as a crow might fly, which is to say, over the coastal hills and then in a straight line across the jungles and the desert. This was the route he took as being the shortest way to Nineveh. He was in a hurry; he was impatient to begin his mission. He was filled with enthusiasm.

How different from his flight to sea, this vigorous return across the land dry with the sun of midsummer. Now he marched with a firm and hurried step, his face darkly radiant with divine purpose, with pious anger. Yes, he would speak; Nineveh would hear him. Let them stone him if they liked, God would amply repay them for it. What glory.

And this was all his, not hers, not for her sake; let her be proud of him if she liked; what did it matter any more? She would hear enough of it in Tyre; Jonah here, and Jonah there . . .

Yes, they would speak of it in Tyre.

As he passed the wayside altars of the baalim with their pillars surmounted by horns of sacrifices, he smiled at them in derision.

"You," he said scornfully, "you . . . what are you gods of, anyway?"

At Kadesh he saw statues of the river deities, Chrysonhoa and Pegai. He spat in the dust before them; fortunately, no one was looking. In the sun of late afternoon their shadows pointed like great spears toward Nineveh.

"Israel will hear my name again," he thought proudly.

The evergreen oaks of the hills gave way to the tamarisks of the Syrian jungles, and the palms and scrub of the desert. He slept the first night in the wilderness between Kadesh and Rehoboth. The jackals were silent, awed by the presence of lions among the rocks. Padding to and fro, the great beasts watched Jonah from afar, with eyes like flames. And Jonah dreamed of Deborah; when he awoke, he remembered her gentle smile.

In the fresh light of early morning a mother goat divided her milk between the prophet and her ewe. "These are stirring times, Jonah," she said; "angels are abroad in great numbers." Recognizing a minor deity, Jonah blessed her and resumed his journey.

At the end of the second day he began to pass the boundary stones of Assyria, set up to warn trespassers upon private property. Thinking them altars, Jonah cursed each one as he went by. The next day he passed kilns in which colored bricks were being baked. As far as he could see, the blue, green, and yellow bricks stood in rows on the red earth.

That night he slept outside the gates of Nineveh. The city rose above him in the dark; he heard the sentries challenge on the walls.

In the morning he entered the city with some farmers on their way to the markets. The sun was rising, gleaming upon the great winged bulls before the temples, the green and yellow lions upon the walls. Under the clear upland sky the city shone with color like a fair. The markets opened; the streets filled with men and women in their colored shawls and clashing ornaments. And Jonah, looking and looking, was astonished. "Why," he thought, "this is strange; there is something bright and bold about all this. This is fine, after all." And he felt a gayety of heart take hold of him. How vigorous these mountain people looked with their insolent faces and their swaggering air. There was nothing old or sad in Nineveh. He forgot why he had come; he was excited, and happy. It was not at all what he had expected; and he forgot himself.

But not for long. As the hours passed, he grew weary; and as the brightness wore off, and he began to think of his own life again, he began to hate Nineveh, to hate the bold colors all around him, the youth that carried itself so proudly and carelessly in the streets. "Yes," he thought, "that is all very well for you; but you know nothing about life." And, lifting his arms, he cried aloud with gloomy satisfaction, "Yet forty days, and Nineveh shall be overthrown."

The success of this remark astonished him. Without waiting to find out any more about it, the Assyrians hurried home and put ashes on their heads. Nineveh repented like a child of its sins; in an orgy of humility the city gave up its business, and dressed itself in sackcloth. The king, even, left his throne, and sat down in some ashes.

Jonah was vexed. This, also, was not what he had expected. He had looked for a wind of fury, for stones, and curses, and a final effect of glory. And when he learned that because of its repentance Nineveh was to be spared, his courage gave way in a flood of disappointment.

"I knew it," he said bitterly to God; "I knew You'd never do it."

And with an angry countenance he retired to an open field on the east side of the city, to see what would happen. His heart was very sore.

"Where is my glory now?" he thought.

Then God, who was anxiously watching, spoke to Jonah from the sky. "Why are you angry?" said the Holy One. "Have I done you a wrong?"

Jonah replied, sighing, "Who will ever believe me now, Lord?"

And for the rest of the day he maintained a silence, full of reproach.

Then because the sun was very hot, and because where Jonah was sitting there was no shade of any sort, God made a vine grow up, overnight, to shelter Jonah.

"There," said God, "there is a vine for you. Rest awhile and see."

That day Jonah sat in comfort beneath his shelter. The wind was in the west, full of agreeable odors; at noon a farmer brought him meal, salt, and oil; he ate, was refreshed, and dozed beneath his vine. The sun went down over the desert; and the evening star grew brighter in the sky, which shone with a peaceful light. The dews descended; and Jonah, wrapped in his cloak, dreamed of home.

But in the morning worms had eaten the leaves of the vine; gorged and comfortable, they regarded Jonah from the ground with pious looks. As the day progressed, the sun beat down upon him without pity, a strong wind blew up from the east, out of the desert, and the prophet grew faint with misery. Too hot even to sweat, he nevertheless refused to move.

"No," he said, "I shall sit here."

An obstinate rage kept him out in the sun, although he half expected to die of it. "Well," he said to himself, "what if I do?"

It seemed to him that he had nothing more to live for.

Then God said to Jonah, "Do you do well to be angry, My son?"

Jonah did not wish to reply. But he was sure of one thing: that he had every right to be angry. "Why did You wither my vine, Lord?" he asked bitterly. "Was that also necessary?"

God, looking down on His prophet, smiled sadly. "What is a vine?" He said gently, "Was it your vine, Jonah? You neither planted it nor cared for it. It came up in a night, and it perished in a night. And now you think I should have spared the vine for your sake. Yes . . . but what of Nineveh, that great city, where there are so many people who cannot discern between their right hand and their left hand? Shall I not spare them, too, for My sake, Jonah?"

Jonah rose wearily to his feet. "Well," he said, "I may as well go home again."

And with bowed head he passed through the city, and out of the western gate. In the streets the citizens made way for him with pious murmurs and anxious looks, but Jonah did not notice them. All his courage was gone, his pride, his hope of glory, all gone down in the dust of God's mercy to others, to all but him. To him alone God had been merciless and exacting. One by one the warm hopes of the youth, the ardors of the man, had been denied him; peace, love, pride, everything had been taken from him. What was there left? Only the desert, stony as life itself . . . only the empty heart, the deliberate mind, the bare and patient spirit. Well, Jonah . . . what a fool to think of anything else. Glory . . . yes, but the glory is God's, not yours.

But he had not learned even that. He was not a good prophet. The flowers of his hope, the bitter blossoms of his grief, sprang up everywhere, where there should have been only waste brown earth. No, he was not a prophet; he was a man, like anybody else, whose love had been false, whose God had been unkind. . . .

And as he trudged dejectedly along, his heart, bare now of pride, filled with loneliness and longing. He thought of Judith, of the happiness that would never be his; and he wept.

High among the clouds, God turned sadly to Moses. "You Jews," He said wearily, "you do not understand beauty. With you it is either glory or despair."

And with a sigh He looked westward to the blue Aegean. Warm and gold the sunlight lay over Greece.

40 Return of the Exiles

In choosing the story of the Second Isaiah as the subject of his fifth biblical novel, Sholem Asch had to invent more than in any of his previous biblical books. Less is known about this Isaiah than about Moses, Jesus, St. Paul or Mary. Skillfully using some of the Isaiah quotations within the context of a largely fictional background, Asch told a story with obvious modern significance. The exile of the Jews to Babylon and their return to Jerusalem was personally meaningful to Asch. The decision which faced the Jews in Babylon was whether to remain in exile where many of them had businesses and property, or to return to a destroyed homeland which they would have to rebuild. The wealthy were prepared to contribute money to send their co-religionists back to Jerusalem, but were themselves reluctant to make the journey. In time it became apparent that only the poor and the very religious would make the necessary sacrifices. It is this story—the return from an early diaspora—which Asch tells in *The Prophet.*

> *Thus saith the Lord, thy redeemer, and he that formed thee from the womb, I am the Lord that maketh all things: that stretcheth forth the heavens alone; that spreadeth abroad the earth by myself;*
>
> *That frustrateth the tokens of the liars, and maketh diviners mad; that turneth wise men backward; and maketh their knowledge foolish;*
>
> *That confirmeth the word of his servant, and performeth the counsel of his messengers; that saith to Jerusalem, Thou shalt be inhabited; and to the cities of Judah, Ye shall be built, and I will raise up the decayed places thereof:*
>
> *That saith to the deep, Be dry, and I will dry up thy rivers:*
>
> *That saith of Cyrus, He is my shepherd, and shall perform all my pleasure: even saying to Jerusalem, Thou shalt be built; and to the temple, Thy foundation shall be laid.*
>
> ISAIAH: XLIV, 24–28

THE PROPHET by SHOLEM ASCH

FINALLY, IN THE MONTH OF Marheshvan, of the year in which he conquered Babylon, Cyrus entered the capital to be anointed emperor of Babylon and ruler of all the kingdom of the earth.

Never, in the whole of its history, had Babylon seen such a triumphal procession. No monarch that had before trod the streets of that metropolis had ever been surrounded by so many kings, by such a multitude of satraps, by governors from so many provinces; accompanied by so many bodyguards and courtiers of so many nations and peoples. Towering head and shoulders above all the retinue and the warriors who marched around him, his Persian garb gleaming beneath the golden robe of Babylonian royalty that flowed from his shoulders, a gold crown upon his head, Cyrus led his bodyguard from the gate of Ishtar in the Avenue of the Processions to the palace of Nebuchadnezzar.

The massed forces of Cyrus, the brilliance of their variegated uniforms, the camels, elephants and leopards, did not excite the Babylonians so much as the three troops of the king's personal bodyguard. They were a sign and a witness that the dominion of the three mighty powers which had, each in its turn for generations, held lands and peoples without number beneath their sway, was now united under one head. One will ruled over them; one king, terrible and fearful, whose power was limitless, now commanded them all. On his right marched the king's personal guards, the Persians clad in short tunics, quivers of arrows on their shoulders. The warriors, with their short beards, stepped out in the full vigor of their youthful strength, in perfect unison with their king. On his left was the Assyrian troop, in their dress of antique mode; their awe-inspiring, full, curled and plaited beards, their conical helmets high on their heads and their copper-covered lances in their hands—lances which had broken the heads of kings and despatched their peoples into slavery. They tramped along with a thunderous tread, in that ominous irresistible inevitability which had in former times struck terror and dread into the hearts of nations and brought them under subjection. Behind the king came his Babylonian bodyguard. These were all high-ranking officers, who had commanded troops that once served the king of Babylon and who had gone over with their men to the service of the victor monarch.

The triumphal processions of the rulers of Assyria and Babylon had always made a great feature of crushed captive kings and their generals, bound in chains and fetters. These three companies of personal bodyguards, composed of officers of the highest rank marching in formation, witnessed and announced more eloquently than any words could do that a great change had taken place in the world. An old era had died; a new era had been born.

Rameses II, king of kings, Tiglath Pileser, Sennacherib, Nebuchadnezzar —none of these mighty conquerors had ever sat so securely on their thrones as did Cyrus, the king of Persia and Media, on the seat of monarchy in the palace of the kings of Babylon with its hanging gardens, with its vast halls embellished with the graven tablets from which stood forth the scenes depicting the overwhelming and crushing triumphs of Nebuchadnezzar. The eternal celestial struggle between Tiamat and Bel Merodach was graven in ivory and embossed in gold upon the throne on which Cyrus now sat. He was arrayed in the Assyrian robe of majesty which Nebuchadnezzar had brought from Ninevah together with the throne as a spoil of war. There was another bas relief upon the throne. It depicted Bel Merodach investing Nebuchadnezzar with the crown and the scepter of Babylon. It was this crown which now graced the high head of Cyrus, the Persian, while the scepter which symbolized dominion over the peoples of the earth was grasped firmly in his hand. Grouped around the king were the great ones and nobles of Assyria and Babylon, satraps and pashas, every one of them lord of a province in the dominions of Cyrus. Each was resplendent in his chain and ring and the golden badge of his authority. To the right and left of the throne stood the two rulers of the city of Babylon itself, Cambyses, the son and heir, and Gubaru, the lord of the governors of Babylon, who had by his craft and diplomacy brought over the priests of E-Sagila to the cause of the new monarch.

The same day, the great king summoned a deputation of the leaders of the Jews who dwelt in Babylon. It included Shaltiel, the senior prince of the House of David, his son, Zerubabel, Jehozedek, the son of the chief priest, Seraiah. There was Jeshu, son of Jehozedek, and notables of the fathers' houses of Babylon and the surrounding settlements of the exiles.

At a signal from the king, Gubaru, Pasha of Babylon, came forward with great ceremony to the rolling of drums and the flourish of herald's trumpets. Two scribes appeared before him and held up a clay tablet before his eyes. He read aloud:

"Thus saith Cyrus, king of Persia, the Lord God of Heaven hath given me all the kingdoms of the earth, and He hath charged me to build Him an house at Jerusalem, which is in Judah.

"Who is there among you of all His people? His God be with him and let him go up to Jerusalem, which is in Judah, and build the House of the Lord God of Israel, He is the God which is in Jerusalem."

While the deputation of the exiles were still staring open-mouthed, trembling, stirred to the depths, their hearts fearful and shaking, the king's voice was heard again.

"And these shall be your boundaries."

At a sign from the king, two scribes brought in a great clay tablet on which a plan of Jerusalem and its environs was engraved. The Pasha of Babylon pointed out the boundaries with his finger. They were cut out from the coastal plain to the seashore, excluding Samaria, Schechem, and Galilee. Jerusalem was shown there and the hills roundabout it as far as Hebron.

Pallor spread over the faces of the exiles, but before they could recover themselves, the king spoke again.

"I am not restoring the kingship of the House of David. I am your monarch and you shall be under my protection and rule. I have extended my grace to you and appointed my own governor over you. His name is Sheshbazzar."

A tall man, dressed in Persian style, came forward and stood before the king.

"This is the governor I have set over you. His title shall be the 'Prince of Judah.' He will lead you back to Judah and I entrust you to his rule. Any prince of Judah who wishes to go with him to help in the building of Jehovah's house is free to do so. But I am not restoring the monarchy of the House of David."

He turned to the man who stood before him.

"Sheshbazzar, Prince of Judah."

The appointed governor fell with his face to the ground at the foot of the king.

"I am entrusting Judah to your care. Take the Judeans who wish to return to Jerusalem and help in rebuilding the sanctuary of their God. And whosoever remaineth in any place where he sojourneth, let the men of his place help him with silver and with gold, and with goods and with beasts, besides the freewill offering for the House of God that is in Jerusalem.

"Make my will in this matter known to return the Judeans to Judah in all the provinces of my empire."

There was a short silence and then Cyrus called:

"The treasurer of the empire of Babylon!"

Mithradates came forward and fell with his face to the ground before the throne.

"Mithradates, bring out the vessels of Jehovah's house, which Nebuchadnezzar took away from Jerusalem and gave to the temple of his own gods. Count them and hand them over to Sheshbazzar, the governor of Judah."

With this latter command, the audience ended, leaving the heads of the Exile both astounded and heartened.

Joy and fear mingled together in the hearts of the exiles. Confusion, jumbled ideas, and bewilderment were the marks of the attitude of the leaders and rulers when Cyrus's manifesto became generally known. By every stall and store in the great market, in all the alleys and courtyards, in the synagogues, in all the points of settlement in city and village; in the metropolis, in Tel Aviv and Tel Melach alike, groups of Jews gathered, weighing, arguing, hairsplitting, and disputing over the great event. Great arguments broke out in the palace of the House of David, among the sons of the prophets, among the elders and the priests. Great as was the joy, not less was the fear of the unknown that the news held.

"They have poured into our land from Sodom and Edom, like a sewer or cesspit that has overflowed, and have flooded the whole country. The Edomites who only yesterday paid servile tribute to us are today the lords of the country. They have come up from the Negev, the south country, from Transjordania. They have come down from the hills and occupied our parts of them and have taken for themselves everything of any value. The Samaritans, our blood cousins, have hurried down from the mountains of Ephraim and settled in Jerusalem. Where then shall we live, having been allocated the dried-up hills of Judah from around Jerusalem to Jericho and Hebron? Where shall we find a place to live? How can we be expected to exchange the fat fertile lands of Babylonia, which drink in water day and night and are nourished by the canals as a child is nourished by the full breasts of its mother, for the craggy hills of Judah whose slopes have been washed clean for years by the early and latter rains? Where shall we get our daily bread, pasture for our cattle and nourishment for our babies?"

To the bazaar came simple peasants who dwelt on the broad meadows near Tel Aviv and in other rural settlements on the network of canals that radiated from the Chebar canal.

"I shall bring those who return a rich gift. Two mules, a horse, and a silver bar I was saving to make a bracelet for my wife. I shall certainly not leave here. I might even go as far as a yoke of two fine oxen, and that is that. My lot is quite all right in Babylon."

So spoke Giddel, the wealthy landowner of Tel Aviv who had recently added a fine field to his estate after a poor peasant had defaulted on a debt to him. The same sort of story was heard from the workers and artisans in the market places and courtyards around the bazaars.

"To whom shall we sell our goods? To the leprous Ammonites who run about the ruins of Jerusalem with their tails sticking out of their torn cloaks? What do these barefoot beggars want with our fine dyed cloths? Maybe they will leap for joy over our women's embroidered sandals? Perhaps they will buy our beautiful girdles for their worn-out and raddled wives."

"Ha! Do you think they will grab for good money our spices and oils out of which half of us make our living, to get rid of the stink that clings about them?"

But more serious and weighty were the considerations pondered by the heads of the Exile and the chiefs of the House of David, the elders, the priests, the sons of the prophets. In those circles the debate went on quietly, without the raising of voices. They turned the matter over and examined it in all its aspects; they gathered all sorts of groups together for mutual consultations. They assembled the heads of houses, the more prominent priests.

"An alien prince shall rule over us, one of the king's satraps, with the title 'Prince of Judah.' He is not of the Davidic stock. It seems as though Cyrus deliberately overlooked the princes of the Davidic house who dwell among us, who are rightly entitled to rule, and chose one of his own people whom no one knows."

So one of those assembled at the palace of the House of David expressed the universal doubts.

"In spite of all these considerations, I feel that the great king nevertheless sanctified Jehovah's name in the sight of everyone, in the presence of all his vassals, satraps, and commanders. In the sight of all the peoples who live in his dominions he called our God the God of Heaven who had given him dominion over all the earth. The position of the people of Israel has risen wonderfully in the eyes of the people of the world. Surely the words of the prophet have been fulfilled."

Thus Zerubabel tried to encourage the people.

"He also ordered the return of the Temple vessels from the royal treasury and their transfer to the keeping of the 'Prince of Judah'!" exclaimed Jeshu, the son of Jehozedek.

"To whom did he hand them over? To the chief priest? He gave them to an uncircumcised stranger. To one impure whose touch alone is sufficient to pollute them," a fanatical priest stormed.

"And as for talk of having sanctified God's name in the sight of all, let us reserve judgment. Cyrus has many gods and is not going to quarrel with any deity. He fights against peoples and states and as soon as he subdues one of them he accepts their god and looks upon him as a partner. Today he says that God handed him the kingdom of the earth. Tomorrow he will say this about the god of another people, about Bel Merodach or some other powerful demon. He does not find it hard to make such statements."

Nevertheless all eyes were lifted up to the young and wonderful prophet. Only yesterday he was banned and made a laughing stock. Today part of his prophecy had been fulfilled and so all hung expectantly on his utterance. Even though the whole redemption he had promised had not been fulfilled, it was patent to every eye that it was God's veritable truth that came out of his mouth. The whole prophecy might well be fulfilled in stages. Accordingly, Zerubabel, Jeshu, and some of the elders and sons of the prophets and priests came to him in his small hut. They wanted to know if he had any message from God to communicate to them. He knew they were perplexed. He saw the fear in their eyes and perceived how their joy was mingled with fear and anxiety. But it was still difficult for him to understand why they were so upset and apprehensive; why they were so utterly dependent upon Cyrus's utterance. Was Cyrus their savior; did the redemption depend upon Cyrus? Who was Cyrus that they should so stand in awe of him? He said to them:

"When Sennacherib set his foot upon the neck of the children of Israel near Lachish he thought that he was the master of the world and would hold dominion for ever and ever, that all peoples were given into his hand for the rod or for lovingkindness. Nebuchadnezzar thought so in his day, too; at the judgment of Riblah when his chief executioner severed the heads of the princes of Judah, the sons of the royal house, and that of Seraiah the High Priest and counted them out before the king. At that moment, Nebuchadnezzar believed he had finally sealed the fate of the kingdom of Judah and that it was doomed to eternal destruction. Where are they today, these magnificent kings? So it is with Cyrus. He is an insect. Today he flies about, tomorrow he is no more. Was it Cyrus who expelled you from your land and took you into exile? Why then do you depend upon him and wait upon him so fearfully to redeem you? He did not sell you. For naught were you sold. No one took money from Cyrus to get possession of you and no one will have to pay Cyrus to redeem you. You will not be redeemed with money. It is not Cyrus that will determine your lot and set rulers over you. God will do this. If today Cyrus writes upon bricks and tablets, he is writing in sand. Tomorrow will bring the rain, and all his fine words will be washed away as though they had not been. Therefore, be not dismayed nor afraid. God and none other shall redeem you."

The prophet was waiting for a sign, for a vision, so that he could bring them a word of encouragement. And indeed one night a vision visited him. He summoned Neraiah and told him of it and asked him to commit it to writing. It was his answer to their fear and confusion. Then he brought the vision to the exiles, the elders, the priests, the fathers' houses, and the sons of the prophets, for they were all awaiting his word. On the following Sabbath, he spoke his consolation in Be Knishta, the great synagogue of the elders. And this is the answer God put in the mouth of the prophet:

> *"Awake, awake, put on thy strength, O Zion;*
> *Put on thy beautiful garments, O Jerusalem, the holy city;*
> *For henceforth there shall no more come into thee the*
> *uncircumcised and the unclean.*
> *Shake thyself from the dust; arise and sit down, O Jerusalem.*
> *Loose thyself from the bands of thy neck, O captive daughter*
> *of Zion.*
> *For thus saith Jehovah:*
> *Ye have sold yourselves for nought;*
> *And ye shall be redeemed without money.*
> *For thus saith Jehovah the Lord.*
> *My people went down aforetime to Egypt to sojourn there;*
> *And the Assyrian oppressed them without cause;*
> *And now—*
> *What have I here, saith Jehovah,*
> *That my people is taken away for naught?*
> *They that rule over them make them to howl, saith Jehovah;*
> *And my name continually every day is blasphemed.*
> *Therefore my people shall know my name;*
> *Therefore they shall know in that day—*
> *That I am He that doth speak:*
> *Behold it is I."*

It was the God of Israel that sent them into exile and it was He that would redeem them thence. He, and not a stranger. He, and not flesh and blood. No one on earth had the power to fix boundaries for them or appoint princelings over them. No! No uncircumcised nor stranger would have dominion over them; no satrap, but one of their own from among them.

A new spirit was stirred up among the exiles. The ancient blood of their forefathers seemed to stream through their veins once again.

The Temple vessels which Sheshbazzar had received from the royal treasurer, Mithradates, were laid in order on tables in the palace of the House of David. Priests attired in their white tunics stood by the tables to prevent any layman touching the holy objects. The sons of the House of Shallum and the Sons of the Servants of Solomon stood on guard at the doors. Five thousand and four hundred was the number of the vessels upon the tables: bowls of silver, basins of gold, goblets, knives, kettles, censers, and other dishes; all pure gold and silver.

The people streamed through to feast their eyes upon the sight of the holy vessels. They had been restored; they seemed to live again. King Solomon who had endowed the Sanctuary with the vessels was not dead; it was Nebuchadnezzar, who had taken them away to destroy them, who was dead. He was no more and the vessels were alive. They had come back to life and the people were being revived along with them.

The first to respond to the proclamation of Cyrus, after it had been disseminated as decreed throughout the empire, were the priests. The king had not announced the restoration of the State but of the Temple and the renewal of its worship. It was thus natural that the priests should be the first to embrace the opportunity of the return to Zion. The Exile had raised their stature immensely in the eyes of the people. If the nation had thronged its courts and offices when the Temple stood in Jerusalem, in the exile it was the priests who went out among the people, visiting them wherever they were to be found and reading them extracts from the Pentateuch and the other Holy Books on Sabbaths and festivals in the synagogues. This scriptural reading had taken the place of the sacrificial service of the Temple. It was to the priests that the religious-minded among the exiles turned for counsel and spiritual direction in matters appertaining to the observance of the commandments. In the Jewish agricultural settlements, the tillers of the ground still paid their tithes to the priests, more out of respect for tradition than because the law required it. The priests were looked to for guidance much more than the rulers and secular chiefs of Judah, even the members of the House of David. The standing of the latter had indeed declined gradually as the Davidic kingship sank into obsolescence. But in place of this maternal regime there was a rise in the importance of the priesthood as the repository of religious truth and the stronghold of the spiritual kingdom.

In those days the head of the priesthood was Jeshu, son of the aged Jehozedek. He contended with the chiefs of Judah in the palace of the House of David.

After Cyrus had issued his manifesto, Zerubabel and Jeshu had gone to the governor, Sheshbazzar, and acknowledged him by his new title of "Prince of Judah."

Despite the fact that Cyrus had not committed the leadership of the exodus from Babylon to a scion of the House of David, to whom it rightly belonged, but had given it to an alien, Zerubabel was still quite ready to serve the governor with goodwill and help him in his difficult task. He accorded him the honor due to his office of Prince of Judah and fulfilled his requests. He was constant in this obedience despite the opposition of his father, Shaltiel, who was legally entitled to the Davidic crown. The aged prince could not forgive Cyrus for discriminating against the House of David. The bitterness of the great merchants and heads of houses also determined Zerubabel to persist in his course of conduct. They had claimed that the redemption was not the real thing because it did not carry political independence with it. Zerubabel, on the other hand, accepted the view of the prophet that redemption did not in any case come from Cyrus but from God and that the monarch was only His tool whom He would cast aside as soon as he had performed the part of the Divine purpose assigned to him, in favor of another who would bring about the perfect redemption.

The priest Jeshu, son of Jehozedek, had the same belief and adopted the same course of conduct as Zerubabel.

The aged Jehozedek was the son of Seraiah, the last High Priest who officiated in the Temple at Jerusalem and who had been led in copper fetters with Zedekiah to the judgment of Nebuchadnezzar at Riblah. Here they were leading forth his father, the High Priest, in his ceremonial garments, his hands bound behind his back. The victim cast one last glance about him before his head was cut off and cast aside. Thereafter, he continued to stare at Jehozedek from the mound as if he wished to tell him something. The son knew what the father wanted to say. His slaughtered father wanted to charge him to keep himself pure and hallow his days so as to be ready for the redemption when God would return with His people to Zion and rebuild the Temple. He was to keep himself fit to officiate as a priest in the Sanctuary; to take his place as Chief Priest and serve in the office he, the father, had filled before Nebuchadnezzar had reft him away and extinguished the flame of his life.

But was this day the one which his father's dead eyes, staring out of his severed head, had charged him to await in holiness and purity? Was it really the day of vengeance and triumph, the day of recompense for all the agony and tribulation? This salvation which came from an alien hand, from a grasping palm which opened but a fraction to release without grace and with reluctance that which it held. The hand that gave back neither the kingship to the House of David, nor independent rule, but appointed a foreign governor who would reign as "Prince of Judah." Was this the redemption?

This was not the view his son, Jeshu, took. Let the nest but be rebuilt. . . . The Holy Temple was Israel's nest. Jerusalem was its place, the tree in which the nest belonged. Let the bird return to its nest, the fledglings were already trying their wings. Cyrus was the beginning of the redemption, the whole restoration could be expected at the end of days. From the beginning until the end of the redemption many waters would pass. The priest, Jeshu, was also ready to serve the governor, Sheshbazzar, faithfully and obediently, and assist him in the task with which he had been entrusted.

Sheshbazzar was an Assyrian aristocrat by birth and breeding and had had a lifetime's experience in high offices of state. His whole mien testified to his ancient noble Assyrian lineage but, nevertheless, his attitude towards the Jews was such that he might have been one of them. He devoted himself utterly to the task with which he had been entrusted. He respected the finest susceptibilities of the exiles and understood their special apprehensions with regard to the sacred vessels, which he did not touch with his own hands nor allow his men to approach. He appointed the priests to take charge of the vessels in the palace of the chiefs of Judah.

All kinds of rumors spread through the Exile about the origin of Sheshbazzar. Some held that he stemmed from an ancient noble Jewish family that had assimilated long ago into the Assyrians and that he really came from an Israel royal house that had been taken captive by Sennacherib. Some of these had afterwards been brought to Babylon by Nebuchadnezzar. Sheshbazzar had been a page in the Babylonian court and in royal service all his life. When

the priests of Bel Merodach made their compact with Cyrus, he, together with
the rulers of Babylon, had gone over to him. Gubaru, the governor of Babylon,
knew of the Israelite descent of Sheshbazzar and had confidence in his loyalty
to the king of the Medes and Persians and so had recommended him to Cyrus
for the office of "Prince of Judah." There was really no foundation for all these
rumors that circulated among the people. Whether they were true or fabricated
out of thin air, the fact was that Sheshbazzar kept his genealogy a secret.
However, his attitude and inclinations towards the Judeans were as clear as
day.

Emissaries went out from Babylon to the settlements of Judeans throughout the kingdom. They came to all the villages, cities, and heads of families
and brought the good tidings of the restoration of Zion. The news was not
universally received with joy and enthusiasm. In the older settlements, Tel
Aviv among them, where the Judeans lived in prosperity and flourished and
waxed rich from the fruitful produce of the soil, the news brought confusion
rather than rejoicing. How could they be expected to leave their solid, well-
built houses, their fat lands which yielded three or four rich harvests a year;
the sleek herds of cattle and their fat sheep which grew so quickly; and go to
a land they no longer knew and which they had heard of only by hearsay in
grandfather's tales? They would give a very handsome donation and help
the establishment of the Temple. But, let others go in the meantime, those who
had not done so well and did not live on such good land. Let the poor, who
lived a hard life in the cities, go.

That is how it fell out. In spite of their disappointment that Cyrus had
failed to fulfill the prophecies of Isaiah, it was as if a new spirit had come
over the people. Some of the Judeans who, with their fathers, had always
been faithful to the prophets' words of instruction and consolation and the
Law the priests had inculcated in their teaching in the synagogue Sabbath by
Sabbath and festival by festival, responded to the call of King Cyrus. They
inclined a sympathetic ear to the exhortations of Zerubabel and Jeshu, who
came to speak to them in the name of Sheshbazzar, the Prince of Judah. The
heads of houses appeared as one man at the great council which Sheshbazzar
convened in Babylon for discussion of the procedure to be followed in the
return to Jerusalem.

The families of the exiles very jealously treasured and preserved, even in
Babylon, the purity of lineage of their fathers' houses. In this genealogical
pride and solidarity they saw the best shield against that assimilation with
the Babylonians which in the course of time had begun to threaten the oldest
Jewish families. The authority of the head of the house was absolute, and
anyone who belonged to it had to obey his dictates willingly and without complaint. The headship of the house was the cement which bound the whole
family together, making it a compact group proud of its ancestry and traditions. The severe patriarchal discipline, which had proven a strong bar against
assimilation while the exile lasted, was now a prime factor when the people had
to gird themselves for the return in bringing it to practical fruition.

Twelve representatives, corresponding to the twelve tribes of Israel, were chosen out of the heads of houses to help the Prince in preparing the exodus. The twelve transmitted decisions to the other heads of houses and these decided, without the possibility of any appeal, which families would have to go back to Judah. Those who had struck strong roots into Babylon, which could not be pulled up without destroying their possessions, and who were, therefore, bound to remain: merchants, tillers of the soil and craftsmen, were made subject to heavy imposts to finance the immigration.

The fathers' houses were called after their heads: the sons of Shephatiah, the sons of Arach, the sons of Pashhur, and the like. Some houses which originated in one city or neighborhood in Judah were similarly constituted in the Exile and they usually formed a single community named after their Judean city; for example, the Bethlehemites, the Anathothies, Kiyat Yearimites, and so forth. This relationship to a city or area in Judah aroused sweet memories in the minds of the group in question and longings for the redemption. The cities and forsaken villages in the homeland, "cities and mothers in Israel," were now calling their children home just as a human mother would.

When he saw the people gathering together into Babylon from the whole of the empire on the first stage of their way back to Zion, the prophet had asked to dwell among them. Consequently, Neraiah had carried him in a padded litter to the court of the Bethlehemites. There in an attic chamber Neraiah carefully tended the prophet, keeping constant watch at his bedside. There was little left of him but a bundle of bones clothed in a white skin and wrapped in a white cloak.

On the straw pallet shaded by palm branches he lay still and silent, like a man in whom there was no longer a breath of life. The pale face was upturned to the sky that could be seen through the palms. His eyes were shut and only the matted hair of his beard and chest stirred slightly as he breathed. Apart from this, there was no sign that he was still alive.

His writing materials were laid on a bench by his bed: stylus, pens, clay tablets, and ink. Neraiah sat beside him devotedly. He was almost afraid to move. He was ever ready and alert to serve him and to note down any words he might utter. But the prophet was silent. His lips were sealed like his eyes. Then later, his heartbeats grew loud, his nostrils were distended as he panted to draw in a breath of air. The rise and fall of his chest, and the nervous distention of his nostrils, told Neraiah that the thoughts of the prophet were lifted up on the wings of vision. So he sat silent, holding his breath, concentrating with all his power not to disturb the prophet from seeing the visions which held him in thrall and kept him captive as his soul prepared to depart from him.

In his vision, he was standing on the Mount of Olives and looking at Mount Moriah opposite. He saw the returned of Zion over against him. They were purifying the site of all its pollution, smashing down the high places of the abominations and laying the foundations of the Sanctuary anew. At their head stood Zerubabel and the priest Jeshu. There was great activity on the mountain. People were carrying stones, planing wood, and dragging along cedar beams. The priests were attending to the cleansing of the Temple vessels, pressing out and refining oil and preparing the hangings. He saw how God was indeed healing the hurt of Zion. God had once again made the sun to shine over Jerusalem. He had returned her light unto her, the radiance of the six days of creation. The light flooded the ruins of Jerusalem with beams dropping down grace. The whole appearance of the desolate city had been altered by the amber effulgence. The ruins became fortresses and citadels now; rays of light wove them into halls of molten splendor. Every one of the stones of Jerusalem again took on its original shape and face, was transformed into an ornamental block, shining, sparkling, and coruscating.

The Kidron River separated him from the new Temple which he could not approach. The Kidron fell into the Valley of the Son of Hinnom which wound around Mount Zion. This valley had been appointed as a place for retribution from the most ancient times. All impurity of Jerusalem flowed into it. The fragments of the idols that had been shattered on the Temple mount were thrown there. There also were cast the remnants of the broken altars which the kings of Judah and Israel had once erected to foreign abominations and idols in order to worship them, fragments of Moloch, Ashtoreth, Baal. In the heap of refuse, too, were mingled the bones of their forsworn priests. In his vision the prophet saw the Valley of the Son of Hinnom filled to overflowing, like a river in springtime, with skeletons of idols and men and mighty heaps of refuse and ashes. But nevertheless, the seven-colored rainbow, God's sign to Noah, was suspended over the valley.

Suddenly he heard a song going up from the Valley of the Son of Hinnom and mingled with the chant of those who were going down from the Hills of Jerusalem, a song of praise and glorification of God. From its dust and rubble, even the Valley of the Son of Hinnom was singing praise of God. This was surely the great day of forgiveness and pardon. God in His glory was Himself purifying the unclean and exalting it unto Him. He was making an end of arrogance while allowing the arrogant to remain in life. He was wiping away tears from all faces. He was removing all boundaries. He was making the crooked straight. He was smoothing all the rough places. He was bringing the righteous and the wicked alike under the shelter of the wings of His grace. To all who were thirsty He was giving pure water to drink, without price and without demanding any return.

Out of his great faintness, the prophet cried in a voice brimming over with joy:

"Ho, every one that thirsteth,
Come ye to the waters!
And he that hath no money,
Come, buy ye and eat!"

"Come ye, every one that is hungry, and eat the bread of God, for this is the day of forgiveness and pardon. The table of Jehovah lies open and laid ready for everyone."

He suddenly beheld a crown of fire lifted up over the Mountain of

Moriah. It was exalted upon wings to the heights. The crown, like a moon surrounded by stars, soared upward higher and higher to the empyrean till it reached the celestial sea of brilliant amber radiance. There it was immersed and hidden from view.

"This can only be the crown of David that God has taken up to heaven." The prophet awoke from his vision.

With the last of his strength, he summoned Neraiah to take the writing materials and put down the message that he was leaving as a testament for the exiles going up to Judah. His last words would restore their hearts, would uphold them and give them comfort and strength for all time to come, in all the flames through which they would have to pass. It would help them to meet all the stumbling blocks and stones that would lie in their path which now began and would lead on to the end of days.

God had taken the crown of David from the earth unto Himself. There it would be guarded and stored for him that would come at the end of days. The kingdom of the House of David was no longer an earthly kingdom; it was henceforth a kingdom of Heaven. God had made an everlasting covenant with Israel through the hand of David, through the grace He had vouchsafed to him, through the Messiah that would come out of David.

The prophet dictated his last testament to the people of Israel:

> "*Incline your ear and come unto me,*
> *Hear and your soul shall live;*
> *And I will make an everlasting covenant with you,*
> *Even the sure mercies of David.*
> "*Nor do I make this eternal covenant for you alone by means of My*
> *grace and the sure mercies of David:*
> "*Behold I have given him for a witness to the people,*
> *A leader and commander to the people.*
> *Behold thou shalt call a nation that thou knowest not,*
> *And nations that knew not thee shall run unto thee,*
> *Because of Jehovah, the God,*
> *And the Holy One of Israel for he hath glorified thee.*"

It was this longing for the Messiah with which the prophet wished to endow Israel. This would be the goal of Israel, her purpose and her mission, and for this she was going back to her land. God was near to every man, and whosoever sought Him would find Him. Even the wicked, if he would only forsake his evil way. If only the transgressor would shake himself free from his arrogant imaginings and return to God, then He would surely have mercy upon him, for He was the eternal and inexhaustible fountain of grace and forgiveness.

> "*For my thoughts are not your thoughts,*
> *Neither are my ways your ways,*
> *Saith Jehovah.*
> *For as the rain cometh down and the snow from heaven*

And returneth not thither,
But watereth the earth
And maketh it bring forth the bud,
That it may give seed to the sower
And bread to the eater,
So shall my word be that goeth forth out of my mouth.
It shall not return unto me void.
But it shall accomplish that which I please,
And it shall prosper in the thing wherein I sent it.
For ye shall go out with joy,
And be led forth with peace.
The mountains and hills shall break forth before you into singing
And all the trees of the field shall clap their hands.
Instead of the thorn shall come up the fir tree,
Instead of the brier shall come up the myrtle,
And it shall be to Jehovah for a name,
For an everlasting sign that shall not be cut off."

When, with the last of his strength, the prophet had ended communicating to Neraiah in writing the words of his final consolation to those going back to Zion, he commanded him to bring Zerubabel to him to his attic chamber. He must come before he departed for Zion with the returning exiles, for it was laid upon the prophet to make known the word of Jehovah concerning him.

Neraiah found Zerubabel near the Camp of Judah, which was the name now given to the place where those who were preparing to go had congregated. He and Jeshu the priest were busily and heavily engaged in the vast labors of final preparation before the expedition set out. But when Neraiah told him that the prophet had sent for him, he left everything and came at once.

Zerubabel bent down over the failing prophet. He looked into his eyes and said to him:

"O eyes of Israel, rise up and come with us. Behold, O prophet, and see that the Camp of Judah stands ready to depart from Babylon. In a day or two we shall be starting. Your prophecy has been fulfilled. Do not forsake us now. Come with us and be our guide along the road to Zion even as you were our guide in the Exile."

The prophet shook his head feebly.

"I shall not be your guide any longer, for the Lord of all the earth has turned aside my path. He has set a bound about me and I can now go only unto Him. Others will come in my place and will be the guides for Israel."

"Tell me, who shall they be?"

"You yourself!" cried the prophet and summoned up his strength to look straight into Zerubabel's eyes.

"I? You know full well that an alien is Prince of Judah."

"No. A stranger shall not be the prince of Judah. You shall be the prince and Jeshu the priest shall stand at your right hand and Haggai the prophet at your left and they will support you when you come to build the House of God."

Zerubabel turned pale. The prophet closed his eyes. He panted heavily as he struggled to draw some breath into his lungs. With his eyes shut, he fumbled blindly, seeking the hand of Zerubabel. When he found it, he grasped it tight with his fingers and said:

"Blessed be this hand that shall build the House of Jehovah, but from this selfsame hand shall the kingdom of David be withheld."

"Only from my own hand," cried out Zerubabel with deep emotion.

"From your hand and that of all that come after you," the prophet pronounced, laboring out every word. "From the hand of all the generations until . . ."

"Will the House of David then be utterly and finally cut off from the earth?" asked Zerubabel, and there was a fearful confusion on his face and in his voice.

"Heaven forbid! The God Jehovah made an eternal covenant with the House of David because of the lovingkindness and sure mercies of David. At the same time that God showed me your pure hands building anew the House of His sanctuary, He also revealed to me the crown of David borne by wings high above the earth unto Heaven . . . so also He told me that the kingdom of David would pass from the earth and be treasured up by Him in heaven for His sake, to await him that would come at the end of days. Because of this, He told me concerning him; 'Behold, I have given him for a witness to the people, and leader and commander to the people.'"

"Who is he?"

"His name was with God in heaven before He created the world. God created the redemption even before He decreed servitude. He prepared forgiveness and pardon before the snares of sin and iniquity. He created peace before He brought war upon the world. The spirit of God moved upon the face of the chaos and formlessness before He breathed order upon them. For His sake are you returning to Judah. For His sake shall you build the Holy Temple so that you may prepare the world to become pure and so that Israel may become purified in order to be a sign for the nations."

"Alas, O my father, the luminary of Israel, open for me just a crevice into the hidden future worlds that are revealed to you. Let me see it. Let me behold him that will come with the crown of David on his head."

"It is not in my power to do this. But there will come to you at some time a moment of Divine grace and lovingkindness. One day the spirit will rest upon you and you will know and understand why the God of Jehovah delivered His people from the furnace of Babylon and brought them back to His holy mountain. Since you will know this you will also see him. And when you behold him, you will understand why Israel suffered chastisement and great afflictions for being the chosen and peculiar people."

"I pray you have pity upon me and tell me, when shall he come, he that shall bring an end to our sufferings? When shall he come that shall free man and the world from the fetters of evil and arrogance and bring eternal peace between man and man, between beast and beast, as you foresaw and also as Isaiah the son of Amoz foresaw before you, just as you both depicted in your visions?"

"This, too, I cannot reveal to you. It is a mystery hidden from all those born of woman. We were given only the longing and expectation of the redemption. We were also given faith, and this is what binds us to the God Jehovah. This faith is the ladder whereby we mount to the Master of the Universe in Heaven. Let this ladder of faith be removed and once more we fall into Sheol. Go, O Zerubabel, and lead the remnant of Israel to Jerusalem. Take with you on the way the faith in the Master of the Universe and the passion for the redemption. These will uphold you. These will turn the wilderness into a paradise before you and remove every stumbling stone that lies in your path to the redemption. Hearken and give good ear: God has entrusted the remnant of his flock to your hand. Hearken and hear: I have chosen you to store up my last message in your heart. These are the latest words that God has spoken to me for the exiles who are now leaving Babylon to go up unto Zion:

> *"For ye shall go out with joy,*
> *And be led forth with peace;*
> *The mountains and hills shall break before you into singing,*
> *And all the trees of the field shall clap their hands."*

The prophet was silent and motionless for a long time. A brooding quiet reigned in the chamber. Then at last Isaiah spoke in a whisper:

"Not for your sake alone do you return to Judah. You go back to Judah for the sake of the salvation of all the nations."

With these words he took his leave of Zerubabel and of the Exile.